Catalog of the

EMILIE AND KARL RIEMENSCHNEIDER MEMORIAL

BACH LIBRARY

Baldwin-Wallace College Series

Catalog of the

Emilie and Karl Riemenschneider Memorial

Bach Library

Edited by Sylvia W. Kenney

Published for Baldwin-Wallace College

by Columbia University Press

New York, 1960

Published in Great Britain, India, and Pakistan
by the Oxford University Press
London, Bombay, and Karachi

Library of Congress Catalog Card Number: 60-7039
Printed in the Netherlands

FOREWORD

I am greatly moved in writing this introduction to a catalog of the Emilie and Karl Riemenschneider Memorial Bach Library. My mind is crowded with memories at this moment, memories of my husband, Albert Riemenschneider, and of his wonderful parents. At his suggestion we are naming this collection of books for his parents, for whom he had the most tender feelings. It was his father in particular who instilled in him, as a child, a passion for fine books, so that from his young boyhood on he had his own collection of various printed matter. His mother, though lacking the very fine education of his father, had an innate leaning towards the fine arts. When my husband was about nineteen years old, after having studied piano and later organ for some twelve years with both his father and Mr. James H. Rogers of Cleveland, he came to the decision that he would devote his gifts as a performer to the organ. Since an organist's repertoire is composed largely of the works of Johann Sebastian Bach, he naturally began to use his carefully hoarded savings to buy various editions of Bach's organ works. The next steps were collecting Bach's numerous works in other fields and searching for biographical and historical material on this great composer.

I feel sure that he had no intention of making a real collection of Bach's works and of books about him until about twenty-five years after this period, though in the meantime he was constantly adding to his material. It was some time after our marriage in 1904, when he realized what a sizable Bach collection we had, that he began to gather catalogs from prominent book dealers in the United States and abroad. This step excited his keenest desire to know much more about the musician whom he had come to revere profoundly. He also made the acquaintance of many of these book dealers, and at every opportunity he and I would pay them a visit.

My husband made seven trips to Europe, practically all for the purpose of studying with Alexandre Guilmant and Charles-Marie Widor, both of whom were influential in directing his growing taste for Bach. During these trips, too, he formed a deep and lasting friendship with Marcel Dupré, who was a fellow student of Guilmant and Widor then. One of the most decisive influences upon my husband's life and work was his friendship with Dr. Albert Schweitzer, who had studied with Widor a few years previously. It was not long before he and my husband began an interesting correspondence, exchanging views on various matters ranging from stamp collecting to Bach and the organ. This relationship was most precious to my husband.

It was when he and I were both studying in Paris after our marriage that we had the privilege of hearing choral works of Bach for the first time. Our very first opportunity was a concert given by the Bach Society of Paris with Guilmant at the organ. It included various cantatas of Bach and proved to be a revelation to both my husband and me. These cantatas inspired him to attempt the presentation of smaller choral works of Bach and even the *Magnificat* on the campus of Baldwin-Wallace College at Berea, Ohio, where he was Director of the growing Conservatory of Music for over fifty years.

The next step in his development was the planning of annual trips to the Bach festivals at Bethlehem, Pennsylvania.

It was at about this same time that Dr. Riemenschneider made the acquaintance of Dr. Henry Drinker of Merion, Pennsylvania. A beautiful friendship developed between the two men, and my husband looked forward to letters from this friend, who shared many of his feelings towards Bach and his works. In addition to hearing the Bach festivals in Bethlehem, my husband and I planned a trip to Europe in 1935 (the two hundred fiftieth anniversary of the birth of Bach) for the express purpose of hearing two great Bach festivals—one at Zürich lasting three days and one at Leipzig lasting ten days. The latter festival was directed by Karl Straube with Ramin at the organ. The concerts were held in many different places identified with the work of Bach in Leipzig, most of them at the St. Thomas Church. Following this festival at Leipzig, we made a trip to Eisenach and to other small towns in the vicinity of Leipzig where Bach had worked. There we saw one of the churches where Bach's first wife had been soprano soloist as well as many of the beautiful small organs which Bach had opened and played. This trip added considerably to the fund of knowledge which my husband had already accumulated on Bach.

A little over twenty-five years ago, as my husband and I returned from one of the Bethlehem festivals, we began to talk over the possibilities of organizing a Bach festival on the Berea campus and again to make an earnest effort to present choral works of Bach. My husband felt strongly that there was a sore lack of such concerts in the Middle West. The outcome of these plans was the first in our series of twenty-five annual Bach festivals. I remember at that time my husband's remark to me that our growing Bach collection would be invaluable for the preparation of these festivals. And so it has proved to be. This Bach library has also been the basis for my husband's published editions of Bach's works, and he used it extensively in preparing his Bach organ recitals, which were given on the Baldwin-Wallace campus. His complete rendition of these organ works in a special series of recitals drew the attention of music lovers throughout our country. My husband also drew on the resources of this library for the many articles he published in various professional journals. Soon scholars began to apply, and many of them came to spend days or weeks in this library.

My husband's ambition was that we constantly add important things to the library, and for this reason we have established a memorial fund in memory of our older daughter, Lois, whose early passing was a severe blow to us both. It is my earnest hope that I may, as long as I live, do my full part in enlarging this library in every possible way in order to make it a place where music lovers from the entire world will come for study and research.

SELMA M. RIEMENSCHNEIDER

PREFACE

The classification and a large part of the cataloging of the Emilie and Karl Riemenschneider Memorial Bach Library were done by the late Edythe Backus. Although it has not been possible to include in the published catalog all the information which Miss Backus compiled in the course of her bibliographical research on the collection, this data is recorded in the card file at the library. Omissions are, for the most part, of material documenting the assigned dates. There are also in the library four other files which Miss Backus set up and which have been completed since her death. These are the plate-number file, the publishers' file, the chronological file, and the association file.

One other aspect of Miss Backus' work on the collection which is not reflected in this catalog is the special classification of a large number of items as "rare material." Three works published during Bach's lifetime, however, seem sufficiently important to warrant special mention here. These are the *Clavierübung*, Part I (Six Partitas); the variations for organ on the chorale "Vom Himmel hoch, da komm ich her"; and the *Clavierübung*, Part IV (Goldberg Variations) which appear here as entry nos. 2274, 1512, and 548.

The preparation of the published catalog has presented a number of problems, some of which have been solved with a view to utility at the expense of a wholly consistent system. The cantatas, for example, have been classified as full scores, vocal-piano scores, vocal scores, and excerpts. While a

similar subdivision is perfectly feasible in some of the other
categories, there are so few editions in some instances that it
has seemed unnecessary to subdivide to the point where each
item has a subheading. These editions are simply listed
alphabetically by title. The composer's name has been
omitted from the body of the entry except in the case of first
editions or where there is an unusual form of spelling. The
cantatas are arranged numerically, and the distinctive
German titles are given in the first heading of each cantata. These titles are omitted from the entries unless the text
is also published in translation. For these editions, as well
as for those without the original German, the distinctive
titles are given in all languages appearing in the text unless they are not given on the title page or as a caption title.

The editions of the *Well-tempered Clavier* have presented the
most difficult problems. A simple alphabetical listing seems
to serve no useful purpose, particularly in view of the
deviations of spelling even within the same language
(*Temperirte, Temperierte; Clavier, Clavir, Klavier, Klavir*). A
chronological listing was rejected partly because many of the
dates are necessarily tentative and partly because date of
issue and date of the original plates may vary widely, and in
many cases the only available date is that of issue. A listing
by publishers has already been published by Albert Riemenschneider in *Notes for the Music Library Association, No. 14*
(August, 1942). The final decision to arrange them by
editors seemed at once the most useful and the most precise.
There is one obvious drawback to this arrangement, in that
some editions have no editor specified. But since all con-
ditions cannot be met, these editions have been placed in a
second group and arranged alphabetically by publisher. In
the case of the *Well-tempered Clavier* a further liberty has been
taken with the system employed for the remainder of the

catalog because the holdings of the Riemenschneider Library represent a very nearly complete collection of this work. Cross references have been used here but not for other works. In the listing of the *Well-tempered Clavier*, cross references are given to particular volumes in collections entered under Complete Works or Clavier Works (Collected or Selected) in order to bring together all the versions prepared by any one editor.

The preparation of this catalog has been a joint effort. Acknowledgments are due above all to two people who guided the project from the beginning through its many vicissitudes: Clyde L. Haselden, librarian of Baldwin-Wallace College, and Cecil W. Munk, Director of the Baldwin-Wallace Conservatory. Jeanette Beebe, reference librarian of Baldwin-Wallace, performed the arduous task of proofreading and checking the manuscript, and Alice Hall, cataloger of the college library, was very helpful in advising on cataloging problems. Mabel Knapp, music cataloger of the Cleveland Public Library, gave generous assistance on bibliographical matters. A great deal of help was provided by Richard S. Hill, William Lichtenwanger, and Frank C. Campbell of the Library of Congress in connection with bibliographical research as well as on the more general problems of publishing a catalog. An indispensable part of the project was the tedious job of typing, filing, and correcting which was done by four students of Baldwin-Wallace College—Barbara Snyder, Lloyd McFarland, June McCord, and Alison Elliott. Finally, thanks are due to Elizabeth Evanson, assistant editor at Columbia University Press, whose considerate and painstaking work eased the manuscript through the last stages of publication.

SYLVIA W. KENNEY

Bryn Mawr, Pennsylvania   August, 1960

Abbreviations Used in Catalog

P.N. = Plate Number

S.   = Schmieder, Wolfgang. *Thematisch-systematisches Verzeichnis der Werke Joh. Seb. Bachs.*

CONTENTS

FOREWORD, by Selma M. Riemenschneider   v

PREFACE   ix

MUSIC LITERATURE   1

MUSIC OF CONTEMPORARIES AND SONS OF
JOHANN SEBASTIAN BACH   49

MANUSCRIPTS   49
PUBLISHED MUSIC   49

MUSIC OF JOHANN SEBASTIAN BACH   51

MANUSCRIPTS   51
PUBLISHED MUSIC   53
Complete Works   53
Selected Works   53
Aria mit 30 Veränderungen   53
     Excerpts and Arrangements, 54
Aria variata alla maniera italiana   54
Arias, Collected   54
Cantatas   56
     Collections, 56; Single Works (Cantatas 1–198, 201–13, 216), 56
Capriccio sopra la lontananza del suo fratello
dilettissimo   144
Chorales   144
     Collections, 144; Arrangement, 149; Single Works, 149
Chorale Preludes   150
     *Collections, 150; Selections, 151; Achtzehn Choräle von
     verschiedener Art, 152; Clavier-Übung III, 152;
     Orgel-Büchlein, 152; Sechs Choräle von verschiedener
     Art, 153; Single Works, 153*

Chorale Variations   153
Chromatische Fantasie und Fuge D-Moll   154
Clavier Works   155
   Collections, 155; Selections, 157; Selections, Arranged, 159
Concertos   160
   Brandenburg, 160; Clavier, 163; Two Claviers, 167;
   Three Claviers, 168; Four Claviers, 169; Clavier, Violin,
   and Flute, 169; Organ, 170; Violin, 170; Two Violins, 173
Duets   174
   Clavier, 174; Voice, 174
Fantasie in C Minor for Clavier   175
Fantasie in G Major for Organ   175
Fantasie and Fugue in A Minor for Clavier   175
Fugues   176
   Clavier, 176; Organ, 176; Violin and Clavier, 177
Inventions   177
   Collections, 177; Selections, 180; Selections, Arranged, 181;
   Two-Part Inventions, 181; Three-Part Inventions
   (Sinfonias), 185
Italienisches Konzert   187
Klavierbüchlein für Wilhelm Friedemann Bach   188
Die Kunst der Fuge   188
   Scores, 188; Arrangements, 189; Excerpts, 190
Magnificat   190
   Full Scores, 190; Vocal-piano Scores, 191; Excerpts, 192
Masses   192
   Collections, 192; Single Works (B Minor, F Major,
   A Major, G Minor, G Major), 192
Minuets, Selected   196
Motets   196
   Collections, 196; Single Works, 197
Musikalisches Opfer   199
   Complete, 199; Excerpts, 200
Notenbuch für Anna Magdalena Bach, No. 2   200
   Complete, 200; Selections, 201
Oratorios   202
   Oster-Oratorium, 202; Weihnachts-Oratorium, 202
Organ Works   204
   Collections, 204; Selections, 206
Passions   207
   Johannespassion, 207; Lukaspassion, 209; Matthäuspassion, 209
Pastorale in F Major (Organ)   214
Preludes   214
   Clavier, 214; Organ, 216
Preludes and Fugues, Clavier   217
Preludes (Fantasies or Toccatas) and Fugues   218
   Organ, Collections, 218; Organ, Arrangement, 219;
   Organ, Selections, 219; Organ, Single Works, 220
Sanctus   223

Sonatas   223
   Flute, Unaccompanied, 223; Flute and Clavier, 223; Flute,
   Clavier, and Violin, 224; Organ, 224; Viola da Gamba and
   Clavier, 226; Violin, Unaccompanied, 226; Violin and
   Clavier, 229; Two Violins and Clavier, Trio Sonatas, 232
Songs, Sacred   232
   Collections, 232; Arrangements, 234
Songs, Secular   234
   Collection, 234; Arrangement, 234
Suites   234
   Clavier, English Suites, 234; Clavier, French Suites, 238;
   Clavier, Partitas, 241; Clavier, Suites in F Major,
   F Minor, and A Major, 245; Orchestra, 246; Violin and
   Clavier, 248; Violoncello, 248
Toccatas   251
   Clavier, Collections, 251; Clavier, Single Works, 251;
   Organ, Single Works, 253
Trios   253
Das Wohltemperierte Klavier, Books I and II   254
   Listed Alphabetically by Editor, 254; Listed Alphabetically
   by Publisher, 265; Selections, Arrangements, 268
Das Wohltemperierte Klavier, Book I   271
   Selections, Arrangements, 271; Single Works, 271
Das Wohltemperierte Klavier, Book II   276
   Selections, Arrangements, 276; Single Works, 276

INDEX TO CANTATAS: Titles   277

GENERAL INDEX   283

Catalog of the

EMILIE AND KARL RIEMENSCHNEIDER MEMORIAL

BACH LIBRARY

MUSIC LITERATURE

1. Adler, Guido. Handbuch der Musikgeschichte. ... Frankfurt, Frankfurter Verlags-Anstalt, 1924. 6 ll., 1097 pp., illus. (incl. music), 26 cm.
2. Albrecht, Otto Edwin. A Census of Autograph Music Manuscripts of European Composers in American Libraries. ... Philadelphia, University of Pennsylvania Press, 1953. vii, 331 pp.; 24 cm.
   Introduction by Carleton Sprague Smith.
3. Allgemeine Musikzeitung. Rhein-Westfälische Musikzeitung und Süddeutscher Musik-Kurier, Wochenschrift für das Musikleben der Gegenwart. Berlin, Breitkopf & Härtel [etc.], 1874-. 1 vol. Weekly. 31 cm.
   Library has Vol. 39, Nos. 36, 38-39 (1912); Vol. 40, Nos. 29-30 (1913); Vol. 58, Nos. 39, 42 (1931); Vol. 61, Nos. 1-52 (1934); Vol. 62, Nos. 12, 26 (1935); also, photostat of Vol. 39, No. 37, pp. 883-84.
4. Ambros, August Wilhelm. Bunte Blätter, Skizzen und Studien für Freunde der Musik und der bildenen Kunst... Neue Folge. Leipzig, F.E.C. Leuckart, 1874. 6 ll., pp. [1]-382, 3 ll., 18 cm.
5. —— Geschichte der Musik, Mit zahlreichen Notenbeispielen und Musikbeilagen. ... Dritte, gänzlich umgearbeitet Auflage. ... Leipzig, F. E. C. Leuckart, 1887, 1891, 1878, 1889. 5 vols. 22 cm.
   Vols. I-III are third ed., the first dated 1887, the second and third dated 1891. Vol. IV is the first ed., dated 1878; Vol. V is the second ed., dated 1889.
6. Apel, Willi. Harvard Dictionary of Music. Cambridge, Mass., Harvard University Press, 1955. x, 833 pp.; 24 cm.
   Ninth printing.
7. Arblay, Mme. Frances (Burney) d'. Memoirs of Doctor Burney, arranged from his own manuscripts, from family papers, and from personal recollections by his daughter, Madame d'Arblay. ... London, Edward Moxon, 1832. 3 vols. 22 cm.
8. Audsley, George Ashdown. The Art of Organ-Building, A comprehensive historical, theoretical, and practical treatise on the tonal appointment and mechanical construction of concert-room, church,

8. *(continued)* and chamber organs. ... New York, Dodd, Mead;
London, Th Vincent Music Company, 1905. 2 vols. Illus., 33 cm.
9. Bach, Carl Philipp Emanuel. Essay on the True Art of Playing
Keyboard Instruments. ... Translated and edited by William J.
Mitchell. ... New York, W. W. Norton [c 1949]. xiii, 449 pp.,
illus. (music); facs., 23 cm.
10. —— Versuch über die wahre Art das Clavier zu spielen mit
Exempeln und achtzehn probe-Stücken in sechs Sonaten erläutert. ...
Zweyte Auflage, In Verlegung des auctoris. Berlin, Georg Ludewig
Winter, 1759, 1762. 2 vols. in 1, separate supp. Illus. (music), 21 cm.
Original mottled boards. Engraved music supp. (41 cm.) unbound.
Pages 235, 261 misnumbered 253, 361 respectively. Title of Vol. II:
Carl Philipp Emanuel Bachs Versuch über die wahre Art das Clavier zu
spielen... in welchem die Lehre von dem Accompagnement und der
freyen Fantasie abgehandelt wird, Nebst einer Kupfertafel....
Musical supp. has half-title only: Exempel nebst achtzehn probe-
Stücken in sechs Sonaten zu Carl Philipp Emanuel Bachs Versuch
über die wahre Art das Clavier zu spielen auf XXVI. Kupfertafeln.
The musical supp. issued with this ed. is the same as that issued
with the 1753 ed. Signature of G. J. Vollweiler on front flyleaf;
signature and *ex libris* of Archer on front pastedown. On half-title of
music supp. are signatures of Eduard Hanslick, J. Brahms, and
Marie Schumann.
11. —— Versuch über die wahre Art, das Klavier zu spielen, Kritisch
revidierter Neudruck nach der unveränderten, jedoch verbesserten
zweiten Auflage des Originals, Berlin 1759 und 1762. Mit einem
Vorwort und erläuternden Anmerkungen versehen von Dr. Walter
Niemann. Fünfte Auflage. Leipzig, C. F. Kahnt, 1925. viii pp.,
3 ll., 94 pp., 4 ll., 130 pp., 3 ll. (ads), illus. (music), 24 cm.
12. Bach, Johann Sebastian. Johann Sebastian Bach Briefe Gesamt-
ausgabe herausgegeben im Auftrage des Internationalen Musiker-
Brief-Archives von Hedwig u. E. H. Müller von Asow. Zweite vermehrte Auflage. Regensburg, Gustav Bosse [c 1950]. 228 pp., illus.
(incl. music), ports. 18 cm. (Deutsche Musikbücherei, Band 1.)
13. —— Johann Sebastian Bach Documenta. Herausgegeben durch
die Niedersächsische Staats- und Universitätsbibliothek von Wilhelm
Martin Luther zum Bachfest 1950 in Göttingen. Kassel & Basel,
Bärenreiter [1950]. 148 pp., illus. (ports.), facs. (incl. music), 2
folding plates, 21 cm.
14. —— Kurtzer, iedoch höchstnöthiger Entwurff einer wohlbestallten
Kirchen Music; nebst einigen unvorgreiflichen Bedencken von dem
Verfall derselben; Leipzig, den 23. August 1730. Herausgegeben vom
Bach-Archiv Leipzig. Leipzig, Deutscher Verlag für Musik [1954?].
Facsimile of MS. Rep. III in the Bach-Archiv. Title page and
commentary by Werner Neumann at end of text.

15. Bach-Fest [Leipzig] anlässlich der Enthüllung des Bach-Denkmal, in Leipzig 16 bis 18 Mai, 1908; Fest- und Programmbuch. [Leipzigs Breitkopf & Härtel, 1908.] 174 pp., illus. (incl. music), 22 cm.
16. Bach-Jahrbuch 1904 [to 1955]. Herausgegeben von der Neuern Bachgesellschaft. Leipzig, Breitkopf & Härtel [1905-]1956. Vols. [1]–42. Illus. (incl. music), ports., folding facs. (incl. music), 22 cm.
17. Bachmann, Luise George. The Heart Ever Faithful, The Story of John Sebastian Bach, 1723-1750. London, Geo. E. J. Coldwell [c 1938]. 440 pp., 19 cm.
Translated from the German by K. T. Stephenson.
18. —— Der Thomaskantor; Introduktion, Toccata und Fuga über B-A-C-H. 4. Auflage. Paderborn, Ferdinand Schöningh, 1948. 461 pp., 19 cm.
19. Baker, Theodore. Baker's Biographical Dictionary of Musicians. Third edition, revised and enlarged by Alfred Remy. New York, G. Schirmer, 1919. 7 ll., 1094 pp., 23 cm.
20. —— A Supplement to the Biographical Dictionary of Musicians. New York, G. Schirmer, 1905. 1 l., pp. 649-95, 23 cm.
21. Baldwin-Wallace College, Conservatory of Music. Bach Festival Programs with Text and Descriptive Notes. [Berea, Ohio,] 1933-57. 2 vols. bound, 4 nos. unbound (1953-57). 23 cm.
22. Barnard, Charles. The Tone Masters, A Musical Series for Young People.... Bach and Beethoven. Boston, Musical Herald Company [c 1870]. 2 ll., 243 pp., illus., 17 cm. (The Tone Masters, Vol. 3.)
Added title page: The Tone Masters. Bach & Beethoven. The New England Conservatory of Music Publishers.
23. Barth, Hermann. Johann Sebastian Bach, Ein Lebensbild von Hermann Barth, Mit elf Bildern. Berlin, Alfred Schall [1901]. 5 ll., 383 pp., illus. (incl. music), ports., facs. (incl. music), 19 cm.
Bookplate of Richard Barth, left-handed violinist, b. 1850.
24. Baser, Friedrich. Johann Sebastian Bach im musikalischen und geistigen Leben Heidelbergs...mit kulturhistorischem Stadtplan, Führer und Zeittafel; Zum Bachfest der Neuen Bach-Gesellschaft Heidelberg 1932. [Heidelberg, Hermann Meister, 1932.] 1 l., pp. 3-28, 1 l., illus. (map), 22 cm.
25. —— Das musikalische Heidelberg seit den Kurfürsten...Dem zaubrischen Dreiklang: Deutscher Geist, Deutscher Musik, Heidelbergs Höhen, Tal und Wälder. Heidelberg, Hermann Meister [1935?]. 112 pp., illus. (ports.), facs. (incl. music), charts, 23 cm.
26. Batka, Richard. J. S. Bach. ... Leipzig, Philipp Reclam, jun. [c 1893]. 119 pp., 15 cm. (Musiker Biographien, 15. Band.)
27. Bellermann, Heinrich. Der Contrapunkt. ... Vierte Auflage. Berlin, Julius Springer, 1901. xviii, 480 pp.; illus. (music); charts; 24 cm.

28. Belval, Maurice. La Trente-Deuxième Cantate de Bach "Liebster Jesu mein Verlangen." Paris, Librairie Fischbacher, 1914. 52 pp., 24 cm.
At head of title: Henry Maubel [pseudonym].

29. Benz, Richard Edmund. Bachs Passion, Die nordische Tragödie. ... Leipzig, Philipp Reclam, jun. [1940?]. 68 pp., 2 ll., 15 cm.

30. Besch, Hans. Johann Sebastian Bach Frömmigkeit und Glaube, Band I: Deutung und Wirklichkeit das Bild Bachs im Wandel der deutschen Kirchen- und Geistesgeschichte. Zweite Auflage. Kassel und Basel, Bärenreiter-Verlag [1950]. xii, 314 pp.; facs.; 22 cm.

31. Beyer, Oskar. Bach; Anmerkungen und Hinweise. ... Zweite, neugestaltete und erweiterte Ausgabe. Berlin, im Furche-Verlag, 1928. 87, [1] pp.; frontis.; 22 cm.

32. —— Bach, Eine Kunde vom Genius. ... Berlin, im Furche-Verlag, 1924. 63 pp., 22 cm.

33. Bitter, Carl Hermann. Carl Philipp Emanuel und Wilhelm Friedemann Bach und deren Brüder. ... Berlin, Wilhelm Müller, 1868. 2 vols. in 1. Illus. (ports.), facs. (incl. music), folding charts, 22 cm.
Vol. I: C. P. E. Bach; Vol. II: C. P. E. Bach, continuation; Johann Christoph Friedrich Bach, Johann Christian Bach, Wilhelm Friedemann Bach

34. —— Johann Sebastian Bach. ... Berlin, Ferdinand Schneider, 1865. 2 vols. Illus. (music), port., facs. (music), 21 cm.
Book plate of Otto Jahn in each vol.

35. —— Johann Sebastian Bach. ... Zweite umgearbeitete und vermehrte Auflage. Berlin, Wilhelm Baensch, 1881. 4 vols. in 2. Illus. (incl. music), facs. (incl. music), 21 cm.

36. —— The Life of J. Sebastian Bach. An abridged translation from the German of C. H. Bitter by Janet E. Kay-Shuttleworth, with preface by Sir Julius Benedict. London, Houlston and Sons [1873]. vi, 153 pp.; (frontis.); 19 cm.

37. Blankenburg, Walter. Einführung in Bachs h-moll-Messe mit vollständigem Text. Kassel und Basel, Bärenreiter [1950]. 48 pp., illus. (music), 19 cm.

38. Blom, Eric Walter. Bach. ... London, Murdoch [ca. 1930]. 30 pp., 1 l., illus. (incl. music), port., facs. (incl. music), 25 cm. (Mayfair Biographies, No. 13.)

39. Blume, Friedrich. Johann Sebastian Bach im Wandel der Geschichte. ... Kassel, Bärenreiter [1947]. 39 pp., 24 cm. (Musikwissenschaftliche Arbeiten, Nr. 1.)
Published by the Gesellschaft für Musikforschung.

40. Blumner, Martin Traugott Wilhelm. Cantatencyclus von Johann Sebastian Bach. Berlin, Horn & Raasch, 1893. 15 pp., 22 cm.

41. Bojanowski, Paul Friedrich Wilhelm von. Das Weimar Johann

Sebastian Bach zur Erinnerung an den 8. April 1703. ... Weimar, Hermann Böhlaus, 1903. 50 pp., frontis., 22 cm.

42. Borkowsky, Ernst Otto. Die Musikerfamilie Bach dargestellt von Ernst Borkowsky. Jena, Eugen Diederichs, 1930. 88 pp., illus. (ports.), facs. (incl. music), 21 cm.

43. Boughton, Rutland. Bach. ... London, John Lane, 1920. xiii, 156 pp.; 2 ll.; illus. (incl. music); 16 cm. (The Music of the Masters, Book V.)
General editor: Wakeling Dry. Second edition.

44. —— Bach, the Master; A new interpretation of his genius. ... New York, London, Harper, 1930. x pp., 1 l., 291 pp., illus. (incl. music facs.), 22 cm.

45. Brachvogel, Albert Emil. Friedemann Bach, Roman von A. E. Brachvogel. Leipzig, H. Fikentscher [not before 1913]. 380 pp., 18 cm.

46. Breitkopf und Härtel, publishers. Verzeichnis des Musikalien-Verlages von Breitkopf und Härtel in Leipzig. Systematischer und alphabetischer Theil nebst Anhang, Vollständig bis Ende 1885 mit Nachträgen bis zur Gegenwart. [Leipzig, Breitkopf und Härtel, 1888.] 1 l., pp. [iii]–clx, [1]–824, [1]–19, [1]–24, [1]–36, 22 cm.

47. British Museum, Department of Printed Books. Catalogue of Printed Music Published before 1801 Now in the British Museum. Second supplement by William C. Smith...London, by Order of the Trustees, 1940. 2 ll., 85 pp., 25 cm.

48. Brodde, Otto. Johann Sebastian Bach, Kleine Biographie...mit einige Auszügen aus der ersten Bach-Biographie von Johann Nikolaus Forkel. Kassel und Basel, Bärenreiter [1950]. 16 pp., 23 cm.
Sonderdruck aus der Zeitschrift "Der Kirchenchor," 10. Jahrg.

49. Bruyck, Carl Debrois van. Technische und ästhetische Analysen des Wohltemperirten Klaviers nebst einer allgemeinen, Sebastian Bach und die sogenannte kontrapuntische Kunst betreffenden Einleitung verfasst von Carl van Bruyck. Dritte Auflage. Leipzig, Breitkopf & Härtel, 1925. iv, [2], 188 pp.; illus. (music); 23 cm.
"Anhang, Die Themen des Wohltemperirten Klaviers und deren Gegensätze," pp. [178]–188.

50. Buhle, Edward. Verzeichnis der Sammlung alter Musikinstrumente im Bachhause zu Eisenbach. Leipzig, Breitkopf & Härtel [1918]. iv, 52 pp.; illus.; 23 cm. (Neue Bach Gesellschaft Publications, Vol. 19, No. 1.)
"Vorwort zur alten Ausgabe" (p. II), signed: Edward Buhle; "Vorwort zur neuen Ausgabe" (p. III), signed: Dr. Curt Sachs.

51. —— Verzeichnis der Sammlung alter Musikinstrumente im Bachhause zu Eisenach. Herausgegeben von der Neuen Bachgesellschaft zu Leipzig. Dritte, vermehrte Ausgabe. Leipzig, Breitkopf und Härtel [1939]. 64 pp., illus., 23 cm.

6 MUSIC LITERATURE

51. *(continued)* "Vorwort zu ersten Ausgabe," signed: Edward Buhle; "Zur Neuausgabe," unsigned, but dated: Ostern, 1939. "Veröffentlichungen der Neuen Bachgesellschaft Vereinsjahre 38,2," on verso of title page.

52. Buhrman, Thomas Scott Godfrey. Bach's Life Chronologically as He Lived It. ... Richmond, Staten Island, N.Y., Organ Interest, Inc., c 1935. 54 pp., illus., 19 cm.
On leaf facing title page: "A reprint from The American Organist."

53. Bukofzer, Manfred F. Music in the Baroque Era from Monteverdi to Bach. ... New York, W. W. Norton [c 1947]. xv, 489 pp.; 1 l.; illus. (incl. music); facs. (incl. music); 24 cm.

54. Bülow, Paul. Johann Sebastian Bach dem Meister evangelischer Kirchenmusik zu seinem 250. Geburtstag. ... Leipzig und Hamburg, Gustav Schloessmann, 1935. 63 pp., illus., facs. (music), 20 cm.

55. Cart, William Adolphe. Etude sur J. S. Bach 1685-1750. ... Paris, Librairie Fischbacher, 1885. iv, 267 pp.; 18 cm.
At head of title: Un maitre deux fois centenaire.

56. —— Etude sur J.-S. Bach 1685-1750. ... Nouvelle édition. ... Paris, Librairie Fischbacher, 1885. iv, 267 pp.; 18 cm.

57. Cellier, Alexandre. Les Passions et l'oratorio de Noël de J. S. Bach précédé d'une notice biographique. ... Paris, Les éditions musicales de la Librairie de France, 1929. 212, [1] pp.; illus. (incl. music); facs. (incl. music); 19 cm. (Collection des Grandes Oeuvres Musicales.) General editor: René Dumesnil.

58. Cherbuliez, Antoine-Elisee Adolphe. Johann Sebastian Bach, sein Leben und sein Werk. Olten [Switzerland], Otto Walter [c 1946]. 235 pp., illus., ports., facs. (incl. music), 19 cm. (Musikerreihe, Band I.) Special foreword concerning the series by general editor, Paul Schaller.

59. Cherubini, Maria Luigi Carlo Zenobio Salvatore. Cours de contrepoint et de fugue. ... 2me édition. Paris, Heugel [18??]. 1 l., 204 pp., illus. (music), 34 cm.
Engraved throughout; plates badly worn. First edition in 1835.
P.N.: H. 4041

60. Ching, James. The Playing and Teaching of Bach, A guide for teachers, students and examination candidates. ... London, Forsyth, c 1931. 59 pp., 1 l., illus. (incl. music), 31 cm.

61. Chop, Max. Joh. Seb. Bach Matthäus-Passion Oratorium, Geschichtlich und musikalisch analysiert mit zahlreichen Notenbeispielen. ... Leipzig, Philipp Reclam, jun. [c 1909]. 88 pp., 15 cm. (Erläuterungen zu Meisterwerken der Tonkunst, 15. Band.)
Reclams Universal Bibliothek No. 5063.

62. Clemens, Charles Edwin. Modern School for the Organ. ... New York, G. Schirmer, c 1903. 3 ll., 81 pp., obl. fol., 23×31 cm.
P.N.: 16395

63. Correspondenzblatt des Evangelischen Kirchengesangsvereins für Deutschland. Herausgegeben von dem Vorstande des Central-ausschusses. Leipzig, Breitkopf & Härtel, 1887-. Monthly. 23 cm.
Library has Vol. 15, No. 12 (Dec., 1901); Vol. 21, No. 4 (March, 1907). Contents: A. Beutter, "Praktische Vorschläge ... der Bachschen Choräle..."; Karl Schmidt, "Zu den Ausgabe der Bachschen Choräle."

64. Cöthen, Heimatmuseum, Bachabteilung. Johann Sebastian Bach, 1685-1750, und sein Wirken in Cöthen, 1717-1723. Ein Führer durch die Bachabteilung des Cöthener Heimatmuseums, Im Auftrage des Arbeitsausschusses des Heimatmuseums in Cöthen bearbeitet von W. Bethge und W. Götze. Cöthen-Anhalt, Verlag des Heimat-museums, 1925. 47 pp., illus. (ports.) facs., 22 cm. (Schriftenreihe des Cöthener Heimatmuseums, Heft 1.)

65. Courrier musical, théâtral et cinématographique, Le, et son supplément; La Semaine musical et théâtral. Paris, Société anonyme du Courrier Musical et Théâtral, 1897-. Semiweekly. 31 cm.
Library has Vol. 37, No. 3 (1 Feb., 1935). Contents: Articles on Bach by Gustav Bret, Léopold Stokowski, Alexandre Cellier, Emmanuel Bondeville, Elisabeth de Mondesir, and others.

66. Cranach-Sichart, Eberhard von. Johann Sebastian Bach, Eine Einführung in sein Leben und seine Musik. ... Leipzig, Karl Robert Langewiesche [1935?]. 48 pp., illus., 21 cm.

67. Crowest, Frederick James. The Great Tone-Poets: Being Short Memoirs of the Greater Musical Composers. ... Cincinnati, John Church, 1877. ix, 210 pp.; 20 cm.

68. Cunliffe Owen, Sidney. Gentlemen! Old Bach is Here. Thirty-One Leipzig Variations on the Theme of John Sebastian Bach. ... London, Hutchinson [1936]. 281 pp., 1 l., 20 pp., illus., facs. (incl. music), 23 cm.

69. Dahms, Walter. Johann Sebastian Bach, Ein Bild seines Lebens zusammengestellt von Walter Dahms. Munich, Musarion Verlag, 1924. 123 pp., 2 ll., frontis., 20 cm.

70. Danckert, Werner. Beiträge zur Bachkritik. Kassel, Bärenreiter, 1934. 72 pp., illus. (music), 23 cm. (Jenaer Studien zur Musik-wissenschaft Bd. 1.)

71. Dannreuther, Edward George. Musical ornamentation, Part I [and Part II]. ... London, Novello [1925?]. 2 vols. in 1. Illus. (music), 28 cm. (Novello's Music Primers and Educational Series.)
P.N.: 8157 & 8205

72. David, Ernest. La Vie et les oeuvres de Jean-Sébastien Bach, sa famille, ses élèves, ses contemporains. ... Paris, Calmann Lévy, 1882. xv, 380 pp.; illus. (music); 18 cm.

73. David, Hans Theodore. The Bach Reader, A life of Johann Sebastian Bach in letters and documents, edited by Hans T. David

73. *(continued)* and Arthur Mendel. New York, W. W. Norton [c 1945]. 431 pp., illus. (incl. charts, music), ports., facs. (incl. music), 24 cm.

74. —— J. S. Bach's Musical Offering; History, Interpretation, and Analysis. ... New York, G. Schirmer [c 1945]. ix, 190 pp.; illus. (music); facs. (incl. music); 22 cm.
> Supplement to the score and parts published by G. Schirmer. Autograph inscription on front flyleaf.

75. Dehn, Siegfried Wilhelm. Analysen dreier Fugen aus Joh. Seb. Bach's Wohltemperirtem Clavier und einer Vocal-Doppelfuge A. M. Bononcini's. ... Leipzig, C. F. Peters, 1858. 2 ll., 37 pp., 1 l., 11 pp. (music), 4 pp., illus. (music), 26 cm.
> Foreword signed by Bernard Scholz, a student of Dehn's. Autograph signature and stamp on title page: Marie Proksch.

76. Dehnert, Max. Das Weltbild Johann Sebastian Bach. ... Zweite Auflage. Stuttgart, S. Hirzel, 1949. 4 ll., 150 pp., 21 cm.
> Foreword by Günther Ramin.

77. Detheridge, Joseph. Chronology of Music Composers. Birmingham, Detheridge, c 1936-37. 2 vols. Illus., ports., map.

78. Deutsches Bach-Fest. Festschrift und Programmbuch. [Leipzig, Breitkopf & Härtel, 1901-56.] 30 vols. (21 bound in 5; 9 unbound). Illus. (incl. music), ports., 22 cm.
> At head of title: Neue Bach-Gesellschaft. Editor: A. F. H. Kretschmar, 1901-24.

79. Dickinson, Alan Edgar Frederic. The Art of J. S. Bach. ... London, Duckworth [1936]. vii, 9-296 pp.; 19 cm.

80. Dienel, Otto. Die Stellung der modernen Orgel zu Seb. Bach's Orgelmusik. ... Berlin, V. Ostrowski, 1889. 19 pp., 21 cm.

81. Dole, Nathan Haskell. A Score of Famous Composers. ... New York, Thomas Y. Crowell [c 1891]. 540 pp., illus. (ports.), 19 cm.

82. Dolmetsch, Arnold. The Interpretation of the Music of the XVIIth and XVIIIth Centuries Revealed by Contemporary Evidence. ... London, Novello [ca. 1928]. x, 493 pp.; illus. (music); 22 cm. (Handbooks for Musicians.)
> General editor: Ernest Newman.

83. Dommer, Arrey von. Musikalisches Lexikon auf Grundlage des Lexikon's von H. Ch. Koch. Heidelberg, J. C. B. Mohr, 1865. 3 ll., pp. [1]-1010, 23 cm.

84. Dörffel, Alfred. Thematisches Verzeichnis der Instrumentalwerke von Joh. Seb. Bach. Auf Grund der Gesammtausgabe von C. F. Peters verfasst. ... Leipzig, C. F. Peters [1882]. Pp. [i]-iv, 5-92 [i.e., 94], 27 cm.

85. Drinker, Henry Sandwith. The Bach Chorale Texts in English Translation, with annotations showing the use of the melodies elsewhere by Bach in his vocal and organ works, and a musical index to

the melodies. ... New York, Association of American Colleges [1941].
Pp. i-xii, 1-105, 25 cm.

86. —— Texts of the Choral Works of Johann Sebastian Bach in
English Translation. ... New York, Association of American Colleges
[1942-43]. 4 vols. in 2. 25 cm.

87. —— Bach's Use of Slurs in Recitativo Secco. ... [n.p., 1946.]
42 pp., 25 cm.
Presentation inscription from the author, signed.

88. Dubois, François Clement Théodore. Traité de contrepoint et de
fugue, 1re partie—Contrepoint simple; 2e partie—Imitations; 3e
partie—Contrepoint double, triple et quadruple; 4e partie—fugue. ...
Paris, Heugel, c 1901. vii, 3-310 pp.; illus. (music); 31 cm.
P.N.: H. & Cie. 20404

89. Dufourcq, Norbert. Un Architecte de la musique, Jean-Sébastien
Bach; Génie allemand? Génie latin? ... Paris, La Colombe [c 1947].
236 pp., 1 l. (table), 22 cm.
Limited edition of 55 numbered copies, of which this is No. 34.

90. —— Jean-Sébastien Bach, le maître de l'orgue. ... Paris, Librairie
Floury, 1948. 431 pp., illus. (incl. music), facs. (incl. music), folding
charts, ports., 26 cm.

91. Dupré, Marcel. Cours complet de fugue en deux volumes. Paris,
Alphonse Leduc [1938]. 2 vols. 30 cm. (Bibliothèque-Leduc Nos.
725, 726.) P.N.: A.L. 19.629, A.L. 19.630

92. Dürr, Alfred. Studien über die frühen Kantaten J. S. Bachs.
Leipzig, Breitkopf & Härtel, 1951. 243 pp., illus. (music), charts
(folding), 24 cm. (Bach-Studien, Band 4.)

93. Ebermayer, Erich. Meister Sebastian, Roman. Vienna, Paul
Zsolnay, 1950. 195, [1] pp., 19 cm.

94. Edinburgh University, Reid Library. The Sixty-Eighth Session of
Reid Orchestral Concerts...Fifteenth Season, Seventh Concert...
March, 1931. ... Edinburgh, Paterson Sons & Co. [1931]. 30 pp.,
illus., 24 cm.
Program notes for the B Minor Mass of Bach, prepared by D. F.
Tovey.

95. Ehlert, Louis. Joh. Seb. Bach.
Fragment (pp. [73]-[88]) of unidentified issue of *Deutsche Rundschau*,
Berlin, Gebrüder Paetel [ca. 1895]. 18 pp., 23 cm.

96. Ehrhardt, Paul. Gisela Agnes—Bach bilder aus Köthens Ver-
gangenheit; Paul Ehrhardt, Pastor an St. Agnus Köthen. [Köthen]
im Selbstverlag des Verfassers, 1935. 105 pp., illus., facs., 18 cm.

97. Ehrlich, Heinrich. Die Ornamentik in Joh. Seb. Bachs Klavierwerken, Studien und Erläuterungen. ... Leipzig, Steingräber [1896?].
19 pp. Illus. (music), 26 cm. (Edition Steingräber, No. 28.)

98. Eitner, Robert. Biographisch-bibliographisches Quellen-Lexikon
der Musiker und Musikgelehrten der Christlichen Zeitrechnung bis

98. *(continued)* zur Mitte des Neunzehnten Jahrhunderts. Leipzig, Breitkopf & Härtel [1898]. 10 vols. 24 cm.
    Ex libris Franz Leclercq.

99. Emery, Walter. Bach's Ornaments. ... London, Novello [c 1935]. 164 pp., illus. (music), facs. (music), 14 cm.

100. Engel, Carl. Alla Breve from Bach to Debussy. ... N[ew] Y[ork], G. Schirmer [c 1921]. xxii, 286 pp.; 19 cm.

101. Engel, Hans. Johann Sebastian Bach. ... Berlin, Walter de Gruyter, 1950. xi, 252 pp.; frontis.; illus. (music); 21 cm.

102. Engelhardt, Franz. Johann Sebastian Bach. Eine Betrachtung über sein Leben und seine Werke, Anlässlich seines 250. Geburtstages verfasst. ... Freudenthal, W. Krommer [1935]. 24 pp., frontis., pl., port., 23 cm.

103. Engelhardt, Walther. Johann Sebastian Bachs geistliche Sologesänge, Ein Führer für den praktischen Gebrauch. ... Kassel, Bärenreiter [1930]. 1 l., pp. 3-26, 1 l., 23 cm.
    "Erweiterter Sonderdruck aus der Zeitschrift 'Musik und Kirche' 1. Jahrgang, Heft 5 und 6."

104. Englund, Karl. Bach-studiet strödda anteckningar av Karl Englund. ... Stockholm, Klioförlaget, 1928-35. 4 vols. in 2. 21 cm.

105. Evangelical Lutheran Synod of Missouri, Ohio and Other States. Kirchen-Gesangbuch für Evangelisch-Lutherische gemeinden ungeänderter Augsburgischer Confession, darin des sel. Dr. Martin Luthers und anderer geistreichen Lehrer gebräuchlichste Kirchen-Lieder enthalten sind. St. Louis, Mo., Concordia, 1905. Pp. [iii]-xx, [1]-468, 14 cm.

106. Evangelisch-Lutherische Landeskirche in Württemberg. Gesangbuch für die evangelische Kirche in Württemberg. Stuttgart, Verlags-Comptoir des neuen evangelischen Gesangbuchs, 1863. 2 l., pp. [iii]-vi, [1]-434, [1]-134, [i]-vi. Frontis. (port.), 17 cm.

107. Feller, Camillo. Ein feste Burg auf einerlei Weise! ... Leipzig, Paul Eger, 1908, 121 pp., illus. (music), 23 cm.

108. [Ferris, George Titus, Ed.] The Great German Composers. New York, D. Appleton, 1881. 218, 4 pp.; 17 cm. (Appleton's New Handy Volume Series, No. 16.)

109. Ferris, George Titus. Great Musical Composers: German, French and Italian. ... Edited by Elizabeth A. Sharp. London and Felling-on-Tyne, Walter Scott Publishing Co. [ca. 1890]. xvi, 334 pp.; 9 ll.; 18 cm.

110. Fest-Aufführungen, zur Erinnerung an die Wiedererweckung der Matthäus-Passion durch die Singakademie zu Berlin am 11 März 1829 unter Leitung von Felix Mendelssohn. [Leipzig, Breitkopf & Härtel, 1929.] 45 pp., illus. (incl. music), facs., 24 cm.

111. Fetis, François Joseph. Traité du contrepoint et de la fugue contenant l'exposé analytique des règles de la composition musicale

depuis deux jusqu' à huit parties réelles, Ouvrage divisé en deux
parties.... Nouvelle édition. ... Paris, Ph. Maquet [1895]. 2 vols. in 1.
Illus. (music), 34 cm.
    Preface dated 10 janvier, 1846.
               P.N.: F.T. et Cie. 1760, F.T. et Cie. 1760 (2)

112. Field, Laurence Nathaniel. Johann Sebastian Bach. ... Minnea-
polis, Augsburg Publishing House, 1943. xxiv, 166 pp.; illus. (port.);
facs.; 22 cm.

113. Findeisen, Kurt Arnold. Gottes Orgel, Roman um Bach und
Händel... Mit einem Anhang. ... Berlin, Rich. Bong [c 1935]. 323,
[1] pp.; 2 ll.; illus.; facs. (incl. music); 20 cm.

114. —— Lockung des Lebens, Drei musikalische Geschichten... Mit
3 Original-Lithographien von Erich Gruner. Leipzig, Fr. Kistner &
C. F. W. Siegel, 1924. 56 pp., illus., 15 cm.

115. Florand, François. Jean-Sébastien Bach, l'oeuvre d'orgue; Suivi
d'un essai sur l'expression musicale du sentiment religieux. Préface
de Marcel Dupré. Paris, Editions du Cerf, 1947. 248 pp., illus. (incl.
music), 22 cm.
    Series: Collection L'Art et Dieu. Copy VII of 50 numbered copies,
of which 25 are in Roman numerals and reserved for M. Ploix, and
25 are in Arabic numerals.

116. Fock, Gustav. Die Wahrheit über Bachs Aufenthalt in Lüneburg...
Richtigstellungen zu Dr. E. W. Böhmes Schrift: Johann Sebastian
Bach in Lüneburg. Hamburg, Hansischer Gildenverlag, Joachim
Heitmann [c 1949]. 32 pp., illus., facs., 21 cm.

117. Forkel, Johann Nicolaus. Johann Sebastian Bach; His Life, Art,
and Work. Translated from the German... with notes and appendices
by Charles Sanford Terry. ... London, Constable, 1920. xxxii,
321 pp.; illus. (incl. ports.); 22 cm.

118. —— Life of John Sebastian Bach; with a critical view of his
compositions. Translated from the German. London, T. Boosey,
1820. xi, 116 pp.; 3 folding ll.; frontis.; 21 cm.
    Music examples on 3 engraved folding ll. at end of book. Frontis.,
engraved by Zollinger and dated 1802, after painting by Haussmann, is in reverse. Translated by A. F. C. Kollmann, according
to letter from Samuel Wesley, November 23, 1820.

119. —— Ueber Johann Sebastian Bachs Leben, Kunst und Kunstwerke; Für patriotische Verehrer echter musikalischer Kunst; Von
J. N. Forkel. ... Leipzig, Hoffmeister und Kühnel, Bureau de musique,
1802. x, 69 pp.; 2 ll. (music examples); frontis.; boards; 23 cm.
    Bach's portrait, engraved by F. W. Nettling, after Haussmann's
painting. Title page bears stamp of Bernhard Friedr. Richter.

120. —— Ueber Johann Sebastian Bach's Leben, Kunst und Kunstwerke; Für patriotische Verehrer echter musikalischer Kunst...Neue,

120. *(continued)* unveränderte Ausgabe. ... Leipzig, C. F. Peters, Bureau de musique, 1855. viii, 48 pp.; 1 l.; 4 pp.; frontis.; 27 cm. Portrait lithographed by Dr. von L. Blau & Co. is frontispiece. Tilet page bears signature of E duard Hanslick and notation Wien, 1860.

121. —— Ueber Johann Sebastian Bachs Leben, Kunst und Kunstwerke...Nach der Originalausgabe von 1802 neu herausgegeben mit Einleitung und ausführlichem Nachwort von Josef M. Müller-Blattau. Augsburg, Bärenreiter, 1925. 111, [1] pp.; illus.; 23 cm.

122. —— Ueber Johann Sebastian Bachs Leben, Kunst und Kunstwerke...Nach der Originalausgabe von 1802 neu herausgegeben mit Einleitung und ausführlichem Nachwort von Josef Müller-Blattau. Vierte, neuarbeitete Auflage. Kassel und Basel, Bärenreiter, 1950. 103, [1] pp.; 24 cm.

123. —— Vie, talents et travaux de Jean-Sébastien Bach. Ouvrage traduit de l'allemand...annoté et précédé d'un aperçu de l'état de la musique en Allemagne aux xvie et xviie siècles par Félix Grenier. ... Paris, J. Baur, 1876. 3 ll., 286 pp., 1 l. (entirely unopened), illus., facs., 18 cm., original wrappers.

124. Franck, Hans. Die Pilgerfahrt nach Lübeck, Eine Bach-Novelle. Gütersloh, C. Bertelsmann, 1950. 94, [1] pp.; 19 cm. (Das kleine Buch 5.)

125. Frank, Ernst. Erläuterungen zur Johannes-Passion von J. S. Bach ... dargeboten von E. Frank. Hannover, Adolf Nagel, 1885. 19 pp., 21 cm.

126. —— Erläuterungen zur Matthaeus-Passion von J. S. Bach... dargeboten von E. Frank. Hannover, Adolph Nagel, n.d. 32 pp., 22 cm.

127. Franke, Friedrich Wilhelm. Johann Sebastian Bachs Kirchen-Kantaten mit einer Einführung in ihre Geschichte, ihr Wesen und ihre Bedeutung herausgegeben von F. W. Franke. Leipzig, Philipp Reclam, jun. [1925]. 2 vols. 15 cm. (Reclams Universal Bibliothek, Nos. 6565, 6818.)

128. Franz, Robert. Gesammelte Schriften über die Wiederbelebung Bach'scher und Händel'scher Werke. Mit einem Begleitwort des königlichen Universitätsmusikdirektors Professor O. Reubke zu Halle a. S. und einem Anhang enthaltend Notenbeispiele herausgegeben von Robert Bethge. Leipzig, F. E. C. Leuckart, 1910. viii, 92 pp.; 2 ll.; 72 pp. (music); illus. (music); 23 cm.

P.N. (music only): F.E.C.L. 6583

129. —— Johann Sebastian Bachs Cantata "Wer da gläubet und getaufft wird" bearbeitet von Robert Franz. ... Königsberg, Verlag der Expedition der Tonkunst [1877]. 4 ll., 79 pp., 4 ll., music supp., illus. (music), 24 cm.

Separat-Abdruck aus "Die Tonkunst." Music supp. has separate pagination, 17-23.   P.N.: F.E.C.L. 2323

130. —— Mittheilungen über Johann Sebastian Bach's "Magnificat" von Robert Franz, Zweite durchgesehene Auflage. Leipzig, F. E. C. Leuckart, 1889. 26 pp., 1 l.; 6 ll. (ads), 22 cm.

131. —— Offener Brief an Eduard Hanslick über Bearbeitungen älterer Tonwerke namentlich Bach'scher und Händel'scher Vocalmusik. ... Leipzig, F. E. C. Leuckart (Constantin Sander), 1871. 40 pp., illus. (music), 23 cm.

132. Fuller-Maitland, John Alexander. The "48" Bach's Wohltemperirtes Clavier...Book I [and Book II]. London, Oxford University Press, Humphrey Milford, 1925. 2 vols. Illus. (music), 17 cm. (The Musical Pilgrim.)
General editor: Arthur Somervell.

133. —— Bach's "Brandenburg" Concertos. ... London, Oxford University Press, Humphrey Milford, 1929. 47, [1] p.; illus. (music); 17 cm. (The Musical Pilgrim.)
General editor: Arthur Somervell.

134. —— The Keyboard Suites of J. S. Bach. ... Second impression. London, Oxford University Press, Humphrey Milford, 1928. 74 pp., 1 l., illus. (music), 17 cm. (The Musical Pilgrim.)
General editor: Arthur Somervell.

135. Galston, Gottfried. Studienbuch von Gottfried Galston...2 (vermehrte) Auflage. Munich, Otto Halbreiter [c 1921]. 4 ll., 45 pp., illus. (music), 24 cm.

136. Gannett, Kent. Bach's Harmonic Progressions (One Thousand Examples). ... Philadelphia, Oliver Ditson [c 1942]. v, 51 pp.; 27 cm. P.N.: 78372-51.

137. Geiringer, Karl. The Bach Family, Seven Generations of Creative Genius. London, George Allen & Unwin [c 1954]. xiv, [2], 514, [2] pp.; illus.; ports.; facs. (incl. music); 24 cm.
At head of title: Karl Geiringer in Collaboration with Irene Geiringer.

138. —— The Lost Portrait of J. S. Bach. ... New York, Oxford University Press, 1950. 2 ll., [8] pp., (illus.), 23 cm.

139. Gerber, Ernst Ludwig. Historisch-biographisches Lexicon der Tonkünstler. ... Leipzig, verlegts J. G. I. Breitkopf, 1790-92. 2 vols. in 1. Ports., 23 cm.

140. —— Neues historisch-biographisches Lexikon der Tonkünstler, welches Nachrichten von dem Leben und den Werken musikalischer Schriftsteller, berühmter Komponisten...älterer und neuerer Zeit, aus aller Nationen enthält. ... Leipzig, A. Kühnel, 1812-14. 4 vols. 24 cm.
Uncut and partly unopened.

141. Gérold, Théodore. J.-S. Bach...biographie critique. ... Paris, Librairie Renouard, 1925. 126 pp., 1 l., illus. (incl. music), facs. (incl. music), 20 cm. (Les Musiciens célèbres.)

142. Gerstenberg, Walter. Die Zeitmasse und ihre Ordnungen in Bachs Musik. ... [Einbeck, Carl Schleicher & Schüll, 1952.] 27, [2] pp.; 21 cm.

143. Gerster, Matthäus. Um Bach und Beethoven; Novellen von Matthäus Gerster, Wilhelm Schäfer, Karl Söhle, Adolf Stern und Richard Wagner; Mit zwei Bildtafeln. Stuttgart, Strecker und Schröder, 1927. 2 ll., 232, [1] pp., 1 l., illus., 19 cm.

144. Goethe, Johann Wolfgang von. Briefwechsel zwischen Goethe und Zelter in den Jahren 1799 bis 1832. Mit Einleitung und Erläuterungen herausgegeben von...Ludwig Geiger. Leipzig, Philipp Reclam, jun., [1902-04]. 3 vols. 14 cm. (Reclams Universal Bibliothek, Nos. 4581-85a, 4591-95a, 4606-10a.)
Vol. I, "Einleitung," dated 1902; Vol. III, "Nachträge und Berichtungen," dated 20 Januar, 1904.

145. Gräbner, Augustus Lawrence. Johann Sebastian Bach. ... Milwaukee, Wis., George Brumder, 1885. 160 pp., frontis. (photograph), 18 cm.

146. Grace, Harvey. Bach. ... London, Novello, [1930?]. 1 l., 22 pp., 19 cm. (Novello's Biographies of Great Musicians.)
General editor: W. McNaught.

147. —— The Organ Works of Bach...with an introduction by Ernest Newman. London, Novello, [1922]. xvi pp., 1 l., 319 pp., illus. (music), 22 cm.
At head of title: Handbooks for musicians edited by Ernest Newman. Author's preface, p. xi, states that this is "...a revised and amplified form of a series of articles that appeared in the *Musical Times* from January, 1920 to August, 1921."

148. Gray, Cecil. Bach and "Das wohltemperirte Klavier". ... [London, The Gramophone Company, 1934?] 33 pp., illus. (music), 24 cm.
Half-title: The Bach Society, Volume One.

149. —— The Forty-Eight Preludes and Fugues of J. S. Bach. ... London, Oxford University Press, 1938. viii, 148 pp.; illus. (music); 19 cm.

150. Grenzeboten, Die. Zeitschrift für Politik, Literatur und Kunst. Leipzig, Fr. Wilh. Grunow, 1841-. 25 cm.
Library has Vol. 65, No. 26 (June 28, 1906).

151. Grew, Eva Mary (Instone), Ed. Bach, by Eva Mary and Sydney Grew. London, J. M. Dent and Sons, [c 1947]. xiv, 239 pp.; illus. (incl. music); facs. (incl. music); 18 cm. (The Master Musicians.)
General editor: Eric Blom.

152. Grey, Robin, Ed. Studies in Music by Various Authors Reprinted from "The Musician" and Edited by Robin Grey. London, Simpkin, Marshall, Hamilton, Kent and Co., 1901. vii, 339 pp.; frontis. (port.); 22 cm.

153. Grolman, Adolf von. Johann Sebastian Bach. Heidelberg, Lambert Schneider [1948]. 223, [1] pp.; illus. (music); 21 cm.
154. Grosse-Weischede, A. Orgelbau, Orgelton und Orgelspiel. ... Bochum, Wilhelm Stumpf, 1910. vi, 183 pp.; illus. (incl. music); 24 cm.
155. Grosser, Johann Emanuel. Lebensbeschreibung des Kapellmeister des Fürsten von Köthen, hernach Musikdirektor an der Thomasschule zu Leipzig und königl. polnischer Hofkomponist Johann Sebastian Bach; Nebst einer Sammlung interessanter Anekdoten und Erzählungen grössentheils aus dem Leben berühmter Tonkünstler und ihrer Kunstverwandten. ... Breslau, J. D. Grüson, [1825?]. 147, xvi pp.; frontis.; 16 cm.
156. Grove, sir George. Grove's Dictionary of Music and Musicians. Fifth edition, edited by Eric Blom. London, Macmillan, 1954. 9 vols. Illus., facs. (incl. music), 23 cm.
157. Gumprecht, Otto. Unsere klassischen Meister, Musikalische Lebens- und Charakterbilder. ... Leipzig, H. Haessel, 1883, 1885. 2 vols. 20 cm.
    Library has Vol. I.
158. Gurlitt, Willibald. Johann Sebastian Bach der Meister und sein Werk. ... Berlin, Furche-Verlag, [1936]. 78, [1] pp.; frontis. (port.); 21 cm.
159. —— Johann Sebastian Bach der Meister und sein Werk. 3. Auflage. Kassel und Basel, Bärenreiter, [1949]. 116 pp., frontis. (port.), 19 cm.
160. Hadden, James Cuthbert. Master Musicians, a Book for Players, Singers & Listeners. ... London, T. N. Foulis, 1913. x pp., 1 l., 254 pp., illus. (ports.), 20 cm.
161. Hamburg. Staats- und Universitäts-Bibliothek. Die Musik Hamburgs im Zeitalter Seb. Bachs; Ausstellung anlässlich des neunten deutschen Bachfestes zu Hamburg 3-7 Juni 1921 in Gemeinschaft mit dem Hamburgischen Staatsarchiv und dem Hamburgischen Museum für Kunst und Gewerbe veranstaltet von der Hamburger Staats- und Universitäts-Bibliothek. Hamburg, 1921. viii, 84 pp.; illus. (frontis., 4 plates at end); 25 cm.
    General editor: G. Wahl.
162. Hamel, Fred. Johann Sebastian Bach geistige Welt. ... Göttingen, Deuerlichsche Verlagsbuchhandlung [c1 961]., xi, 243, [1] pp.; illus (ports.); facs. (incl. music.); 20 cm.
163. Handke ,Robert, Bachsche Choralkunst uud Gemeindegesang. Berlin, Trowitzsch & Sohn [1915?]. 24 pp., illus. (music), 24 cm.
    Sonderabdruck aus: Die Stimme. Centralblatt für Stimm- und Tonbildung...Jahrgang 1914/15.
164. Hannam, William S. Notes on the Church Cantatas of John Sebastian Bach. ... London, Oxford University Press, 1928. 3 ll., 128 pp., 19 cm.

165.   Hartog, Jacques. Joh. Seb. Bach. ... Amsterdam, Scheltens &
Giltay, [1915?]. viii, 155 pp.; illus. (incl. music); ports.; facs. (incl.
music); 25 cm.

166.   Hashagen, D. Fr. Johann Sebastian Bach als Sänger und Musiker
des Evangeliums und der Lutherischen Reformation; Skizzen von
D. Fr. Hashagen. ... Wismar, Mecklenburg, Hans Bartholdi, 1909.
163 pp., 23 cm.

167.   —— Johann Sebastian Bach als Sänger und Musiker des
Evangeliums und der Lutherischen Reformation; Skizzen von
D. Fr. Hashagen. ... 4. Auflage. Emmishofen, Switzerland, Evange-
lischen Buchhandlung, c 1925. 163 pp., 22 cm.

168.   Hasse, Karl. Johann Sebastian Bach. ... Bielefeld und Leipzig,
Velhagen und Klasing, 1925. 178, [1] pp.; illus.; ports.; facs. (incl.
music); 22 cm.

169.   Hauptmann, Moritz. Briefe von Moritz Hauptmann Kantor und
Musikdirektor an der Thomasschule zu Leipzig an Franz Hauser.
Herausgegeben von Prof. Dr. Alfred Schöne. Erster (Zweiter) Band.
Mit Hauptmann's Bildniss. Leipzig, Breitkopf & Härtel, 1871.
2 vols. Illus. (port.), (incl. music), 20 cm.

170.   —— Erläuterungen zu Joh. Sebastian Bachs Kunst der Fuge. ...
Leipzig, C. F. Peters, 1841. 14 pp., illus. (music), 27 cm.

171.   —— Erläuterungen zu Joh. Sebastian Bach's Kunst der Fuge. ...
Neue, unveränderte Ausgabe. Leipzig, C. F. Peters, 1881. 14 pp.,
illus. (music), 27 cm.

172.   —— Erläuterungen zu Joh. Sebastian Bach's Kunst der Fuge. ...
Neue unveränderte Ausgabe. Leipzig, C. F. Peters [1929]. 14 pp.,
illus. (music), 27 cm. (Edition Peters, No. 8.)

173.   Hausegger, Friedrich von. Unsere deutschen Meister; Bach,
Mozart, Beethoven, Wagner. ... Munich, F. Bruckmann A.-G., 1901.
xv, 244 pp.; 26 cm.

174.   Hausvater, Der. Evangelisch-kirchliches Monatsblatt für Leipzig
und Umgegend. Leipzig, E. Haberland, 1908. 24 cm.
        Library has Vol. 17, No. 8 (May, 1908).

175.   Hayes, Gerald Ravenscourt. The Viols and Other Bowed
Instruments. With an Introduction by Arnold Dolmetsch. ... London,
Oxford University Press, Humphrey Milford, 1930. xxii, 265 pp.;
XI plates; illus. (incl. music); 20 cm. (Musical Instruments and
Their Music 1500-1750, No. 2.)

176.   Heinrich, E. Johann Sebastian Bach, Ein kurzes Lebensbild. ...
Berlin, Wilhelm Baensch, 1885. 56 pp., 22 cm.

177.   Henderson, William James. The Story of Music. ... New York,
Longmans, Green, 1890. xvii, 212 pp., 19 cm.
        Second edition, revised.

178.   Henrici, Christian Friedrich [pseud.: Picander]. La Passion selon
Saint Matthieu de J.-S. Bach. Geneva, H. Jarrys, 1911. 32 pp., 23 cm.

Translated into French by M. Ch. Bannelier. At head of title: Société de chant sacré de Genève (LXXXIIIe année).

179. —— Passionsmusik nach dem Evangelium Matthäi Cap. 26 und 27 von Johann Sebastian Bach. Leipzig, C. F. Peters, n.d. 40 pp., 18 cm. Foreword by Hermann Kretzschmar.

180. Herz, Gerhard. Johann Sebastian Bach im Zeitalter des Rationalismus und der Frühromantik, Zur Geschichte der Bachbewegung von ihren Anfängen bis zur Wiederaufführung der Matthäuspassion im Jahre 1829. Kassel, Bärenreiter, 1935. vi, 104 pp.; 23 cm.

181. Hesselbacher, Karl. Le Cinquième Évangéliste Jean-Sébastien Bach, Sa vie et son oeuvre racontées au peuple par Charles Hesselbacher. Traduit de l'allemand par Madame J. Paris. Neuchatel, Paris, Delachaux & Niestlé [c 1937]. 91 pp. (entirely unopened), illus., ports., facs. (music), 19 cm.

182. —— Der fünfte Evangelist, Das Leben von Johann Sebastian Bach dem Volk erzählt von Karl Hesselbacher. Stuttgart, Quell-Verlag [c 1934]. 95 pp., frontis., 17 cm.

183. Heuss, Alfred Valentin. Johann Sebastian Bachs Matthäuspassion von Alfred Heuss. Leipzig, Breitkopf & Härtel [c 1909]. viii, 166 pp.; illus. (music); 19 cm.

184. —— Magnificat von Johann Sebastian Bach, Kleiner Konzertführer von Alfred Heuss. Leipzig, Breitkopf & Härtel, n.d. 14 pp., illus. (music), 17 cm. (Breitkopf & Härtels Musikbücher, No. 635.)

185. Heydt, Johann Daniel von der. Johann Sebastian Bach. ... Berlin, Verlag des Evangelischen Bundes, 1935. 16 pp., chart, 20 cm. (Der Heliand, Volksmissionarische Hefte Nr. 24, II Reihe: Geschichte.)

186. Hilgenfeldt, C. L. Johann Sebastian Bach's Leben, Wirken und Werke; Ein Beitrag zur Kunstgeschichte des achtzehnten Jahrhunderts...Als Programm zu dem am 28. Julius 1850 eintretenden Säcularlage des Todes von Johann Sebastian Bach, Mit einer genealogischen Tabelle und Notenbeilagen. Leipzig, Friedrich Hofmeister [1850]. 1 l.; x, 182 pp.; 5 ll.; folding plate; 28 cm.

187. Hiller, Johann Adam. Lebensbeschreibungen berühmter Musikgelehrten und Tonkunstler, neuerer Zeit...Erster Theil. Leipzig, Dykische Buchhandlung, 1784. 7 ll., pp. [1]-320, illus. (music), 20 cm.

188. Hindemith, Paul. Johann Sebastian Bach, Heritage and Obligation. ... New Haven, Yale University Press; London, Oxford University Press, 1952. 1 l., 44 pp., illus. (incl. music), 20 cm.
     Note on p. [3]: Johann Sebastian Bach. A speech delivered on September 12, 1950 at the Bach commemoration of the city of Hamburg, Germany.

189. Hinrichs, Friedrich. Johann Sebastian Bach (J. S. Bach von C. H. Bitter, Berlin, 1865, 2 Bände.) Berlin, Georg Reimer, 1865. pp. [305]-324, 24 cm.
     Review reprinted from Preussische Jahrbücher, Bd. XVI, Heft 4.

190.   His, Wilhelm. Anatomische Forschungen über Johann Sebastian
Bach's Gebeine und Antlitz nebst Bemerkungen über dessen Bilder. ...
Leipzig, S. Hirzel, 1895. 2 ll., pp. [381]-420, illus., folding charts,
26 cm. (Abhandlung der mathematisch-physischen Classe der
Königl. Sächsischen Gesellschaft der Wissenchaften, Band 22, No. 5.)
191.   Hitzig, Wilhelm. Johann Sebastian Bach 1685-1750, Sein Leben
in Bildern. ... Leipzig, Bibliographisches Institut [c 1935]. 32 pp.,
23 ll. (45 plates), illus., 18 cm.
192.   Hoelty-Nickel, Theodore, Ed. The Little Bach Book. Valparaiso,
Indiana, Valparaiso University Press [c 1950]. 6 ll., 162 pp., illus.,
facs. (incl. music), 22 cm.
    Contents: Bach essays by Kretzmann, Naumann, Nettl, Rosenwald,
    Fleischer, Buszin, Farmer and Brady.
193.   Hofmeister, Adolph, Ed. C. F. Whistling's Handbuch der musikalischen Literatur... Dritte, bis Anfang des Jahres 1844 ergänzte
Auflage. ... Leipzig, Friedrich Hofmeister, 1845, 1844. 3 vols. 29 cm.
    Library has Vols. 1 and 2.
    General title page dated 1845; title page for Vols. 1 and 2 dated
    1844.
194.   Hopkinson, Cecil. A Dictionary of Parisian Music Publishers,
1700-1950. ... London, printed for the author, 1954. xiv, 131 pp.;
illus. (facs); 29 cm.
    Copy, numbered 120, of a limited edition of 300 copies.
195.   Hubbard, Elbert. Little Journeys to the Homes of Great
Musicians: Sebastian Bach. ... East Aurora, N. Y., Roycrofters, 1901.
4 ll., pp. 111-136, 3 ll., illus. (port.), 20 cm. (Vol. VIII, No. 5 of
series.)
    Signature on cover: Franklin Brooks.
196.   Huber, Anna Gertrud. Johann Sebastian Bach als Meister der
"Gemüthsergoetzung". ... Zürich, Speer, 1948. 72 pp., 18 plates,
illus., facs. (incl. music), 24 cm.
197.   Huggler, Hans Erwin. Johann Sebastian Bachs Orgelbüchlein.
Inaugural-Dissertation der philosophischen Facultät i. der Universität
Bern... vorgelegt von Hans Erwin Huggler von Bern. Bern, O. Wehrlin
[1930?]. viii, 128 pp.,; 6 ll.; 11 pp. (separate music supp.); 24 cm.
198.   Hull, Arthur Eaglefield. Bach's Organ Works...With a complete
list of arrangements of the organ works for pianoforte and other
instruments by Harold T. Scull. ... London, Office of "Musical
Opinion," 1929. 4 ll., 189 pp., 1 l., illus. (music), 19 cm.
199.   Humiston, William Henry. The Lighter Side of Bach. ... New
York City [1922]. 1 l., pp. 148-57, illus., 22 cm.
    Reprinted from M.T.N.A. *Proceedings*, 1922.
200.   —— Little Biographies...with Illustrations, Bach. New York,
Breitkopf Publications [c 1921]. 24 pp., 4 ll., illus., facs., 15 cm.
(Little Biographies, Series I: Musicians.)

201. Hutchins, Farley Kennan. Dietrich Buxtehude, the Man, His Misic, His Era. ... Paterson (New Jersey), Music Textbook Company, c 1955. 68 pp., 1 l., illus. (music), 23 cm.

Autographed by the author.

202. Iliffe, Frederick. The Forty-Eight Preludes and Fugues of John Sebastian Bach, Analysed for the Use of Students. ... London, Novello [1927?]. v, 194 pp.; illus. (music), 28 cm. (Novello's Music Primers and Educational Series.)

203. Inselschiff, Das. Eine Zweimonatsschrift für die Freunde des Insel-Verlages. Leipzig, Insel-Verlag, 1919-. 23 cm.

Library has Vol. 3, No. 6 (August, 1922). Contents include: Wilhelm Altmann, "Zu Johann Sebastian Bachs Passionsmusik nach dem Evangelium Matthäi."

204. Internationale Bach-Gesellschaft. Bach-Gedenkschrift 1950 im Auftrag der Internationalen Bach-Gesellschaft herausgegeben von Karl Matthaei. Zurich, Atlantis [c 1950]. 216 pp., illus. (music), 22 cm.

Contents: essays by Straube, Besch, Blankenburg, Ferchault, Smend, Schrade, Schweitzer, Reinhart, Westrup, Matthaei, von Fischer, Ansbacher, Husmann, Schmieder, Ramin, Pfatteicher, and Ebner.

205. Jadassohn, Salomon. Erläuterungen der in Joh. Seb. Bach's Kunst der Fuge enthaltenen Fugen und Kanons...Sonderausgabe des Anhanges zu des Verfassers "Lehre vom Kanon und von der Fuge." Leipzig, Breitkopf & Härtel, 1899. 43 pp., illus. (music), 23 cm.

206. —— Erläuterungen zu ausgewählten Fugen aus Johann Sebastian Bach's Wohltemperirtem Clavier...Supplement zu des Verfassers Lehrbuch des Canons und der Fuge. Leipzig, F. E. C. Leuckart [1877]. 58 pp., 1 l., illus. (music), 23 cm.

207. —— Zur Einführung in J. S. Bach's Passionsmusik nach dem Evangelisten Matthaeus. ... Berlin, "Harmonie" Verlagsgesellschaft [1898]. 56 pp., 2 ll., illus. (music), 23 cm.

208. Jähne, Margarete. Die Passion des Johann Sebastian Bach, Eine kleine Erzählung von Christine Holstein. Leipzig, Koehler & Amelang [c 1935]. 166, [2] pp.; frontis.; 19 cm.

209. Jahrbuch der Musikbibliothek Peters. Leipzig, C. F. Peters, 1895-1939. 45 vols., 26 cm.

210. Jöde, Fritz. Die Kunst Bachs dargestellt an seinen Inventionen. ... Wolfenbüttel, Georg Kallmeyer, 1926. 223, [1] pp.; illus. (music); 21 cm. (Organik, Band 1.)

211. Johannes-Passion. Oratorium von Johann Sebastian Bach. Leipzig, C. F. Peters, n.d. 1 l., 19 pp., 18 cm.

Libretto only. Foreword signed by Hermann Kretzschmar, who edited the text.

212. Julian, John, Ed. A Dictionary of Hymnology, Setting Forth the Origin and History of Christian Hymns. ... London, John

212. *(continued)* Murray, 1892. 2 ll., pp. [v]-xii, [1]-1616, 21 cm. Handwritten note on last page: Mr John Murray, the Publisher of this Dictionary, died April 1892, in his 84th year. The publication of this work cost him £3700.

213. Kehrer, Jodok. Joh. Seb. Bach als Orgelkomponist und seine Bedeutung für den kath. Organisten. ... Regensburg, Friedrich Pustet, 1920. 175 pp., illus. (music), 17 cm. (Sam mlung "Kirchenmusik" herausgegeben von ... Karl Weinmann ... Doppelbändchen I XX und XX.)

214. Kekule, Stephan. Festrede zum Gedenktage des fünfzigjährigen Bestehens des "Herold," Gehalten am 4 November 1919 von Dr. Stephan Kekule von Stradonitz, Sonderdruck aus der Zeitschrift "Der Deutsche Herold" 1920 Nr. 1. [Berlin, Julius Sittenfeld, 1920.] Anniversary paper concerning the work done by a genealogical society, including studies on the Bach family tree. Autograph inscription, signed by author and dated 21.2.20.

215. Keller, Hermann. Johann Sebastian Bach der Künstler und sein Werk. Stuttgart, Alfons Bürger-Verlag, 1947. 96 pp., illus. (incl. music), facs. (incl. music), 19 cm.

216. —— Die musikalische Artikulation inbesondere bei Joh. Seb. Bach ... Mit 342 Notenbeispielen und einem Anhang: Versuch einer Artikulation der Fugenthemen des Wohltemperierten Klaviers und der Orgelwerke. Stuttgart, C. L. Schultheiss-Musikverlag, 1925. 4 ll., pp. 1-144, illus. (music), 22 cm. (Veröffentlichungen des Musik-Instituts der Universität Tübingen. Heft II.) Foreword signed by Karl Hasse, general editor of series.

217. —— Die Orgelwerke Bachs; Ein Beitrag zu ihrer Geschichte, Form, Deutung und Wiedergabe. Leipzig, C. F. Peters [c 1948]. 228 pp., illus. (incl. music), 27 cm.

218. Kenyon, Max. Harpsichord Music: A survey of the virginals, spinet, harpsichord and their Continental equivalents; the people who played upon them; the composers for them; and the music they wrote. ... London, Toronto, Melbourne, etc., Cassell. 1949. 256 pp., illus. (incl. music), 22 cm.

219. Kinsky, Georg. Die Originalausgaben der Werke Johann Sebastian Bachs, Ein Beitrag zur Musikbibliographie. ... Vienna, Leipzig, etc., Herbert Reichner [c 1937]. 134 pp., 21 cm.

220. —— Pedalklavier oder Orgel bei Bach. ... Basel [Bärenreiter], 1937. Pp. 158-61, 26 cm. Reprinted from *Acta Musicologica*, January, 1937. Inscribed to Albert Riemenschneider and annotated by the author.

221. Kirchenchor, Der. Zeitschrift des Kirchenchorverbandes der sächsischen Landeskirche, herausgegeben vom Vorstande des Verbandes. Rötha, G. Apitz, 1908-19. 26 cm. Library has Vol. 19, No. 6 (1908); Vol. 21, No. 2 (1910); Vol. 27, No. 3 (1916).

222. Kirchenmusikalisches Jahrbuch. Gegrundet von Dr. F. X. Haberl.
Regensburg, Rome, New York, etc., Friedrich Pustet [neue Folge]
[1886]-19-. 25 cm.
   No volumes issued for 1904, 1906. Library has Vols. 21-24 (1908-11),
   bound in 2 vols.
223. Kirnberger, Johann Philipp. Die Kunst des reinen Satzes in der
Musik aus sicheren Grundsätzen hergeleitet und mit deutlichen
Beyspielen erläutert von Joh. Phil. Kirnberger. ... Berlin und
Königsberg, G. J. Decker und G. L. Hartung, 1774-79. 2 vols. in 1.
Illus. (music), laid paper, music examples printed, 21 cm.
   Vol. II in 3 parts, each having special title page, with imprint, and
   dated 1776, 1777, 1779.
   Errors in pagination: Vol. I has 134 for 234; Vol. II, part 1, has
   [3] unnumbered; Vol. II, part 2, has 27 for 72.
224. —— Die wahren Grundsätze zum Gebrauch der Harmonie,
darinn deutlich gezeiget wird, wie alle möglichen Accorde aus dem
Dreyklang und dem wesentlichen Septimenaccord, und deren dis-
sonirdenden Vorhälten, herzuleiten und zu erklären sind, als ein
Zusatz zu der Kunst der reinen Satzes in der Musik, von Johann
Philipp Kirnberger, ... Berlin und Königsberg, G. J. Decker und
G. L. Hartung, 1773. 115 [i.e., 113] pp., illus. (music), laid paper,
music examples printed, 22 cm.
   Signature of C. Pohsner on front flyleaf; signature of Ludwig
   Wachtel [?] on front flyleaf and title page. Page 113 misnumbered
   115.
225. Klee, Ludwig. Die Ornamentik der klassischen Klavier-Musik;
Enthaltend: die Verzierungen der klassischen Klavier-Musik, von
J. S. Bach bis auf L. van Beethoven, leicht fasslich erklärt und...
erläutert. ... Leipzig, Breitkopf & Härtel [1879?]. 3 ll., 45 pp.,
33 cm.
   At head of title: Herrn Professor Dr. Theodor Kullak verehrungsvoll
   zugeeignet.   P.N.: 14925
226. Kleinert, Paul. Musik und Religion, Gottesdienst und Volksfeier,
Rückschau und Ausblick. ... Leipzig, J. C. Hinrichs'sche Buchhandlung, 1908. 4 ll., 106 pp., 20 cm.
227. Knorr, Iwan Otto Armand. Die Fugen des "Wohltemperierten
Klaviers" von Joh. Seb. Bach in bildlicher Darstellung als Anhang
und Ergänzung zu seinem Lehrbuch der Fugen-Komposition herausgegeben von Iwan Knorr. Leipzig, Breitkopf & Härtel, 1912. 5 ll.,
48 pp., 23 cm.
   Added title page in English and French; all explanatory notes in
   German, English, and French.
228. Kobelt, Martin. J. S. Bachs 'Grosses Magnificat in D-dur' und
die für Anlage der Composition massgebenden, günstigen und un-
günstigen Factoren; Inaugural-Dissertation zur Erlangung der

228. *(continued)* Doctorwürde. ... Greifswald, F. W. Kunike, 1902.
71 pp., 1 folding l., 2 ll., 4 ll., illus. (music), 23 cm.

229. Kollmann, August Friedrich Christoph. An Essay on Musical
Harmony, according to the nature of that science and the principles
of the greatest musical authors. ... London, J. Dale, M,DCC,XCVI
[1796]. xviii, 128, 40 pp. (engraved music); laid paper; 34 cm.
   Signature of A. F. C. Kollmann on title page. Ex libris of A. H. Fox
   Strangways on front pastedown.

230. —— An Essay on Practical Musical Composition, according to
the nature of that science and the principles of the greatest musical
authors. ... London, printed for the author, M,DCC,XCIX [1799].
xx, 106 pp.; 1 l.; 67 pp. (engraved music); laid paper; 34 cm.
   Signatures of A. F. C. Kollmann and I. Evan on title page;
   signature of Robert Lindley, April 20th, 1809, on front pastedown.

231. Korte, Werner. Johann Sebastian Bach. ... Berlin, Max Hesse
[1935]. 16 pp., illus., 24 cm. (Musikalische Schriftenreihe No. 11.)
   General editor: Walter Stang.

232. Kreisler, Fritz. Valuable and Important Incunabula and Other
Rare Early Printed Books and Illuminated Manuscripts Together
with Notable Specimens of Later Periods Collected by Fritz Kreisler
and Sold by Order of The Golden Rule Foundation...and the Lenox
Hill Hospital...Public auction sale...Parke-Bernet Galleries, Inc.
New York, Parke-Bernet Galleries, 1949. 3 ll., 127 pp., illus., facs.,
27 cm.

233. Kretzschmar, August Ferdinand Hermann. Bach-Kolleg, Vorlesungen über Johann Sebastian Bach gehalten an der Universität
zu Berlin. ... Leipzig, Breitkopf & Härtel, 1922. 1 l., 90 pp., illus.
(music), 23 cm.

234. —— Führer durch den Konzertsaal...I. Abteilung: Sinfonie und
Suite. I. Band [and II. Band]. Vierte, vollständig neuarbeitete
Auflage. Leipzig, Breitkopf & Härtel, 1913. 2 vols. in 1. 21 cm.
   Incomplete: Abteilung II and III wanting.

235. —— J. S. Bach's "Christmas Oratorio"; Separate Issue from
"Guide Through the Concert-Room," by Hermann Kretzschmar.
English translation by Percy Pinkerton. Leipzig, Breitkopf & Härtel,
n.d. 16 pp., illus. (music), 17 cm. (Breitkopf & Härtel's Music Books,
No. 552a.)

236. —— Joh. Seb. Bach's Mass in B minor; Separate issue from
"Guide Through the Concert-Room," by Herman Kretzschmar.
English Translation by Francis Weber. Leipzig, Breitkopf & Härtel,
n.d. 18 pp., illus. (music), 17 cm. (Breitkopf & Härtel's Music Books,
No. 503.)

237. —— Johannes-Passion von Joh. Seb. Bach, Einzelausgabe aus
dem "Führer durch den Konzertsaal". ... Leipzig, Breitkopf & Härtel,
n.d. 20 pp., 17 cm. (Breitkopf & Härtels Musikbücher, No. 501.)

238. —— Matthäus-Passion von Joh. Seb. Bach, Einzelausgabe aus dem "Führer durch den Konzertsaal" ... Leipzig, Breitkopf & Härtel, [1898]. 23 pp., illus. (music), 17 cm. (Breitkopf & Härtels Musikbücher, No. 502.)

239. —— Matthäus-Passion von Joh. Seb. Bach, Einzelausgabe aus dem "Führer durch den Konzertsaal". ... Mit dem Texte des Werkes. Leipzig, Breitkopf & Härtel, n.d. 47 pp., illus. (music), 17 cm. (Breitkopf & Härtels Musikbücher, No. $\frac{26}{502}$.)

240. —— Weihnachtsoratorium von Sebastian Bach, Einzelausgab, aus dem "Führer durch den Konzertsaal". ... Leipzig, Breitkopf & Härtel, n.d. 14 pp., illus. (music), 17 cm. (Breitkopf & Härtel's Musikbücher, No. 552.)

241. Kruse, Georg Richard. Joh. Seb. Bach Matthäus-Passion, Johannes-Passion und H-moll Messe. Zweite Auflage. ... Leipzig, Philipp Reclam, jun. [1920?]. 55 pp., 15 cm. (Oratorientexte, 1. Band.)
Reclams Universal Bibliothek, No. 5918.

242. Kurth, Ernst. Grundlagen des linearen Kontrapunkts Bachs melodische Polyphonie. ... Zweite Auflage. Berlin, Max Hesse, 1922. xii, 532 pp.; illus. (music); 24 cm.

243. Lahee, Henry Charles. The Organ and Its Masters, A short account of the most celebrated organists... together with a brief sketchof the development of organ construction, organ music and organ playing. ... Boston, L. C. Page, 1903. 5 ll., 345 pp., illus., 20 cm.

244. Landowska, Wanda. Bach et ses interprètes, Sur l'interprétation des oeuvres de clavecin de J.-S. Bach. [Poitiers, Blais et Roy, 1905.] 16, 8 pp.; 22 cm.
Reprint from November 15, 1905 issue of the *Mercure de France*.

245. —— Le Clavecin chez Bach. N.p. [ca. 1912]. 16 pp., 26 cm.
Inscribed by author: Au docteur Edgar Istel très sympathiquement, Wanda Landowska. 1912.

246. Landshoff, Ludwig. Joh. Seb. Bach, Die 15 zweistimmigen Inventionen und die dreistimmigen Sinfonien, Urtext-Ausgabe Revisionsbericht. ... Leipzig, C. F. Peters, 1933. 104 pp., illus. (music), facs. (incl. music), 27 cm.
To accompany Landshoff's Urtext edition of the Two- and Three-Part Inventions.

247. Langer, Gunther. Die Rhythmik der J. S. Bachschen Praeludien und Fugen für die Orgel. Ein Beitrag zur Entwicklungsgeschichte des Bachschen Personalstils. ... Dresden, M. Dittert, 1937. 91 pp., illus. (music), charts, 21 cm.

248. Lanning, Russell. Bach Ornamentation. ... Ann Arbor, Michigan, J. W. Edwards [1953]. 61 pp., photolithographed, 31 cm.

249.   Leichtentritt, Hugo.   Everybody's Little History of Music. ...
English translation by Arnold Elston. ... New York, Associated Music
Publishers [c 1938].   2 ll., 61 pp., 20 cm.
Note on title page: In the chapter on Music in America the author
is indebted to Daniel Wolfert for valuable assistance.

250.   —— Geschichte der Motette. ... Leipzig, Breitkopf & Härtel,
1908.   4 ll., 453 pp., illus. (music), 22 cm.   (Kleine Handbücher der
Musikgeschichte nach Gattungen, No. 2.)
General editor: Hermann Kretzschmar.

251.   Leipzig.   Ein Blick in das Wesen und Werden einer deutschen
Stadt, Festgabe der Stadt Leipzig 1913.   [Leipzig, Peoschel & Trepte,
1913.]   2 ll., 187 pp., illus. (woodcuts), 24 cm.
On front flyleaf, dedicatory inscription to Bernhard Friedrich
Richter, dated 3.X.13, signed by Alfred Heuss.

252.   Leipzig, Bach Festival.   Bachfest zu Leipzig. ... [Leipzig, Breitkopf & Härtel, 1911-.   Illus. (incl. music), 22 cm.
Library has Vol. 2 (1911); Vol. 3 (1914).   Title preceded by
appropriate numerical adjective: Zweites, Drittes, etc.

253.   Leipzig, City.   Johann Sebastian Bach und Leipzig zu seiner Zeit
herausgegeben von der Superintendentur Leipzig-Stadt.   Leipzig,
Breitkopf & Härtel, 1950.   36 pp., 10 ll. of 20 plates, illus., facs.
(incl. music), 21 cm.
Foreword by Heinrich Schumann, Oberkirchenrat, dated 8 April,
1950.   Symposium in honor of 200th anniversary of Bach's death.

254.   Leipzig, Thomasschule.   Philologos Germaniae Lipsiae congre-
gatos M. Maio A. MDCCCLXXII perofficiose salutant Scholae
Thomanae magistri; Sumptus suppeditavit Senatus Lipsiensis.
Leipzig, B. G. Teubner, 1872.   iv, 54 pp., 27 cm.
Preface signed Fr. A. Eckstein.

255.   Leipziger Beobachter und Wochen-Programm.   Wochenschrift
für Verkehr, Wirtschaft und Kultur. ... Leipzig, Hermann Eichblatt-
Verlag, 19??-.   26 cm.
Library has Vol. 12, Nos. 12 and 13 (June, 1935), a special Bach
issue.

256.   Leipziger Zeitung.   Wissenschaftliche Beilage der Leipziger
Zeitung.   Leipzig, B. G. Teubner, 18??-.   31 cm.   Semi-weekly until
15 May, 1888; then three times a week.
Library has No. 90 (29 July, 1897); No. 65 (5 June, 1906).

257.   Leonhardt, Gustav M.   The Art of Fugue, Bach's Last Harpsichord Work; An Argument.   The Hague, Martinus Nijhoff, 1952.
3 ll.; 58, [1] pp.; illus. (music); folding plate, containing music, bound
after p. 58; 26 cm.

258.   Levin, Julius. Johann Sebastian Bach ... mit Noten-, Handschriften-
proben und 14 Illustrationen.   Berlin, Volsverband der Bücherfreunde,

Wegweiser Verlag, g.m.b.h. [c 1930]. 243, [1] pp., illus., ports., facs. (incl. music), 21 cm.

259. Liess, Andreas. Johann Joseph Fux, ein steirischer Meister des Barock; Nebst einem Verzeichnis neuer Werkfunde. Vienna, Ludwig Doblinger [c 1948]. 90 pp., illus., facs. (incl. music), 24 cm. Thematic indices of unrecorded works, pp. 61-89.

260. —— Wiener Barockmusik. ... Vienna, Ludwig Doblinger (Bernard Herzmansky), 1946. 236 pp., 28 plates (incl. ports.), facs. (incl. music) on 14 ll., 24 cm. (Wiener Musik-Bücherei Band 3.)

261. Lightwood, James Thomas. Samuel Wesley, Musician. The Story of His Life. ... London, The Epworth Press [1937]. 238 pp., illus., 19 cm.

262. Lillie, (Mrs.) Lucy Cecil (White). The Story of Music and Musicians. ... New York, Harper [c 1886]. xii, [1], 242 pp., illus., 19 cm.

263. Lindner, Ernst Otto Timotheus. Zur Tonkunst, Abhandlungen von Ernst Otto Lindner. Berlin, I. Guttentag, 1864. 3 ll., 378 pp., 1 folding plate (music), 21 cm.

264. Lipsius, Ida Marie. Johann Sebastian Bach von La Mara neubearbeiteter Einzeldruck aus den musikalischen Studienköpfen. 8. u. 9. Auflage. Leipzig, Breitkopf & Härtel, 1921. 90 pp., frontis., 19 cm.

265. Lissauer, Ernst. Bach Idyllen und Mythen. Zweites und drittes Tausend. Jena, Eugen Diederichs, 1919. 51 pp., 2 ll., 21 cm.

266. Locard, Paul. Les Maîtres contemporains de l'orgue. Paris, Editions du Courrier Musical, Bruxelles [1901]. 48 pp., illus. (ports.), 18 cm.

267. Lowe, Claude Egerton. Word-Phrases to Bach's 48 Fugues with Hints on the Renderings of the Preludes and Fugues. ... London, A. Weekes [1924]. 47, [1] pp., illus. (music), 21 cm.

268. Lüneburg, St. Michael's School. Programm des Johanneums zu Lüneburg. Ostern 1870. ... Lüneburg, Sternschen Buchdruckerei, 1870. 50 pp., 27 cm.
Contents include: Johann Sebastian Bach als Schüler der Partikularschule zu St. Michaelis in Lüneburg ... (Junghans).

269. MacPherson, Stewart. A Commentary on Book I of The Forty-Eight Preludes and Fugues (Das wohltemperirte Klavier) of Johann Sebastian Bach. ... London, Novello [1933]. 1 l., 107 pp., 1 l., illus. (music), 21 cm. (Novello's Music Primers and Educational Series.)

270. —— A Commentary on Book II of The Forty-Eight Preludes and Fugues of Johann Sebastian Bach. ... London, Novello [1937?]. 1 l., 79 pp., illus. (music), 22 cm. (Novello's Music Primers and Educational Series.)

271. Mahrenholz, Christhard. Luther und die Kirchenmusik. Kassel, Bärenreiter, 1937. 22 pp., 1 l., 24 cm.

26   MUSIC LITERATURE

272. Marx, Adolf Bernhard. Die Musik des neunzehnten Jahrhundrts
      und ihre Pflege, Methode der Musik von Adolf Bernard Marx. ...
      Leipzig, Breitkopf & Härtel, 1855. viii, 572 pp., illus. (incl. music),
      22 cm.
273. —— Über Tondichter und Tonkunst, Aufsätze von Adolph
      Bernhard Marx, Zum erstenmal gesammelt und herausgegeben von
      Leopold Hirschberg. ... Hildburghausen, F. W. Gadow, 1912-22.
      3 vols. in 1. 22 cm. (Schriften über Musik und Musiker.)
274. Mattheson, Johann. Kern melodisches Wissenschaft, bestehend
      in den auserlesensten Haupt- und Grund-Lehren der musicalischen
      Setz-Kunst oder Composition, als ein Vorläuffer des Vollkommenen
      Capellmeisters, ausgearbeitet von Mattheson. Hamburg, Christian
      Herold, MDCCXXXVII [1737]. 9 ll., 182, [8] pp., illus. (incl.
      music), printed music examples, 22 cm.
      Ex libris Ch.-Martin Loeffler.
275. Mayrhofer, P. Isidor. Bach-Studien; Aesthetische und technische
      Fingerzeige zum Studium der Bach'schen Orgel- und Klavierwerke;
      Einbegleitet von einer Abhandlung über Polyphonie, das Verständnis
      polyphoner Tonwerke und das Verhältnis Johann Sebastian Bachs
      zur modernen Musik. ... Leipzig, Breitkopf & Härtel, 1901-. 23 cm.
      Library has Vol. I only.
276. Mendel, Hermann. Musikalisches Conversations-Lexikon, Eine
      Encyklopädie der gesammten musikalischen Wissenschaften, Für
      Gebildete aller Stände, unter Mitwirkung der literarischen Com-
      mission des Berliner Tonkünstlervereins. ... Berlin, L. Heimann
      [R. Oppenheim], 1870-83. 12 vols. 24 cm.
      Vols. 4-12 are "Vollendet von Dr. August Reissmann. Zweite
      Ausgabe, 1880 (1881, 1883)."
277. Menke, Werner. History of the Trumpet of Bach and Handel,
      A new point of view and new instruments forming a history of the
      trumpet and its music, from its earliest use as an artistic instrument to
      the middle of the eighteenth century...Englished by Gerald Abraham.
      London, William Reeves, [1934]. xiii, 223 pp., 6 ll., illus. (incl. music),
      19 cm.
      Title, text, and labels in German and English.
278. Merseburger, Carl Wilhelm. Geschichte der Tonkunst, Ein
      Handbüchlein für Musiker und Musikfreunde...Herausgegeben von
      Paul Frank. ... Leipzig, Carl Merseburger, 1863. vi, 282 pp., 17 cm.
      "Paul Frank" is pseudonym of Carl Wilhelm Merseburger.
279. Metropolitan Museum of Art Bulletin. New York, The Metro-
      politan Museum of Art, 1942-. 26 cm.
      Library has Vol. XII, No. 9 (May, 1954), a special number
      devoted to an exhibition of Baroque musical instruments.
280. Meyer, Paul. Johann Sebastian Bach. ... Basel, Benno Schwabe,
      1887. 39 pp., 22 cm. (Oeffentliche Vorträge, IX. Band 6. Heft.)

281. Meynell, (Mrs.) Esther Hallam (Moorhouse). Bach. ... London, Duckworth, [1934]. 136 pp., 19 cm. (Great Lives. No. 25.)
282. —— Die kleine Chronik der Anna Magdalena Bach. ... Leipzig, Koehler & Amelang, 1931. 300 pp., 2 ll., illus., facs. (incl. music), 19 cm.
283. —— The Little Chronicle of Magdalena Bach. ... Garden City, Doubleday, Page, 1925. 3 ll.; 183, [1] pp.; frontis.; 21 cm.
284. —— La Petite Chronique d'Anna Magdalena Bach ... Traduction par Marguerite et Edmond Buchet. Paris, Éditions R. A. Corréa [c 1935]. 249, [6] pp.; 2 ll.; illus.; 18 cm.
285. Michaelis, Otto. Heinrich Schütz, Eine Lichtgestallt des deutschen Volkes. ... Leipzig, Hamburg, Gustav Schloessmann [1935]. 70 pp., 1 l., illus., facs. (incl. music).
286. Mojsisovics, Roderich von. Bach-Probleme; Polyphone Klaviermusik (Inventionen, Wohltemperiertes Klavier, Klavierübertragungen von Orgelwerken) mit Notenbeispielen, zwei Textfiguren und fortlaufenden Anmerkungen. Würzburg, Universitätsdruckerei H. Stürtz, A. G., 1930. 2 ll., 69 pp., illus. (music), 21 cm.
287. Monatschrift für Gottesdienst und Kirchliche Kunst, herausgegeben von Dr. Friedrich Spitta und Dr. Julius Smend. Göttingen, Vandenhoeck & Ruprecht, 1896-. 25 cm.
   Library has Vol. 1, No. 2 (May, 1896).
288. Monatshefte für Musik-Geschichte herausgegeben von der Gesellschaft für Musikforschung. Leipzig, Breitkopf & Härtel, 1899.
   Library has Vol. 31 (Nos. 1-12), 1899.
289. Monde Musical, Le. Paris, 1889-. Monthly. 32 cm.
   Library has Vol. 44, No. 12 (Dec., 1933); Vol. 45, Nos. 5-7 (May-July, 1934), Nos. 8-10, 12 (Sept.-Oct., Dec., 1934); Vol. 46, Nos. 1-3 (Jan.-March, 1935).
290. Moser, Hans Joachim. Ein Bachscher Familientag, Ein fröhliches Spiel um Bachs Hochzeits-Quodlibet und weltliche Kantaten. Leipzig, Breitkopf & Härtel [1932]. 56 pp., 18 cm. (Veröffentlichungen der Neue Bachgesellschaft, Vol. 32, No. 3.)
291. —— Joh. Seb. Bach. ... Berlin, Max Hesse [c 1935]. vii, 271 pp.; illus. (incl. music); facs. (incl. music); 23 cm.
292. Mosewius, Johann Theodor. Johann Sebastian Bach in seinen Kirchen-Cantaten und Choralgesängen, Dargestellt von Johann Theodor Mosewius. ... Berlin, T. Trautwein'schen Buch- und Musikalien-Handlung (J. Guttentag), 1845. viii, 31 [3]-26 pp.; 30 cm.
   Last section contains engraved music. Republished, with alterations, from the Allgemeine musikalische Zeitung of 1844. Stamp of Fritz Lubrich on both front flyleaf and title page.
293. —— Johann Sebastian Bach's Matthäus-Passion, musikalisch-aesthetisch dargestellt von Johann Theodor Mosewius ... Mit Musik-

293. *(continued)* Beilagen. Berlin, J. Guttentag (Trautwein), 1852.
vi, 70, 7 pp.; 32 cm.
  Last 7 pages contain engraved music. Presentation inscription from
  the author to K[arl] Kossmaly on verso of front wrapper; Kossmaly's
  signature on recto.   P.N.: 401
294. Müller, Karl Franz. Johann Sebastian Bach. Vienna, Emerich
Florian [c 1950]. 48 pp., frontis., 24 cm.
  Limited edition of 100 copies, of which this is No. 81, autographed
  by the author.
295. Müller-Blattau, Joseph Maria. Genealogie der musikalisch-
Bachischen Familie nach Ph. E. Bachs Aufzeichnungen wieder-
hergestellt und erläutert von Joseph Müller-Blattau. Kassel und
Basel, Bärenreiter [1940?]. 24 pp., illus., 21 cm.
296. —— Grundzüge einer Geschichte der Fuge. ... Königsberg,
K. Jüterbock, 1923. 2 ll., 140 pp., 8 ll., lith. music, 22 cm. (Königs-
berger Studien zur Musikwissenschaft, Band 1.)
297. —— Johann Sebastian Bach, Leben und Schaffen. ... Leipzig,
Philipp Reclam, jun. [1935]. 77, [2] pp., 15 cm. (Musiker-Bio-
graphien. 15. Band.)
  Reclams Universal Bibliothek, No. 7294.
298. Musical Quarterly. New York, G. Schirmer, 1915-. 25 cm.
  Library has Vol. 21, No. 2 (April, 1935); Vol. 23, No. 3 (July, 1937);
  Vol. 35, No. 1 (January, 1949); Vol. 36, No. 2 (April, 1950).
299. Musical Record. Philadelphia, The Musical Record, 1933-.
Monthly. 25 cm.
  Library has Vol. I, No. 2 (July, 1933).
300. Musical Times and Singing-Class Circular. [London] 1844-.
Monthly. 25 cm.
  Library has Vol. 71, Nos. 1048, 1052-54 (June, Oct.-Dec., 1930);
  Vol. 72, No. 1056 (Feb., 1931); Vol. 79, No. 1146 (Aug., 1938);
  Vol. 85, No. 1214 (April, 1944); Vol. 86, No. 1231 (Sept., 1945).
  These are special numbers, containing articles on J. S. Bach.
301. Musik, Die. Monatsschrift herausgegeben von Bernhard Schuster.
Berlin, Max Hesse, 1901-15, 1922-1936. 20 vols. Illus., ports., facs.
(music), 28 cm.
  Title varies: Die Musik, Illustrierte Halb-Monatsschrift (Vols. 1-6);
  Die Musik, Halbmonatsschrift mit Beilagen und Noten) Vols. 7-14).
  Library wants: Vol. 1 (1st, 3rd quarters); Vol. 22 (Nos. 1-3, 5-11);
  Vol. 24 (Nos. 1-3); Vol. 26 (Nos. 4-12); Vol. 27 (Nos. 1-3); Vol. 29
  (Nos. 4-12).
302. Musikalisches Wochenblatt. Organ für Musiker und Musik-
freunde. Leipzig, E. W. Fritzsch, 1870-1910. 28 cm.
  Library has Vol. 6, Nos. 36-44 (Sept. 3-Oct. 29, 1875); Vol. 14,
  Nos. 19-23 (May 3-31, 1883); Vol. 35, No. 40 (Sept. 29, 1904).

303. Musikführer, Der. Gemeinverständliche Erläuterungen hervorragender Werke aus dem Gebiete der Instrumental- und Vokalmusik, Mit zahlreichen Notenbeispielen, Redigiert von A. Morin. Leipzig, Hermann Seemann Nachfolger [1900?-1903?]. 6 vols. Illus. (music), 17 cm.
    Library has 241 nos., many without numbering, in 6 vols.

304. Musik-Woche, Die. Berlin, 1933-35. Facs. (music), 31 cm. Vol. 1, No. 35 (1933); Vol. 3, No. ? (Aug. 31, 1935) appeared during this period under the title "Musik im Zeitbewusstsein." Library has Vol. 3, No. 11 (March 16, 1935).

305. Naumann, Emil. Deutsche Tondichter von Sebastian Bach bis auf die Gegenwart; Vorträge, gehalten im Wintersemester von 1870 auf 1871. ... Berlin, Robert Oppenheim, 1871. xi, 313 pp., illus. (port.), 22 cm.

306. Nef, Karl. Geschichte der Sinfonie und Suite...mit vielen Notenbeispiel. Leipzig, Breitkopf & Härtel, 1921. viii, 344 pp., illus. (music), 22 cm. (Kleine Handbücher der Musikgeschichte nach Gattungen, No. 14.)
    General editor: Hermann Kretzschmar.

307. Nettl, Paul. Luther and Music...Translated by Frida Best and Ralph Weed. Philadelphia, The Muhlenburg Press [c 1948]. 5 ll., 174 pp., 19 cm.

308. Neue Bachgesellschaft, Leipzig. Bach-Urkunden, Ursprung der musikalisch-Bachischen Familie, Nachrichten über Johann Sebastian Bach von Carl Philipp Emanuel Bach herausgegeben von Max Schneider. Leipzig, Breitkopf & Härtel [1917]. 18 ll. (13 ll. facs.), 30 cm. (Veröffentlichungen der Neuen Bachgesellschaft. Jahrgang XVII, Heft 3.)

309. —— Eisenacher Dokumente um Sebastian Bach im Auftrage der Neuen Bachgesellschaft herausgegeben von Conrad Freyse. Leipzig, Breitkopf & Härtel [1933]. 47 pp., illus., facs. (incl. music), 30 cm. (Veröffentlichungen der Neue Bachgesellschaft, Jahrgang XXXIII, Heft 2.)

310. —— Johann Sebastian Bachs Geburtshaus, Zwölf Federzeichnungen von Hanns Bock mit einer Einführung von Conrad Freyse. ... Leipzig, E. V. Sitz [1931]. [4] pp. text; 12 ll., each with mounted print; 19 cm.

311. Neumann, Werner. J. S. Bachs Chorfuge, Ein Beitrag zur Kompositionstechnik Bachs. Zweite Auflage. Leipzig, Breitkopf & Härtel, 1950. 3 ll., 110 pp., 16 ll. of 30 tables, illus. (music), 24 cm. (Bach-Studien, Band 3.)

312. —— Handbuch der Kantaten Joh. Seb. Bachs. 2. wesentlich erweiterte Auflage. Leipzig, Breitkopf & Härtel, 1953. 236 pp., 22 cm. (Neue Bach Gesellschaft Publications, Vol. 53.)

30 MUSIC LITERATURE

313. Nietschmann, Hermann Otto. Johann Sebastian Bach, Bilder aus dem Leben des grossen Meisters von Armin Stein, Mit Zeichnungen von Max Grunwald. ... Berlin, Acker-Verlag [1934]. 46 pp., 1 l., illus. 16 cm. (Führer und Freunde, No. 15.)

314. —— Johann Sebastian Bach, Ein Kunstlerleben von Armin Stein (H. Nietschmann). Halle, Verlag der Buchhandlung des Waisenhauses, 1896. viii, 278 pp.; 19 cm. (Deutsche Geschichts- und Lebensbilder, No. 23.)

315. Nohl, Ludwig. Allgemeine Musikgeschichte, Populär dargestellt von Dr. Ludwig Nohl. ... Leipzig, Philipp Reclam, jun. [1905?]. 320 pp., 1 l., 14 cm.

316. Norlén, Karl Gunnar. Johann Sebastian Bach. ... Uppsala, J. A. Lindblads [1922]. 172 pp., 2 ll., illus. (incl. music), facs. (incl. music), 22 cm.
Partly unopened.

317. Notes, A magazine devoted to music and its literature, with bibliographies and reviews of books, records, music. Washington, D.C., Music Library Association, 1934-42; 1943-. 23 cm. Irregular, 1934-42; quarterly, 1943-.
Library wants: 1st series, Nos. 1, 2, and 5.

318. Novello and Company, Limited, Publishers. The Complete Catalogue of Music Published by Novello and Company, Limited. London, Novello, [1907]. 8 catalogues in 16 parts, with separate pagination and varying dates. 26 cm.

319. Nuelsen, Bishop John Louis. John Wesley und das deutsche Kirchenlied. ... Bremen, Anker-Verlag, 1938. 222 pp., 22 cm. (Beiträge zur Geschichte des Methodismus, No. 4.)

320. Orgel, Die. Centralblatt für Kirchenmusiker u. Freunde kirchlicher Tonkunst, mit Musikbeilagen. Leipzig, Carl Klinner, 1901-. 31 cm.
Library has Sonderdruck aus ... "Die Orgel," 9. Jahrgang, Heft 9; 10. Jahrgang, Heft 9 (Sept., 1910).

321. Oxford History of Music, The. Oxford, Clarendon, 1901-34. 7 vols. Illus. (music), 22 cm.
Vol. IV is the second edition, 1931.

322. Parke, William Thomas. Musical Memoirs; comprising an account of the general state of music in England, from the first commemoration of Handel, in 1784, to the year 1830; Interspersed with numerous anecdotes, musical, histrionic, etc. ... London, Henry Colburn and Richard Bentley, 1830. 2 vols. 19 cm.

323. Parry, Sir Charles Hubert Hastings. Johann Sebastian Bach, The Story of the Development of a Great Personality. ... New York, G. P. Putnam [c 1909]. xi, 584 pp.; illus. (incl. music); facs. (incl. music); 21 cm.

324. —— Studies of Great Composers. ... Eighteenth edition. London, George Routledge [ca. 1915]. vii, 376 pp.; 19 cm.

325. Paumgartner, Bernhard. Johann Sebastian Bach, Leben und
   Werk. Leipzig, Atlantis [c 1950]. 543, [1] pp.; frontis.; illus; facs.;
   music; 22 cm.
      Announcement of second volume pending at end of table of
      contents, p. 543. Library has Vol. I only.
326. Payne, May de Forest. Melodic Index to the Works of Johann
   Sebastian Bach, Compiled by May de Forest Payne. New York,
   G. Schirmer [c 1938]. Pp. [i]-xvi, 1 l., pp. 1-101, 31 cm.
327. Perrachio, Luigi. G. S. Bach, Il clavicembalo ben temperato.
   Milan, Bottega di poesia [c 1926]. 308, [1] pp.; illus. (music).
   (I facioli musicali scelti da Giovanni da Nova.)
328. Peters, C. F., Publishers. Katalog der Edition Peters. Leipzig,
   C. F. Peters, 1917. 6 ll., pp. 1-370, 1 l., pp. 1-32, ports., 27 cm.
      Appendix (pp. 1-32) comprises a thematic catalog.
329. Pfeiffer, Theodor. Studien bei Hans von Bülow. ... Berlin,
   Friedrich Luckhardt, 1894-96. 2 vols. in 1. Illus. (incl. music),
   20 cm.
      Title of Vol. II: Nachtrag zu Studien bei Hans von Bülow von
      Theodor Pfeiffer, von J. Vianna da Motta.
330. Philobiblon. Eine Zeitschrift für Bücherliebhaber. Vienna,
   Herbert Reichner, 1928-35. Illus., plates, ports., facs., 23 cm.
   Monthly except July and August.
      Library has Vol. 8, No. 3 (1935). Autograph presentation in-
      scription on cover and numerous notes throughout article by Georg
      Kinsky.
331. Pirro, André. Dietrich Buxtehude. ... Paris, Librairie Fischbacher,
   1913. 2 ll., 506 pp., 1 l., illus. (music), 24 cm.
332. —— L'Esthétique de Jean-Sébastien Bach. ... Paris, Librairie
   Fischbacher, 1907. 2 ll.; 538, [1] pp.; illus. (music); 25 cm.
      Author's signature on half-title.
333. —— J.-S. Bach. ... Sixième édition. Paris, Librairie Félix Alcan,
   1924. 2 ll., 244 pp., 2 ll., illus. (music), 19 cm. (Les Maîtres de la
   Musique.)
334. —— Johann Sebastian Bach, sein Leben und seine Werke. ...
   Vom Verfasser autorisierte deutsche Ausgabe von Bernhard Engelke.
   Berlin, Schuster & Loeffler, 1910. 192, [2] pp.; 3 ll.; illus. (incl.
   music); 25 cm.
335. —— Johann Sebastian Bach the Organist, and His Works for
   the Organ...with a preface by Ch.-M. Widor, Translated from the
   French by Wallace Goodrich. New York, G. Schirmer, 1902. xxi,
   116 pp.; illus. (music); 23 cm.
336. —— L'Orgue de Jean-Sébastien Bach...avec une préface de
   Ch.-M. Widor. Paris, Librairie Fischbacher, 1895. xl, 204, [1] pp.;
   illus. (music); 18 cm.
      "Ex libris de Archer," bookplate inside front cover.

337. —— Schütz. ... Deuxième mille. Paris, Félix Alcan, 1924.
239 pp., 2 ll., illus. (music), 19 cm. (Les Maîtres de la Musique.)

338. Pitrou, Robert. Jean-Sébastien Bach. Paris, Albin Michel
[c 1941]. 309 pp., 5 ll. (partly unopened), illus., facs. (music), 21 cm.

339. Polko, (Frau) Elise (Vogel). Musical Sketches by Elise Polko.
Translated from the fifteenth German edition. Philadelphia, Theodore
Presser [c 1915]. ix, 345 pp.; illus.; 19 cm.

340. Poole, Reginald Lane. Johann Sebastian Bach, 1685-1750. ...
Foreword by Francesco Berger. London, Sampson Low, Marston
[1911?]. viii pp., 1 l., 138 pp., 19 cm.

341. —— Sebastian Bach. ... London, Sampson Low, Marston,
Searle & Rivington, 1882. viii, 138 pp.; 1 l.; 32 pp.; 19 cm. (The
Great Musicians.)

342. Preuss, Hans. Bachs Bibliothek...Sonderabdruck aus der Zahn-
Festgabe. Leipzig, D. Werner Scholl, 1928. 25 pp., 24 cm.
    Handwritten note on first page: "Zur Erinnerung Hans Löffler
    3.1.1929."

343. —— Dürer und Bach. ... Gütersloh, C. Bertelsmann, 1935.
35 pp., 20 cm.

344. —— Johann Sebastian Bach, der Lutheraner. Erlangen, Verlag
des Martin Luther-Bundes, 1935. 30 pp., incl. frontis.; 1 plate; 20 cm.
(1.-5. Tausend. Der zweiten Reihe, 9. Heft.)

345. Prieger, Erich. Echt oder unecht? Zur Lucas-Passion. ... Berlin,
C. F. Conrad, 1889. 28 pp., illus. (music), 22 cm.
    A revised and expanded form of a series of articles which originally
    appeared in the "Deutschen Musiker-Zeitung," Nos. 21-23 (May
    26, June 2, and 9, 1888).

346. Prout, Ebenezer. Analysis of J. S. Bach's Forty-Eight Fugues (Das
Wohltemperirte Clavier). ... Edited by Louis B. Prout. London,
Edwin Ashdown [c 1910]. ix, 11-90 pp.; illus. (music); 19 cm.

347. —— Fugal Analysis: A Companion to "Fugue"; being a collection of fugues of various styles, put into score and analyzed by
Ebenezer Prout. ... Second edition. London, Augener [1892]. viii,
249, [3] pp.; illus. (music); 21 cm. (Augener's Edition, No. 9186.)

348. —— Fugue. ... Fifth impression. London, Augener [1891]. xi,
258 pp.; illus. (music); 21 cm. (Augener's Edition, No. 9185.)

349. —— Some Notes on Bach's Church-Cantatas. ... London,
Breitkopf & Härtel, 1907. 32, 16 pp.; frontis.; facs. (music); illus.
(music); 22 cm.

350. Prüfer, Arthur. Sebastian Bach und die Tonkunst des neunzehnten Jahrhunderts; Antrittsvorlesung gehalten am 10 Mai 1902
in der Aula der Universität zu Leipzig. ... Leipzig, Poeschel & Trepte,
1902. 23 pp., 23 cm.
    Autograph inscription on title page: "Herrn Organisten F. B.

[*i.e.*, B. F.] Richter/hochachtungsvoll zugeeignet/vom/Verfasser/
Leipzig 4/IX°²".

351. Ramann, Lina. Bach und Händel; Eine Monographie; Vorträge,
gehalten an der Ramann-Volkmann'schen Musikschule in Nürnberg
im Winter 1866. ... Leipzig, Hermann Weissbach, 1869. vi pp., 1 l.,
87 pp., 19 cm.
Inscription on verso of title page: "Zür freundlichen Erinnerung
von den 27 Dez. 1869 v.d.F."

352. Rameau, Jean Philippe. Generation harmonique, ou traité de
musique theorique et pratique, Par M. Rameau. Paris, Chez Prault
fils, M.DCC.XXXVII. [1737]. 8 ll.; 227, [13] pp.; 12 folding ll. of
examples; illus. (charts); 20 cm.
Pages misnumbered 92, 208, 201 for 82, 226, 227, respectively.

353. Ramin, Günther. Gedanken zur Klärung des Orgelproblems.
Kassel, Bärenreiter, 1929. 40 pp., 23 cm.

354. Rau, Arthur (Book Dealer). Musique ancienne, Catalogue V,
Octobre 1935. Paris, Arthur Rau [1935]. 2 ll., pp. [3]-177, illus.,
facs., 25 cm.

355. Reeser, Eduard. The Sons of Bach. ... Stockholm, The Continental Book Company [1940?]. 63 pp., illus. (incl. music), facs. (incl.
music). (Symphonia Books.)
Translated from the Dutch by W. A. G. Doyle-Davidson.

356. Reichardt, Johann Friedrich. Musikalisches Kunstmagazin.
Berlin, for the author, 1782, 1791. 2 vols. in 1. 30 cm.
Error in pagination: 581 for 185.

357. Reimann, Heinrich. Johann Sebastian Bach. ... Zweite Auflage,
neu bearbeitet und erweitert von Bruno Schrader. Berlin, Schlesische
Verlagsanstalt [c 1921]. 110 pp., illus. (incl. music), ports., facs.
(incl. music), 25 cm. (Berühmte Musiker Lebens- und Charakterbilder nebst Einführung in der Werke der Meister. [No.] XVIII. ...)

358. Reinhart, Walther. Die Aufführung der Johannes-Passion von
J. S. Bach und deren Probleme. Leipzig, Carl Merseburger [c 1933].
90 pp., 1 l., illus. (music), 25 cm.

359. Reissmann, August. Johann Sebastian Bach, Sein Leben und
seine Werke. ... Berlin, Leipzig, J. Guttentag, 1881. viii, 283, 15 pp.;
illus. (music); 21 cm.

360. Revue Musicale, La. Paris, Éditions de la Nouvelle Revue
Française, 1920-. Monthly. 26 cm.
Library has Special Bach No. (Dec., 1932); Vol. 20, No. 190
(April, 1939).

361. Richardson, Alfred Madeley. Helps to Fugue Writing Based on
Bach's "Das wohltemperirte Klavier"... With a foreword by Rubin
Goldmark. ... New York, H. W. Gray [c 1930]. 90 pp., 2 ll., illus.
(music), 23 cm.

362. Riemann, Hugo. Analysis of J. S. Bach's Wohltemperirtes Clavier. Translated from the German by J. S. Shedlock. ... Fifth impression. London, Augener [1922? 1925?]. 2 vols. Illus. (music), 19 cm. (Augener's Edition, Nos. 9205, 9206.)

363. —— Encyclopaedic Dictionary of Music. ... Translated by J. S. Shedlock...revised to 1897. Philadelphia, Presser, 1899. 2 ll., pp. [1]-884, 1 l., 22 cm.

364. —— Katechismus der Fugen-Komposition (Analyse von J. S. Bachs "Wohltemperiertem Klavier" und "Kunst der Fuge"). ... Zweite Auflage. Leipzig, Max Hesse, 1906, 1907. 2 vols. in 1. Illus. (music), 18 cm. (Max Hesses illustrierte Katechismen, Nos. 18, 19.)

365. —— Katechismus der Fugen-Komposition...Dritter Teil: Analyse von J. S. Bachs "Kunst der Fuge". ... Leipzig, Max Hesse [1894]. viii, 166 pp.; 1 l.; illus. (music); 18 cm. (Max Hesse's illustrierte Katechismen, No. 29.)

366. Riemenschneider, Albert. The Fall and Rise of the Recognition and Appreciation of Bach. ... [Pittsburgh, Pa., 1934.] Reprinted from M.T.N.A. Proceedings, 1934.

367. Rietschel, Georg Christian. Die Aufgabe der Orgel im Gottesdienst bis in das 18. Jahrhundert, Geschichtlich dargelegt von Georg Rietschel. ... Leipzig, Dürr'schen Buchhandlung, 1893. iv, 72 pp.; 1 l.; partly unopened; 26 cm.

368. [Rimbault, Edward Francis.] Johann Sebastian Bach: His Life and Writings. Adapted from the German of Hilgenfeldt and Forkel with additions from original sources. London, Metzler, 1869. vii, 122 pp.; illus.; facs.; 17 cm.
   Preface signed: E. F. R. [Edward Francis Rimbault]. Signature on front flyleaf: W. A. Bellamy.

369. Ritter, August Gottfried. Zur Geschichte des Orgelspiels, vornehmlich das deutschen, im 14. bis zum Anfange des 18. Jahrhunderts. ... Leipzig, Max Hesse, 1884. 2 vols. in 1. Illus. (music), 27 cm.
   Vol. I: text; Vol. II: music examples. P.N. (Vol. II): M.H.V.

370. Ritter, Max. Der Stil Joh. Seb. Bachs in seinem Choralsatze. ... Bremen, Schweers & Haake, 1913. viii, 237, [3] pp.; illus. (music); 21 cm. (Kirchenmusikalisches Archiv, Heft 20.)
   General editor: Fritz Lubrich.

371. Robert, Gustave. Le Descriptif chez Bach. Paris, Librairie Fischbacher, 1909. 2 ll., 75 pp., illus. (music), 24 cm.

372. Rochlitz, Friedrich Johann. Für Freunde der Tonkunst. ... Zweite Auflage. Leipzig, Carl Cnobloch, 1830-32. 4 vols. Ports., 18 cm.
   Library lacks Vol. 1.

373. —— Wege zu Bach, Drei Abhandlungen von Friedrich Rochlitz 1769-1842, Eingeleitet und herausgegeben von Joseph M. Müller-Blattau. Augsburg, Bärenreiter, 1926. 47 pp., 24 cm.

374. Roethlisberger, Edmond. Le Clavecin dans l'oeuvre de J.-S. Bach, Étude...publiée par l'Association des musiciens suisses. Geneva, Édition Henn, H. Jarrys, 1920 [i.e., 1921]. 142 pp., illus. (music), 24 cm.
This copy is numbered 504. Memorial to the author, signed by Gustave Doret, precedes text.

375. Rolland, Romain. Haendel. ... Sixième édition. Paris, Félix Alcan, 1924. 2 ll., 244 pp., illus. (music), 19 cm. (Les Maîtres de la Musique.)

376. Rosen, Waldemar. Johann Sebastian Bach Leben und Werk... mit einem Geleitwort von Präsident D. Dr. Walter Simons, Vorsitzendem der Neuen Bachgesellschaft. Leipzig, Breitkopf & Härtel [c 1935]. 48 pp., illus., ports., facs. (incl. music), 21 cm.

377. Rossy, Gustav Christian. Kantor und König, Eine Bach-Novelle. ... Munich, Zentralverlag der NSDUP, Frz. Eher Nachf. [4. Auflage, 1942]. 98, [2] pp., 19 cm.
Blank paper pasted over imprint, which is still legible.

378. Rothschild, Fritz. The Lost Tradition in Music, Rhythm and Tempo in J. S. Bach's Time. ... London, Adam and Charles Black [c 1953]. xi, 325 pp.; illus. (music); tables; 25 cm.

379. Röttger, Karl. Die Berufung des Johann Sebastian Bach. Leipzig, Paul List [c 1933]. 60 pp., 19 cm.

380. Rücker, Curt. Johann Sebastian Bach der Deutsche. ... Weimar, Fritz Fink, 1935. 31 pp., 23 cm.

381. Rumberger, Marian S. A Conspectus of the Works of Johann Sebastian Bach, Compiled for the Bach-Gesellschaft Edition. ... Ann Arbor, J. W. Edwards, 1948. ix, 48 pp.; 1 l.; 22 cm.

382. Rupp, J. F. Emile. Die Entwicklungsgeschichte der Orgelbaukunst. ... Einsiedeln, Benziger, 1929. xvi, 467 pp.; 5 ll.; illus.; 25 cm.
Foreword by Charles-Marie Widor.

383. Sachs, Curt. The Commonwealth of Art. A lecture delivered... in the Whittall Pavilion of the Library of Congress, April 25, 1949. Washington, D.C., 1950. 19 pp., 23 cm.
At head of title: The Library of Congress, The Louis Charles Elson Memorial Fund.

384. Sampson, Brook. A Digest of the Analyses of J. S. Bach's Forty-Eight Fugues from The Well-Tempered Clavier. ... London, Vincent Music Company [c 1905-c 1907]. 5 parts in 1. 1 l., 404 pp. continuous pagination, illus. (music), 25 cm.

385. ―― The Forty-Eight Fugues in the Well-Tempered Clavier... analyzed by Brook Sampson. ... London, Vincent Music Company [c 1907]. 48 parts. Illus. (music), 26 cm.
Library has Nos. 4, 9, 16, 18, 24, 28, 29, 34, 36, 38, and 40.

386. —— Outline Analysis of Each of J. S. Bach's Forty-Eight Fugues (in the "Das wohltemperirte Clavier"). ... London, Vincent Music Company [1907?]. 2 ll., 36 pp., illus. (music), 25 cm.

387. Schaeffer, Julius. Seb. Bach's Cantate: "Sie werden aus Saba alle kommen" in den Ausgaben von Robert Franz und dem Leipziger Bach-Verein kritisch beleuchtet. ... Leipzig, F. E. C. Leuckart, 1877. 1 l., 77 pp., illus. (music), 23 cm.

388. Schäfer, Wilhelm. Johann Sebastian Bach, Eine Rede. Munich, Albert Langen [&] Georg Müller, 1935. Pp. 3-[15], 22 cm.

389. —— Johann Sebastian Bach, Eine Rede, gehalten auf dem einundzwanzigsten deutschen Bachfeste in Bremen am 8 Oktober 1934. [Leipzig, Breitkopf & Härtel, 1935?]. 18 pp., 24 cm.
On verso of title page: "Den Mitgliedern der Neuen Bachgesellschaft überreicht."

390. Schallenberg, Evert Willem. Joh. Seb. Bach. ... Stockholm, The Continental Book Company [1940?]. 63 pp., illus., ports., facs. (incl. music). (Symphonia Books.)
Translated from the Dutch by W. A. G. Doyle-Davidson.

391. Schauer, J. K. Johann Sebastian Bach's Lebensbild; Eine Denkschrift auf seinen 100-jährigen Todestag, den 28. Juli 1850, aus Thüringen, seinem Vaterlande. Jena, Friedrich Luden, 1850. Pp. [i]-vii, 1-38; 19 cm.
Dedicated to Franz Liszt. Stamped on title page: Museums Bibliothek.

392. Scheibe, Johann Adolph. Critischer Musikus; Neue, vermehrte und verbesserte Auflage. Leipzig, Bernhard Christoph Breitkopf, 1745. 24 ll., 1059 [i.e., 1056] pp., 12 ll., 20 cm.
Appeared in (irregular) weekly numbers from 1737-40. This edition (Vorrede signed Copenhagen, 17 April, 1745) is the second and contains all the original numbers, plus the entire Scheibe-Birnbaum controversy about J. S. Bach.

393. Schenker, Heinrich. Ein Beitrag zur Ornamentik als Einführung zu Ph. Em. Bachs Klavierwerken mitumfassend auch die Ornamentik Haydns, Mozarts, Beethovens, etc. ... Neue revidierte und vermehrte Auflage. Vienna, Universal-Edition, A.G. [1908]. 72, [1] pp.; illus. (music); 31 cm.   P.N.: U.-E. 812

394. Schering, Arnold. Bach's Texthandlung, Ein Beitrag zum Verständnis Joh. Seb. Bach'scher Vokal-Schöpfungen. ... Leipzig, C. F. Kahnt, 1900. 38 pp., illus. (music), 21 cm.

395. —— Geschichte des Instrumentalkonzerts bis auf die Gegenwart. ... Zweite, mit Nachträgen versehene Auflage. Leipzig, Breitkopf & Härtel, 1927. 4 ll., 235 pp., illus. (music), 22 cm. (Kleine Handbücher der Musikgeschichte nach Gattungen, No. 1.)
General editor: Hermann Kretzschmar.

396. —— Geschichte des Oratoriums. ... Leipzig, Breitkopf & Härtel,

1911. 4 ll.; 647, xxxix pp.; illus. (music); 22 cm. (Kleine Handbücher der Musikgeschichte nach Gattungen, No. 3.)
Anhang II (music), pp. xiii-xxxix. General editor: Hermann Kretzschmar.

397. ——— Johann Sebastian Bachs Leipziger Kirchenmusik, Studien und Wege zu ihrer Erkenntnis. ... Leipzig, Breitkopf & Härtel, 1936. viii, 206 pp.; 16 plates; illus. (music); facs.; 22 cm. (Neue Bach Gesellschaft Publications, Vol. 36, No. 2.)

398. ——— Der Thomaskantor. Ein Gemüth-erfreuend Spiel von deme Herren *Cantori* Sebastian Bachen vorgestellt in zween Auffzügen durch Bernhard Christoph Breitkopfen seel. Erben. [Leipzig] Breitkopf & Härtel, 1917. 1 l., 69 pp., 21 cm.

399. ——— Der Thomaskantor. Ein Gemüth-erfreuend Spiel von deme Herren *Cantori* Sebastian Bachen vorgestellt in zween Auffzügen durch Bernhard Christoph Breitkopfen seel. Erben. ... Zweyte Auflage. Leipzig, Breitkopf & Härtel, 1925. 69 pp., 18 cm.

400. ——— Über Kantaten Johann Sebastian Bachs mit einen Vorwort von Friedrich Blume. Zweite Auflage im Bachgedenkjahr 1950. Leipzig, Koehler & Amelang [c 1942, i.e., 1950]. 202, [1] pp.; 19 cm.

401. Schick, M. Joh. Sebastian Bach; ein musikalisches Lebensbild aus der ersten Hälfte des 18. Jahrhunderts. ... Reutlingen, Wilhelm Baur, 1873. 89 pp., incl. frontis., folding genealogical table, 19 cm.

402. Schiedermair, Ludwig. Einführung in das Studium der Musikgeschichte; Leitsätze, Quellen, Zusammenstellung und Ratschläge für akademische Vorlesungen. ... 3. erweiterte Auflage. Bonn & Leipzig, Kurt Schröder, 1930. 4 ll., pp. 1-111, 22 cm.
Slip, pasted over original imprint, reads: Ferd. Dümmlers Verlag, Berlin und Bonn.

403. Schirmer, G. (Publishers). A Catalogue of the Music and Books Published by G. Schirmer. New York [G. Schirmer], 1905. 1 l., pp. [iii]-vi, 2 ll., pp. [1]-311, 23 cm.

404. Schlesisches Blatt für Evangelische Kirchenmusik, herausgegeben vom Schlesischen evangelischen Kirchenmusikverein. Sagan, Benjamin Krause. 2 vols. 28 cm.
Library has Vol. 60, No. 9 (Sept., 1929); Vol. 62, No. 7 (April, 1931).

405. Schloezer, Boris Fedorovich de. Introduction à J.-S. Bach (Essai d'esthétique musicale). ... Paris, Librairie Gallimard, 1947. 309 pp., 1 l. (entirely unopened), illus. (music), 23 cm. (Bibliothèque des Idées.)
Third edition.

406. Schmidt, Leopold. Zur Einführung in Joh. Seb. Bach's Hohe Messe in H-moll. ... Drittes Tausend. Berlin, "Harmonie," n.d. 39 pp., illus. (music), 24 cm.

407. Schmieder, Wolfgang, (Editor). Thematisch-systematisches Verzeichnis der musikalischen Werke von Johann Sebastian Bach. ... Leipzig, Breitkopf & Härtel, 1950. Pp. [i]-xxii, 1 l., pp. 1-747, 27 cm.

408. Schmitz, Eugen. Geschichte der Kantate und des geistlichen Konzerts. I. Teil: Geschichte der weltlichen Solokantate. ... Leipzig, Breitkopf & Härtel, 1914. vii, 327 pp.; illus. (music); 22 cm. (Kleine Handbücher der Musikgeschichte nach Gattungen, No. 5.) General editor: Hermann Kretzschmar.

409. Scholes, Percy Alfred. The Oxford Companion to Music. ... London, Oxford University Press, 1938. 3 ll., pp. [vii]-lv, [1]-1091, 4 ll., ports., illus., 24 cm.

410. Scholz, Robert. Bach's The Art of the Fugue...reprinted from *Musicology*, Autumn, 1945, for the first performance of Robert Scholz' orchestration 1948-49. ... [New York, 1950.] 1 l., 24 pp., illus. (music), 23 cm.

411. Schreyer, Johannes. Beiträge zur Bach-Kritik. ... Dresden, Holz & Pahl, 1910; Leipzig, Carl Merseburger, 1913. 2 parts. Illus. (music), 22 cm.

412. Schubart, Christian Friedrich Daniel. Ideen auf einer Ästhethik der Tonkunst. Herausgegeben von Ludwig Schubart. ... Vienna, J. V. Degen, 1806. 1 l.; viii, 382 pp.; 3 ll.; illus. (music); 21 cm. Corrections in ink throughout. Music examples printed.

413. Schumann, Eugenie. Eugenie Schumann, Erinnerungen; Mit 16 Bildnissen. Stuttgart, Engelhornverlag Adolf Spemann [c 1925]. 256 pp., illus., 20 cm.

414. Schumann, Robert Alexander. Gesammelte Schriften über Musik und Musiker. ... Vierte Auflge, mit Nachträgen und Erläuterungen von F. Gustav Jansen. Leipzig, Breitkopf & Härtel, 1891. 2 vols. Illus. (music), 23 cm.

415. Schwebsch, Erich. Joh. Seb. Bach und Die Kunst der Fuge. Stuttgart, Orient-Occident Verlag, 1931. 355 pp., illus. (music), 24 cm.

416. Schweitzer, Albert. Deutsche und französische Orgelbaukunst und Orgelkunst 1906, Nachwort über den gegenwärtigen Stand der Frage des Orgelbaues 1927. Leipzig, Breitkopf & Härtel, 1927. 2 ll.; 73, [3] pp.; 23 cm.

417. —— J. S. Bach...With a preface by C. M. Widor. English translation in two volumes by Ernest Newman. ... London, A. & C. Black [1935]. 2 vols. Illus. (incl. music), 22 cm.

418. —— J. S. Bach le musicien-poète, avec la collaboration de M. Hubert Gillot. ... Préface de Ch. M. Widor. Leipzig, Breitkopf & Härtel, 1905. xx, 455 pp.; illus. (incl. music); 21 cm.

419. —— J. S. Bach, Vorrede von Charles Marie Widor. ... Leipzig, Breitkopf & Härtel, 1908. xvi, 844 pp.; illus. (incl. music); 21 cm.

420. —— Memoirs of Childhood and Youth. Translated by C. T. Campion. First American edition. New York, Macmillan, 1950. 78 pp., 21 cm.
421. —— Out of My Life and Thought, An Autobiography. Translated by C. T. Campion. New York, Henry Holt [c 1933]. 288 pp., illus. (incl. port.), 21 cm.
422. —— The Philosophy of Civilization. ... Translated by C. T. Campion. First American edition. New York, Macmillan, 1950. xvii, 347 pp.; 21 cm.
423. Schweizerische Musikpädagogische Blätter. Offizielles Organ des Schweizerischen Musikpädagogischen Verbandes. Zürich, Gebrüder Hug, 1912-. 23 cm. Semi-monthly.
    Library has Vol. 19, Nos. 15, 16 (Aug. 1 and 15, 1930); Vol. 24, Nos. 14, 15 (July 15, 1935, and Aug. 1, 1935).
424. Schweizerische Musikzeitung und Sängerblatt. Gazette musicale suisse. ... Zürich, Gebrüder Hug, 1861-. 25 cm.
    Library has Vol. 70, Nos. 21-22 (Nov., 1930); Vol. 72, No. 3 (March, 1932); Vol. 73, Nos. 18, 23 (Sept., Dec., 1933); Vol. 74, No. 8 (April, 1934); Vol. 75, Nos. 4, 11, 13-15, 21 (Feb., June-Aug., Nov., 1935); Beilage for Oct., 1930 (music).
425. Sharp, Robert Farquharson. Makers of Music, Biographical sketches of the great composers with chronological summaries of their works, facsimiles of their compositions and general chronological tables. ... New York, Charles Scribner's, 1898. 3 ll., 337 pp., 1 l., 1 folding chart, illus. (ports.), facs. (music).
426. [Siebick, Christian Albrecht.] Johann Sebastian Bach, Nebst einer kurzen Darstellung seines Lebens und seiner Manier. [Erfurt] 1801. 30 pp., 18 cm.
427. Signale für die Musikalische Welt. Gegründet von Bartholf Senff im Jahre 1842. Berlin, Franz Weber, 1842-. 24 cm. Weekly.
    Library has Vol. 71, No. 26 (June 25, 1913); Vol. 88, No. 31 (Aug. 30, 1930); Vol. 90, No. 12 (March 23, 1932); Vol. 92, No. 3 (Jan. 17, 1934).
428. Simrock, Nikolaus (Music Publisher). Zum Gebrauch für Singvereine. Messen, Oratorien, Cantaten etc., im Clavierauszuge mit Beiliegenden einzelnen Sing.- u. Chorstimmen. ... Bonn, bei N. Simrock [1830?]. Single sheet, 34 cm.
429. —— Jahrbuch. Berlin [N. Simrock], 1928-. 21 cm.
    Library has Vol. 1 (1928); Vol. 2 (1929).
430. Sitte, Heinrich. Bachs "Chromatische" eingeleitet und erklärt von...Heinrich Sitte. [Innsbruck and] Berlin, Georg Stilke, 1921. 63 pp., 23 cm.
    At head of title: Schriftenreihe der Preussischen Jahrbücher Nr. 5.
431. —— Johann Sebastian Bach als "Legende" erzählt von Heinrich Sitte. Zweite, verbesserte und um ein Geleitwort vermehrte Auflage.

431. *(continued)* Innsbruck, Universitäts-Verlag Wagner, 1931. 136 pp., illus. (incl.music), facs. (incl. music), 24 cm.

432. Smend, Friedrich. Joh. Seb. Bach Kirchen-Kantaten... Erläutert von Friedrich Smend. Berlin-Dahlem, Christlicher Zeitschriftenverlag, 1947-50. 6 parts. Illus. (music), facs. (incl. music), 21 cm.

433. —— Johann Sebastian Bach bei seinem Namen gerufen, Eine Noteninschrift und ihre Deutung. ... Kassel und Basel, Bärenreiter, 1950. 36 pp., separate music supp., illus. (incl. music).
Bach's Canon triplex à 6 voci, expanded and published as separate supplement.

434. Söhle, Karl. Die letzte Perfectionierung, Eine Bach-Novelle... mit 3 Original-Lithographien von Paul Horst-Schulze. Leipzig, Fr. Kistner & C. F. W. Siegel, 1924. 82 pp., illus., 15 cm.

435. —— Seb. Bach in Arnstadt. ... Zweite Auflage. Berlin, B. Behr, 1904. 3 ll., 132 pp., 3 ll., illus. (music), 19 cm.

436. —— Sebastian Bach in Arnstadt, Ein musikalisches Kulturbild aus dem Anfang des 18. Jahrhunderts. ... Neue Ausgabe. Leipzig, L. Staackmann, 1927. 139 pp., 2 ll., 18 cm.

437. Spitta, Friedrich. Haendel und Bach, Zwei Festreden von Friedrich Spitta. Bonn, Math. Hochgürtel, 1885. 34 pp., 22 cm.

438. Spitta, Philipp. Händel, Bach und Schütz.... Berlin, Gebrüder Paetel, n.d. Pp. [36]-54, 24 cm.
Fragment of unidentified issue of Deutsche Rundschau. Bookplate of A. H. Fox Strangways.

439. —— Johann Sebastian Bach gekürzte Ausgabe mit Anmerkungen und Zuzätzen von Wolfgang Schmieder. Leipzig, Breitkopf & Härtel, 1935. xi, 388 pp.; frontis.; 22 cm.

440. —— Johann Sebastian Bach, His Work and Influence on the Music of Germany, 1685-1750. Translated from the German by Clara Bell and J. A. Fuller-Maitland. New York, Dover Publications [c 1951]. 3 vols. in 2. Illus. (incl. music), 21 cm.

441. —— Johann Sebastian Bach. ... Leipzig, Breitkof & Härtel, 1873, 1880. 2 vols. Illus. (incl. music), 23 cm.
Name and stamp of former owners, V. Trier and Hortense Panum, on front flyleaf of each volume.

442. —— Musikgeschichtliche Aufsätze von Philipp Spitta. Berlin, Gebrüder Paetel, 1894. vii, 470 pp.; illus. (music); 23 cm.

443. —— Die Passionsmusiken von Sebastian Bach und Heinrich Schütz, Vortrag gehalten in Kasino zu Elberfeld; für den Druck erweitert von Prof. Philipp Spitta in Berlin. Hamburg, Verlagsanstalt und Druckerei (Vormals J. F. Richter), 1893. 40 pp., 22 cm.

444. Sponer, Alfred von. Johann Sebastian Bach in Leipzig, 1723-1750. Im Anhang: Einige Lebensdaten von Bachs Schwiegersohn Johann Christoph Altnikol; Biographische Skizzen von Alfred von Sponer. Leipzig, 1945. 34 pp., 21 cm.

In Kommission bei Musikalienhandlung Franz Jost. Typescript reproduced by multigraphic means.

445. Springer, Herman Wilhelm. Miscellanea musicae bio-bibliographica, Musikgeschichtliche Quellennachweise als Nachträge und Verbesserungen zu Eitners Quellenlexikon in Verbindung mit der Bibliographischen Kommission der Internationalen Musikgesellschaft herausgegeben von...Max Schneider und Werner Wolffheim. Leipzig, Kommissionverlag von Breitkopf & Härtel, 1912-16. 3 vols. in 1. 24 cm.
    Jahrgang 1 (1912-13); Jahrgang 2 (1913-14); Jahrgang 3 (1914-16).

446. Stabenow, Karl. Johann Sebastians Sohn, Ein Musikerschicksal zur Zeit Friedrichs des Grossen. ... Leipzig, Hamburg, Gustav Schloessmann [c 1935]. 125, [3] pp.; illus.; facs. (incl. music); 19 cm.

447. Steglich, Rudolf. Johann Sebastian Bach. ... Potsdam, Akademische Verlagsgesellschaft Athenaion [c 1935]. 2 ll., 160 pp., illus. (incl. music), facs. (incl. music), 29 cm. (Die grossen Meister der Musik.)

448. Stellhorn, Martin H. Index to Hymn Preludes including also postludes, voluntaries, paraphrases, variations, and other organ compositions, based on hymns, chorales, and carols. A listing of 2,200 selections of various publishers according to key, difficulty, and length. ... St. Louis, Missouri, Concordia [c 1948]. 151 pp., 26 cm.

449. Stuart, Elsa Marianne. Johann Sebastian Bach. ... Stockholm, Wahlström & Widstrand [1922]. 176 pp., illus. (incl. music), facs. (incl. music), 21 cm.

450. Succo, Friedrich. Rhythmischer Choral, Altarweisen und griechischen Rhythmen in ihrem Wesen dargestellt durch eine Rhythmik des einstimmigen Gesanges auf Grund der Accente. ... Gütersloh, C. Bertelsmann, 1906. 405 pp., 1 l., illus. (incl. music), 23 cm.

451. Sylvia, Heinrich Mohr de. Soli Deo gloria! Gott allein die Ehre; Ein Führer für die Jugend zu Johann Sebastian Bach. ... Stuttgart, Verlag Junge Gemeinde, 1950. 24 pp., illus., 21 cm. (Gotteszeugen, Eine Schriftenreihe für Jugend und Gemeinde, Heft 1.)
    Autograph presentation inscription signed: F[red] Roehm.

452. Tamme, Carl. Joh. Seb. Bach, Thematisches Verzeichnis der Gesangswerke auf Grund der Gesamtausgaben von C. F. Peters und der Bach-Gesellschaft verfasst von Carl Tamme. Leipzig, C. F. Peters [1890]. Pp. [i]-xvi, 1-156; 27 cm.   P.N.: 7035

453. Tapper, Thomas. First Studies in Music Biography. ... Philadelphia, Presser [c 1900]. 316 pp., illus. (incl. ports.), facs. (music), 17 cm.

454. —— Pictures From the Lives of the Great Composers for Children. ... Philadelphia, Presser [c 1899]. iv pp., 3 ll., 11-185 pp., illus. (music), 18 cm.

455. Tappert, Wilhelm. Sebastian Bachs Compositionen für die Laute.
... [Berlin, 1901]. 16 pp., illus. (music), 27 cm.
Sonderabdruck aus den "Redenden Künsten," VI. Jahrgang,
Heft 36-40.

456. Taylor, Sedley. The Life of John Sebastian Bach in Relation to
His Work as a Church Musician and Composer. A lecture by
Sedley Taylor. ... Cambridge, Macmillan & Bowes, 1897. 55 pp.
20 cm.

457. Taylor, Stainton de Boufflers. The Chorale Preludes of J. S. Bach,
A Handbook. ... London, Oxford University Press, 1942. xii, 126 pp.;
illus. (music); 22 cm.
Foreword by W. Gillies Whittaker.

458. Terry, Charles Sanford. Bach, A Biography. ... London, Oxford
University Press, 1928. xix, 292 pp.; 76 plates; illus. (incl. music);
facs.; 22 cm.

459. —— Joh. Seb. Bach Cantata Texts, Sacred and Secular; With a
reconstruction of the Leipzig liturgy of his period. ... London,
Constable, 1926. xx, 656 pp.; illus. (incl. music); 26 cm.
Copy No. 308 of 550 numbered copies.

460. —— Bach, The Cantatas and Oratorios. ... Book I [and Book II].
London, Oxford University Press, Humphrey Milford, 1925. 2 vols.
Illus. (music), 17 cm. (The Musical Pilgrim.)
General editor: Arthur Somervell.

461. —— Bach, The Historical Approach. ... London, Oxford
University Press, 1930. 157 pp., folding table, 21 cm.

462. —— Bach: The Magnificat, Lutheran Masses and Motets. ...
London, Oxford University Press, Humphrey Milford, 1929. 60 pp.,
illus. (music), 17 cm. (The Musical Pilgrim.)
General editor: Arthur Somervell.

463. —— Bach: The Mass in B Minor. ... London, Oxford University
Press, Humphrey Milford, 1924. 47 pp., illus. (music), 17 cm. (The
Musical Pilgrim.)
General editor: Arthur Somervell.

464. —— Bach: The Passions. Book I, 1723-25 [Book II, 1729-31].
London, Oxford University Press, Humphrey Milford, 1926. 2 vols.
Illus. (music), 17 cm. (The Musical Pilgrim.)
General editor: Arthur Somervell.

465. —— Bach's Chorals. ... Cambridge, University Press, 1915,
1917, 1921. 3 vols. Illus. (music), 22 cm.

466. —— Bach's Orchestra. ... London, Oxford University Press,
1932. xv, 250 pp.; illus. (incl. music); facs.; 21 tables; 23 cm.

467. —— Johann Sebastian Bach, Eine Biographie mit einem
Geleitwort von Karl Straube. Leipzig, Insel-Verlag [1929]. xvi,
396 pp.; 55 plates; illus. (incl. music); facs. (incl. music); 23 cm.
Translated by Alice Klengel.

468. —— The Music of Bach, An Introduction. ... London, Oxford
University Press, 1933. 6 ll., 104 pp., 3 folding tables, illus. (music),
facs. (music), folding plates, 20 cm.

469. —— The Origin of the Family of Bach Musicians; Ursprung der
musikalisch-Bachischen Familie. Edited with pedigree tables and a
facsimile of Bach's manuscript by Charles Sanford Terry. London,
Humphrey Milford, Oxford University Press, 1929. 22 pp., 1 l.,
illus., facs., folding charts, 29 cm.
Front flyleaf has signature: W. C. Gill.

470. Theatrum Ceremoniale Historico-Politicum, oder historisch- und
politischer Schau-Platz aller Ceremonien, welche so wohl an Euro-
päischen Höfen, als auch sonsten bey vielen Illustren fällen beobachtet
worden. Anderer Theil, nebst unterschiedlichen Hof-Ordnungen,
Rang-Reglementen, und anderen curieusen Piecen, wie auch dem
Europäischen Lantzley-Ceremoniale, Elenchis und Registern; Ans
Licht gegeben von Johann Christian Lünig. Leipzig, bey Moritz
Georg Weidmann, 1720. [Vienna, Bors & Müller, 1953.] 6 ll., 32 cm.
Facsimile of title and pages 352-359 of this work. Preface to
facsimile edition by Ahlgrimm-Fiala, dated 17 December, 1953.
Copy No. 369 of privately printed limited edition of 500 numbered
copies.

471. Thiele, Eugen. Die Chorfugen Johann Sebastian Bachs, Inaugural-Dissertation...zur Erlangung der Doktorwürde vorgelegt. ...
Bern, Leipzig, Paul Haupt, 1936. 223 ,[1] pp.; illus. (music); 25 cm.

472. Thomas, Friedrich August Wilhelm. Einige Ergebnisse über
Johann Sebastian Bachs Ohrdrufer Schulzeit, aus der Matrikel des
Lyceums geschöpft. ... Ohrdruf, 1900. 20 pp. (pp. 13-16 lacking),
folding geneal. table, 26 cm.
Beilage zum Jahresbericht des Gräflich Gleichenschen Gymnasiums
zu Ohrdruf. Pages [17]-20: "Der Stammbaum des Ohrdrufer
Zweigs der Familie von Johann Sebastian Bach ... [Aus Jahres-
bericht des Gräfl. Gleichenschen Gymnasiums, Ohrdruf, 1899
(Progr. Nr. 750)]."
Another copy, complete up to p. 16, pages [17]-25: "Schul-
nachrichten vom Direktor."

473. Tiersot, Julien. J.-S. Bach. ... Paris, Les Éditions Rieder [c 1934].
103 pp., illus., facs. (incl. music), 21 cm. (Maîtres de la Musique
Ancienne et Moderne.)

474. Todt, B. Vademecum durch die Bachschen Cantaten mit Hin-
weisen auf ihre Verwendbarkeit auch für Schülerchöre. ... Essen,
H. L. Geck [1895]. 1 l.; viii, 69 pp.; 22 cm.
Note on title page: 1895. Progr. Nr. 452.

475. Tovey, Donald Francis. A Companion to "The art of fugue"...
J. S. Bach. ... London, Oxford University Press, Humphrey Milford,
1931. 3 ll., 79 pp., illus. (music), 19 cm.

475. *(continued)* Published to accompany Professor Tovey's open-score edition of Der Kunst der Fuge.

476. Trömer, Johann Christian. Die avantures von Deutsch Francos mit all sein Scriptures und mit viel schoen Kuffer-Blatt viel lustigk ssu les uff krost kross Allerknäd; Comentement es iss kedruck. Leipzig, Vienna, Prague, Nurnberg, bey Jean George Lochner [1745]. [Vienna, Bors & Müller, 1954.]
Facsimile of title and pages 24-31 of this work. Preface to facsimile edition by Ahlgrimm-Fiala, dated 19 May, 1954. Date of imprint given in form of a rebus. Text describes festivities (in rhymed dialect) in connection with birthday visit of King August II to Leipzig on 12 May, 1727, at which time Bach's lost cantata, *Entfernet euch, ihr heitern Sterne,* was performed. Copy No. 367 of privately printed edition, limited to 500 copies.

477. Tweedy, Donald Nichols. Manual of Harmonic Technique Based on the Practice of J. S. Bach...Published by the Eastman School of Music of the University of Rochester. Boston, Oliver Ditson [c 1928]. xix, 307 pp.; illus. (music); 22 cm.

478. Upton, George Putnam. The Standard Cantatas, Their Stories, Their Music, and Their Composers; A Handbook. ... Eighth edition. Chicago, A. C. McClurg, 1903. 367 pp., 18 cm. (Upton's Musical Handbooks, No. 3.)

479. —— The Standard Oratorios, Their Stories, Their Music, and Their Composers; A Handbook. ... Chicago, A. C. McClurg, 1888. 1 l., 335 pp., 7 ll., 18 cm. (Upton's Musical Handbooks, No. 2.)

480. Urbino, L. B. Biographical Sketches of Eminent Musical Composers, Arranged in Chronological Order. ... Boston, Oliver Ditson [c 1876]. 379 pp., 20 cm.

481. Vetter, Walther. Johann Sebastian Bach, Leben und Werk. Leipzig, Breitkopf & Härtel [c 1938]. 104 pp., 1 folding l., illus. (incl. music), facs. (music), 18 cm.

482. —— Der Kapellmeister Bach, Versuch einer Deutung Bachs auf Grund seines Wirkens als Kapellmeister in Köthen. Potsdam, Akademische Verlagsgesellschaft Athenaion [c 1950]. 3 ll., 405 pp., illus. (music), 21 cm.

483. Voigt, Woldemar. Händels Samson und Bachs Matthäus-Passion, Ein Vortrag gehalten von Prof. W. Voigt. Göttingen, Vandenhoeck & Ruprecht's Verlag, 1885. 31 pp., 22 cm.

484. —— Die Kirchenkantaten Johann Sebastian Bachs, Ein Führer bei ihrem Studium und ein Berater für ihre Aufführung ... herausgegeben vom Württembergischen Bachverein. Stuttgart, J. B. Metzlersche Buchhandlung, 1918. 2 ll., 176 pp., illus. (music), 24 cm.
Label pasted over original imprint: Leipzig, Breitkopf & Härtel (1918).

485. —— Ueber die Kirchenmusik J. S. Bach's, Ein Vortrag gehalten von Prof. W. Voigt. ... Königsberg, Bruno Meyer [1881]. 51 pp., 22 cm.

486. Waldersee, Paul Hermann Otto, Graf von. Sammlung musikalischer Vorträge. Leipzig, Breitkopf & Härtel, 1879-. 5 vols. 24 cm.

   Library has Vols. 1-5, Nos. 1-60 (1879-84).

487. Walters, Raymond. The Bethlehem Bach Choir, A history and a critical compendium. ... Silver anniversary edition. Boston, New York, Houghton Mifflin, 1923. xix, 344 pp.; illus.; 22 cm.

488. Walther, Johann Gottfried. Musicalisches Lexicon oder musicalische Bibliothec. ... Leipzig, Wolffgang Deer, 1732. 8 ll., pp. [1]-659, 6 ll., 22 numbered folding plates, frontis., 22 cm.

   Page 64 contains first known listing of J. S. Bach in a bibliographical dictionary.

489. Was Weisst Du von Bach. Leipzig, Breitkopf & Härtel, n.d. 25 pp., illus., facs. (incl. music), 31 cm.

   Contains two articles by Adolf Aber: "Johann Sebastian Bachs Leben," and "Johann Sebastian Bachs Werke."

490. Weihnachts-Oratorium, nach dem Evangelisten Lucas und Matthäus von Johann Sebastian Bach. Leipzig, Breitkopf & Härtel, n.d. 20 pp., 17 cm.

   Libretto only.

491. Weihnachts-Oratorium, nach den Evangelisten Lucas und Matthäus von Johann Sebastian Bach. Leipzig, C. F. Peters, n.d. 1 l., 19 pp., 18 cm.

   Foreword signed by Hermann Kretzschmar. Libretto only.

492. Weissgerber, Deacon. Johann Sebastian Bach in Arnstadt, Festrede. ... Arnstadt, Karl Brettinger, 1904. pp. [3]-14, [1]-13; 25 cm.

   In Furstliche Realschule in Arnstadt. Jahresbericht über das Schuljahr von Ostern 1903 bis Ostern 1904, erstattet von Professor Dr. Stille, Direktor. Pages [1]-13: Schulnachrichten. Vom Direktor.

493. Werker, Wilhelm. Studien über die Symmetrie im Bau der Fugen und die motivische Zusammengehörigkeit der Präludien und Fugen des "Wohltemperierten Klaviers" von Johann Sebastian Bach. ... Leipzig, Breitkopf & Härtel, 1922-23. 2 vols. in 1. Illus. (incl. music), 24 cm.

   Added title page: Abhandlung der Sächs. Staatl. Forschungsinstitut zu Leipzig, Heft III.

   Vol. II title: Bach Studien Bd. II. Die Matthäus-Passion. ...

494. Wesley, Samuel. Letters of Samuel Wesley to Mr. Jacobs [sic], organist of Surrey Chapel, relating to the introduction into this country of the works of John Sebastian Bach ... Edited by his daughter Eliza Wesley. Second edition. London, William Reeves, 1878. 2 ll., 60 pp., illus. (music), 21 cm.

495. Westerby, Herbert. How to Study the Pianoforte Works of Bach...With Musical Examples. London, William Reeves, n.d. iv pp., pp. [25]-60, illus. (music), 19 cm.

496. Westphal, Rudolph Georg Hermann. Allgemeine Theorie der musikalischen Rhythmik seit J. S. Bach auf Grundlage der Antiken und unter Bezugnahme auf ihren historischen Anschluss an die Mittelalterliche, Mit besondere Berücksichtigung von Bach's Fugen und Beethoven's Sonaten. ... Leipzig, Breitkopf & Härtel, 1880. lxxiv, 298, [1] pp.; illus. (music); 23 cm.

497. Whittaker, William Gillies. Collected Essays. London, Oxford University Press, 1940. 6 ll., pp. [1]-235, frontis., facs., folding plat e 21 cm.

498. —— Fugitive Notes on Certain Cantatas and the Motets of J. S. Bach. ... London, Oxford University Press [1924]. xii, 298, [1] pp.; illus. (music); 22 cm.

499. Widor, Charles-Marie Jean Albert. Initiation musicale. ... Paris, Librairie Hachette [c 1923]. 159, [1] pp.; illus. (music); 18 cm. (Collection des initiations.)
    Dedicatory inscription to Albert Riemenschneider signed by Widor.

500. Wilkinson, Charles W. How to Play Bach's 48 Preludes and Fugues, A guide book for the use of piano students. ... London, William Reeves [1939?]. ix, 135 pp.; 19 cm.

501. Williams, Charles Francis Abdy. Bach. ... London, J. M. Dent & Co., 1906. x, 223 pp.; illus. (incl. music); facs., (music); 18 cm. (The Master Musicians.)
    General editor: F. J. Crowest.

502. Winterfeld, Carl Georg August Vivigens von. Der evangelische Kirchengesang und sein Verhältniss zur Kunst des Tonsatzes, dargestellt von Carl von Winterfeld. ... Leipzig, Breitkopf & Härtel, 1843-47. 3 vols. Illus. (music), 27 cm.
    Defective: Musikbeilage for all 3 vols. wanting.

503. [Wit, Paul Marie Guillaume Joseph de.] Das fragwürdige Todtenbein von Leipzig, Satire auf die lieftraurige Historie vom Leben, Sterben u. d. Ausgrabung der Gebeine J. S. Bachs. Leipzig, Verlegt bei Paul de Wit [printed by Frankenstein & Wagner, 1906]. 18 pp., illus., 28 cm.

504. Wolff, Leonhard. J. Sebastian Bachs Kirchenkantaten, Ein Nachschlagebuch für Dirigenten und Musikfreunde. ... Leipzig, Breitkopf & Härtel, 1930. 240 pp., 1 l., 20 cm.
    Type facsimile of the 1913 edition.

505. Wolffheim, Werner Joachim. Versteigerung der Musikbibliothek des Herrn Dr. Werner Wolffheim...Versteigerung durch die Firmen: Breslauer & Leo Liepmannssohn. Berlin, Breslauer & Liepmannssohn, 1928. 4 vols. in 2. Illus. (ports.), facs. (incl. music), plates, 24 cm.

506. Wolfrum, Philipp. Die Entstehung und erste Entwicklung des Deutschen evangelischen Kirchenliedes in musikalischer Beziehung, Für Theologen und kirchliche Musiker dargestellt. ... Leipzig, Breitkopf & Härtel, 1890. xvi, 250 pp.; 24 cm. (Musikalische Handbibliothek, No. 8.)

Rubber-stamped facsimile signature on title page: Carl Böhm.

507. —— Die evangelische Kirchenmusik, ihr Stand und ihre Weiterentwicklung, Vortrag auf dem ersten Preussischen Kirchenmusikertag am 15. April 1914 in Berlin gehalten von D. Dr. Philipp Wolfrum. ... Bremen, Verlag von Schweers & Haake, 1914. 39 pp., 2 ll., 22 cm. (Kirchenmusikalisches Archiv, Heft 22.)

508. —— Johann Sebastian Bach. ... Leipzig, Breitkopf & Härtel, 1910. 2 vols. Illus. (incl. music), facs. (incl. music), 19 cm.

509. Wolgast, Johannes. Karl Straube, Eine Würdigung seiner Musikerpersönlichkeit anlässlich seiner 25 jährigen Tätigkeit in Leipzig. ... Leipzig, Breitkopf & Härtel, 1928. 3 ll., 54 pp., illus. (ports.).

510. Wolzogen, Hans Paul, Freiherr von W. und Neuhaus. Grossmeister deutscher Musik: Bach, Mozart, Beethoven, Weber...mit den Bildnissen der Meister. Berlin, Georg Minuth [1897]. 4 ll., 110 pp., 29 cm.

Preface dated 22. Mai 1897.

511. Wustmann, Rudolf. Joh. Seb. Bachs Kantatentexte im Auftrage der Neuen Bachgesellschaft herausgegeben von Rudolf Wustmann. Leipzig, Breitkopf & Härtel, 1913. xxxi, 298 pp.; 26 cm. (Vol. 14, No. 1.)

512. Yale University Library Gazette. New Haven, Yale University Library, 1934. Vol. 8, No. 3 (January, 1934), 25 cm.

Contents include: Eva J. O'Meara, "The Clavier-Büchlein vor Wilhelm Friedemann Bach," pp. 95-99.

513. Young, Filson. Mastersingers. ... Philadelphia, J. B. Lippincott, 1906. ix, 216 pp.; 19 cm.

514. Zahn, Johannes (Ed.). Die Melodien der deutschen evangelischen Kirchenlieder aus den Quellen geschöpft und mitgeteilt von Johannes Zahn. ... Gütersloh, C. Bertelsmann, 1889-93. 6 vols. 23 cm.

515. Zeitschrift für Evangelische Kirchenmusik. Vereinigung der Monatsschriften: "Siona,"..."Kirchenmusikalische Blätter". ... Hildburghausen, F. W. Gadow & Sohn, 1923-. 26 cm.

Library has Vol. 8, Nos. 8-9, 11. (Aug.-Sept., Nov., 1930); Vol. 9, Nos. 1, 4 (Jan., April, 1931); Vol. 10, Nos. 7, 8, 10, 11 (July-Aug., Oct.-Nov., 1932). Editor: Wilhelm Herold.

516. Zeitschrift für Musik. Monatsschrift für eine geistige Erneuerung der deutschen Musik, Gegrundet 1834 als "Neue Zeitschrift für Musik" von Robert Schumann, Seit 1906 vereinigt mit dem

48 MUSIC LITERATURE

516. *(continued)* "Musikalischen Wochenblatt." Regensburg, Gustav Bosse, 1834-. 25 cm.

Libray has Vol. 71, No. 100 (Sept. 28, 1904); Vol. 78, No. 20 (May 18, 1911); Vol. 82, Nos. 35, 36 (Sept. 2, 1915); Vol. 91, No. 1 (Jan., 1924); Vol. 97, No. 10 (Oct., 1930); Vol. 99, Nos. 4, 12 (April, Dec., 1932); Vol. 101, Nos. 1-3 (Jan.-March, 1934); Vol. 102, No. 8 (Aug., 1935). Organ of the Allgemeiner deutscher Musikverein, Jan., 1883-May, 1892. Organ of the Verband Deutscher Orchester- und Chorleiter, Jan., 1911-March, 1914.

517. Zeitschrift für Musikwissenschaft. Herausgegeben von der deutschen Musikgesellschaft. Leipzig, Breitkopf & Härtel, 1918-. 27 cm.

Library has Vol. 12, No. 8 (May, 1930); Vol. 15, No. 5 (Feb., 1933).

518. Ziebler, Karl. Das Symbol in der Kirchenmusik Joh. Seb. Bachs. Kassel, Bärenreiter, 1930. 94 pp., illus. (music), charts, folding plate, 23 cm.

Issued as an inaugural doctoral dissertation at Münster.

519. Zulauf, Max. Die Harmonik J. S. Bachs, Inaugural-Dissertation der philosophischen Facultät der Universität Bern zur Erlangung der Doctorwürder vorgelegt. ... Bern, Stämpfli, 1927. viii, 186 pp.; illus. (music); 23 cm.

520. Zürich, Allgemeine Musik-Gesellschaft in Zürich. Biographie von Johann Sebastian Bach und seinen Söhnen. Zürich, Orell, Füssli und Compagnie, 1839. 15 pp., front., folding geneal. table, 24 cm. (Siebenundzwanzigstes Neujahrs-Stück der Allgemeinen Musik-Gesellschaft in Zürich.)

Title on wrapper: XXVII. Neujahrsgeschenk an die Zürcherische Jugend von der Allgemeinen Musik-Gesellschaft in Zürich auf das Jahr 1839.

MUSIC OF CONTEMPORARIES AND SONS
OF JOHANN SEBASTIAN BACH

Manuscripts

521. [Collection of 6 Sonatas for Harpsichord.] 6 ll., laid paper, 33 × 21 cm.
   18th-century copy in unidentified hand. Imperfect: At least 1 outer folio and either one or two inner folios missing.

522. Cramer, J. G. Fuga di J. G. C. 2 ll., fol., laid paper, 33 × 21 cm.
   Two inside pages contain another fugue with caption: Fuga | di Cramer. Contents: Fugues in G minor (on outside pages) and B-♭ major (on inside pages). Mid-18th-century hand, unidentified.

523. [Cramer, J. G.] Fuga. 2 ll., fol., laid paper, 33 × 20 cm.
   Two inside pages contain another fugue with caption: Fuga di Cramer. Contents: Fugues in F major (on outside pages) and G major (on inside pages.) Mid-18th-century hand, unidentified.

Published Music

524. Bach, Carl Philipp Emanuel. 4 Orchester Sinfonien componirt 1776 ... Nach der in der Königl. Bibliothek zu Berlin befindlichen Original-Handschrift des Componisten. ... No. 1. Leipzig und Berlin, im Bureau de musique von C. F. Peters [1861]. 1 l., 37 pp., wove paper, 25 cm.
   Preface signed and dated: Fr.[anz] Espagne. December, 1860.
   P.N.: 4270

525. —— 4 Orchester Sinfonien componirt 1776 ... Nach der in der Königl. Bibliothek zu Berlin befindlichen Original-Handschrift des Componisten. ... No. III. Leipzig und Berlin, im Bureau de musique von C. F. Peters [1861?]. 1 l., 33 pp., wove paper, 25 cm.
   Edited by Franz Espagne. P.N.: 4295

50 PUBLISHED MUSIC OF SONS OF J. S. BACH

526. Bach, Johann Christoph. I Wrestle and Pray; Motett Composed by J. Sebastian Bach [*sic*]. The words rendered and adapted by W. Bartholomew. London, Novello; New York, Novello, Ewer [1927?]. 12 pp., 25 cm. (Novello's Octavo Choruses, No. 353.)

527. —— I Will Not Let Thee Go, Ich lasse dich nicht. For eight-part chorus of mixed voices a cappella or with organ accompaniment. ... Transcribed by Karl Geiringer, English version by Willis Wager. New York, G. Schirmer, c 1941. 19 pp., 27 cm. (Old Masters of Choral Song, No. 20.)   P.N.: 38685

528. —— Ich lasse dich nicht, I Let Thee Not Go. [Philadelphia] Association of American Choruses [1947?]. 15 pp., 26 cm. (Choral Series, No. 106.)
  Edited by Henry S. Drinker. English text only. Also included: J. S. Bach, three settings of chorale "Warum betrübst du dich, mein Herz."

529. —— Motetten...Ausgabe für den praktischen Gebrauch von Victor Junk. Leipzig, Breitkopf & Härtel [1922?].
  Preface dated 1922.
  Contents: (1) Fürchte dich nicht. (2) Lieber Herr Gott, wecke uns auf. (3) Herr, nun lässest du deinen Diener in Friede fahren.
                                                        P.N.: Part B. 2544

530. —— The Righteous, Der Gerechte. For five-part chorus of mixed voices a cappella or with organ accompaniment...Adapted by Karl Geiringer, English version by Willis Wager. New York, G. Schirmer, c 1941. 16 pp., 27 cm. (Old Masters of Choral Song, No. 19.)   P.N.: 38684

531. Bach, Johann Ludwig. Messa a 8 voci reali e 4 ripiene coll' accompagnamento di due orchestre composta da Giov. Sebast. Bach [J. L. Bach], Partitura copiata dalla partitura autografa dell' Autore. ... A Lipsia, presso Breitkopf e Härtel [1805?]. 57 pp., laid paper, 36 cm.
  Signature on title page: Vincent Novello. This Mass in G major has been variously attributed to Lotti and J. L. Bach. (Schmieder, Anhang 167).

MUSIC OF JOHANN SEBASTIAN BACH

Manuscripts

532. Cantate | Dominica post festum circumcisionis Christi | Dialogus. | "Ach Gott wie manches Herzeleid." | von I. S. Bach | Organo. 2 parts. Fol., wove paper, 33 × 26 cm; 34 × 26 cm.
    Organ part: [1], 2-19 pp.; violin part: [7] pp. Title of violin part is the same except that the German line is underscored and the word "Organo" replaced by "Violino 1 me". This is a truncated version of Cantata 58, arranged for organ, and copied in a neat, 19th-century hand. Dynamic markings added in pencil to violin part.

533. Concerto à violino, violoncello et contrabasso von S. Bach [caption-title]. 3 parts. Fol., wove paper, 34 × 26 cm.
    Violin: [2] pp.; Cello: [2] pp.; Bass: [2] pp.
    This is a neat, 19th-century MS. of a concerto of three movements, arranged after the manner of the Bach-Mozart trios, and transposed to C major from the original keys. Arranger unknown. Contents: 1st movement, Organ sonata No. 1 (S. 525); 2nd movement, Flute and harpsichord sonata No. 3 (S. 1032); 3rd movement, Organ sonata No. 1 (S. 525).

534. [Cantata] No. 26. | Ihr seid Gottes Kinder, etc. | Joh. Seb. Bach. | 4 Voci | 2 Violini | 1 Viola | 2 Oboi | 2 Flauti | 2 Corni in f | Contin. 55 pp., fol., wove paper, black cloth, 33 × 26 cm.
    Although labeled No. 26, this is actually Cantata 40 with a variant first line. 19th-century hand, unidentified, same as that of Item 535. Name written or stamped on title twice: Emil Kahn.

535. [Cantata] No. 108. | Der Herr denket an uns. | Joh. Seb. Bach. | 4 Voci | 2 Violini | 1 Viola | Baſso Viocell. | Contin. 15 pp., fol., wove paper, 33 × 26 cm.
    Although labeled No. 108, this is actually Cantata 196. 19th-century hand, unidentified, same as that of Item 534. Imperfect: All wanting after m. 59 of Aria No. 4.

536. Prelude. | del Sigᵉ. | Iean Sebast. Bach. 4 unnumbered ll., fol., laid paper, 34 × 21 cm.
    18th-century copy in two unidentified hands; title and caption in

536. *(continued)* different hand from remainder of the MS. Contents: Prelude and Gigue of E minor English Suite (S. 810).

537. Prelude. | del Sig^e. | Iean Sebast. Bach. 4 unnumbered ll., fol., laid paper, 34 × 21 cm.

    18th-century copy in two unidentified hands; title and caption in different hand from remainder of the MS. Contents: Prelude to D minor English Suite (S. 811).

538. [Six trios for violin, viola and violoncello.] 3 parts. Fol., wove paper, 34 × 26 cm.

    Violin: [16] pp.; Viola: [16] pp.; Cello: [16] pp. A neat, 19th-century copy of the collection of six trios, based on selected compositions by J. S. and W. F. Bach, arranged by Mozart, with Mozart's own adagios preceding Nos. 1, 2, 3 and 6. At head of each part is the caption: Trio v. J. S. Bach. (Mozart u. W. Rust).

539. Svite Premiere avec Prelude | del Sig^e. | Iean Sebast. Bach. 6 unnumbered ll., fol., laid paper, 34 × 21 cm.

    18th-century copy in two unidentified hands; title and caption of G minor suite in different hand from remainder of the MS. Contents: Prelude of A major English Suite (S. 806); Prelude and Gigue of G minor English Suite (S. 808); Gigue of D minor English Suite (S. 811).

540. The | Well-temper'd Clavier; | or | Forty-eight Preludes and Fugues | by Sebastian Bach | Da Vincenzo Novello | Al suo stimatiſsimo Amico | Dragonetti. 85 unnumbered ll., 4° in 8's, wove paper, ¾ black calf, mottled boards.

    Colophon: R. H. Billings | music copyist | Decr 1833. Lengthy presentation inscription and description on front flyleaf, signed by Vincent Novello and dated June 8, 1846. In this, Novello explains original gift to Dragonetti, the reversion of it to him at Dragonetti's death, and his final disposal of the MS. to [C. G.] Whittaker, whose bookplate is on the front pastedown. Morocco label on cover reads: Fuge di Sebastian Bach. | Contrabasse | Da Vincenzo Novello | al suo Stimatissimo Amico | Dragonetti | 1833. Contents: Bass part of each of the 48 preludes and fugues suitable for the double bass, with appropriate cues for the clavier part.

541. Wo soll ich fliehen hin [No. 2 of the Schübler Chorales]. 1 l., pencil copy, 35 × 28 cm.

    Realization of continuo by Arthur Shepherd for the 1938 Bach Festival at Baldwin-Wallace College.

542. Das wohl temperirte Clavir | oder | Preludia und Fugen | durch alle Tone und Semitonia | so wohl Tertiam majorem oder Ut, Re, Mi, | anlagend | als auch | Tertiam minorem oder Re, Mi, Fa, betreffend. | Zum Nützen und Gebrauch der Lehr- | begierigen Muſicaliſchen Jugend, | als auch derer in die- | ſem Studio ſchon |

habil ſeyenden | Beſonderen Zeit Vertreib auff geſetz und | Verfertigt
Von | Johann Sebaſtian Bach. H. | Cöth. Capell Meiſter und Dir. der
Cam. M. | ae 1723. | Decopirt | H N Gerber. | Lipſia. die 31. [sic]
Novemb. | 17.25. 41 unnumbered ll., fol., laid paper (3 sorts),
½ black cloth, boards, 32×21 cm. (1st 5 ll.); 34×21 cm. (ll. 6-41).
First 29 leaves in same hand, leaves 30-41 in different hand.
Contents: Book I only. Imperfect: Preludes and Fugues 3 through
6 wanting. At top of verso of title page, in faint pencil: Kam mit
einem grossen Theil von Gerber's | Nachlass in März 1876 in meinen
Besitz | E. P. | seh. Bach-Ausgabe XXIII Jahre T XIV tum.
543. [Das wohltemperierte Klavier. Book II]. n.p., n.d. 55 ll.,
laid paper, ¾ calf, marbled boards, 23×31 cm.
Fugues only. Name on front flyleaf: John Foster. Unidentified
hand, probably late 18th or early 19th century.

Published Music

COMPLETE WORKS

544. Johann Sebastian Bach's Werke. Herausgegeben von der Bach-
Gesellschaft zu Leipzig. Leipzig, Breitkopf & Härtel [1851]-1926.
47 vols. (64 parts) in 56. Illus., facs. (incl. music), 35 cm.
P.N.: B.W. I to B.W. XLVII
545. Neue Ausgabe sämtlicher Werke, herausgegeben vom Johann-
Sebastian-Bach-Institut Göttingen und vom Bach-Archiv Leipzig.
Kassel, Bärenreiter, 1954-. Facs., 33 cm.
"Kritischer Bericht" in separate volumes: Kassel, Bärenreiter,
1955-; illus. (music), 25 cm.

SELECTED WORKS

546. Joh. Seb. Bachs Werke. Nach der Ausgabe der Bachgesellschaft.
. . Leipzig, Breitkopf & Härtel [1901]-1950. 48/50 vols. (58 parts)
in 23. Facs., varying sizes. (Veröffentlichungen der Neue Bach-
gesellschaft.)
Library wants: Vol 16, Part 1; Vol 38; Vol 41/46, Part 2.
P.N.: N.B. I, 1 to N.B. XXXIX, 2; 31337

ARIA MIT 30 VERÄNDERUNGEN (S. 988)

547. Aria mit 30 Variationen ("Goldberg-Variationen") ... Ein-
gerichtet und herausgegeben von Richard Robert. Vienna, New
York, Universal-Edition A.G. [ca. 1926]. 1 l., 52 pp., 31 cm.
Preface in German, French, and English, signed by Hans Gál.
P.N.: U.E. 8133

54 PUBLISHED MUSIC OF J. S. BACH

548. Clavier Ubung bestehend in einer Aria mit verschiedenen Veraenderungen vors Clavicimbal mit 2 Manualen. Denen Liebhabern
zur Gemüths-Ergetzung verfertigeɩ von Johann Sebastian Bach
Königl. Pohl. u. Churfl. Saechss. Hoff-Compositeur, Capellmeister u.
Directore Chori Musici in Leipzig. Nürnberg, Balthasar Schmid
[1742]. 1 l., 32 pp., laid paper, original floral boards, 32 cm.
Title-page in facsimile.

549. Exercices pour le clavecin par J. S. Bach, Oeuvre II. Leizpg, au
Bureau de musique de A. Kühnel [after 1805]. 35 pp., obl. fol.,
wove paper, 24 × 34 cm.
Imprint shows evidence of erasure and addition of Kühnel's name.
P.N.: 185

550. Exercices pour le clavecin par J. S. Bach. Oeuv. II. Leipzig, au
Bureau de musique de C. F. Peters [1817?]. 47 pp., obl. fol., wove
paper, original boards, 25 × 33 cm.
First of eleven items bound in one pamphlet-volume formerly
belonging to Clara Schumann. P.N.: 1621

551. Keyboard Practice consisting of an aria with thirty variations for
the harpsichord with 2 manuals prepared for the enjoyment of Music-
Lovers by Johann Sebastian Bach. Edited for the harpsichord or
piano by Ralph Kirkpatrick. New York, G. Schirmer [c 1938].
xxviii, 83 pp., illus., facs (incl. music), 30 cm. P.N.: 37149

552. Klavierübung IV. Teil, Aria mit verschiedenen Veränderungen…
nach dem Erstdruck revidiert und herausgegeben von Kurt Soldan;
Fingersatz von C. A. Martienssen. Leipzig, C. F. Peters [1937?].
2 ll., 51 pp., illus., facs. (music), 30 cm. P.N.: 11329

553. Variationen für das Clavier von Johann Sebastian Bach. Zürich,
Hans Georg Nägeli [1809?]. 1 l., 2-63 pp., laid paper, 26 cm.
Imperfect: pages 55-58 wanting.

Excerpts and Arrangements

554. Quodlibet aus den Goldberg-Variationen. Für Soloquartett ausge-
setzt von Fritz Müller. Regensburg, Gustav Bosse, 1934. 4 pp., 33 cm.
First line: Ich bin so lang bei dir gewest.

ARIA VARIATA ALLA MANIERA ITALIANA (S. 989)

555. Heinrich Germer's Akademische Ausgabe klassischer Pianoforte-
Werke für den Unterricht…J. S. Bach, Aria Variata. … Leipzig,
Hug [c 1903]. 9, [1] pp., 34 cm. P.N.: G. 90

ARIAS, COLLECTED

556. Bach Songs & Airs for Bass. Book I [and Book II]. [Edited by
E. Prout]. London, Augener [c 1909]. 2 books. 30 cm. (Augener's
Edition, Nos. 4721C, 4721D.) P.N.: 13849

557. Bach Songs & Airs for Contralto. Book I [and Book II], edited
by E. Prout. London, Augener [c 1909]. 2 books. 30 cm. (Augener's
Edition, Nos. 4721A, 4721B.) P.N.: 13849
558. Bach Songs & Airs for Soprano. Book I [and Book II], edited by
E. Prout. London, Augener [c 1908]. 2 books. 30 cm. (Augener's
Edition, Nos. 4720A, 4720B.) P.N.: 13801
559. Bach Songs & Airs for Tenor. Book I [and Book II], edited by
E. Prout. London, Augener [c 1908]. 2 books. 30 cm. (Augener's
Edition, Nos. 4720C, 4720D.) P.N.: 13801
560. Fünfzehn Arien für eine Altstimme aus Kantaten von Joh. Seb.
Bach, ausgewählt von Karl Straube, herausgegeben von Max
Schneider. Leipzig, C. F. Peters [ca. 1916]. 79 pp., 27 cm. (Edition
Peters, No. 3335b.)
Also included: Arias from the Easter Oratorio and the Mass in
G minor. P.N.: 10042
561. Fünfzehn Arien für eine Bassstimme aus Kantaten von Joh. Seb.
Bach, ausgewählt von Karl Straube, herausgegeben von Max
Schneider. Leipzig, C. F. Peters [ca. 1916]. 73 pp., 27 cm. (Edition
Peters, No. 3335d.) P.N.: 10165
562. Fünfzehn Arien für eine Sopranstimme aus Kantaten von Joh.
Seb. Bach, ausgewählt von Karl Straube, herausgegeben von Max
Schneider. Leipzig, C. F. Peters [ca. 1916]. 96 pp., 27 cm. (Edition
Peters, No. 3335a.) P.N.: 10041
563. Fünfzehn Arien für eine Tenorstimme aus Kantaten von Joh. Seb.
Bach, ausgewählt von Karl Straube, herausgegeben von Max
Schneider. Leipzig, C. F. Peters [ca. 1916]. 80 pp., 27 cm. (Edition
Peters, No. 3335c.)
Also included: One aria from the Easter Oratorio. P.N.: 10136
564. 9 Alt-Arien aus verschiedenen Cantaten und Messen mit Be-
gleitung des Pianoforte, bearbeitet von Robert Franz. Neue Ausgabe.
Leipzig, F. Whistling; Vienna, F. Glöggl, 1861. 60 pp., 32 cm.
P.N.: 910.911 to 910.919
565. 9 Alt-Arien von Joh. Seb. Bach mit Begleitung des Pianoforte,
bearbeitet von Robert Franz. Leipzig, C. F. Peters, n.d. 1 l., 60 pp.,
34 cm. (Edition Peters, No. 2958b.)
Same plates as Whistling edition. P.N.: 910.911 to 910.919
566. 9 Bass-Arien aud verschiedenen Cantaten mit Begleitung des
Pianoforte, bearbeitet von Robert Franz. Leipzig, F. Whistling;
Vienna, F. Glöggl, 1861. 67 pp., 32 cm. P.N.: 920.921 to 920.929.
567. 9 Sopran-Arien aus verschiedenen Cantaten mit Begleitung des
Pianoforte, bearbeitet von Robert Franz. Leipzig, F. Whistling;
Vienna, F. Glöggl, 1861. 57 pp., 32 cm. P.N.: 930.931 to 930.939
568. 9 Tenor-Arien aus verschiedenen Cantaten mit Begleitung des
Pianoforte, bearbeitet von Robert Franz. Leipzig, F. Whistling;
Vienna, F. Glöggl, 1861. 73 pp., 32 cm. P.N.: 940.941 to 940.949

569. The Oxford Series of Bach Arias. Arranged and edited by W. G. Whittaker [with translations by Charles Sanford Terry and others]. London, Oxford University Press, c 1925-29. 22 parts in 1, with separate pagination. 25 cm.
   Issued as individual arias.

570. Solos from the Cantatas, Sacred and Secular. Edited by J. Michael Diack. Glasgow, Paterson [ca. 1928]. 13 parts in 1. 31 cm.
   Also included: Solos from Bach's Magnificat, St. Matthew Passion, and St. John Passion.

571. Solos from the Sacred Cantatas of J. S. Bach. London, Novello; New York, H. W. Gray [ca. 1923]. 12 books in 1 (soprano, sets I-III; contralto, sets I-III; tenor, sets I-III; bass, sets I-III). 27 cm.

CANTATAS (S. 1-224)

Collections

572. Kirchen-Musik von Joh. Seb. Bach. Herausgegeben von Adolph Bernhard Marx. Clavierauszug. ... Bonn, bei N. Simrock [1830?]. 6 nos. in 2 parts. Obl. fol., wove paper, 26 × 33 cm.
   On inside of front cover is signature: Alf Angel.
   Cantatas 101-06.   P.N.: 2890 to 2895

573. Ten Instrumental Movements from the Cantatas. Transcribed for organ by Harvey Grace. New York, Oxford University Press [c 1928]. 36 pp., 32 cm.

Single Works

CANTATA NO. 1. Wie schön leuchtet der Morgenstern (S. 1): Full score

574. Wie schön leuchtet der Morgenstern... Nach der Ausgabe der Bach-Gesellschaft und den Originalstimmen revidiert und mit Einführung versehen von Arnold Schering. Leipzig, Eulenburg [1928?]. 3 ll., 66 pp., 2 ll., 19 cm. (Eulenburgs kleine Partitur-Ausgabe, No. 1012.)   P.N.: E.E. 4809

CANTATA NO. 1: Vocal-piano scores

575. Cantate am Feste Mariä Verkündigung... Klavier-Auszug von G. Rösler. ... Leipzig, C. F. Peters [1875]. 30 pp., 27 cm. (Edition Peters, No. 1193.)   P.N.: 5739

576. How Bright and Fair the Morningstar. ... [Philadelphia] Association of American Choruses [1947?]. 31 pp., 26 cm. (Choral Series, No. 88.)
   Photo-offset lithograph process. Translation by Henry S. Drinker.

577. How Brightly Shines yon Star of Morn... Edited by John E. West, English version by Paul England. London, Novello [1927?]. 1 l., 40 pp., 26 cm. (Novello's Original Octavo Edition.)
   Two copies.   P.N.: 12076

578.   Kantate am Feste Mariae Verkündigung. ... Leipzig, Breitkopf
& Härtel [ca. 1890]. 1 l., 34 pp., 27 cm. (Joh. Seb. Bach Kirchenkantaten, No. 1.)   P.N.: J.S.B.I. 1.

579.   "Wie schön leuchtet der Morgenstern"..."All glorious doth the
day-star shine"...English version by Mevanwy Roberts..."Brillante
étoile du matin"...traduction française de Mme. Henriette Fuchs...
Klavierauszug von Günter Raphael. Leipzig, Breitkopf & Härtel
[c 1932]. 1 l., 39 pp., 27 cm. (Joh. Seb. Bach Kirchenkantaten,
No. 1.)   P.N.: J.S.B.I. 1.

CANTATA NO. 1: Excerpts

580.   Wie schön leuchtet der Morgenstern, How Brightly Shines yon
Morning Star, two choruses for mixed voices from Cantata No. 1...
English version by Charles Sanford Terry, edited...by Canon Walter
Williams. Boston, E. C. Schirmer [c 1933]. 29, [3] pp.; 27 cm.
(St. Dunstan Edition, No. 1247.)   P.N.: E.C.S.N°. 693)

CANTATA NO. 2. Ach Gott, vom Himmel sieh darein (S. 2): Vocal-
piano scores

581.   Ah, God, from Heaven Look Anew. ... [Philadelphia] Association
of American Choruses [1948?]. 1l., 24 pp., 1 l., 26 cm. (Choral
Series, No. 140.)
       Photo-offset lithograph process. Translation by Henry S. Drinker.

582.   Ah God, in Mercy Look from Heaven...Vocal score by B. Todt,
English words by E. W. Naylor. ... Leipzig, Breitkopf & Härtel
[c 1904]. 24 pp., 27 cm.   P.N.: 24156

583.   Cantate am 2ten Sonntage nach Trinitatis...Klavier-Auszug von
G. Rösler. Leipzig, C. F. Peters [1875]. 1 l., 23 pp., 28 cm. (Edition
Peters, No. 1194.)   P.N.: 5740

584.   Kantate am zweiten Sonntage nach Trinitatis. ... Leipzig,
Breitkopf & Härtel [1890?]. 24 pp. (pp. 35-58), 27 cm. (Joh. Seb.
Bach Kirchenkantaten, No. 2.)
       This is B. Todt's vocal-piano edition.   P.N.: J.S.B.I. 2.

CANTATA NO. 2: Vocal scores

585.   Cantata Number Two...with two earlier harmonizations by
Bach of the choral melody. [Philadelphia] University of Pennsylvania
[1939?]. 16 pp., 27 cm. (Choral Series, No. 39.)
       English text. Edited by Henry S. Drinker.

CANTATA NO. 3. Ach Gott, wie manches Herzeleid (S. 3): Full scores

586.   Dominica 2 poſt Epiphanias Gross Gott! Wie manches Herzeleid
à 4 voci 2 hautb. d'amour 2 violini viola e continuo. ... 9 ll., 35 cm.
       Photostat of MS. whose present whereabouts is unknown.

CANTATA NO. 3: Vocal-piano scores

587.   Ah God, How Sad and Sick at Heart. ... [Philadelphia] Associ-

58 PUBLISHED MUSIC OF J. S. BACH

587. *(continued)* ation of American Choruses [1945?]. 1 l., 22 pp., 26 cm. (Choral Series, No. 23.)
Photo-offset lithograph process. Translation by Henry S. Drinker.
588. Kantate am zweiten Sonntage nach Epiphanias. ... Leipzig, Breitkopf & Härtel [1890?]. 1 l., 22 pp. (pp. 59-80), 27 cm. (Joh. Seb. Bach Kirchenkantaten, No. 3.)   P.N.: J.S.B.I. 3
589. Kantate am 2ten Sonntage nach Epiphanias...Klavier-Auszug von G. Rösler. Leipzig, C. F. Peters [1875]. 25 pp., 28 cm. (Edition Peters, No. 1159.)   P.N.: 5741
590. "Ach Gott, wie manches Herzeleid"..."O God, How Many Pains of Heart"...English version by E. H. Thorne and Revd. Rosslyn Bruce...Klavierauszug von Günter Raphael. Leipzig, Breitkopf & Härtel [c 1930]. 1 l., 28 pp., 27 cm. (Joh. Seb. Bach Kirchenkantaten, No. 3.)   P.N.: J.S.B.I. 3

CANTATA NO. 3: Excerpts

591. Three Choruses for Mixed Voices from Cantata No. 3...English version by Charles Sanford Terry, edited...by H. Clough-Leighter. Boston, E. C. Schirmer [c 1931]. 21, [3] pp.; 27 cm. (E. C. Schirmer Sacred Music, No. 1613.)   P.N.: E.C.S. N°. 666

CANTATA NO. 4. Christ lag in Todesbanden (S. 4): Full scores

592. Christ lag in Todesbanden...Nach der Ausgabe der Bach-Gesellschaft herausgegeben und mit Vorwort versehen von Arnold Schering. Leipzig, Eulenburg [1932?]. viii, 42 pp., 2 ll., 19 cm. (Eulenburgs kleine Partitur-Ausgabe, No. 1011.)   P.N.: E.E. 3897

CANTATA NO. 4: Vocal-piano scores

593. Cantate am Osterfeste. ... Leipzig, C. F. Peters [ca. 1907]. 35 pp., 27 cm. (Edition Peters, No. 1196.)
Edited by Gustav Rösler.   P.N.: E.E. 9239
594. Christ Lay by Death Enshrouded. ... [Philadelphia] Association of American Choruses [1947?]. 36 pp., 26 cm. (Choral Series, No. 86.)
Photo-offset lithograph process. Translation by Henry S. Drinker.
595. "Christ Lay Fast Bound in Death's Harsh Chain". ... Vocal score by G. Schreck, English version by E. H. Thorne and Mrs. Newmarch. Leipzig, Breitkopf & Härtel [c 1903]. 1 l., 34 pp., 27 cm. (Joh. Seb. Bach Vocal Scores, No. 4.)   P.N.: 23808
596. Christ Lay in Death's Dark Prison...Edited by John E. West, English version by Paul England. London, Novello; New York, H. W. Gray [ca. 1920]. 1 l., 49 pp., 26 cm. (Novello's Original Octavo Edition.)
Two copies.   P.N.: 12053
597. Christ nous donna sa vie. Paroles françaises de Maurice Bouchor,

Partition chant et piano de A. Guilmant. Paris, Choudens [1935?].
1 l., 35 pp., 31 cm. (Edition française de musique classique, No. 1.)
Page 2 has plate number 11703. P.N.: 22

598. Kantate am Osterfeste...Klavierauszug von Gustav Schreck.
Leipzig, Breitkopf & Härtel [ca. 1900]. 35 pp., 27 cm. (Joh. Seb.
Bach Kirchenkantaten, No. 4.) P.N.: N.B. II. 2

CANTATA NO. 4: Vocal scores

599. Cantata No. 4...for the feast of Easter. ... [Philadelphia,
University of Pennsylvania, ca. 1935]. 24 pp., 27 cm.
Edited by Henry S. Drinker.

600. Cantata No. 4. ... For the Easter festival ... [Philadelphia] University of Pennsylvania [1941?]. 28 pp., 27 cm. (Choral Series, No. 1.)
MS. note opposite title: New Edition | July 28, 1941. Series
edited by Henry S. Drinker

CANTATA NO. 5. Wo soll ich fliehen hin (S. 5): Vocal-piano scores

601. Cantate am 19ten Sonntage nach Trinitatis...Clavier-Auszug
von G. Rösler. ... Leipzig, C. F. Peters [1875]. 23 pp., 27 cm.
(Edition Peters, No. 1197.) P.N.: 5743

602. Kantate am neunzehnten Sonntage nach Trinitatis. ... Leipzig,
Breitkopf & Härtel [1890?] 1 l., 28 pp. 27 cm. (Joh. Seb. Bach
Kirchenkantaten, No. 5.) P.N.: J.S.B.I. 5.

603. Where may I fly, O where? ... [Philadelphia] Association of
American Choruses [1945?]. 1 l., 28 pp., 1 l., 26 cm. (Choral Series,
No. 15.)
Photo-offset lithograph process. Translation by Henry S. Drinker.

CANTATA NO. 6. Bleib' bei uns, denn es will Abend werden (S. 6):
Full scores

604. Bleib' bei uns, denn es will Abend werden... Nach der Ausgabe
der Bach-Gesellschaft und nach dem in der Preussischen Staatsbibliothek zu Berlin befindlichen Autograph revidiert und mit Einführung versehen von Arnold Schering. Leipzig, Eulenburg [1926?].
xi, 28 pp.; 2 ll.; 19 cm. (Eulenburgs kleine Partitur-Ausgabe,
No. 1004.) P.N.: E.E. 4621

605. Bleib bei uns Kantate...Partitur mit Cembalo- und Orgelstimme
herausgegeben von Max Seiffert. Leipzig, C. F. Peters [1924?].
26 pp., 34 cm. (Edition Peters, No. 3749b.) P.N.: 10292

CANTATA NO. 6: Vocal-piano scores

606. Bide With Us...The English translation and adaptation by the
Rev. John Troutbeck, D. D. London, Novello; New York, H. W. Gray
[1935?]. 1 l.; 29, [1] pp.; 26 cm. (Novello's Original Octavo Edition.)
Two copies. P.N.: Bach's Cantata, "Bide with us."
Novello, Ewer and Co.'s Octavo Edition.

607. Bide With Us. ... [Philadelphia] Association of American Choruses [1947?]. 24 pp., 26 cm. (Choral Series, No. 89.)
Photo-offset lithograph process. Translation by Henry S. Drinker.
608. "Bleib bei uns, denn es will Abend werden!"..."Stay With Us, the Evening Approaches!"...English version by E. H. Thorne and G. W. Daisley...Klavierauszug von Günter Raphael. Leipzig, Breitkopf & Härtel [c 1933]. 1 l., 27 pp., 27 cm. (Joh. Seb. Bach Kirchenkantaten, No. 6.)   P.N.: J.S.B.I. 6.
609. Kantate am zweiten Osterfesttage. ... Leipzig, Breitkopf & Härtel [1890?]. 1 l., 22 pp. (pp. 143-64), 27 cm. (Joh. Seb. Bach Kirchenkantaten, No. 6.)
Edited by Günter Raphael.   P.N.: J.S.B.I. 6.
610. Kantate am 2ten Osterfesttage...Klavierauszug von G. Rösler. Leipzig, C. F. Peters [ca. 1895]. 23 pp., 28 cm. (Edition Peters, No. 1015.)   P.N.: 8342
611. "Stay With Us, the Evening Approaches!"...Vocal score by B. Todt, English version by E. H. Thorne and G. W. Daisley. ... Leipzig, Breitkopf & Härtel, c 1903. 22 pp., 28 cm.   P.N.: 23807

CANTATA NO. 6: Vocal scores

612. Cantata 6. ... [Philadelphia] University of Pennsylvania [ca. 1935]. 14 pp., 27 cm. (Choral Series, No. 65.)
Edited by Henry S. Drinker.

CANTATA NO. 7. Christ unser Herr zum Jordan kam (S. 7): Vocal-piano scores

613. Cantate am Feste Johannis des Täufers...Klavier-Auszug von G. Rösler. Leipzig, C. F. Peters [1875]. 30 pp., 27 cm. (Edition Peters, No. 1198.)   P.N.: 5744
614. "Christ unser Herr zum Jordan kam"..."Lord Christ of Old to Jordan Came."...English version by Charles Sansford Terry... Klavierauszug von Günter Raphael. Leipzig, Breitkopf & Härtel, c 1930. 1 l., 32 pp., 27 cm. (Joh. Seb. Bach Kirchenkantaten, No. 7.)
Two copies.   P.N.: J.S.B.I. 7.
615. To Jordan's Stream Came Christ our Lord. ... [Philadelphia] Association of American Choruses [1945?]. 1 l., 32 pp., 1 l., 26 cm. (Choral Series, No. 16.)
Photo-offset lithograph process. Translation by Henry S. Drinker.

CANTATA NO. 7: Excerpts

616. Recitativ und Arie aus der Cantate "Christ unser Herr zum Jordan kam"...Arrang. von W. Rust. Berlin, Schlesinger'sche Buch- und Musikhandlung [ca. 1855]. 5 pp., wove paper, 34 cm. (Sion, Vol. 3, No. 49.)
First line: Als Jesus dort, nach seinen Leiden.   P.N.: S. 4192

CANTATA NO. 8. Liebster Gott, wann werd' ich sterben? (S. 8):
Full score

617. Liebster Gott, wann werd' ich sterben?...Nach der Ausgabe der
Bach-Gesellschaft mit Einführung versehen von Arnold Schering.
Leipzig, Eulenburg [1932?]. 1 l., iv, 44 pp., 3 ll., 19 cm. (Eulenburg's
kleine Partitur-Ausgabe, No. 1028.)   P.N.: E.E. 4828

CANTATA NO. 8: Vocal-piano scores

618. Dearest God, When Wilt Thou Call Me? ... [Philadelphia]
Association of American Choruses [1945?]. 1 l., 32 pp., 1 l., 26 cm.
(Choral Series, No. 17.)
Photo-offset lithograph process. Translation by Henry S. Drinker.
619. Dieu que j'aime quand mourrai je? Paroles françaises de Maurice
Bouchor, partition chant et piano de A. Guilmant. Paris, Choudens
[ca. 1935]. 2 ll., 36 pp., 31 cm. (Edition française de musique
classique, No. 10.)   P.N.: 11712
620. Kantate am sechzehnten Sonntage nach Trinitatis. ... Leipzig,
Breitkopf & Härtel [1890?]. 26 pp. (pp. 195-220), 27 cm. (Joh. Seb.
Bach Kirchenkantaten, No. 8.)   P.N.: J.S.B.I. 8.
621. Kantate am 16. Sonntage nach Trinitatis...Klavier-Auszug von
G. Rösler. ... Leipzig, C. F. Peters [1875]. 27 pp., 27 cm. (Edition
Peters, No. 1199.)   P.N.: 5745
622. "Liebster Gott, wann werd' ich sterben?"..."Gracious God,
When Wilt Thou Call Me?" ... English version by J. Michael Diack...
Klavierauszug von Günter Raphael. Leipzig, Breitkopf & Härtel
[c 1931]. 1 l., 32 pp., 27 cm. (Joh. Seb. Bach Kirchenkantaten,
No. 8.)   P.N.: J.S.B.I. 8.
623. When Will God Recall My Spirit...Translated from the German
of Kaspar Neumann, 1690, by Rev. Dr. Troutbeck. London,
Novello; New York, H. W. Gray [ca. 1905]. 1 l., 26 pp., 25 cm.
(Novello's Original Octavo Edition.)
                    P.N.: J. S. Bach – "When will God recall my spirit." –
                                Novello, Ewer and Co.'s Octavo Edition)
CANTATA NO. 8: Excerpts

624. Liebster Gott, wann werd' ich sterben? When Will God Recall
My Spirit?...Two choruses for mixed voices from Cantata No. 8...
English version by the Rev. John Troutbeck...edited...by H. Clough-
Leighter. Boston, E. C. Schirmer [c 1935]. 17, [3] pp.; 28 cm.
(E. C. Schirmer Sacred Music, No. 1674.)
Contents: 1. Liebster Gott...(When Will God Recall My Spirit).
2. Herrscher über Tod und Leben (Thou That Life and Death
Ordainest).   P.N.: E.C.S. No. 909

CANTATA NO. 9. Es ist das Heil uns kommen her (S. 9): Full score
625. Doica 6 poʃt Trinitatis. Es iʃt das Heyl uns kommen her. a 4

625. *(continued)* Voci 1 Trav. 1 Haut: | 2 Violin. Viola & Continuo.
9 ll., 36 cm.
Photostat of MS. now at Library of Congress.

CANTATA NO. 9: Vocal-piano scores
626.   Cantate am 6. Sonntage nach Trinitatis...Klavier Auszug von
G. Rösler. Leipzig, C. F. Peters [1875?]. 28 pp., 27 cm. (Edition
Peters, No. 1281.)   P.N.: 5748
627.   Cantate am sechsten Sonntage nach Trinitatis. ... Leipzig,
Breitkopf & Härtel [1890?]. 1 l., 30 pp., 27 cm. (Joh. Seb. Bach
Kirchenkantaten, No. 9.)   P.N.: J.S.B.I. 9.
628.   Salvation Sure Has Come to Man. ... [Philadelphia] Association
of American Choruses [1947?]. 1 l., 30 pp., 26 cm. (Choral Series,
No. 14.)
Photo-offset lithograph process. Translation by Henry S. Drinker.

CANTATA NO. 10.   Meine Seel' erhebt den Herren (S. 10): Full score
629.   Festo Viſitationis Maria Meine Seel erhebt den Herren à 4 Voc:
Tromba 2 Hautbois 2 Violini Viola e Continuo di Sign. I. S. Bach.
10 ll., 36 cm.
Photostat of MS. now at Library of Congress.

CANTATA NO. 10: Vocal-piano scores
630.   Cantate am Feste Mariä Heimsuchung...Klavier-Auszug von
G. Rösler. Leipzig, C. F. Peters [1875]. 26 pp., 1 l., 27 cm. (Edition
Peters, No. 1278.)   P.N.: 5746
631.   Cantate am Feste Mariae Heimsuchung. ... Leipzig, Breitkopf &
Härtel [1890?]. 1 l., 28 pp. (pp. 251-78), 27 cm.
Vocal score is by B. Todt.   P.N.: J.S.B.I. 10.
632.   My Soul Doth Exhalt the Lord God.... [Philadelphia] Association
of American Choruses [1948?]. 1 l., 26 pp., 26 cm. (Choral Series,
No. 138.)
Photo-offset lithograph process. Translation by Henry S. Drinker.
633.   "My Soul Doth Magnify the Lord"...Vocal score by B. Todt,
English version by E. H. Thorne and G. W. Daisley. ... Leipzig,
Breitkopf & Härtel, c 1903. 28 pp., 27 cm.

CANTATA NO. 10: Vocal scores
634.   Cantata 10...The Magnificat. ... [Philadelphia] University of
Pennsylvania [1941?]. 19 pp., 26 cm. (Choral Series, No. 133.)
Edited by Henry S. Drinker.
635.   Meine Seel' erhebt den Herrn; My soul doth magnify the Lord.
Two choruses for mixed voices from Cantata No. 10...German and
English words from the "Magnificat"...Edited by H. Clough-
Leighter. Boston, E. C. Schirmer [1931]. 19, [1] pp.; 27 cm.
(E. C. Schirmer Sacred Music, No. 1614.)

Contents: 1. Meine Seel' erhebt den Herrn (My Soul Doth Magnify the Lord). 2. Lob und Preis sei Gott dem Vater (Glory Be to the Father). P.N.: E.C.S. No. 667

CANTATA NO. 11. Lobet Gott in seinen Reichen (S. 11): Full score

636. Lobet Gott in seinen Reichen...Nach der Ausgabe der Bach-Gesellschaft und nach dem in der Preussischen Staatsbibliothek zu Berlin befindlichen Autograph revidiert und mit Einführung versehen von Arnold Schering. Leipzig, Eulenburg [1925?]. 4 ll., 56 pp., 2 ll., 19 cm. (Eulenburgs kleine Partitur-Ausgabe, No. 1002.)
P.N.: E.E. 4534

CANTATA NO. 11: Vocal-piano scores

637. Cantate (Oratorium) am Feste der Himmelfahrt Christi. ... Leipzig, C. F. Peters [ca. 1903]. 36 pp., 27 cm. (Edition Peters, No. 1279.)
Edited by Gustav Rösler. P.N.: 8927

638. Gloire à Dicu parmi les anges. Paroles françaises de *** partition chant et piano par A. Guilmant. Paris, Choudens [ca. 1930]. 56 pp., 31 cm. (Edition française de musique classique, No. 9.)
P.N.: A.C. 11711

639. Johann Sebastian Bach, Vocalwerke im Clavier Auszuge bearbeitet von Robert Franz, Kirchen-Cantaten...6, Lobet Gott in seinen Reichen. ... F. E. C. Leuckart (Constantin Sander) [ca. 1890]. 46, [1] pp.; 27 cm. P.N.: F.E.C.L. 3030

640. Kantate am Feste der Himmelfahrt Christi...Klavierauszug von Ernst Naumann. Leipzig, Breitkopf & Härtel [1891?]. 1 l., 36 pp., 27 cm. (Joh. Seb. Bach Kirchenkantaten, No. 11.)
P.N.: J.S.B.I. 11.

641. "Praise Jehovah in His Splendour."...Vocal score by Ernst Naumann, English version by John E. Borland. Leipzig, Breitkopf & Härtel [c 1904]. 1 l., 36 pp., 27 cm. (Joh. Seb. Bach Vocal Score, No. 11.)
P.N.: 24157

642. Praise our God in All His Splendor, Lobet Gott in seinen Reichen ...Edited and accompaniment arranged by Ifor Jones, English version by J. M. Stein and Ifor Jones. New York, G. Schirmer [c 1941]. 1 l., 53 pp., 26 cm.
P.N.: 39194

643. Praise our God Who Reigns in Heaven..Edited by John E. West, the English version by Paul England. London, Novello; New York, H. W. Gray, c 1906. 2 ll., 48 pp., 25 cm. (Novello's Original Octavo Edition.)
P.N.: 12126

644. Praise to God on High in Heaven. ... [Philadelphia] Association of American Choruses [1947?]. 1 l., 38 pp., 26 cm. (Choral Series, No. 117.)
Photo-offset lithograph process. Translation by Henry S. Drinker.

CANTATA NO. 11 : Vocal scores

645.   Cantata No. 11, Ascension Oratorio. ... [Philadelphia, University
of Pennsylvania, ca. 1935.] 16 pp., 27 cm.
Edited by Henry S. Drinker.
646.   Cantata 11...The Ascension Oratorio. ... [Philadelphia] University of Pennsylvania [ca. 1935]. 24 pp., 26 cm. (Choral Series,
No. 30-A.)
Edited by Henry S. Drinker.

CANTATA NO. 12. Weinen, Klagen, Sorgen, Zagen (S. 12): Full score

647.   Weinen, Klagen, Sorgen, Zagen...Nach der Ausgabe der Bach-
Gesellschaft und dem in der Preussischen Staatsbibliothek zu Berlin
befindlichen Autograph revidiert und mit Einführung versehen von
Arnold Schering. Leipzig, Eulenburg [1926?]. 4 ll., 24 pp., 2 ll., 19 cm.
(Eulenburgs kleine Partitur-Ausgabe, No. 1001.)   P.N.: E.E. 4548

CANTATA NO. 12 : Vocal-piano scores

648.   Cantate am Sonntage Jubilate...Klavier-Auszug von G. Rösler.
Leipzig, C. F. Peters [1876]. (Edition Peters, No. 1283.)   P.N.: 5832
649.   "Weinen, Klagen, Sorgen, Zagen,"..."Larmes, plaintes, transes,
craintes," traduction française de E. Goblot. ... Leipzig, Breitkopf &
Härtel [1891?]. 1 l., 24 pp., 27 cm. (Joh. Seb. Bach Kirchenkantaten,
No. 12.)
B. Todt's edition.   P.N.: J.S.B.I. 12.
650.   Wailing, Crying, Mourning, Sighing...Edited by John E. West,
English version by Paul England. London, Novello; New York,
H. W. Gray, c 1911. 1 l., 29 pp., 25 cm. (Novello's Original Octavo
Edition.)   P.N.: 13163
651.   Weeping, Crying Sorrow, Sighing. ... [Philadelphia] Association
of American Choruses [1946?]. 1 l., 20 pp., 1 l., 26 cm. (Choral
Series, No. 25.)
Photo-offset lithograph process. Translation by Henry S. Drinker.
652.   "Weeping, Wailing, Mourning, Fearing."...Vocal score by
B. Todt, English version by E. H. Thorne and Mrs. Rosa Newmarch.
Leipzig, Breitkopf & Härtel, c 1904. 20 pp., 27 cm.   P.N.: 24155

CANTATA NO. 12 : Excerpts

653.   Sinfonia to "Weinen, Klagen, Sorgen, Zagen"...Arranged by
Harvey Grace [Organ]. [London] Oxford University Press [c 1928].
1 l., 4 pp., 32 cm.

CANTATA NO. 13. Meine Seufzer, meine Tränen (S. 13): Vocal-piano
score

654.   Kantate am zweiten Sonntage nach Epiphanias. ... Leipzig,
Breitkopf & Härtel [1891?]. 1 l., 20 pp., 27 cm. (Joh. Seb. Bach
Kirchenkantaten, No. 13.)   P.N.: J.S.B.I. 13.

CANTATA NO. 14. Wär Gott nicht mit uns diese Zeit (S. 14): Parts

655. Originalstimmensatz der Kantate "Wär Gott nicht mit uns diese Zeit," Herausgegeben vom Bach-Archiv Leipzig. Leipzig, Deutscher Verlag für Musik [1956]. 11 parts and loose-leaf title page with foreword. 35 cm. (Faksimile-Reihe Bachscher Werke und Schriftstücke, Band 2.)
Facsimile of MS. in possession of Thomasschule. Original title page: Domin: 4 poſt Epiphin. | Wär Gott nicht mit uns dieſe Zeit | a 4 Voc. | 1. Corne da caccia | 2. Hautbois | 2. Violini | Viola | e | Continuo | di | J. S. Bach. Foreword by Werner Neumann.

CANTATA NO. 14: Vocal-piano scores

656. Cantate am 4ten Sonntage nach Epiphanias. ... Leipzig, C. F. Peters [1876]. 30 pp., 1 l., 27 cm. (Edition Peters, No. 1297.)
Edited by Gustav Rösler. P.N.: 5890

657. Kantate am vierten Sonntage nach Epiphanias. ... Leipzig, Breitkopf & Härtel [1891?]. 30 pp. (pp. 77-106), 27 cm. (Joh. Seb. Bach Kirchenkantaten, No. 14.) P.N.: J.S.B.I. 14.

658. Were God Not With Us. ... [Philadelphia] Association of American Choruses [1949?]. 1 l., 30 pp., 26 cm. (Choral Series, No. 160.)
Photo-offset lithograph process. Translation by Henry S. Drinker.

CANTATA NO. 14: Vocal score

659. Cantata 14. ... [Philadelphia] University of Pennsylvania [ca. 1935]. 19 pp., 26 cm. (Choral Series, No. 134.)
Edited by Henry S. Drinker.

CANTATA NO. 15. Denn du wirst meine Seele nicht in der Hölle lassen (S. 15): Vocal-piano score

660. Kantate am ersten Osterfesttage. ... Leipzig, Breitkopf & Härtel [1891?]. 28 pp. (pp. 107-34), 27 cm. (Joh. Seb. Bach Kirchenkantaten, No. 15.) P.N.: J.S.B.I. 15.

CANTATA No. 15: Vocal score

661. Cantatas 15 and 116. ... [Philadelphia] University of Pennsylvania [ca. 1935]. 36 pp., 27 cm. (Choral Series, No. 48.)
Edited by Henry S. Drinker.

CANTATA NO. 16. Herr Gott, dich loben wir (S. 16): Vocal-piano scores

662. Cantate am Feste der Beschneidung Christi. ... Leipzig, C. F. Peters [1876]. 23 pp., 27 cm. (Edition Peters, No. 1286.)
Edited by Gustav Rösler. P.N.: 8355

663. Kantate am Feste der Beschneidung Christi. ... Leipzig, Breitkopf & Härtel [1891?]. 24 pp. (pp. 135-58), 27 cm. (Joh. Seb. Bach Kirchenkantaten, No. 16.) P.N.: J.S.B.I. 16.

664. Lord God, Thy Praise We Sing. ... [Philadelphia] Association of
American Choruses [1943?]. 1 l., 24 pp., 1 l., 26 cm. (Choral Series,
No. 161.)
Photo-offset lithograph process. Translation by Henry S. Drinker.

CANTATA NO. 16: Vocal score

665. Cantata 16. ... [Philadelphia] University of Pennsylvania
[ca. 1935]. 16 pp., 26 cm. (Choral Series, No. 131.)
Edited by Henry S. Drinker.

CANTATA NO. 17. Wer Dank opfert, der preiset mich (S. 17): Vocal-
piano scores

666. By Praise Offered. ... [Philadelphia] Association of American
Choruses [1947?]. 1 l., 28 pp., 1 l., 26 cm. (Choral Series, No. 13.)
Photo-offset lithograph process. Translation by Henry S. Drinker.

667. Cantate am 14. Sonntage nach Trinitatis...Klavier-Auszug von
G. Rösler. ... Leipzig, C. F. Peters [1875]. 26 pp., 27 cm. (Edition
Peters, No. 1282.)   P.N.: 5787

668. Kantate am vierzehnten Sonntage nach Trinitatis. ... Leipzig,
Breitkopf & Härtel [1891?] 28 pp. (pp. 159-86), 27 cm. (Joh. Seb.
Bach Kirchenkantaten, No. 17.)   P.N.: J.S.B.I. 17.

669. Kirchen-Cantaten von Joh. Seb. Bach. Im Clavierauszuge mit
unterlegter Orgelstimme herausgegeben vom Bach-Vereine in Leipzig,
No. 2. Am vierzehnten Sonntage nach Trinitatis (On the Fourteenth
Sunday after Trinity), Bearbeitet von H. von Herzogenberg. Leipzig
& Winterthur, J. Rieter-Biedermann; London, Stanley Lucas,
Weber & Co. [ca. 1875]. 39 pp., 28 cm.
English version by R. H. Benson.   P.N.: 871

670. "Who Thanks Offers, He Praiseth Me." Edited and arranged by
W. G. Whittaker, the English words by C. Sanford Terry. [London]
Oxford University Press [c 1928]. 2 ll., 36 pp., 25 cm.

671. Whoso Doth Offer Thanks...Edited by John E. West, English
version by W. G. Rothery. London, Novello; New York, H. W. Gray
[1921?]. 2 ll., 35 pp., 25 cm. (Novello's Original Octavo Edition.)
P.N.: 14881

CANTATA NO. 18. Gleich wie der Regen und Schnee vom Himmel fällt
(S. 18): Vocal-piano scores

672. Cantate am Sonntage Sexagesimae. ... Leipzig, C. F. Peters
[1883]. 17 pp., 27 cm. (Edition Peters, No. 2141.)
Edited by Gustav Rösler.   P.N.: 6653

673. For As the Rain and Snow from Heaven Fall, Gleich wie der
Regen und Schnee vom Himmel fällt...Edited and accompaniment
arranged by Ifor Jones...English version by J. M. Stein and Ifor Jones.
New York, G. Schirmer [c 1947]. 25 pp. 1 l., 26 cm.   P.N.: 41547

674. "Gleich wie der Regen und Schnee vom Himmel fällt"..."For as the rain cometh down, and snow from Heaven"...English version by Mevanwy Roberts...Klavierauszug von Otto Schroder. Leipzig, Breitkopf & Härtel [c 1932]. 1 l., 18 pp., 27 cm. (Joh. Seb. Bach Kirchenkantaten, No. 18.)   P.N.: N.B.XXXI.2.

675. Kantate am Sonntage Sexagesimae. ... Leipzig, Breitkopf & Härtel [1891?]. 1 l., 18 pp. (pp. 187-204), 27 cm. (Joh. Seb. Bach Kirchenkantaten, No. 18.)   P.N.: J.S.B.I.18.

676. Like As the Raindrops and Snow. ... [Philadelphia] Association of American Choruses [1946?]. 1 l., 18 pp., 26 cm. (Choral Series, No. 43.)
Photo-offset lithograph process. Translation by Henry S. Drinker.

677. Telles la pluie et la neige tombent du ciel. Paroles françaises de Jules Ruelle, Partition chant et piano par A. Guilmant. Paris, Choudens [1926?]. 1 l., 15 pp., 31 cm. (Edition française de musique classique, No. 3.)   P.N.: 117.05

CANTATA NO. 18: Excerpts

678. Sinfonia from "Gleich wie der Regen und Schnee vom Himmel fällt"...arranged by Harvey Grace [for organ]. [London] Oxford University Press [c 1928]. 1 l., 4 pp., 32 cm. (Ten Instrumental Movements from the Cantatas, No. 9.)

CANTATA NO. 19. Es erhub sich ein Streit (S. 19): Full score

679. Es erhub sich ein Streit...Nach der Ausgabe der Bachgesellschaft und nach dem Autograph revidiert und mit Einführung versehen von Arnold Schering. Leipzig, Eulenburg [1931?]. viii, 40 pp.; 2 ll.; 19 cm. (Eulenburgs kleine Partitur-Ausgabe, No. 1027.)
          P.N.: E.E. 4827

CANTATA NO. 19: Vocal-piano scores

680. Cantate am Michaelisfeste. ... Leipzig, C. F. Peters [1876]. 27 pp., 27 cm. (Edition Peters, No. 1284.)
Edited by Gustav Rösler.   P.N.: 5833

681. Kantate am Michaelisfeste. ... Leipzig, Breitkopf & Härtel [1891?]. 28 pp., 27 cm. (Joh. Seb. Bach Kirchenkantaten, No. 19.)
          P.N.: J.S.B.I.19.

682. See How Fiercely They Fight. ... [Philadelphia] Association of American Choruses [1948?]. 1 l., 28 pp., 1 l., 26 cm. (Choral Series, No. 18.)
Photo-offset lithograph process. Translation by Henry S. Drinker.

683. There Uprose a Great Strife, Es erhub sich ein Streit...Edited and accompaniment arranged by Ifor Jones, English version by J. M. Stein and Ifor Jones. New York, G. Schirmer [c 1942]. 43 pp., 26 cm.   P.N.: 39750

CANTATA NO. 19: Vocal score

684.   See How Fiercely They Fight. ... [Philadelphia] Associacion of American Choruses [1943?]. 19 pp., 26 cm. (Choral Series, No. 18.) Edited by Henry S. Drinker.

CANTATA NO. 19: Excerpts

685.   Es erhub sich ein Streit. ... Cleveland, Ohio, The Bach Chorus of Cleveland [ca. 1940]. 12 pp., 28 cm.
This edition is made from the first 12 pp. of Gustav Rösler's edition, published by C. F. Peters, with P.N.: 5833. Markings added by F. W. Strieter, director of Cleveland Bach Chorus, 1931-43. Two copies.

CANTATA NO. 20. O Ewigkeit, du Donnerwort (S. 20): Vocal-piano scores

686.   Cantate am ersten Sonntage nach Trinitatis. ... Leipzig, C. F. Peters [1876]. 33 pp., 27 cm. (Edition Peters, No. 1285.)
Edited by Gustav Rösler.   P.N.: 5834
687.   Eternity, Thou Thunder Word. ... [Philadelphia] Association of American Choruses [1945?]. 1 l., 42 pp., 26 cm. (Choral Series, No. 19.)
Photo-offset lithograph process. Translation by Henry S. Drinker.
688.   "O Ewigkeit, du donnerwort!"..."Eternité, terrible mot!", Traduction française de Gustave Bret. ... Leipzig, Breitkopf & Härtel [1891?]. 1 l., 42 pp., 27 cm. (Joh. Seb. Bach Kirchenkantaten, No. 20.)   P.N.: J.S.B.I.20.

CANTATA NO. 21. Ich hatte viel Bekümmernis (S. 21): Full scores

689.   "Ich hatte viel Bekümmerniss"...bearbeitet von Robert Franz. ... Leipzig, F. E. C. Leuckart [ca. 1865]. 94 pp., 1 l., 34 cm.
P.N.: F.E.C.L.1986
690.   Ich hatte viel Bekümmernis...Nach der Ausgabe der Bach-Gesellschaft mit Einführung versehen von Arnold Schering. Leipzig, Eulenburg [1933?]. vi, 86 pp.; 3 ll.; 19 cm. (Eulenburgs kleine Partitur-Ausgabe, No. 1029.)   P.N.: E.E. 4829

CANTATA NO. 21: Vocal-piano scores

691.   Cantata 21. ... [Philadelphia] Association of American Choruses [1947?]. 1 l., 54 pp., 26 cm. (Choral Series, No. 87.)
Photo-offset lithograph process. Translation by Henry S. Drinker.
692.   I Suffered with Great Heaviness, Ich hatte viel Bekümmernis... Edited and accompaniment arranged by Ifor Jones, English version by J. M. Stein and Ifor Jones. New York, G. Schirmer [c 1941]. 1 l., 85 pp., 26 cm.   P.N.: 39174
693.   "Ich hatte viel Bekümmernis"..."I Had Great Heaviness of Heart." English version by E. H. Thorne and G. W. Daisley...

Klavierauszug von Günter Raphael. Leipzig, Breitkopf & Härtel
[c 1930]. 1 l., 54 pp., 27 cm. (Joh. Seb. Bach Kirchenkantaten,
No. 21.) P.N.: J.S.B.I.21.

694. J'avais de l'ombre plein le coeur. Paroles française de Maurice
Bouchor, partition chant et piano par A. Guilmant. Paris, Choudens
[1930?]. 1 l., 63 pp., 30 cm. (Edition française de musique classique,
No. 8.) P.N.: A.C. 11710, and 26

695. Johann Sebastian Bach, Vocalwerke im Clavier Auszuge bearbeitet von Robert Franz...2. Ich hatte viel Bekümmerniss. ...
Breslau, F. E. C. Leuckart (Constantin Sander) [ca. 1865]. 50 pp.,
27 cm.

696. Kantate für jede Zeit. "Ich hatte viel Bekümmernis."...Leipzig,
Breitkopf & Härtel [1891?]. 1 l., 54 pp., 27 cm. (Joh. Seb. Bach
Kirchenkantaten, No. 21.) P.N.: J.S.B.I.21.

697. Kantate für jede Zeit. ... Leipzig, C. F. Peters [1878]. 51 pp.,
27 cm. (Edition Peters, No. 41.)
Edited by Gustav Rösler. P.N.: 6244

698. My Spirit Was in Heaviness...The English translation and
adaptation by the Rev. John Troutbeck. ... London, Novello [1928?].
2 ll.; 57, [1] pp.; 1 l.; 26 cm. (Novello's Original Octavo Edition.)
P.N.: Bach's "My Spirit was in heaviness."
Novello, Ewer and Co.'s Octavo Edition.

699. Vocal Compositions by Johann Sebastian Bach, edited by Robert
Franz...No. III..."Deep Within My Heart". ... Leipzig, F. E. C.
Leuckart (Constantin Sander) [ca. 1870]. 1 l., 85 pp., 30 cm.
Front cover stamped with name of former owner, A. J. Balfour.
P.N.: F.E.C.L.1631

CANTATA NO. 21: Vocal scores

700. Cantata No. 21. ... [Philadelphia, University of Pennsylvania,
ca. 1935]. 31 pp., 27 cm. (Choral Series, No. 32.)
Edited by Henry S. Drinker.

CANTATA NO. 21: Excerpts

701. Sinfonia to "Ich hatte viel Bekümmernis"...Arranged by Harvey
Grace [for organ]. [London] Oxford University Press [c 1928]. 1 l.,
[4] pp., 32 cm. (Ten Instrumental Movements from the Cantatas,
No. 5.)

CANTATA NO. 22. Jesus nahm zu sich die Zwölf (S. 22): Vocal-piano
scores

702. "Jesus Called to Him the Twelve." Edited and arranged by
W. G. Whittaker, the English words by C. Sanford Terry. [London]
Oxford University Press [c 1927]. 2 ll., 36 pp., 25 cm.

703. Jesus, Calling Then the Twelve. ... [Philadelphia] Association of

703. *(continued)* American Choruses [1945?]. 1 l., 24 pp., 1 l., 26 cm.
(Choral Series, No. 20.)
   Photo-offset lithograph process. Translation by Henry S. Drinker.
704. Kantate am Sonntage Esto mihi. ... Leipzig, Breitkopf & Härtel
[1891?]. 1 l., 24 pp. (pp. 55-78), 27 cm. (Joh. Seb. Bach Kirchenkantaten, No. 22.)   P.N.: J.S.B.I.22.
705. Kantate am Sonntage vor der Fasten. ... Leipzig, C. F. Peters
[1876]. 23 pp., 27 cm. (Edition Peters, No. 1290.)
   Edited by Gustav Rösler.   P.N.: 5839

CANTATA NO. 22: Excerpts

706. Jesus Took to Him the Twelve. English translation by J. Steuart
Wilson, edited for the Bach Choir by R. Vaughan Williams. London,
Goodwin and Tabb, c 1921. 12 pp., 26 cm.
   Contents: Two choruses: 1. But They Understood Not; 2. O Loose
Us from Our Bondage.

CANTATA NO. 23. Du wahrer Gott und Davids Sohn (S. 23): Vocal-
piano scores

707. Cantata 23. ... [Philadelphia] Association of American Choruses
[1948?]. 24 pp., 26 cm. (Choral Series, No. 139.)
   Photo-offset lithograph process. Translation by Henry S. Drinker.
708. Kantate am Sonntage Esto mihi. ... Leipzig, Breitkopf & Härtel
[1891?]. 28 pp. (pp. 79-106), 27 cm. (Joh. Seb. Bach Kirchenkantaten, No. 23.)   P.N.: J.S.B.I.23.
709. Kantate am Sonntage vor den Fasten. ... Leipzig, C. F. Peters
[1876]. 24 pp., 27 cm. (Edition Peters, No. 1651.)
   Edited by Gustav Rösler.   P.N.: 5830
710. Thou Very God and David's Son, Du wahrer Gott und Davids
Sohn...edited and accompaniment arranged by Ifor Jones, English
version by J. M. Stein and Ifor Jones. New York, G. Schirmer
[c 1947]. 37 pp., 1 l., 26 cm.   P.N.: 41548
711. Thou Very God and David's Son...Vocal score by B. Todt,
English version by E. H. Thorne and G. W. Daisley. ... Leipzig,
Breitkopf & Härtel, c 1904. 28 pp., 27 cm. (Joh. Seb. Bach Kirchenkantaten, No. 23.)   P.N.: 24154

CANTATA NO. 23: Vocal score

712. Cantata 23. ... [Philadelphia] University of Pennsylvania [1941?].
20 pp., 26 cm. (Choral Series, No. 124.)
   Edited by Henry S. Drinker.

CANTATA NO. 23: Excerpts

713. Aller Augen warten, Herr; On Thee Mortal Eyes Wait, Lord;
two choruses for mixed voices from Cantata No. 23...English version
by Charles Sanford Terry, Edited by H. Clough-Leighter. Boston,

E. C. Schirmer [c 1931]. 31, [1] pp.; 27 cm. (E. C. Schirmer Sacred Music, No. 1615 & No. 1165.)
Second chorus: Christe, du Lamm Gottes (Lamb of God, Our Saviour). Two copies.   P N.: E.C.S. No. 668

714. Anthem: Ah Pass Me Not, My Saviour; from the cantata "Du wahrer Gott". ... [London, Henry Frowde, for the Church Music Society, ca. 1910]. 20 pp., 26 cm. (Church Music Society Reprints, No. 19.)

CANTATA NO. 24. Ein ungefärbt Gemüte (S. 24): Vocal-piano scores

715. Cantata am 4. Sonntage nach Trinitatis. ... Leipzig, C. F. Peters [1881]. 24 pp., 27 cm. (Edition Peters, No. 1696.)
Edited by Gustav Rösler.   P.N.: 6465

716. Kantate am vierten Sonntage nach Trinitatis. ... Leipzig, Breitkopf & Härtel [1891?]. 24 pp., 27 cm. (Joh. Seb. Bach Kirchenkantaten, No. 24.)   P.N.: J.S.B.I.24.

717. A Spirit Pure and Holy. ... [Philadelphia] Association of American Choruses [1947?]. 1 l., 24 pp., 1 l., 26 cm. (Choral Series, No. 21.)
Photo-offset lithograph process. Translation by Henry S. Drinker.

CANTATA NO. 24: Excerpts

718. A Chorale by J. S. Bach: God Is Our Hope and Strength, In Bach's Cantata "Ein ungefärbt Gemüthe"...Edited by H. P. Allen. ... [London, Oxford University Press, for Society for Promoting Christian Knowledge, 1925]. 7, [1] pp.; 25 cm. (Church Music Society Reprints, No. 16c.)

CANTATA NO. 25. Es ist nichts Gesundes an meinem Leibe (S. 25): Vocal-piano scores

719. Cantate am 14ten Sonntage nach Trinitatis...Klavier-Auszug von G. Rösler. Leipzig, C. F. Peters [1876]. 22 pp., 27 cm. (Edition Peters, No. 1650.)   P.N.: 5829

720. Kantate am vierzehnten Sonntage nach Trinitatis. ... Leipzig, Breitkopf & Härtel [1891?]. 22 pp. (pp. 131-52), 27 cm. (Joh. Seb. Bach Kirchenkantaten, No. 25.)
This is B. Todt's edition.   P.N.: J.S.B.I.25.

721. There Is Naught of Soundness. ... [Philadelphia] Association of American Choruses [1948?]. 1 l., 22 pp. (Choral Series, No. 127.)
Photo-offset lithograph process. Translation by Henry S. Drinker.

722. There Is No More Soundness in All My Body...Vocal score by B. Todt, English version by Lucy E. Broadwood. Leipzig, Breitkopf & Härtel, c 1905. 22 pp., 27 cm. (Joh. Seb. Bach Kirchenkantaten, No. 25.)   P.N.: 24160

723. There Is Naught of Soundness in All My Body...Edited by John E. West, English version by Miss G. E. Troutbeck. London, Novello; New York, H. W. Gray, c 1906. 2 ll., 31 pp., 25 cm. (Novello's Original Octavo Edition.)   P.N.: 12151

CANTATA NO. 25: Vocal scores

724. Cantata 25. ... [Philadelphia] University of Pennsylvania [1941?]
16 pp., 26 cm. (Choral Series, No. 123.)
Edited by Henry S. Drinker.

CANTATA NO. 26. Ach wie flüchtig, ach wie nichtig (S. 26): Full score

725. Ach wie flüchtig, ach wie nichtig (Vain and Fleeting)...be-
arbeitet von Robert Franz. ... Leipzig, F. E. C. Leuckart (Constantin
Sander) [1877?]. 2 ll., 55 pp., 33 cm.   P.N.: F.E.C.L. 3036

CANTATA NO. 26: Vocal-piano scores

726. "Ach wie flüchtig, ach wie nichtig"..."Ah How Weary, ah How
Fleeting." English version by J. Michael Diack..."Ombre vaine,
fugitive!" traduction française de G. Bret et Ch. Schweitzer...
Klavierauszug von Günter Raphael. Leipzig, Breitkopf & Härtel
[c 1929]. 1 l., 27 pp., 27 cm. (Joh. Seb. Bach Kirchenkantaten,
No. 26.)   P.N.: J.S.B.I. 26.
727. "Ach wie flüchtig, ach wie nichtig"..."Ombre vaine, fugitive."
Traduction française de G. Bret et Ch. Schweitzer. ... Leipzig,
Breitkopf & Härtel [ca. 1895]. 24 pp., 27 cm. (Joh. Seb. Bach
Kirchenkantaten, No. 26.)   P.N.: J.S.B.I.26.
728. Ah How Fleeting, Ah How Futile. ... [Philadelphia] Association
of American Choruses [1946?]. 1 l., 24 pp., 1 l., 26 cm. (Choral
Series, No. 41.)
    Photo-offset lithograph process. Translation by Henry S. Drinker.
729. "Ah How Fleeting." Edited, arranged and with English text by
W. G. Whittaker. [London] Oxford University Press [c 1929]. 3 ll.,
30 pp., 25 cm.
730. Johann Sebastian Bach, Vocalwerke im Clavier Auszuge bearbeitet von Robert Franz...[No.] 8. ... Leipzig, F. E. C. Leuckart
(Constantin Sander) [ca. 1890]. 31, [1] pp.; 27 cm.
731. Kantate am 24. Sonntage nach Trinitatis. ... Leipzig, C. F. Peters
[ca. 1881]. 23 pp., 28 cm. (Edition Peters, No. 43.)
Edited by Gustav Rösler.   P.N.: 6548

CANTATA NO. 27. Wer weiss, wie nahe mir mein Ende (S. 27): Full
score

732. Zur Todtenfeier, "Wer weiss, wie nahe mir mein Ende"...mit
ausgeführte, Accompagnement herausgegeben von Robert Franz. ...
Leipzig, F. E. C. Leuckart (Constantin Sander) [1886?]. 52 pp.,
34 cm.   P.N.: F.E.C.L.: 3883

CANTATA NO. 27: Vocal-piano scores

733. Kantate am 16ten Sonntage nach Trinitatis. ... Leipzig, C. F.
Peters [1876]. 21 pp., 27 cm. (Edition Peters, No. 1288.)
Edited by Gustav Rösler.   P.N.: 5837

CANTATAS 73

734. O Teach Me, Lord, My Days to Number...Edited by John E.
West, English version by Miss G. E. Troutbeck. ... London, Novello,
c 1906. 2 ll., 28 pp., 26 cm. (Novello's Original Octavo Edition.)
P.N.: 12187
375. "Wer weiss, wie nahe mir meine Ende?"..."Qui peut prévoir sa
dernière heure?" traduction française de Mme Henriette Fuchs. ...
Leipzig, Breitkopf & Härtel [ca. 1905]. 1 l., 24 pp. (Joh. Seb. Bach
Kirchenkantaten, No. 27.) P.N.: J.S.B.I.27.
736. Who Knows How Near Is My Last Hour. ... [Philadelphia]
Association of American Choruses [1948?]. 1 l., 24 pp., 1 l., 26 cm.
(Choral Series, No. 126.)
Photo-offset lithograph process. Translation by Henry S. Drinker.
737. "Who Knows, How Near My Latter Ending?"...Vocal score by
B. Todt, English version by Lucy E. Broadwood. Leipzig, Breitkopf
& Härtel, c 1905. 22 pp., 27 cm. (Joh. Seb. Bach Kirchenkantaten,
No. 27.) P.N.: 24161

CANTATA NO. 27: Vocal score

738. Cantata 27. ... [Philadelphia] University of Pennsylvania
[1939?]. 12 pp., 27 cm. (Choral Series, No. 59.)
Edited by Henry S. Drinker.

CANTATA NO. 28. Gottlob, nun geht das Jahr zu Ende (S. 28): Vocal-
piano scores

739. Cantate am Sonntage nach Weihnachten.... Leipzig, C. F. Peters
[1881]. 25 pp., 27 cm. (Edition Peters, No. 1692.)
Edited by Gustav Rösler. P.N.: 6461
740. Kantate am Sonntage nach Weihnachten...Klavierauszug von
Gustav Schreck. Leipzig, Breitkopf & Härtel [ca. 1900]. 1 l., 26 pp.,
27 cm. (Joh. Seb. Bach Kirchenkantaten, No. 28.) P.N.: N.B.II.2.
741. O Praise the Lord for All His Mercies...Edited by John Pointer,
the English version by W. G. Rothery. ... London, Novello, c 1911.
1 l.; 33, 8 pp.; 26 cm. (Novello's Original Octavo Edition.)
P.N.: 13095
742. "Praise God! The Year Draws To Its Closing"...Vocal score by
G. Schreck, English version by E. H. Thorne and G. W. Daisley. ...
Leipzig, Breitkopf & Härtel, c 1904. 26 pp., 27 cm. (Joh. Seb. Bach
Kirchenkantaten, No. 28.) P.N.: 23810
743. Rejoice! The Passing Year is Ended. ... [Philadelphia] Associ-
ation of American Choruses [1948?]. 1 l., 26 pp. (Choral Series,
No. 125.)
Photo-offset lithograph process. Translation by Henry S. Drinker.

CANTATA NO. 28: Excerpts

744. Harvest Anthem, O Lord of Life, Whose Glory...from the
cantata "Gottlob! nun geht das Jahr zu Ende."...[London, Henry

744. *(continued)* Frowde for The Church Music Society, ca. 1910].
13, [1] pp.; 1 l.; 26 cm. (Church Music Society Reprints, No. 9.)
745. Motet from Cantata No. 28. Gottlob! nun geht das Jahr zu
Ende. ... [Philadelphia, University of Pennsylvania, ca. 1935]. 8 pp.,
27 cm.
Contents: "Bless the Lord, O my soul." On page 8 appears a
chorale from Cantata No. 17.

CANTATA NO. 29: Wir danken dir Gott, wir danken dir (S. 29): Vocal-
piano scores

746. Kantate bei der Rathswahl zu Leipzig 1731. ... Leipzig, Breitkof
& Härtel [1891?]. 1 l., 28 pp., 27 cm. (Joh. Seb. Bach Kirchen-
kantaten, No. 29.)   P.N.: J.S.B.I.29.
747. Kantate bei der Ratswahl zu Leipzig 1731. ... Leipzig, C. F.
Peters [ca. 1925]. 27 pp., 27 cm. (Edition Peters, No. 1289.)
Edited by Gustav Rösler.   P.N.: 10453
748. We Thank Thee, Lord God. ... [Philadelphia] Association of
American Choruses [1947?]. 1 l., 28 pp., 1 l., 26 cm. (Choral Series,
No. 22.)
Photo-offset lithograph process. Translation by Henry S. Drinker.

CANTATA NO. 29: Excerpts

749. Chorale...My Soul, Now Praise Thy Maker...from Cantata
No. 29. ... [London, Oxford University Press, for the Society for
Promoting Christian Knowledge, 1930]. 3, [1] pp.; 26 cm. (Church
Music Society Reprints, No. 22 B.)

CANTATA NO. 30. Freue dich, erlöste Schar (S. 30): Vocal-piano scores

750. Cantata 30. ... [Philadelphia] Association of American Choruses
[1946?]. 1 l., 48 pp., 1 l., 26 cm. (Choral Series, No. 26).
Photo-offset lithograph process. Translation by Henry S. Drinker.
751. Cantate am Feste Johannis des Täufers...Klavier-Auszug von
G. Rösler. Leipzig, C. F. Peters [1872]. 47 pp., 27 cm. (Edition
Peters, No. 1017.)   P.N.: 5429
752. Johann Sebastian Bach, Vocalwerke im Clavier Auszuge bearbeitet von Robert Franz... [No.] 9. ... Leipzig, F. E. C. Leuckart
(Constantin Sander) [ca. 1890]. 59, [1] pp.; 27 cm.
                                                     P.N.: F.E.C.L.1893
753. Kantate am Feste Johannis des Täufers. ... Leipzig, Breitkopf &
Härtel [1891?]. 1 l., 48 pp., 27 cm. (Joh. Seb. Bach Kirchenkantaten,
No. 30.)   P.N.: J.S.B.I.30.
754. O Sion, dans tes chaumières. Paroles françaises de V. Durdilly,
partition chant et piano par A. Guilmant. Paris, Choudens [ca. 1925].
1 l., 40 pp., 1 l., 30 cm. (Edition française de musique classique,
No. 5.)   P.N.: 117.07 and 21.
755. Sing For Joy ye Ransomed Band; Freue dich, erloste Schaar...

Vocal score with piano accompaniment arranged by Robert Franz,
edited and provided with an English translation by Alfred G. Langley.
... New York, Carl Fischer [c 1926]. 1 l., 60 pp., 1 l., 27 cm. (Carl
Fischer's Choir Music Edition.)   P.N.: C.M. 225-60

CANTATA NO. 31. Der Himmel lacht, die Erde jubilieret (S. 31):
Full score

756. Der Himmel lacht die Erde jubilieret...Nach der Ausgabe der
Bach-Gesellschaft und den Originalstimmen revidiert und mit Einführung versehen von Arnold Schering. Leipzig, Eulenburg [1929?].
1 l.; v, 62 pp.; 2 ll.; 19 cm. (Eulenburgs kleine Partitur-Ausgabe,
No. 1016.)   P.N.: E.E. 4816.

CANTATA NO. 31: Vocal-piano scores

757. Cantata 31. ... [Philadelphia] Association of American Choruses
[1946?]. 1 l., 30 pp., 26 cm. (Choral Series, No. 27.)
Photo-offset lithograph process. Translation by Henry S. Drinker.
758. Cantate am ersten Osterfesttage. ... Leipzig, C. F. Peters [1881].
30 pp., 27 cm. (Edition Peters, No. 1695.)
Edited by Gustav Rösler.   P.N.: 6464
759. The Heavens Shout. Edited and arranged by W. G. Whittaker,
the English words by C. Sanford Terry. [London] Oxford University
Press [c 1927]. 4 ll., 43 pp., 25 cm.
760. "Der Himmel lacht, die Erde jubilieret"..."The Heavens
Rejoice"...English version by J. Michael Diack...Klavierauszug
von Günter Raphael. Leipzig, Breitkopf & Härtel [c 1931]. 1 l.,
34 pp., 27 cm. (Joh. Seb. Bach Kirchenkantaten, No. 31.)
                                            P.N.: J.S.B.I.31.
761. Kantate am ersten Osterfesttage. ... Leipzig, Breitkopf & Härtel
[1891?]. 30 pp., 27 cm. (Joh. Seb. Bach Kirchenkantaten, No. 31.)
                                            P.N.: J.S.B.I.31.

CANTATA NO. 32. Liebster Jesu, mein Verlangen (S. 32): Vocal-piano
scores

762. "Blessed Jesus, Priceless Treasure"...English version by C. V.
Gorton. Leipzig, Breitkopf & Härtel, c 1911. 23 pp., 27 cm. (Joh.
Seb. Bach Kirchenkantaten, No. 32.)   P.N.: 26795
763. Cantate...am 1ten Sonntage nach Epiphanias. ... Leipzig,
C. F. Peters [1877]. 22 pp., 27 cm. (Edition Peters, No. 1663.)
Edited by Gustav Rösler.   P.N.: 5932
764. "Liebster Jesu, mein Verlangen"..."O Mon Jésus, mon seul
désir." Traduction française par G. Bret. Leipzig, Breitkopf &
Härtel [ca. 1910]. 1 l., 20 pp. (pp. 31-50), 27 cm. (Joh. Seb. Bach
Kirchenkantaten, No. 32.)   P.N.: J.S.B.I.32.

CANTATA NO. 33. Allein zu dir, Herr Jesu Christ (S. 33): Vocal-piano scores

765.   Kantate am dreizehnten Sonntage nach Trinitatis. ... Leipzig, Breitkopf & Härtel [1891?]. 28 pp. (pp. 51-78), 27 cm. (Joh. Seb. Bach Kirchenkantaten, No. 33.)   P.N.: J.S.B.I.33.
766.   Thou Art Alone, Lord Jesus Christ. ... [Philadelphia] Association of American Choruses [ca. 1943]. 1 l., 28 pp., 1 l., 26 cm. (Choral Series, No. 33.)
Photo-offset lithograph process. Translation by Henry S. Drinker.

CANTATA NO. 33: Vocal score

767.   Cantata 33. ... [Philadelphia] University of Pennsylvania [ca. 1935]. 16 pp., 26 cm. (Choral Series, No. 137.)
Edited by Henry S. Drinker.

CANTATA NO. 34. O ewiges Feuer, O Ursprung der Liebe (S. 34): Full scores

768.   "O ewiges Feuer, O Ursprung der Liebe"...bearbeitet von Robert Franz. ... Leipzig, F. E. C. Leuckart (Constantin Sander) [ca. 1890]. 1 l., 55 pp., 28 cm.   P.N.: F.E.C.L.2076.
769.   O ewiges Feuer, Ursprung der Liebe...Nach der Ausgabe der Bach-Gesellschaft und dem Autograph revidiert und mit Einführung versehen von Arnold Schering. Leipzig, Eulenburg [1929?]. 1 l.; vi, 50 pp.; 3 ll.; 19 cm. (Eulenburgs kleine Partitur-Ausgabe, No. 1013.)
P.N.: E.E. 4812

CANTATA NO. 34: Vocal-piano scores

770.   Cantate am Pfingstfeste. ... Leipzig, C. F. Peters [1876]. 24 pp., 27 cm. (Edition Peters, No. 1291.)
Edited by Gustav Rösler.   P.N.: 5840
771.   Johann Sebastian Bach, Vocalwerke im Clavier Auszuge bearbeitet von Robert Franz...[No.] 3. ... Breslau, F. E. C. Leuckart (Constantin Sander) [ca. 1865]. 28 pp., 27 cm.
P.N.: F.E.C.L. 2065
772.   Kantate am Pfingstfeste. ... Leipzig, Breitkopf & Härtel [1891?]. 1 l., 24 pp., 27 cm. (Joh. Seb. Bach Kirchenkantaten, No. 34.)
P.N.: J.S.B.I.34.
773.   "O Fire Everlasting, O Fount of Affection"...Vocal score by Ernst Naumann, English version by E. H. Thorne and G. W. Daisley. ... Leipzig, Breitkopf & Härtel, c 1903. 24 pp., 27 cm. (Joh. Seb. Bach Kirchenkantaten, No. 34.)   P.N.: 24025
774.   O Flamme immortelle. Paroles françaises de Maurice Bouchor, partition chant et piano par A. Guilmant. Paris, Choudens [ca. 1930], 2 ll., 32 pp., 1 l., 30 cm. (Edition française de musique classique. No. 7.)   P.N.: 11709 and D.24.

775. O Light Everlasting...The pianoforte accompaniment arranged by Robert Franz, the English version translated and adapted by the Rev. John Troutbeck. ... London, Novello [1930?]. 1 l., 26 pp., 2 ll., 26 cm. (Novello's Original Octavo Edition.)
Two copies.   P.N.: Bach's "O Light everlasting."
                                                          Novello, Ewer and Co.'s Octavo Edition
CANTATA NO. 34: Vocal score

776. Cantata 34. ... [Philadelphia] University of Pennsylvania [ca. 1935]. 15 pp., 27 cm. (Choral Series, No. 60.)
Edited by Henry S. Drinker.

CANTATA NO. 34: Excerpts

777. O Light Everlasting, O ewiges Feuer. Two choruses for mixed voices from Cantata No. 34...English version by Rev. John T. Troutbeck, edited by H. Clough-Leighter. Boston, E. C. Schirmer [1931]. 33, [3] pp.; 27 cm. (E. C. Schirmer Sacred Music, No. 1195.)
Second chorus: Peace be unto Israel (Fricde über Israel).
                                                          P.N.: E.C.S. N°. 585

CANTATA NO. 35. Geist und Seele wird verwirret (S. 35): Vocal-piano score

778. Kantate am zwölften Sonntage nach Trinitatis. ... Leipzig, Breitkopf & Härtel [1891?]. 1 l., 32 pp. (pp. 103-34), 27 cm. (Joh. Seb. Bach Kirchenkantaten, No. 35.)   P.N.: J.S.B.I.35.

CANTATA NO. 36. Schwingt freudig euch empor (S. 36): Vocal-piano scores

779. Cantate am ersten Advent. ... Leipzig, C. F. Peters [1876]. 36 pp , 27 cm. (Edition Peters, No. 1292.)
Edited by Gustav Rösler.   P.N.: 5841

780. Kantate am ersten Advent. ... Leipzig, Breitkopf & Härtel [1891?]. 1 l., 40 pp., 27 cm. (Joh. Seb. Bach Kirchenkantaten, No. 36.)   P.N.: J.S.B.I.36.

781. Kantate zum 1. Advent...Herausgegeben von Alfred Dürr, Klavier-auszug von Gottfried Müller. Kassel und Basel, Bärenreiter [1956]. 46 pp., 1 l., 27 cm. (Bärenreiter-Ausgabe 5101a.)
On verso of title page: "In Teilauflage Veröffentlichung der Neuen Bachgesellschaft, Jahrgang LVI, 1."

782. Up, Joyous Raise Your Song. ... [Philadelphia] Association of American Choruses [1948?]. 36 pp., 26 cm. (Choral Series, No. 149.)
Photo-offset lithograph process. Translation by Henry S. Drinker.

CANTATA NO. 36: Vocal score

783. Cantata 36. ... [Philadelphia] University of Pennsylvania [ca. 1935]. 24 pp., 26 cm. (Choral Series, No. 129.)
Edited by Henry S. Drinker.

CANTATA NO. 37. Wer da glaubet und getauft wird (S. 37): Vocal-piano scores

784. Cantate am Feste der Himmelfahrt Christi. ... Leipzig, C. F. Peters [1881]. 23 pp., 27 cm. (Edition Peters, No. 1693.) Edited by Gustav Rösler. P.N.: 6462

785. Johann Sebastian Bach, Vocalwerke im Clavier Auszuge bearbeitet von Robert Franz, Kirchen-Cantaten...[No.] 7: Wer da glaubet und getauft wird [Who Believeth and Obeyeth]. Leipzig, F. E. C. Leuckart (Constantin Sander) [ca. 1890]. 33, [1] pp.; 27 cm. P.N.: F.E.C.L.1713

786. Kantate am Feste der Himmelfahrt Christi. ... Leipzig, Breitkopf & Härtel [1891?]. 1 l., 24 pp., 27 cm. (Joh. Seb. Bach Kirchenkantaten, No. 37.) P.N.: J.S.B.I.37.

787. True Believers. ... [Philadelphia] Association of American Choruses [1948?]. 1 l., 24 pp., 1 l., 26 cm. (Choral Series, No. 132.) Photo-offset lithograph process. Translation by Henry S. Drinker.

CANTATA NO. 37: Vocal score

788. Cantata 37. [Philadelphia] University of Pennsylvania [1941?]. 16 pp., 26 cm. (Choral Series, No. 130.) Edited by Henry S. Drinker.

CANTATA NO. 37: Excerpts

789. Psalm CXXI, for chorus and semi-chorus. Arranged by Ivor Atkins and J. Michael Diack. Glasgow, Paterson's Publications, c 1925. 1 l., 30 pp., 27 cm.
Chorus No. 1 also issued separately by Paterson in The Lyric Collection of Part Songs, No. 1578. P.N.: Psalm CXXI

CANTATA NO. 38. Aus tiefer Not schrei' ich zu dir (S. 38): Vocal-piano scores

790. Cantate am 21. Sonntage nach Trinitatis. ... Leipzig, C. F. Peters [1881]. 23 pp., 28 cm. (Edition Peters, No. 1694.) Edited by Gustav Rösler. P.N.: 6463

791. From Depths of Woe I Call on Thee...Edited by John E. West, English version by Paul England. London, Novello; New York, H. W. Gray, c 1906. 1 l., 30 pp., 25 cm. (Novello's Original Octavo Edition.) P.N.: 12354

792. In My Despair I Cry to Thee. ... [Philadelphia] Association of American Choruses [1946?]. 1 l., 22 pp., 26 cm. (Choral Series, No. 40.)
Photo-offset lithograph process. Translation by Henry S. Drinker.

793. Kantate nach ein und zwanzigsten Sonntage nach Trinitatis. ... Leipzig, Breitkopf & Härtel [1891?]. 22 pp. (pp. 199-220), 27 cm. (Joh. Seb. Bach Kirchenkantaten, No. 38.) P.N.: J.S.B.I.38.

CANTATA NO. 38: Excerpts

794. Motet from Cantata 38 [In My Despair I Cry to Thee]. ...
[Philadelphia] University of Pennsylvania [ca. 1935]. 8 pp., 27 cm.
Edited by Henry S. Drinker.
795. Out of the Depths I Cry to Thee, Aus tiefer Noth schrei' ich zu
dir; chorus and choral from Cantata No. 38...English version by
Catherine Winkworth, edited, and the organ part arranged, by the
Rev. Walter Williams. Boston, E. C. Schirmer [c 1938]. 18 pp., 1 l.,
28 cm. (St. Dunstan's Edition, No. 1246.)   P.N.: E.C.S. N°. 692

CANTATA NO. 39. Brich dem Hungrigen dein Brot (S. 39): Full score

796. Brich dem Hungrigen dein Brot...Based on the Bach-Gesellschaft
edition. New York, Broude Brothers [ca. 1940]. 3 ll., 40 pp., front.
(facs.), 20 cm.
Edited by Arnold Schering, whose introduction is printed in English
translation. Three leaves, issued separately, contain Henry S.
Drinker's translation of the text.   P.N.: 36

CANTATA NO. 39: Vocal-piano scores

797. Cantate am 1sten Sonntage nach Trinitatis. ... Leipzig, C. F.
Peters [1876]. 31 pp., 27 cm. (Edition Peters, No. 1295.)
Edited by Gustav Rösler.   P.N.: 5888
798. Deal the Hungry Ones Thy Bread. ... [Philadelphia] Association
of American Choruses [1948?]. 1 l., 30 pp., 26 cm. (Choral Series,
No. 143.)
Photo-offset lithograph process. Translation by Henry S. Drinker.
799. Give the Hungry Man Thy Bread...Edited by John E. West,
English version by Paul England. London, Novello; New York,
H. W. Gray, c 1907. 2 ll., 44 pp., 26 cm. (Novello's Original Octavo
Edition.)   P.N.: 12509
800. Kantate am ersten Sonntage nach Trinitatis. ... Leipzig, Breit-
kopf & Härtel [1891?]. 1 l., 30 pp. (pp. 221-50), 27 cm. (Joh. Seb.
Bach Kirchenkantaten, No. 39.)   P.N.: J.S.B.I.39.

CANTATA NO. 39: Vocal score

801. Cantata 39. ... [Philadelphia] University of Pennsylvania [ca.
1935]. 23 pp., 26 cm. (Choral Series, No. 135.)
Edited by Henry S. Drinker.

CANTATA NO. 39: Excerpts

802. Arie aus der Cantate "Brich dem Hungrigen dein Brod"...
arrangirt von W. Rust. Berlin, Schlesinger'schen Buch- & Musikhandlung [ca. 1855]. 7 pp., 34 cm., wove paper. (Hosianna, Vol. 2,
No. 34.)
First line reads: Höchster, was ich habe.   P.N.: S. 5253

80   PUBLISHED MUSIC OF J. S. BACH

CANTATA NO. 40. Dazu ist erschienen der Sohn Gottes (S. 40):
Vocal-piano scores

803.   Cantata 40. ... [Philadelphia] Association of American Choruses
[1946?]. 1 l., 28 pp., 1 l., 26 cm. (Choral Series, No. 28.)
       Photo-offset lithograph process. Translation by Henry S. Drinker.
804.   Cantate am 2ten Weihnachtsfesttage. ... Leipzig, C. F. Peters
[1876]. 28 pp., 27 cm. (Edition Peters, No. 1296.)
       Edited by Gustav Rösler.   P.N.: 5889
805.   Kantate am zweiten Weihnachtsfesttage. ... Leipzig, Breitkopf &
Härtel [1891?]. 1 l., 28 pp. (pp. 251-78), 27 cm. (Joh. Seb. Bach
Kirchenkantaten, No. 40.)   P.N.: J.S.B.I.40.
806.   "To this End Appeared the Son of God"... Vocal score by B. Todt,
English version by E. H. Thorne and G. W. Daisley. ... Leipzig,
Breitkopf & Härtel, c 1903. 1 l., 28 pp., 27 cm. (Joh. Seb. Bach
Vocal Scores, No. 40.)   P.N.: 24027

CANTATA NO. 41. Jesu, nun sei gepreiset (S. 41): Vocal-piano scores

807.   Cantate am Feste der Beschneidung Christi. ... Leipzig, C. F.
Peters [1877]. 31 pp., 27 cm. (Edition Peters, No. 1656.)
       Edited by Gustav Rösler.   P.N.: 5925
808.   Jesus, Now Will We Praise Thee...The English version by the
Rev. Dr. Troutbeck. London, Novello; New York, H. W. Gray
[1925?]. 1 l., 33 pp., 25 cm. (Novello's Original Octavo Edition.)
                                                                   P.N.: 8086
809.   Kantate am Feste der Beschneidung Christi. ... Leipzig, Breitkopf
& Härtel [1891?]. 1 l., 34 pp., 27 cm. (Joh. Seb. Bach Kirchenkantaten, No. 41.)   P.N.: J.S.B.I.41.
810.   O Lord, We Come to Praise Thee. ... [Philadelphia] Association
of American Choruses [1948?]. 1 l., 34 pp., 26 cm. (Choral Series,
No. 141.)
       Photo-offset lithograph process. Translation by Henry S. Drinker.

CANTATA NO. 41: Vocal score

811.   Cantata 41. ... [Philadelphia] University of Pennsylvania [ca.
1935]. 20 pp., 27 cm. (Choral Series, No. 62.)
       Edited by Henry S. Drinker.

CANTATA NO. 41: Excerpts

812.   Two Chorales. ... London, Oxford University Press, for the
Society for Promoting Christian Knowledge, 1930. 4 pp., 26 cm.
(Church Music Society Reprints, No. 22A.)
       Contents: While Yet the Morn Is Breaking (From Cantata 41);
O Rejoice, ye Christians, Loudly (From Cantata 40).

CANTATA NO. 42. Am Abend aber desselbigen Sabbats (S. 42): Vocal-
piano scores

813.   "Am Abend aber desselbigen Sabbaths"..."Le Soir venu de la

même journée"...Traduction française de G. Bret et Ch. Schweitzer
...Leipzig, Breitkopf & Härtel [ca. 1900]. 1 l., 28 pp. (pp. 35-62),
27 cm. P.N.: J.S.B.I.42.
814. Cantate am Sonntage Quasimodogeniti. ... Leipzig, C. F. Peters
[1883]. 27 pp., 28 cm. (Edition Peters, No. 2144.)
Edited by Gustav Rösler. P.N.: 6648

CANTATA NO. 43. Gott fähret auf mit Jauchzen (S. 43): Vocal-piano
scores
815. Cantata 43. ... [Philadelphia] Association of American Choruses
[1946?]. 1 l., 30 pp., 26 cm. (Choral Series, No. 29.)
Photo-offset lithograph process. Translation by Henry S. Drinker.
816. Cantate am Feste der Himmelfahrt Christi. ... Leipzig, C. F.
Peters [1877]. 31 pp., 27 cm. (Edition Peters, No. 1658.)
Edited by Gustav Rösler. P.N.: 5927
817. "Dieu monte au ciel." Traduction française et adaptation de
Félix Raugel. Paris, Choudens [c 1930]. 1 l., 40 pp., 1 l., 30 cm.
(Edition française de musique classique, No. 9.) P.N : A C. 17195.
818. God Goeth Up with Shouting. ... The pianoforte accompaniment
arranged by Robert Franz, the English words translated from the
German and adapted by the Rev. W. H. Milman. ... London,
Novello; New York, H. W. Gray [1925?]. 1 l., 37 pp., 26 cm.
(Novello's Original Octavo Edition.)
P.N.: Bach's Cantata, "God goeth up with shouting." –
Novello, Ewer and Co.'s Octavo Edition
819. Johann Sebastian Bach, Vocalwerke im Clavier Auszuge be-
arbeitet von Robert Franz, Kirchen-Cantaten...[No.] 2. ... Leipzig,
F. E. C. Leuckart (Constantin Sander) [ca. 1890]. 41, [1] pp.;
27 cm. P.N.: F.E.C.L.1626.
820. Kantate am Feste der Himmelfahrt Christi. ... Leipzig, Breitkopf
& Härtel [1891?]. 30 pp. (pp. 63-92), 27 cm. (Joh. Seb. Bach
Kirchenkantaten, No. 43.) P.N.: J.S.B.I.43.

CANTATA NO. 44. Sie werden euch in den Bann tun (S. 44): Vocal-
piano scores
821. Kantate am Sonntage Exaudi. ... Leipzig, Breitkopf & Härtel,
1891. 22 pp. (pp. 93-114), 27 cm. (Joh. Seb. Bach Kirchenkantaten,
No. 44.) P.N.: J.S.B.I.44.
822. Kantate am Sonntage Exaudi. ... Leipzig, C. F. Peters [1877].
20 pp., 27 cm. (Edition Peters, No. 1659.)
Edited by Gustav Rösler. P.N.: 5928
823. "Sie werden euch in den Bann tun"..."You Will They Put
Under Ban"...English version by E. H. Thorne and G. W. Daisley,
Klavierauszug von Günter Raphael. Leipzig, Breitkopf & Härtel
[c 1932]. 1 l., 24 pp., 27 cm. (Joh. Seb. Bach Kirchenkantaten,
No. 44.) P.N.: J.S.B.I.44.

824. Out From Their Temples They Cast You. ... [Philadelphia] Association of American Choruses [1946?]. 1 l., 22 pp., 26 cm. (Choral Series, No. 44.)
     Photo-offset lithograph process. Translation by Henry S. Drinker.
825. "You They Will Put Under Ban"...Vocal score by B. Todt, English version by E. H. Thorne and G. W. Daisley. Leipzig, Breitkopf & Härtel, c 1904. 22 pp., 29 cm. (Joh. Seb. Bach Vocal Scores, No. 44.)   P.N.: 24026

CANTATA NO. 45. Es ist dir gesagt, Mensch, was gut ist (S. 45): Full score

826. "Es ist dir gesagt, Mensch, was gut ist"...mit ausgeführtem Accompagnement herausgegeben von Robert Franz. ... Leipzig, F. E. C. Leuckart (Constantin Sander) [ca. 1890]. 85 pp., 1 l., 34 cm.   P.N.: F.E.C.L.3699.

CANTATA NO. 45: Vocal-piano scores

827. Cantate am 8ten Sonntage nach Trinitatis...Klavierauszug von G. Rösler. Leipzig, C. F. Peters [1872]. 35 pp., 27 cm. (Edition Peters, No. 1016.)   P.N.: 5428
828. [Es ist dir gesagt, Mensch, was gut ist] To Thee He Hath Shown ...Words from the Bible translated and edited by Alfred G. Langley. ... New York, G. Schirmer [c 1901]. 2 ll., 54 pp., 1 l., 26 cm.
                                                        P.N.: 15650
829. He Showeth To Thee, Man, What Right Is. ... [Philadelphia] Association of American Choruses [1948?]. 1 l., 34 pp., 26 cm. (Choral Series, No. 142.)
     Photo-offset lithograph process. Translation by Henry S. Drinker.
830. Johann Sebastian Bach, Vocalwerke im Clavier Auszuge bearbeitet von Robert Franz, Kirchen-Cantaten. No. 1. ... Leipzig, F. E. C. Leuckart (Constantin Sander) [ca. 1890]. 57, [1] pp.; 27 cm.
831. Kantate am achten Sonntage nach Trinitatis...Klavierauszug von Ernst Naumann. Leipzig, Breitkopf & Härtel [ca. 1900]. 1 l., 34 pp., 27 cm. (Joh. Seb. Bach Kirchenkantaten, No. 45.)
                                                     P.N.: N.B.III.1.

CANTATA NO. 45: Vocal score

832. Cantata 45. ... [Philadelphia] University of Pennsylvania [1941?]. 22 pp., 1 l., 26 cm. (Choral Series, No. 138.)
     Edited by Henry S. Drinker.

CANTATA NO. 46. Schauet doch und sehet, ob irgend ein Schmerz sei (S. 46): Full score

833. Schauet doch und sehet...Auf Grund der Ausgabe der Bach-Gesellschaft nach den Originalstimmen revidiert sowie mit Einführung versehen von Arnold Schering. Leipzig, Eulenburg [1931?].

viii, 52 pp.; 2 ll.; 19 cm.   (Eulenburgs kleine Partitur-Ausgabe,
No. 1025.)   P.N.: E.E.4825
CANTATA NO. 46: Vocal-piano scores

834. Cantate am zehnten Sonntage nach Trinitatis. ... Leipzig,
C. F. Peters [1877]. 31 pp., 27 cm. (Edition Peters, No. 1660.)
Edited by Gustav Rösler.   P.N.: 5929
835. Kantate am zehnten Sonntage nach Trinitatis. ... Leipzig,
Breitkopf & Härtel [1891?]. 1 l., 30 pp., 27 cm. (Joh. Seb. Bach
Kirchenkantaten, No. 46.)   P.N.: J.S.B.I.46.
836. Look Ye Now...[Philadelphia] Association of American Choruses
[1948?]. 1 l., 30 pp., 26 cm. (Choral Series, No. 165.)
Photo-offset lithograph process. Translation by Henry S. Drinker.

CANTATA NO. 46: Vocal score

837. Cantata 46. ... [Philadelphia] University of Pennsylvania [ca.
1935]. 20 pp., 26 cm. (Choral Series, No. 139.)

CANTATA NO. 47. Wer sich selbst erhöhet, der soll erniedriget werden
(S. 47): Vocal-piano scores

838. He Who Self Exalteth. ... [Philadelphia] Association of American
Choruses [1949?]. 1 l., 28 pp., 1 l., 26 cm. (Choral Series, No. 144.)
Photo-offset lithograph process. Translation by Henry S. Drinker.
839. Johann Sebastian Bach, Vocalwerke im Clavier Auszuge be-
arbeitet von Robert Franz, Kirchen-Cantaten...[No.] 4. ... Leipzig,
F.E.C. Leuckart (Constantin Sander) [ca. 1890]. 47, [1] pp.; 27 cm.
840. Kantate am siebzehnten Sonntage nach Trinitatis. ... Leipzig,
Breitkopf & Härtel [1891?]. 1 l., 28 pp., 27 cm. (Joh. Seb. Bach
Kirchenkantaten, No. 47.)   P.N.: J.S.B.I.47.
841. Kantate am 17. Sonntage nach Trinitatis. ... Leipzig, C. F. Peters
[1881]. 27 pp., 27 cm. (Edition Peters, No. 1698.)
Edited by Gustav Rösler.   P.N.: 6467

CANTATA NO. 47: Vocal score

842. Cantata 47. ... [Philadelphia] University of Pennsylvania [1941?].
19 pp., 26 cm. (Choral Series, No. 114.)
Edited by Henry S. Drinker.

CANTATA NO. 48. Ich elender Mensch, wer wird mich erlösen (S. 48):
Vocal-piano scores

843. Cantate am 19. Sonntage nach Trinitatis. ... Leipzig, C. F. Peters
[1881]. 19 pp., 27 cm. (Edition Peters, No. 1699.)
Edited by Gustav Rösler.   P.N.: 6468
844. Kantate am neunzehnten Sonntage nach Trinitatis. ... Leipzig,
Breitkopf & Härtel [1891?]. 1 l., 16 pp., 27 cm. (Joh. Seb. Bach
Kirchenkantaten, No. 48.)   P.N.: J.S.B.I.48.

845.   O Wretched Man, I. ... [Philadelphia] Association of American Choruses [1948?]. 19 pp., 25 cm. (Choral Series, No. 145.) Photo-offset lithograph process. Translation by Henry S. Drinker.

CANTATA NO. 48: Vocal scores

846.   Cantata 48. ... [Philadelphia] University of Pennsylvania [1941?]. 12 pp., 26 cm. (Choral Series, No. 132.) Edited by Henry S. Drinker.

CANTATA NO. 49.   Ich geh' und suche mit Verlangen (S. 49): Vocal-piano scores

847.   Kantate am zwanzigsten Sonntage nach Trinitatis. ... Leipzig, Breitkopf & Härtel [1891?]. 40 pp. (pp. 223-62), 27 cm. (Joh. Seb. Bach Kirchenkantaten, No. 49.)   P.N.: J.S.B.I.49.

CANTATA NO. 50.   Nun ist das Heil und die Kraft (S. 50): Full scores

848.   "Now Shall the Grace." The English translation is by the Rev. J. Troutbeck, published by Novello & Co., London, by whose kind permission that translation is used in this edition. Vienna, Wiener Philharmonischer Verlag, A.G. [1923?]. 4 ll., 32 pp., 1 l., illus., 19 cm. (Philharmonia Partituren, No. 111.) Edited by Wilhelm Fischer.   P.N.: W.Ph.V.111

849.   Nun ist das Heil und die Kraft...Nach der Ausgabe der Bach-Gesellschaft revidiert und mit Einführung versehen von Arnold Schering. Leipzig, Eulenburg [1929?]. 1 l.; vi, 30 pp.; 3 ll.; 19 cm. (Eulenburgs kleine Partitur-Ausgabe, No. 1018.)   P.N.: E.E. 4818

CANTATA NO. 50: Vocal-piano scores

850.   Cantate "Nun ist das Heil und die Kraft". ... Leipzig, C. F. Peters [1877]. 15 pp., 27 cm. (Edition Peters, No. 1657.) Edited by Gustav Rösler.   P.N.: 5926

851.   Kantate "Nun ist das Heil und die Kraft". ... Leipzig, Breitkopf & Härtel [1891?]. 1 l., 22 pp. (pp. 263-84), 27 cm. (Joh. Seb. Bach Kirchenkantaten, No. 50.)   P.N.: J.S.B.I.50.

852.   "Notre Dieu seul est le maître éternel"...Paroles françaises de Paul Collin, édition revue par Francis Casadesus. Paris, Choudens [ca. 1930]. 1 l., 17 pp., 30 cm. (Edition française, de musique classique.)   P.N.: A.C.14,279

853.   Now Has the Hope and the Strength. ... [Philadelphia] Association of American Choruses [1948?]. 1 l., 22 pp., 26 cm. (Choral Series, No. 123.) Photo-offset lithograph process. Translation by Henry S. Drinker.

854.   "Now Hath Salvation and Strength"...English version by E. H. Thorne. Leipzig (London), Breitkopf & Härtel, c 1903. 22 pp., 28 cm. (Joh. Seb. Bach Vocal Scores, No. 50.) P.N.: 23806

855. "Now Hath Salvation and Strength"...English version by
E. H. Thorne. Leipzig (London, New York), Breitkopf & Härtel,
c 1903. 22 pp., 28 cm. (Joh. Seb. Bach Vocal Scores, No. 50.)
Plates like those of Item 855, but with no P.N.

856. "Now Hath the Grace and the Strength." Edited and arranged
by W. G. Whittaker, the English words by C. Sanford Terry. [London]
Oxford University Press [c 1927]. 2 ll., 32 pp., 25 cm.

857. Now Shall the Grace. Edited...by Otto Goldschmidt...the
pianoforte arrangement from the full score by Stephen Kemp, translated from the German by the Rev. J. Troutbeck. London, Novello
[ca. 1880]. Pp. 52-66, 28 cm.
At head of title: No. 8. The Bach Choir Magazine, No. 8. Two
copies.

858. Now Shall the Grace...The pianoforte arrangement from the full
score by Stephen Kemp...translated from the German by the Rev
J. Troutbeck. Chicago, H. T. FitzSimons [ca. 1885]. 17 pp., 1 l.,
28 cm. (Aeolian Series of Choral Music, No. 2034.)   P.N.: 2034-15

859. "Nun ist das Heil und die Kraft"..."Now Hath Salvation and
Strength"...English version by E. H. Thorne, Klavierauszug von
Günter Raphael. Leipzig, Breitkopf & Härtel [c 1930]. 1 l., 27 pp.,
27 cm. (Joh. Seb. Bach Kirchenkantaten, No. 50.) P.N.: J.S.B.I.50.

CANTATA NO. 50: Vocal score

860. Cantata 50. ... [Philadelphia] University of Pennsylvania [ca.
1935]. 15 pp., 27 cm. (Choral Series, No. 45.)
Edited by Henry S. Drinker.

CANTATA NO. 51. Jauchzet Gott in allen Landen (S. 51): Full score

861. Jauchzet Gott in allen Landen. ... Based on the Bach-Gesellschaft
edition. New York, Broude [ca. 1940]. 2 ll., 26 pp., frontis. (facs.),
19 cm.
Edited by Arnold Schering, whose introduction is printed in English
translation. Two leaves, issued separately, contain Henry S.
Drinker's translation of the text.

CANTATA NO. 51: Vocal-piano scores

862. Cantate...am 15. Sonntage nach Trinitatis und für alle Zeit. ...
Leipzig, C. F. Peters [1877]. 20 pp., 27 cm. (Edition Peters, No. 1655.)
Edited by Gustav Rösler.   P.N.: 5924

863. "Jauchzet Gott in allen Landen"..."Gloire à Dieu partout sur
terre"...traduction française de G. Bret et Ch. Schweitzer. ... Leipzig,
Breitkopf & Härtel [ca. 1900]. 1 l., 24 pp., 27 cm. (Joh. Seb. Bach
Kirchenkantaten, No. 51.)   P.N.: J.S.B.I.51.

864. "Jauchzet Gott in allen Landen"..."Praise Jehovah, All ye
People"...English version by J. Michael Diack..."Gloire à Dieu
partout sur terre"...traduction française de G. Bret et Ch. Schweitzer

864. *(continued)* ...Klavierauszug von Günter Raphael. Leipzig, Breitkopf & Härtel [c 1932]. 1 l., 26 pp., 27 cm. (Joh. Seb. Bach Kirchenkantaten, No. 51.)   P.N.: J.S.B.I.51.

CANTATA NO. 52. Falsche Welt, dir trau' ich nicht (S. 52): Vocal-
piano score

865. Kantate am drei und zwanzigsten Sonntage nach Trinitatis. ...
Leipzig, Breitkopf & Härtel [1892?]. 20 pp. (pp. 25-44), 27 cm.
(Joh. Seb. Bach Kirchenkantaten, No. 52.)   P.N.: J.S.B.I.52.

CANTATA NO. 53. Schlage doch, gewünschte Stunde (S. 53): Full score

866. "Schlage doch, gewünschte Stunde," "Strike, thou hour." The
English translation is by Paul England, published by Novello & Co.,
London, by whose kind permission that translation is used in this
edition. Vienna, Wiener Philharmonischer Verlag, A. G.[1923?].
4 ll., 8 pp., frontis. (port.), 19 cm. (Philharmonia Partituren, No. 102.)
Edited by Wilhelm Fischer.   P.N.: W.Ph.V.102

CANTATA NO. 53: Vocal-piano scores

867. La Cloche des agonisants. ... Traduction française de J. Guil-
liaume. [Paris, Henry Lemoine, ca. 1895]. 7 pp., 31 cm. (Répertoire
français de l'ancien chant classique, No. 343.)
Autograph signature on title page: J. Gerville-Réache.
                                                          P.N.: 18332.H.
868. Kantate Schlage doch gewünschte Stunde...Klavierauszug mit
Text von Herman Roth. Leipzig, C. F. Peters [1911]. 10 pp., 27 cm.
(Edition Peters, No. 3351.)   P.N.: 9583
869. "Schlage doch, gewünschte Stunde"..."Sound your Knell, Blest
Hour of Parting." English version by Lucy E. Broadwood...Klavier-
auszug von Günter Raphael. Leipzig, Breitkopf & Härtel [ca. 1930].
1 l., 8 pp., 27 cm. (Joh. Seb. Bach Kirchenkantaten, No. 53.)
Two copies.   P.N.: J.S.B.I.53.
870. "Sound your Knell, Blest Hour of Parting," "Schlage doch, gewünschte Stunde"...English version by Lucy E. Broadwood. Leipzig,
Breitkopf & Härtel [ca. 1925]. 5 pp., 28 cm. (Joh. Seb. Bach's Church
Cantatas and Motets, Vocal Scores, Cantatas, No. 53.) P.N.: 25980
871. Strike, Thou Hour so Long Expected...English version by Paul
England, edited by John Pointer. London, Novello [ca. 1906]. 1 l.,
6 pp., 31 cm.   P.N.: 12390

CANTATA NO. 54. Widerstehe doch der Sünde (S. 54): Full score

872. Widerstehe doch der Sünde...Nach der Ausgabe der Bach-
Gesellschaft revidiert und mit Einführung versehen von Arnold
Schering. Leipzig, Vienna, Eulenburg [1928?]. viii, 3-16 pp.; 3 ll.;
19 cm. (Eulenburgs kleine Partitur-Ausgabe, No. 1010.)
                                                          P.N.: E.E.4807

CANTATA NO. 54: Vocal-piano scores

873. Kantate "Widerstehe doch der Sünde". ... Leipzig, Breitkopf &
Härtel [1892?] 1 l., 12 pp. (pp. 49-60), 27 cm. (Joh. Seb. Bach
Kirchenkantaten, No. 54.)   P.N.: J.S.B.I.54.

874. "Watch and Pray When Trials Beset Thee"... English version by
J. Michael Diack. Leipzig, Breitkopf & Härtel, c 1913. 12 pp.,
27 cm. (Joh. Seb. Bach Vocal Scores, No. 54.)   P.N.: 27128

CANTATA NO. 55. Ich armer Mensch, ich Sündenknecht (S. 55):
Full score

875. Ich armer Mensch, ich Sündenknecht...Nach der Ausgabe der
Bach-Gesellschaft und dem Autograph revidiert und mit Einführung
versehen von Arnold Schering. Leipzig, Eulenburg [1930?]. 1 l.;
v, 15 pp.; 2 ll.; 19 cm. (Eulenburgs kleine Partitur-Ausgabe,
No. 1021.)   P.N.: E.E.4821.

CANTATA NO. 55: Vocal-piano scores

876. Kantate am zwei und zwanzigsten Sonntage nach Trinitatis. ...
Leipzig, Breitkopf & Härtel [1892?]. 14 pp. (pp. 61-74), 27 cm.
(Joh. Seb. Bach Kirchenkantaten, No. 55.)   P.N.: J.S.B.I.55,

877. Kantate: "Ich armer Mensch, ich Sündenknecht". ... Leipzig.
C. F. Peters [1912]. 19 pp., 27 cm. (Edition Peters, No. 3357.)
Edited by Herman Roth.   P.N.: 9671

CANTATA NO. 56. Ich will den Kreuzstab gerne tragen (S. 56):
Full scores

878. [Original MS. title:] Dominica XIX poſt Trinit: Ich will den
Xſtab gerne tragen a 2 Hautbois ò Violini Viola u Taille S. A. T. et
Baſſo Conc: con Continuo di Sigr. Joh. Seb. Bach. Munich, Drei
Masken Verlag, 1921. 7 ll. (title & 12 unnumbered pp.), 34 cm.
Facsimile of MS. p. 18 is in the Berlin Staatsbibliothek.

879. Ich will den Kreuzstab gerne tragen, I with My Cross-Staff
Gladly Wander. Bearbeitet von Phil. Wolfrum...Partitur. Leipzig,
Breitkopf & Härtel [c 1902]. 1 l., 30 pp., 34 cm. (Breitkopf & Härtels
Partiturbibliothek, No. 1665.)   P.N.: Part. B. 1665

880. Ich will den Kreuzstab gerne tragen...Nach der Ausgabe der
Bach-Gesellschaft und dem in der Preussischen Staatsbibliothek zu
Berlin befindlichen Autograph revidiert und mit Einführung versehen
von Arnold Schering. Leipzig, Vienna, Eulenburg [1927?]. 3 ll.,
22 pp., 2 ll., 19 cm. (Eulenburgs kleine Partitur-Ausgabe, No. 1008.)
                                                   P.N.: E.E. 4670

881. Kantate No. 56. ... Vienna, Wiener Philharmonischer Verlag,
A.G., 1924. 4 ll., 24 pp., 1 l., 19 cm. (Philharmonia Partituren,
No. 104.)
Edited by Wilhelm Fischer.   P.N.: W.Ph.V.104

88 PUBLISHED MUSIC OF J. S. BACH

CANTATA NO. 56: Vocal-piano scores

882. "Ich will den Kreuzstab gerne tragen"... "I with My Cross-Staff Gladly Wander"... English translation by Constance Bache, Klavier-auszug von Otto Taubmann unter Mitbenutzung der Continuo-Bearbeitung von Max Seiffert neu herausgegeben von Carl Ettler. Leipzig, Breitkopf & Härtel [c 1931]. 1 l., 18 pp., 27 cm. (Joh. Seb. Bach Kirchenkantaten, No. 56.)   P.N.: J.S.B.I.56.

883. Kantate am neunzehnten Sonntage nach Trinitatis. ... Leipzig, Breitkopf & Härtel [1892?]. 1 l., 18 pp. (pp. 75-92), 27 cm. (Joh. Seb. Bach Kirchenkantaten, No. 56.)   P.N.: J.S.B.I.56.

884. Kantate...am 19ten Sonntage nach Trinitatis. ... Leipzig, C. F. Peters [1877]. 19 pp., 27 cm. (Edition Peters, No. 1644.) Edited by Gustav Rösler.   P.N.: 5933

885. My Cross of Trouble Glad I Carry. ... [Philadelphia] Association of American Choruses [1948?]. 1 l., 18 pp., 26 cm. (Solo Series, No. 59.)

Photo-offset lithograph process. Translation by Henry S. Drinker.

CANTATA NO. 57. Selig ist der Mann (S. 57): Vocal-piano scores

886. Blessed Is the Man. ... [Philadelphia] Association of American Choruses [1952]. 1 l., 26 pp., 26 cm. (Solo Series, No. 62.)

Photo-offset lithograph process. Translation by Henry S. Drinker.

887. Cantata am 2ten Weihnachtsfesttage. ... Leipzig, C. F. Peters [1877]. 25 pp., 27 cm. (Edition Peters, No. 1661.) Edited by Gustav Rösler.   P.N.: 5930

888. "Selig ist der Mann"... "Heureux est l'homme"... Traduction française de Mme Henriette Fuchs. ... Leipzig, Breitkopf & Härtel [ca. 1900]. 1 l., 26 pp., 27 cm. (Joh. Seb. Bach Kirchenkantaten, No. 57.)   P.N.: J.S.B.I.57.

CANTATA NO. 58. Ach Gott, wie manches Herzeleid (S. 58): Vocal-piano scores

889. Kantate am Sonntage nach der Beschneidung Christi...Zweite Komposition. ... Leipzig, Breitkopf & Härtel [1892?]. 18 pp. (pp. 119-36), 27 cm. (Joh. Seb. Bach Kirchenkantaten, No. 58.)

P.N.: J.S.B.I.58.

CANTATA NO. 59. Wer mich liebet, der wird mein Wort halten (S. 59): Vocal-piano score

890. Kantate am ersten Pfingstfesttage...Erste Composition. Leipzig, Breitkopf & Härtel [1892?]. 1 l., 14 pp., 27 cm. (Joh. Seb. Bach Kirchenkantaten, No. 59.)   P.N.: J.S.B.I.59.

CANTATA NO. 60. O Ewigkeit, du Donnerwort (S. 60): Full scores

891. "Eternity, Thou Awful Word." English translation by Dr. C. Sanford Terry, Kontinuobearbeitung von...Arthur Willner. ...

Vienna, Wiener Philharmonischer Verlag, A.G., 1925. 5 ll., 36 pp.,
frontis. (port.), 19 cm. (Philharmonia Partituren, No. 105.)
P.N.: W.Ph.V.105

892. O Ewigkeit, du Donnerwort...Nach der Ausgabe der Bach-
gesellschaft und den Originalstimmen revidiert und mit Einführung
versehen von Arnold Schering. Leipzig, Eulenburg [1929?]. 1 l.;
vii, 26 pp., 2 ll., 19 cm. (Eulenburgs kleine Partitur-Ausgabe,
No. 1017.) P.N.: E.E.4817

CANTATA NO. 60: Vocal-piano scores

893. Cantate...am 24ten Sonntage nach Trinitatis...(Zweite Com-
position). ... Leipzig, C. F. Peters [1877]. 23 pp., 27 cm. (Edition
Peters, No. 1665.)
Edited by Gustav Rösler. P.N.: 5934

894. Kantate am vier und zwanzigsten Sonntage nach Trinitatis...
Zweite Composition. ... Leipzig, Breitkopf & Härtel [1892?]. 20 pp.
(pp. 151-70). 27 cm. (Joh. Seb. Bach Kirchenkantaten, No. 60.)
P.N.: J.S.B.I.60.

CANTATA NO. 61. Nun komm, der Heiden Heiland (S. 61): Vocal-
piano scores

895. Cantate am ersten Advent...(Erste Composition: 1714). ...
Leipzig, C. F. Peters [1879]. 17 pp., 27 cm. (Edition Peters, No. 1668.)
Edited by Gustav Rösler. P.N.: 6287

896. Come, Redeemer of Our Race...Erste Composition...Edited for
the Worcester Festival, 1905, by Ivor Atkins, the English version by
B. M. Craster. London, Novello; New York, H. W. Gray [ca. 1906].
2 ll., 23 pp., 25 cm. (Novello's Original Octavo Edition.)
Two copies. P.N.: 12166

897. Come, Thou Blessed Saviour, Come...Vocal score by B. Todt,
English version by Canon C. V. Gorton. Leipzig, Breitkopf & Härtel
[c 1911]. 1 l., 18 pp., 27 cm. (Joh. Seb. Bach Vocal Scores, No. 61.)
P.N.: 26729

898. Come Thou Now to Save Mankind. ... [Philadelphia] Association
of American Choruses [1947?]. 1 l., 21 pp., 26 cm. (Choral Series,
No. 94.)
Photo-offset lithograph process. Translation by Henry S. Drinker.

899. "Nun komm, der Heiden Heiland"..."Oh Viens, Jésus notre
Sauveur"...Traduction française de G. Bret et Ch. Schweitzer...
Klavierauszug von Gustav Schreck. Leipzig, Breitkopf & Härtel
[ca. 1910]. 1 l., 21 pp., 27 cm. (Joh. Seb. Bach Kirchenkantaten,
No. 61.) P.N.: J.S.B.I.61

CANTATA NO. 62. Nun komm, der Heiden Heiland (S. 62): Vocal-
piano scores

900. Come Thou of Man the Saviour. ... [Philadelphia] Association of

900. *(continued)* American Choruses [1947?]. 1 l., 24 pp., 1 l., 26 cm.
(Choral Series, No. 95.)
    Photo-offset lithograph process. Translation by Henry S. Drinker.
901. Kantate am ersten Advent...Zweite Composition. ... Leipzig,
Breitkopf & Härtel [1892?] 1 l., 24 pp., 27 cm. (Joh. Seb. Bach
Kirchenkantaten, No. 62.)   P.N.: J.S.B.I.62.

CANTATA NO. 63. Christen, ätzet diesen Tag (S. 63): Vocal-piano scores
902. Cantate am 1. Weihnachtsfesttage. ... Leipzig, C. F. Peters
[ca. 1881]. 35 pp., 27 cm. (Edition Peters, No. 1649.)
    Edited by Gustav Rösler.   P.N.: 6513
903. Christians, Grave Ye this Glad Day...Edited by John E. West,
English version by Claude Aveling. London, Novello; New York,
H. W. Gray [1925?]. 2 ll., 45 pp., 1 l., 8 pp., 25 cm. (Novello's
Original Octavo Edition.)   P.N.: 14942
904. Christians, Mark Ye Well this Day. ... [Philadelphia] Association
of American Choruses [1948?]. 1 l., 34 pp., 26 cm. (Choral Series,
No. 146.)
    Photo-offset lithograph process. Translation by Henry S. Drinker.
905. Kantate am ersten Weihnachtsfesttage. ... Leipzig, Breitkopf &
Härtel [1892?]. 34 pp. (pp. 43-76), 27 cm. (Joh. Seb. Bach Kirchenkantaten, No. 63.)   P.N.: J.S.B.I.63.
906. O Chrétien, bénis ce jour. Paroles françaises de Victor Wilder,
partition chant et piano par A. Guilmant. Paris, Choudens [1925?].
1 l., 34 pp., 2 ll., 30 cm. (Edition française de musique classique,
No. 2.)   P.N.: A.C.11709

CANTATA NO. 63: Vocal score

907. "Christians, Mark Ye Well this Day"....[Philadelphia] University
of Pennsylvania [1940?]. 22 pp., 1 l., 27 cm. (Choral Series, No. 79.)
Edited by Henry S. Drinker.

CANTATA NO. 64. Sehet, welch eine Liebe hat uns der Vater erzeiget
(S. 64): Vocal-piano scores

908. Cantate am 3ten Weihnachtsfesttage. ... Leipzig, C. F. Peters
[1876]. 23 pp., 27 cm. (Edition Peters, No. 1652.)
    Edited by Gustav Rösler.   P.N.: 5831
909. Kantate am dritten Weihnachtsfesttage...Klavierauszug von
Ernst Naumann. Leipzig, Breitkopf & Härtel [ca. 1900]. 1 l.,
2 ‡pp., 27 cm. (Joh. Seb. Bach Kirchenkantaten, No. 64.)
                                                   P.N.: N.B.II.2.
910. "See Now." Edited and arranged by W. G. Whittaker, the
English words by C. Sanford Terry. [London] Oxford University
Press [1925]. 2 ll., 38 pp., 1 l., 25 cm.
911. See Ye, Behold what Love. ... [Philadelphia] Association of

American Choruses [1947?]. 1 l., 24 pp., 1 l., 26 cm. (Choral Series, No. 120.)

Photo-offset lithograph process. Translation by Henry S. Drinker.

912. "Voyez quel amour le Père nous a témoigné"...Adaptation française et annotations de Jean de Valois. Paris, Choudens [c 1928]. 1 l., 32 pp., 1 l., 30 cm. (Edition française de musique classique.)
P.N.: A.C. 17097

913. Cantata 64. ... [Philadelphia] University of Pennsylvania [ca. 1935]. 16 pp., 27 cm. (Choral Series, No. 40.)

Edited by Henry S. Drinker.

CANTATA NO. 65. Sie werden aus Saba alle kommen (S. 65): Full scores

914. "Sie werden aus Saba alle kommen"...bearbeitet von Robert Franz. ... Leipzig, F. E. C. Leuckart (Constantin Sander) [1876?]. 1 l., 43 pp., 34 cm. P.N.: F.E.C.L.3080

915. Sie werden aus Saba alle kommen...Nach der Ausgabe der Bach-Gesellschaft und dem Autograph revidiert und mit Vorwort versehen von Arnold Schering. Leipzig, Eulenburg [1930?]. 1 l.; vi, 36 pp.; 2 ll.; 19 cm. (Eulenburgs kleine Partitur-Ausgabe, No. 1019.) P.N.: E.E.4819

CANTATA NO. 65: Vocal-piano scores

916. All They from Saba Shall Come...English version by R. H. Benson. ... New York, G. Schirmer [ca. 1910]. 25, [1] pp.; 1 l.; 26 cm. (Schirmer's Standard Secular Choruses, No. 2029.)

This edition follows K. E. Naumann's editing. P.N.: 4075

917. From Sheba Will Many Men Be Coming. ... [Philadelphia] Association of American Choruses [1947?]. 1 l., 26 pp., 26 cm. (Choral Series, No. 109.)

Photo-offset lithograph process. Translation by Henry S. Drinker.

918. Kantate am Feste der heiligen drei Könige. ... Leipzig, C. F. Peters [ca. 1930]. 23 pp., 27 cm. (Edition Peters, No. 1280.)

Edited by Gustav Rösler. P.N.: 10600

919. Kirchen-Cantaten von Joh. Seb. Bach im Clavierauszuge mit unterlegter Orgelstimme herausgegeben vom Bach-Vereine in Leipzig, No. 1 Am Feste der Erscheinung Christi (On the Feast of the Epiphany) bearbeitet von Alfred Volkland. ... Leipzig, J. Rieter-Biedermann [1876?]. 38 pp., 1 l., 28 cm.

English version (by R. H. Benson): They All Shall Come from Saba. Both piano and organ accompaniment throughout.
P.N.: 864

920. The Sages of Sheba...Edited by John Pointer, English version by Paul England. London, Novello; New York, H. W. Gray [1926?]. 1 l., 29 pp., 25 cm. (Novello's Original Octavo Edition.)
P.N.: 12104

921. "Sie werden aus Saba alle kommen"...bearbeitet von Robert
Franz. ...Leipzig, F. E. C. Leuckart (Constantin Sander) [ca. 1890].
29 pp., 27 cm.   P.N.: F.E.C.L.3082
922. "Sie werden aus Saba alle kommen"..."Ensemble ils viendront
les rois de Saba," traduction française de G. Bret...Klavierauszug
von Ernst Naumann. Leipzig, Breitkopf & Härtel [1892?]. 1 l.,
27 pp., 27 cm. (Joh. Seb. Bach Kirchenkantaten, No. 65.)
                                                   P.N.: J.S.B.I.65.
CANTATA NO. 65: Vocal score
923. "From Sheba Shall Many Men be Coming". ... [Philadelphia]
University of Pennsylvania [1939?]. 15 pp., 27 cm. (Choral Series,
No. 63.)
Edited by Henry S. Drinker.

CANTATA NO. 66. Erfreut euch, ihr Herzen (S. 66): Vocal-piano scores
924. Cantate am 2. Osterfesttage. ... Leipzig, C. F. Peters [1883].
36 pp., 27 cm. (Edition Peters, No. 2145.)
Edited by Gustav Rösler.   P.N.: 6649
925. "Erfreut euch ihr Herzen." Klavierauszug von Gustav Schreck
..."Joyeuse est votre âme." Traduction française de M me Henriette
Fuchs. ... Leipzig, Breitkopf & Härtel [ca. 1915]. 44 pp., 27 cm.
(Joh. Seb. Bach Kirchenkantaten, No. 66.)   P.N.: 27317
926. Rejoice Now, in Gladness. ... [Philadelphia] Association of
American Choruses [1946?]. 1 l., 40 pp., 1 l., 26 cm. (Choral Series,
No. 34.)
Photo-offset lithograph process. Translation by Henry S. Drinker.

CANTATA NO. 67. Halt' im Gedächtnis Jesum Christ (S. 67): Vocal-
piano scores
927. Cantate am 1sten Sonntag nach Ostern. ... Leipzig, C. F. Peters
[1876]. 25 pp., 27 cm. (Edition Peters, No. 1239.)
Edited by Gustav Rösler.   P.N.: 5842
928. "Halt' im Gedächtnis Jesum Christ"..."Garde en mémoire Jésus-
Christ." Traduction française de G. Bret et Ch. Schweitzer. ...
Leipzig, Breitkopf & Härtel [ca. 1933]. 1 l., 32 pp., 27 cm. (Joh. Seb.
Bach Kirchenkantaten, No. 67.)   P.N.: J.S.B.I.67.
929. "Halt' im Gedächtnis Jesum Christ"..."Hold in Remembrance
Jesus Christ"...English version by Lucy E. Broadwood..."Garde en
mémoire Jésus-Christ"...traduction française de G. Bret et Ch.
Schweitzer...Klavierauszug von Günter Raphael. Leipzig, Breitkopf
& Härtel [c 1933]. 1 l., 33 pp., 27 cm. (Joh. Seb. Bach Kirchen-
kantaten, No. 67.)   P.N.: J.S.B.I.67.
930. Hold in Affection Jesus Christ...Edited by John Pointer, English
text by Charles Sanford Terry. London, Novello; New York,
H. W. Gray [1929?]. 3 ll., 31 pp., 1 l., 26 cm. (Novello's Original
Octavo Edition.)   P.N.: 15620

CANTATAS 93

931. Hold in Remembrance Jesus Christ.... [Philadelphia] Association of American Choruses [1948?]. 1 l., 26 pp., 26 cm. (Choral Series, No. 42.)
Photo-offset lithograph process. Translation by Henry S. Drinker.

CANTATA NO. 68. Also hat Gott die Welt geliebt (S. 68):Vocal-piano scores

932. Cantate am 2ten Festtage der heil. Pfingsten. ... Leipzig, C. F. Peters [1876]. 29 pp., 28 cm. (Edition Peters, No. 1287.)
Edited by Gustav Rösler.   P.N.: 5836

933. God so Loved the World...The English adaptation by the Rev. J. Troutbeck. London, Novello; New York, H. W. Gray [1927?]. 1 l., 29 pp., 26 cm. (Novello's Original Octavo Edition.)
Two copies.   P.N.: Bach's "God so loved the World." –
Novello Ewer and Co.'s Octavo Edition

934. Kantate am zweiten Festtage der h. Pfingsten. ... Leipzig, Breitkopf & Härtel [1892?]. 1 l., 28 pp., 27 cm. (Joh. Seb. Bach Kirchenkantaten, No. 68.)   P.N.: J.S.B.I.68.

CANTATA NO. 68: Vocal score

935. "For God has Loved the World so Well". ... [Philadelphia] University of Pennsylvania [ca. 1935]. 16 pp., 27 cm. (Choral Series, No. 76.)
Edited by Henry S. Drinker.

CANTATA NO. 68: Excerpts

936. My Heart Ever Faithful, Mein gläubiges Herze, from Church Cantata No. 68...Arranged and edited by W. G. Whittaker. London, Oxford University Press, c 1929. 6 pp., 26 cm. (The Oxford Choral Songs from the Old Masters, No. 1455.)

CANTATA NO. 69. Lobe den Herrn, meine Seele (S. 69): Vocal-piano scores

937. Bless the Lord, O My Spirit. ... [Philadelphia] Association of American Choruses [1948?]. 1 l., 26 pp., 26 cm. (Choral Series, No. 147.)
Photo-offset lithograph process. Translation by Henry S. Drinker.

938. Cantate am 12. Sonntage nach Trinitatis. ... Leipzig, C. F. Peters [1879]. 25 pp., 27 cm. (Edition Peters, No. 1667.)
Edited by Gustav Rösler.   P.N.: 6286

939. Kantate am zwölften Sonntage nach Trinitatis. ... Leipzig, Breitkopf & Härtel [1892?]. 1 l., 26 pp., 27 cm. (Joh. Seb. Bach Kirchenkantaten, No. 69.)   P.N.: J.S.B.I.69.

CANTATA NO. 69: Vocal score

940. Bless Thou the Lord, O My Spirit. ... [Philadelphia] University

940. *(continued)* of Pennsylvania [1940?]. 18 pp., 1 l., 26 cm. (Choral Series, No. 80.)
    Edited by Henry S. Drinker.

CANTATA NO. 70. Wachet, betet, seid bereit allezeit (S. 70): Vocal-piano scores

941. Cantate am 26. Sonntage nach Trinitatis. ... Leipzig, C. F. Peters [1879]. 31 pp., 27 cm. (Edition Peters, No. 1666.)
    Edited by Gustav Rösler.   P.N.: 6258

942. Kantate am sechs und zwanzigsten Sonntage nach Trinitatis. ... Leipzig, Breitkopf & Härtel [1892?]. 34 pp. (pp. 243-76), 27 cm. (Joh. Seb. Bach Kirchenkantaten, No. 70.)   P.N.: J.S.B.I.70.

943. Watch Ye, Pray Ye... Edited by E. H. Thorne, English version by Claude Aveling. London, Novello; New York, H. W. Gray, c 1907. 2 ll., 47 pp., 25 cm. (Novello's Original Octavo Edition.)   P.N.: 12668

944. Watch Ye, Pray Ye. ... [Philadelphia] Association of American Choruses [1948?]. 1 l., 34 pp., 26 cm. (Choral Series, No. 122.)
    Photo-offset lithograph process. Translation by Henry S. Drinker.

CANTATA NO. 70: Vocal score

945. Cantata 70. ... [Philadelphia] University of Pennsylvania [1943?]. 20 pp., 26 cm. (Choral Series, No. 148.)
    Edited by Henry S. Drinker.

CANTATA NO. 71. Gott ist mein König (S. 71): Vocal-piano scores

946. Cantate bei der Rathswahl in der kaiserlichen freien Reichsstadt Mühlhausen... 1708. ... Leipzig, C. F. Peters [1876]. 32 pp., 27 cm. (Edition Peters, No. 1298.)
    Edited by Gustav Rösler.   P.N.: 5891

947. God Is My Ruler. ... [Philadelphia] Association of American Choruses [1948?]. 1 l., 32 pp., 26 cm. (Choral Series, No. 148.)
    Photo-offset lithograph process. Translation by Henry S. Drinker.

948. Kantate bei der Rathswahl in der kaiserlichen freien Reichsstadt Mühlhausen... 1708. ... Leipzig, Breitkopf & Härtel, 1892. 1 l., 32 pp., 27 cm. (Johann Sebastian Bach's Werke... Gesammtausgabe für den praktischen Gebrauch. I. Kantaten. Nr. 71.) P.N.: J.S.B.I.71.

CANTATA NO. 71: Vocal score

949. Cantata 71. ... [Philadelphia] University of Pennsylvania [1941?]. 24 pp., 26 cm. (Choral Series, No. 140.)
    Edited by Henry S. Drinker.

CANTATA NO. 71: Excerpts

950. Psalm CXXI... The Lord Will Not Suffer Thy Foot to be Moved ... from Cantata No. 71. Glasgow, Patersons Publications, n.d. [8] pp., 26 cm. (The Lyric Collection of Part Songs, No. 1567.)
                                                    P.N.: Psalm CXXI

CANTATAS

CANTATA NO. 72. Alles nur nach Gottes Willen (S. 72): Vocal-piano scores

951. All Must be as God Doth Will It. ... [Philadelphia] Association of American Chorus [1946?]. 1 l., 28 pp., 26 cm. (Choral Series, No. 45.)
Photo-offset lithograph process. Translation by Henry S. Drinker.
952. "Alles nur nach Gottes Willen"..."All Things are by God Ordained"...English version by J. Michael Diack...Klavierauszug von Günter Raphael. Leipzig, Breitkopf & Härtel [c 1931]. 1 l., 32 pp., 27 cm. (Joh. Seb. Bach Kirchenkantaten, No. 72.)
P.N.: J.S.B.I.72.
953. Cantate am 3ten Sonntage nach Epiphanias. ... Leipzig, C. F. Peters [1876]. 27 pp., 28 cm. (Edition Peters, No. 1299.)
Edited by Gustav Rösler. P.N.: 5892.
954. Kantate am dritten Sonntage nach Epiphanias. ... Leipzig, Breitkopf & Härtel [1892?]. 28 pp. (pp. 33-60), 27 cm. (Joh. Seb. Bach Kirchenkantaten, No. 72.) P.N.: J.S.B.I.72.
955. Tout d'après la volonté de Dieu seul. Paroles française, de Jules Ruelle, partition chant et piano par A. Guilmant. Paris, Choudens, [1934?]. 2 ll., 25 pp., 1 l., 30 cm. (Edition française de musique classique, No. 4.) P.N.: 17706

CANTATA NO. 73. Herr, wie du willt, so schick's mit mir (S. 73): Vocal-piano scores

956. Cantata am 3. Sonntage nach Epiphanias. ... Leipzig, C. F. Peters [1879]. 16 pp., 27 cm. (Edition Peters, No. 1676.)
Edited by Gustav Rösler. P.N.: 6303
957. "Herr, wie du willt, so schick's mit mir"..."Dieu, fais de moi ce que tu veux." Traduction française par G. Bret. ... Leipzig, Breitkopf & Härtel [1892?]. 18 pp. (pp. 61-78), 27 cm. (Joh. Seb. Bach Kirchenkantaten, No. 73.) P.N.: J.S.B.I.73.
958. Lord, As Thou Wilt. ... [Philadelphia] Association of American Choruses [1948?]. 16 pp., 26 cm. (Choral Series, No. 151.)
Photo-offset lithograph process. Translation by Henry S. Drinker.

CANTATA NO. 73: Vocal score

959. Three Cantatas of J. S. Bach Using the Choral Melody "Wo Gott du Herr nicht bei uns hält," Cantata 73 "Herr, wie du willt"... Cantata 114 "Ach lieben Christen, seid getrost"...Cantata 178 "Wo Gott der Herr nicht bei uns hält". ... [Philadelphia] University of Pennsylvania [1939?]. 50 pp., 1 l., 27 cm. (Choral Series, No. 61.)
Edited by Henry S. Drinker.

CANTATA NO. 74. Wer mich liebet, der wird mein Wort halten (S. 74): Vocal-piano scores

960. He Who Loves Me. ... [Philadelphia] Association of American

960. *(continued)*   Choruses [1946?].   1 l., 30 pp., 26 cm.   (Choral Series, No. 74.)
   Photo-offset lithograph process. Translation by Henry S. Drinker.
961.   Kantate am ersten Pfingstfesttage...Zweite, grössere Bearbeitung.
   ... Leipzig, Breitkopf & Härtel [1892?].   30 pp. (pp. 79-108), 27 cm.
   (Joh. Seb. Bach Kirchenkantaten, No. 74.)   P.N.: J.S.B.I.74.

CANTATA NO. 75.   Die Elenden sollen essen. (S. 75): Vocal-piano scores

962.   Cantate am 1. Sonntage nach Trinitatis. ... Leipzig, C. F. Peters
   [1879].   33 pp., 27 cm.   (Edition Peters, No. 1670.)
   Edited by Gustav Rösler.   P.N.: 6289
963.   "Die Elenden sollen essen"...Klavierauszug von B. Todt...
   "Pravdy alchushchii da nasytitsîa". ... Leipzig, Breitkopf & Härtel
   [ca. 1910].   1 l., 44 pp., 27 cm.   P.N.: 26583
964.   For the Meek Shall Not Go Empty. ... [Philadelphia] Association
   of American Choruses [1946?].   1 l., 42 pp., 26 cm.   (Choral Series,
   No. 36.)
   Photo-offset lithograph process. Translation by Henry S. Drinker·

CANTATA NO. 75: Excerpts

965.   Sinfonia from Church Cantata No. 75...Chorale 'Was Gott thut,
   das ist wohlgethan.' Edited by W. G. Whittaker, translation by
   C. S. Terry. London, Oxford University Press, c 1925.   2 pp., 26 cm.
   (The Oxford Choral Songs from the Old Masters, No. 348.)
966.   Sinfonia to Part II of "Die Elenden sollen essen"...Arranged by
   Harvey Grace [for organ].   [London] Oxford University Press
   [c 1928].   1 l., 5 pp., 32 cm.   (Ten Instrumental Movements from the
   Cantatas, No. 7.)

CANTATA NO. 76.   Die Himmel erzählen die Ehre Gottes (S. 76):
Vocal-piano scores

967.   Cantate am 2. Sonntage nach Trinitatis. ... Leipzig, C. F. Peters
   [1879].   39 pp., 27 cm.   (Edition Peters, No. 1677.)
   Edited by Gustav Rösler.   P.N.: 6304
968.   The Glory of God are the Heav'ns Declaring. ... [Philadelphia]
   Association of American Choruses [1946?].   1 l., 42 pp., 26 cm.
   (Choral Series, No. 38.)
   Photo-offset lithograph process. Translation by Henry S. Drinker.
969.   Kantate am zweiten Sonntage nach Trinitatis. ... Leipzig,
   Breitkopf & Härtel [1892?].   42 pp. (pp. 151-92), 27 cm. (Joh. Seb.
   Bach Kirchenkantaten, No. 76.)   P.N.: J.S.B.I.76.

CANTATA NO. 76: Excerpts

970.   Aria—Love Ye Faithful, from Church Cantata No. 76...arranged
   and edited by W. G. Whittaker, English text by C. S. Terry. London,

Oxford University Press, c 1928. 6 pp., 26 cm. (The Oxford Choral Songs from the Old Masters, No. 1441.)

CANTATA NO. 77. Du sollst Gott, deinen Herren, lieben (S. 77): Vocal-piano scores

971. Cantate am 13. Sonntage nach Trinitatis. ... Leipzig, C. F. Peters [1879]. 20 pp., 27 cm. (Edition Peters, No. 1675.)
    Edited by Gustav Rösler.   P.N.: 6302
972. Love Thou Thy God. ... [Philadelphia] Association of American Choruses [1946?]. 1 l., 22 pp., 26 cm. (Choral Series, No. 46.)
    Photo-offset lithograph process. Translation by Henry S. Drinker.
973. Kantate am dreizehnten Sonntage nach Trinitatis. ... Leipzig, Breitkopf & Härtel [1892?]. 1 l., 22 pp., 27 cm. (Joh. Seb. Bach Kirchenkantaten, No. 77.)   P.N.: J.S.B.I.77.

CANTATA NO. 78. Jesu, der du meine Seele (S. 78): Full score

974. Jesu, der du meine Seele...Nach der Ausgabe der Bach-Gesellschaft mit Einführung versehen von Arnold Schering. Leipzig, Eulenburg [1934?]. 1 l.; v, 38 pp.; 3 ll.; 19 cm. (Eulenburgs kleine Partitur-Ausgabe, No. 1031.)   P.N.: E.E.4831.

CANTATA NO. 78: Vocal-piano scores

975. "Jesu, der du meine Seele"..."Jesus, My Beloved Saviour". ... English version by J. Michael Diack...Klavierauszug von Günter Raphael. Leipzig, Breitkopf & Härtel [c 1933]. 1 l., 27 pp., 27 cm. (Joh. Seb. Bach Kirchenkantaten, No. 78.)   P.N.: J.S.B.I.78.
976. Jesus By Thy Cross and Passion. ... [Philadelphia] Association of American Choruses [1947?]. 1 l., 30 pp., 26 cm. (Choral Series, No. 110.)
    Photo-offset lithograph process. Translation by Henry S. Drinker.
977. Jesus, Thou My Wearied Spirit; Jesu, der du meine Seele... Edited and accompaniment arranged by Ifor Jones, English version by J. M. Stein and Ifor Jones. New York, G. Schirmer [c 1940]. 47 pp., 26 cm.
    Two copies.   P.N.: 39113
978. Kantate am vierzehnten Sonntage nach Trinitatis. ... Leipzig, Breitkopf & Härtel [1892?]. 1 l., 30 pp., 27 cm. (Joh. Seb. Bach Kirchenkantaten, No. 78.)   P.N.: J.S.B.I.78.
979. Kantate am 14. Sonntage nach Trinitatis. ... Leipzig, C. F. Peters [ca. 1903]. 30 pp., 1 l., 27 cm. (Edition Peters, No. 1294.)
    Edited by Gustav Rösler.   P.N.: 8904

CANTATA NO. 78: Vocal scores

980. Cantata 78. ... [Philadelphia] University of Pennsylvania [1941?]. 20 pp., 26 cm. (Choral Series, No. 71-A.)
    Edited by Henry S. Drinker.

98 PUBLISHED MUSIC OF J. S. BACH

CANTATA NO. 79. Gott, der Herr, ist Sonn' und Schild (S. 79): Full
score

981. Gott der Herr ist Sonn' und Schild...Nach der Ausgabe der
Bach-Gesellschaft revidiert und mit Einführung versehen von Arnold
Schering. Leipzig, Vienna, Eulenburg [1927?]. 4 ll., 40 pp., 2 ll.,
19 cm. (Eulenburgs kleine Partitur-Ausgabe, No. 1009.)
P.N.: E.E.4802.

CANTATA NO. 79: Vocal-piano scores

982. Cantate am Reformations-Feste...Klavier-Auszug von G. Rösler.
Leipzig, C. F. Peters [1872]. 27 pp., 27 cm. (Edition Peters, No. 1013.)
P.N.: 5412.

983. God, the Lord, Is Sun and Shield. ... [Philadelphia] Association
of American Choruses [1948?.] 1 l., 28 pp., 26 cm. (Choral Series,
No. 128.)
Photo-offset lithograph process. Translation by Henry S. Drinker.

984. "Gott, der Herr, ist Sonn' und Schild"..."God, Our Lord, Is
Sun and Shield"...English version by J. Michael Diack...Klavier-
auszug von Günter Raphael. Leipzig, Breitkopf & Härtel [c 1932].
1 l., 36 pp., 27 cm. (Joh. Seb. Bach Kirchenkantaten, No. 79.)
P.N.: J.S.B.I.79.

985. Kantate am Reformations-Feste. ... Leipzig, Breitkopf & Härtel
[1892?]. 1 l., 28 pp. (pp. 245-72), 27 cm. (Joh. Seb. Bach Kirchenkantaten, No. 79.)
P.N.: J.S.B.I.79.

986. The Lord Is a Sun and Shield...Edited for the Worcester Festival,
1902, by Ivor Atkins. London, Novello; New York, H. W. Gray,
c 1902. 2 ll.; 35, 8 pp.; 25 cm. (Novello's Original Octavo Edition.)
P.N.: 11496

CANTATA NO. 79: Vocal score

987. Cantata 79. ... [Philadelphia] University of Pennsylvania, n.d.
16 pp., 27 cm. (Choral Series, No. 44.)
[Edited by Henry S. Drinker.]

CANTATA NO. 80. Ein' feste Burg ist unser Gott (S. 80): Full scores

988. Eine feste Burg ist unser Gott, Cantate für 4 Singstimmen mit
Begleitung des Orchesters in Musik gesetzt von Joh. Sebastian Bach.
Partitur nach J. S. Bach's Original-Handschrift. Leipzig, Breitkopf &
Härtel [ca. 1820]. 1 l., 3-34 pp., title page laid paper; text wove paper,
original marbled wrapper, 35 cm.
Below imprint is the stamp: Prag bei Marco Berra. Stamp of
Musik Bildungs Anstalt des Jos. Proksch on title page and large
label showing Proksch shelf-mark (2547) on front cover. P.N.: 3513

989. Ein' feste Burg ist unser Gott...Nach der Ausgabe der Bach-
Gesellschaft und auf Grund der Handschriftlichen Quellen revidiert
und mit Einführung versehen von Arnold Schering. Leipzig, Eulen-

burg [1926?]. 4 ll., 68 pp., 2 ll., 19 cm. (Eulenburgs kleine Partitur-Ausgabe, No. 1003.)   P.N.: E.E. 4601.

990. Ein' feste Burg ist unser Gott...Nach der Partitur der Bach-gesellschaft zum practischen Gebrauch (mit Orgel ad. lib.) eingerichtet von Albert Becker. ... Leipzig, Brussels, Breitkopf & Härtel [1886?]. 2 ll., 85 pp., 33 cm.   P.N.: 17133

991. Ein feste Burg...Partitur mit Cembalo- und Orgelstimme herausgegeben von Max Seiffert. Leipzig, C. F. Peters [1924?]. 62 pp., 34 cm. (Edition Peters, No. 3749d.)   P.N.: 10303

CANTATA NO. 80: Vocal-piano scores

992. Cantata for the Festival of the Reformation [A Stronghold Sure] ... English version by Rev. G. W. Daisley. ... Leipzig, Breitkopf & Härtel [ca. 1908]. 1 l., 43 pp., 27 cm. (Joh. Seb. Bach Vocal Scores, Cantatas, No. 80.)   P.N.: 26005

993. Cantate am Reformations-Feste...Klavierauszug von G. Rösler. Leipzig, C. F. Peters [ca. 1889]. 40 pp., 27 cm. (Edition Peters, No. 1012.)   P.N.: 7286

994. Kantate am Reformations-Feste. ... Leipzig, Breitkopf & Härtel [ca. 1903]. 44 pp. (pp. 273-316), 27 cm. (Joh. Seb. Bach Kirchenkantaten, No. 80.)   P.N.: N.B.III.1.

995. A Stronghold Sure...The English translation and adaptation by the Rev. J. Troutbeck. London, Novello; New York, H. W. Gray [1930?]. 1 l., 54 pp., 25 cm. (Novello's Original Octavo Edition.)   P.N.: Bach's Cantata, "A stronghold sure." – Novello, Ewer and Co.'s Octavo Edition.

996. A Stronghold Sure. ... New York, G. Schirmer; Boston, The Boston Music Co., [ca. 1910]. 2 ll., 52 pp., 26 cm.
Two other copies bearing imprint of G. Schirmer only, and having P.N. 31099. Copy 2 has signature "W. Neff" on outside wrapper.

997. A Stronghold Sure Is God Our Lord. ... [Philadelphia] Association of American Choruses [1948?]. 1 l., 44 pp., 26 cm. (Choral Series, No. 129.)
Photo-offset lithograph process. Translation by Henry S. Drinker.

CANTATA NO. 80: Vocal score

998. Cantata 80. ... [Philadelphia] University of Pennsylvania [1941?]. 31 pp., 26 cm. (Choral Series, No. 127.)
Edited by Henry S. Drinker.

CANTATA NO. 80: Excerpts

999. Chorus—"A Stronghold Sure Our God Remains." London, Novello [1925]. 19 pp., 27 cm. (Novello's Octavo Choruses, No. 811.)
Translated by J. Troutbeck.   P.N.: Bach's Cantata "A stronghold sure." – Novello, Ewer and Co.'s Octavo Edition

1000.   A Mighty Fortress Is Our God. Cleveland, Greater Cleveland Choral Society, n.d. 2 pp., 27 cm.

CANTATA NO. 81. Jesus schläft, was soll ich hoffen (S. 81): Full score

1001.   Jesus schläft, was soll ich hoffen...Nach der Ausgabe der Bach-Gesellschaft revidiert und mit Einführung versehen von Arnold Schering. Leipzig, Vienna, Eulenburg [1929?]. 1 l.; vi, 34 pp.; 3 ll.; 19 cm. (Eulenburgs kleine Partitur-Ausgabe, No. 1014.)
                                                            P.N.: E.E.4813
CANTATA NO. 81: Vocal-piano scores

1002.   "Jesus Sleeps, Vain All My Hoping,"...Vocal score by B. Todt, English version by Lucy E. Broadwood. Leipzig, Breitkopf & Härtel, c 1905. 22 pp., 27 cm. (Joh. Seb. Bach Vocal Scores, Cantatas, No. 81.)
                                                            P.N.: 24162
1003.   Jesus Sleeps, What Hope Remaineth...Edited for the Hereford Festival, 1903, by Ivor Atkins. London, Novello; New York, Novello, Ewer and Co. [ca. 1903]. 2 ll., 27 pp., 8 pp., 25 cm. (Novello's Original Octavo Edition.)
                                                            P.N.: 11741
1004.   Kantate am vierten Sonntage nach Epiphanias. ... Leipzig, Breitkopf & Härtel [1892?]. 20 pp., 27 cm. (Joh. Seb. Bach Kirchen-kantaten, No. 81.)
                                                            P.N.: J.S.B.I.81.

CANTATA NO. 82. Ich habe genug (S. 82): Vocal-piano scores

1005.   Cantate...am Feste der Maria Reinigung. ... Leipzig, C. F. Peters [1883]. 23 pp., 27 cm. (Edition Peters, No. 2149.)
Edited by Gustav Rösler.   P.N.: 6644
1006.   I Ask for No More. ... [Philadelphia] Association of American Choruses [1950?]. 1 l., 20 pp., 25 cm. (Solo Series, No. 60.)
Photo-offset lithograph process. Translation by Henry S. Drinker.
1007.   "It Is Enough"...Vocal score by B. Todt, English version by J. Michael Diack. Leipzig, Breitkopf & Härtel [c. 1911]. 1 l., 20 pp., 27 cm. (Joh. Seb. Bach's Church Cantatas and Motets, Vocal Scores, Cantatas, No. 82.)
                                                            P.N.: 26655
1008.   Kantate am Feste der Maria Reinigung. ... Leipzig, Breitkopf & Härtel [1893?]. 20 pp. (pp. 21-40), 27 cm. (Joh. Seb. Bach Kirchenkantaten, No. 82.)
                                                            P.N.: J.S.B.I.82.

CANTATA NO. 83. Erfreute Zeit im neuen Bunde (S. 83): Vocal-piano score

1009.   Kantate am Feste der Maria Reinigung. ...Leipzig, Breitkopf & Härtel [1893?]. 1 l., 18 pp. (pp. 41-58), 27 cm. (Joh. Seb. Bach Kirchenkantaten, No. 83.)
                                                            P.N.: J.S.B.I.83.

CANTATA NO. 84. Ich bin vergnügt mit meinem Glücke (S. 84): Vocal-piano score

1010.   Kantate am Sonntage Septuagesimae. ... Leipzig, Breitkopf &

Härtel [1893?]. 1 l., 18 pp. (pp. 59-76), 27 cm. (Joh. Seb. Bach
Kirchenkantaten, No. 84.)   P.N.: J.S.B.I.84.

CANTATA NO. 85. Ich bin ein guter Hirt (S. 85): Full score

1011. Ich bin ein guter Hirt...Nach der Ausgabe der Bach-Gesellschaft
und auf Grund des Autographs revidiert und mit Einführung versehen
von Arnold Schering. Leipzig, Vienna, Eulenburg [1929?]. 2 ll.;
vi, 22 pp.; 2 ll.; 19 cm. (Eulenburgs kleine Partitur-Ausgabe,
No. 1015.)   P.N.: E.E. 4814.

CANTATA NO. 85: Vocal-piano scores

1012. Cantate am Sonntage Misericordias Domini. ... Leipzig,
C. F. Peters [1883]. 19 pp., 27 cm. (Edition Peters, No. 2140.)
Edited by Gustav Rösler.   P.N.: 6623.

1013. Kantate No. 85: "Ich bin ein guter Hirt"...Bearbeitet von
Max Seiffert, Klavierauszug von Max Schneider. Leipzig, Breitkopf
& Härtel [1908]. 18 pp., 27 cm.   P.N.: N.B.IX.2.

CANTATA NO. 86. Wahrlich, wahrlich, ich sage euch. (S. 86): Vocal-
piano score

1014. Kantate am Sonntage Rogate. ... Leipzig, Breitkopf & Härtel
[1893?]. 20 pp. (pp. 95-114), 27 cm. (Joh. Seb. Bach Kirchenkantaten, No. 86.)   P.N.: J.S.B.I.86.

CANTATA NO. 87. Bisher habt ihr nichts gebeten in meinem Namen
(S. 87): Vocal-piano score

1015. Kantate am Sonntage Rogate. ... Leipzig, Breitkopf & Härtel
[1893?]. 18 pp. (pp. 115-32), 27 cm. (Joh. Seb. Bach Kirchenkantaten, No. 87.)   P.N.: J.S.B.I.87.

CANTATA NO. 88. Siehe, ich will viel Fischer aussenden, spricht der
Herr (S. 88): Vocal-piano score

1016. Kantate No. 88...(5. Sonntag nach Trinitatis)...Bearbeitet
von Max Seiffert, Klavierauszug von Otto Taubmann. Leipzig,
Breitkopf & Härtel [1907]. 1 l., 27 pp., 27 cm. (J. S. Bach's Werke
für Gesang. Gesammtausgabe für den praktischen Gebrauch,
Cantaten, No. 88.)   P.N.: N.B.VII.2.

CANTATA NO. 89. Was soll ich aus dir machen, Ephraim? (S. 89):
Vocal-piano score

1017. Kantate am zwei und zwanzigsten Sonntage nach Trinitatis. ...
Leipzig, Breitkopf & Härtel [1893?]. 1 l., 16 pp., 27 cm. (Joh. Seb.
Bach Kirchenkantaten, No. 89.)   P.N.: J.S.B.I.89.

CANTATA NO. 90. Es reifet euch ein schrecklich Ende (S. 90): Vocal-
piano score

1018. Kantate am fünf und zwanzigsten Sonntage nach Trinitatis. ...

1018. *(continued)* Leipzig, Breitkopf & Härtel [1893?]. 16 pp. (pp. 177-92), 27 cm.   P.N.: J.S.B.I.90.

CANTATA NO. 91. Gelobet seist du, Jesu Christ [S. 91]: Vocal-piano scores

1019. Cantate am 1. Weihnachtsfesttage. ... Leipzig, C. F. Peters [1883]. 24 pp., 27 cm. (Edition Peters, No. 2147.)
Edited by Gustav Rösler.   P.N.: 6651
1020. Kantate am ersten Weihnachtsfesttage. ... Leipzig, Breitkopf & Härtel [1893?]. 1 l., 22 pp., 27 cm. (Joh. Seb. Bach Kirchenkantaten, No. 91.)   P.N.: J.S.B.I.91.
1021. We Praise Thee All, Our Saviour Dear. ... [Philadelphia] Association of American Choruses, n.d. 1 l., 22 pp., 26 cm. (Choral Series, No. 35.)
Photo-offset lithograph process. Translation by Henry S. Drinker.

CANTATA NO. 92. Ich hab in Gottes Herz und Sinn (S. 92): Vocal-piano scores

1022. Cantate am Sonntage Septuagesimä. ... Leipzig, C. F. Peters [1883]. 37 pp., 27 cm. (Edition Peters, No. 2143.)
Edited by Gustav Rösler.   P.N.: 6647
1023. Kantate am Sonntage Septuagesimae. ... Leipzig, Breitkopf & Härtel [1893?]. 1 l., 36 pp., 27 cm. (Joh. Seb. Bach Kirchenkantaten, No. 92.)   P.N.: J.S.B.I.92
1024. To God I Give My Heart and Soul. ... [Philadelphia] Association of American Choruses [1946?]. 39 pp., 26 cm. (Choral Series, No. 37.)
Photo-offset lithograph process. Translation by Henry S. Drinker.

CANTATA NO. 93. Wer nur den lieben Gott lässt walten (S. 93): Vocal-piano scores

1025. Cantata of the Fifth Sunday after Trinity on the Hymn He Who Relies on God's Compassion...Vocal score by B. Todt, English version by E. H. Thorne and G. W. Daisley. Leipzig, Breitkopf & Härtel, c 1904. 26 pp., 27 cm. (Joh. Seb. Bach Church Cantatas and Motets, Vocal Scores, Cantatas, No. 93.)   P.N.: 24028
1026. Cantate am 5. Sonntage nach Trinitatis. ... Leipzig, C. F. Peters [1879]. 27 pp., 27 cm. (Edition Peters, No. 1671.)
Edited by Gustav Rösler.   P.N.: 6290
1027. If Thou but Sufferest God to Guide Thee...Edited by John Pointer, English version by Miss G. E. Troutbeck. London, Novello; New York, H. W. Gray, c 1907. 2 ll., 39 pp., 25 cm. (Novello's Original Octavo Edition.)   P.N.: 12429
1028. If Thou Wilt Suffer God to Guide Thee, Wer nur den lieben Gott lässt walten...Edited and accompaniment arranged by Ifor

Jones...English version by J. M. Stein and Ifor Jones. New York,
G. Schirmer [c 1941]. 1 l., 41 pp., 26 cm.   P.N.: 39315
1029. Kantate am fünften Sonntage nach Trinitatis. ... Leipzig,
Breitkopf & Härtel [1893?]. 1 l., 26 pp. (pp. 59-84), 27 cm. (Joh.
Seb. Bach Kirchenkantaten, No. 93.)   P.N.: J.S.B.I. 93.
1030. Whoso Will Suffer God to Guide Him. ... [Philadelphia]
Association of American Choruses [1948?]. 27 pp., 26 cm. (Choral
Series, No. 124.)
    Photo-offset lithograph process. Translation by Henry S. Drinker.

CANTATA NO. 93: Vocal score

1031. The Chorale "Wer nur den lieben Gott lasst walten" in the
Choral Works of J. S. Bach. [Philadelphia] University of Pennsylvania, n.d. 32 pp., 27 cm. (Choral Series, No. 13.)
    Edited, with English text, by Henry S. Drinker.

CANTATA NO. 94. Was frag ich nach der Welt (S. 94): Vocal-piano
scores

1032. Cantate am 9. Sonntage nach Trinitatis. ... Leipzig, C. F. Peters
[1883]. 34 pp., 1 l., 27 cm. (Edition Peters, No. 2146.)
    Edited by Gustav Rösler.   P.N.: 6650
1033. Kantate am neunten Sonntage nach Trinitatis. ... Leipzig,
Breitkopf & Härtel [1893?]. 1 l., 36 pp., 27 cm. (Joh. Seb. Bach
Kirchenkantaten, No. 94.)   P.N.: J.S.B.I.94.
1034. What Care I for the World? ... [Philadelphia] Association of
American Choruses [1947?]. 1 l., 36 pp., 26 cm. (Choral Series,
No. 100.)
    Photo-offset lithograph process. Translation by Henry S. Drinker.

CANTATA NO. 94: Excerpts

1035. Aria für Soprano von Joh. Scb. Bach (Nach der Orig. Partitur
auf der Königliche Bibliothek zu Berlin) "Es halt' es mit der blinden
Welt." Arrang. von W. Rust. Berlin, Verlag der Schlesinger'schcn
Buch u. Musikhandlung [ca. 1850]. 6 pp., 34 cm., wove paper.
(Hosianna, No. 34.)   P.N.: S. 4357

CANTATA NO. 95. Christus, der ist mein Leben (S. 95): Vocal-piano
scores

1036. Cantate am 16. Sonntage nach Trinitatis. ... Leipzig, C. F.
Peters [1879]. 20 pp., 27 cm. (Edition Peters, No. 1673.)
    Edited by Gustav Rösler.   P.N.: 6292
1037. "Christus, der ist mein Leben"..."Since Christ Is All My
Being"...English version by Margaret Bridges...Klavierauszug von
Günter Raphael. Leipzig, Breitkopf & Härtel [c 1930]. 27 pp.,
27 cm. (Joh. Seb. Bach Kirchenkantaten, Klavierauszüge, No. 95.)
    Two copies.   P.N.: J.S.B.I.95.

1038.   For Christ My Saviour Live I. ... [Philadelphia] Association of American Choruses [1946?]. 1 l., 22 pp., 26 cm. (Choral Series, No. 48.)
Photo-offset lithograph process. Translation by Henry S. Drinker.

1039.   O Christ, My All in Living...Edited by John E. West, English text by Claude Aveling. London, Novello [1925?]. 2 ll., 31 pp. (Novello's Original Octavo Edition.)   P.N.: 14964

CANTATA NO. 95: Excerpts

1040.   Chorale by J. S. Bach, All Glory, Laud, and Honour. From Cantata (No. 95 B. & H.). ... New York, Oxford University Press, n.d. 6 pp., 26 cm. (Church Music Society Reprints, No. 17A.)

CANTATA NO. 96. Herr Christ, der ein'ge Gottes-Sohn (S. 96): Vocal-piano scores

1041.   Cantate am 18. Sonntage nach Trinitatis. ... Leipzig, C. F. Peters [1883]. 25 pp., 27 cm. (Edition Peters, No. 2142.)
Edited by Gustav Rösler.   P.N.: 6646

1042.   Kantate am achtzehnten Sonntage nach Trinitatis. ... Leipzig, Breitkopf & Härtel [1893?]. 1 l., 24 pp. (pp. 143-66), 27 cm. (Joh. Seb. Bach Kirchenkantaten, No. 96.)   P.N.: J.S.B.I.96.

1043.   Lord Christ, the Son of God Alone. ... [Philadelphia] Association of American Choruses [1946?]. 1 l., 24 pp., 26 cm. (Choral Series, No. 49.)
Photo-offset lithograph process. Translation by Henry S. Drinker.

CANTATA NO. 97. In allen meinen Taten (S. 97): Vocal-piano scores

1044.   Cantate über Dr. Paul Flemming's Lied: "In allen meinen Thaten". ... Leipzig, C. F. Peters [1879]. 31 pp., 27 cm. (Edition Peters, No. 1647.)
Edited by Gustav Rösler.   P.N.: 6293

1045.   In All That I Am Doing. ... [Philadelphia] Association of American Choruses [1948?]. 1 l., 36 pp., 26 cm. (Choral Series, No. 133.)
Photo-offset lithograph process. Translation by Henry S. Drinker.

1046.   Kantate über das Lied: "In allen meinen Thaten". ... Leipzig, Breitkopf & Härtel [1893?]. 36 pp. (pp. 167-202), 27 cm.
P.N.: J.S.B.I.97.

CANTATA NO. 97: Vocal score

1047.   Cantata 97. ... [Philadelphia] Association of American Choruses, n.d. 24 pp., 26 cm. (Choral Series, No. 4.)
Edited by Henry S. Drinker.

CANTATA NO. 98. Was Gott tut, das ist wohlgetan (S. 98): Vocal-piano scores

1048.   Kantate am einundzwanzigsten Sonntage nach Trinitatis...

Erste Composition. Leipzig, rBeitkopf & Härtel [1893?]. 20 pp.
(pp. 203-22.)   P.N.: J.S.B.I.98.
1049. What God Does Is with Reason Done. ... [Philadelphia] Association of American Choruses [1947?]. 1 l., 20 pp., 26 cm. (Choral Series, No. 96.)
    Photo-offset lithograph process. Translation by Henry S. Drinker.
1050. "What God Doth, Surely That Is Right." Edited and arranged by W. G. Whittaker, the English words by C. Sanford Terry. [London] Oxford University Press [c 1927]. 2 ll., 31 pp., 25 cm.

CANTATA NO. 99. Was Gott tut, das ist wohlgetan (S. 99): Vocal-piano scores

1051. Kantate am fünfzehnten Sonntage nach Trinitatis...Zweite Composition. ... Leipzig, Breitkopf & Härtel [1893?]. 24 pp. (pp. 223-46), 27 cm. (Johann Seb. Bach, Sämtliche Kirchen-Kantaten, No. 99.)   P.N.: J.S.B.I.99.
1052. What God Does Is with Reason Done. ... [Philadelphia] Association of American Choruses [1947?]. 1 l., 24 pp., 26 cm. (Choral Series, No. 97.)
    Photo-offset lithograph process. Translation by Henry S. Drinker.

CANTATA NO. 100. Was Gott tut, das ist wohlgetan (S. 100): Vocal-piano scores

1053. Cantate über M. Samuel Rodigast's Lied: "Was Gott thut, das ist wohlgethan". ... Leipzig, C. F. Peters [1879]. 33 pp., 27 cm. (Edition Peters, No. 1669.)   P.N.: 6288
1054. Kantate über das Lied "Was Gott thut, das ist wohlgethan"... Dritte Composition. ... Leipzig, Breitkopf & Härtel [1893?]. 36 pp. (pp. 247-82), 27 cm.   P.N.: J.S.B.I.100.
1055. What God Does Is with Reason Done. ... [Philadelphia] Association of American Choruses [1947?]. 1 l., 36 pp., 26 cm. (Choral Series, No. 98.)
    Photo-offset lithograph process. Translation by Henry S. Drinker.

CANTATA NO. 101. Nimm von uns, Herr, du treuer Gott (S. 101): Full score

1056. Litaney von Martin Luther und Johann Sebastian Bach. [Bonn, Simrock, 1830?] 15 pp., 34 cm., wove paper, ½ mottled calf. (Kirchen Musik, Band 1.)
    Stamp with facsimile signature on title page: August Grüters. Series edited by Adolph Bernhard Marx. Contents: First chorus only from Cantata 101.   P.N.: 2745

CANTATA NO. 101: Vocal-piano scores

1057. Cantate am 10. Sonntage nach Trinitatis. ... Leipzig, C. F. Peters

1057. *(continued)* [1880]. 31 pp., 27 cm. (Edition Peters, No. 1678.)
Edited by Gustav Rösler.   P.N.: 6305
1058.   Have Mercy, Lord. ... [Philadelphia] Association of American
Choruses [1948?]. 1 l., 34 pp., 26 cm. (Choral Series, No. 166).
Photo-offset lithograph process. Translation by Henry S. Drinker.
1059.   Kantate am zehnten Sonntage nach Trinitatis. ... Leipzig,
Breitkopf & Härtel [1893?]. 1 l., 34 pp., 27 cm. (Joh. Seb. Bach
Kirchenkantaten, No. 101.)   P.N.: J.S.B.I.101.

CANTATA NO. 101: Vocal score

1060.   Cantata 101...with three additional harmonizations by Bach
of the choral-melody "Vater unser in Himmelreich." [Philadelphia]
University of Pennsylvania [1939?]. 20 pp., 27 cm. (Choral Series,
No. 43.)
Edited by Henry S. Drinker.

CANTATA NO. 102. Herr, deine Augen sehen nach dem Glauben
(S. 102): Full score

1061.   Herr deine Augen sehen nach dem Glauben. ... [Bonn, Simrock,
1830?] 25 pp., 34 cm., wove paper. (Kirchen Music, Band 1.)
Stamp with facsimile signature on half-title: August Grüters.
Edited by Adolph Bernhard Marx.   Complete cantata except for
Aria No. 3.   P.N.: 2765

CANTATA NO. 102: Vocal-piano scores

1062.   Cantate am 10. Sonntage nach Trinitatis. ... Leipzig, C. F.
Peters [1880]. 29 pp., 27 cm. (Edition Peters, No. 1679.)
Edited by Gustav Rösler.   P.N.: 6306
1063.   Kantate am zehnten Sonntage nach Trinitatis. ... Leipzig,
Breitkopf & Härtel [1893?]. 1 l., 34 pp., 27 cm. (Joh. Seb. Bach
Kirchenkantaten, No. 102.)   P.N.: J.S.B.I.102.
1064.   Lord, Are Thine Eyes Not Searching for the Righteous; Herr,
deine Augen sehen nach dem Glauben...Edited by Ifor Jones,
English version by J. M. Stein and Ifor Jones. New York, G. Schirmer
[c 1941]. 53 pp., 26 cm.   P.N.: 39165
1065.   Lord, Do Not Thine Eyes Turn on Unbelievers....[Philadelphia]
Association of American Choruses [1948?]. 1 l., 34 pp., 26 cm.
(Choral Series, No. 150.)
Photo-offset lithograph process. Translation by Henry S. Drinker.

CANTATA NO. 102: Vocal score

1066.   Cantata 102. ... [Philadelphia] University of Pennsylvania,
n.d. 20 pp., 26 cm. (Choral Series, No. 100.)
Edited by Henry S. Drinker.

CANTATA NO. 103. Ihr werdet weinen und heulen (S. 103): Full score

1067.   Ihr werdet weinen und heulen, aber die Welt wird sich freuen....

[Bonn, Simrock, 1830?] 24 pp., 34 cm., wove paper. (Kirchen Musick, Band 1.)
Stamp with facsimile signature on half-title page: August Grüters.
Edited by Adolph Bernhard Marx.   P.N.: 2857

CANTATA NO. 103: Vocal-piano scores

1068. "Ihr werdet weinen und heulen"..."Pour vous les larmes, les plaintes"...Traduction française de G. Bret. ... Leipzig, Breitkopf & Härtel [1893?]. 1 l., 34 pp., 27 cm. (Joh. Seb. Bach Kirchenkantaten, No. 103.)   P.N.: J.S.B.I.103.

1069. Kantate am Sonntage Jubilate. ... Leipzig, C. F. Peters [1881]. 24 pp., 27 cm. (Edition Peters, No. 1697.)
Edited by Gustav Rösler.   P.N.: 6466.

1070. Ye Shall Be Weeping and Wailing. ... [Philadelphia] Association of American Choruses [1946?]. 1 l., 34 pp., 26 cm. (Choral Series, No. 62.)
Photo-offset lithograph process. Translation by Henry S. Drinker.

CANTATA NO. 104. Du Hirte Israel, höre (S. 104): Full scores

1071. Du Hirte Israel...herausgegeben von Adolph Bernhard Marx. Bonn, Simrock [1830?]. [3], 4-21 pp.; 34 cm.; wove paper. (Kirchen Musik, Band 2.)
Stamp with facsimile signature on title page: August Grüters.
                                                              P.N.: 2884

1072. Du Hirte Israel, höre... herausgegeben und mit Vortragszeichen versehen von Siegfried Ochs. Leipzig, Eulenburg [1929?]. 1 l.; 48, [1] pp.; 3 ll.; 19 cm. (Eulenburgs kleine Partitur-Ausgabe, No. 1023.)   P.N.: E.E. 3898

CANTATA NO. 104: Vocal-piano scores

1073. Kantate am Sonntage Misericordias Domini...Klavierauszug von Ernst Naumann. Leipzig, Breitkopf & Härtel [ca. 1903]. 1 l., 20 pp., 27 cm. (Joh. Seb. Bach Kirchenkantaten, No. 104.)
                                                              P.N.: N.B.III.1.

1074. Kantate am Sonntage Misericordias Domini. ... Leipzig, C. F. Peters [1880]. 20 pp., 27 cm. (Edition Peters, No. 1680.)
Edited by Gustav Rösler.   P.N.: 6326

1075. Thou Guide of Israel...The English adaptation by the Rev. J. Troutbeck. London, Novello; New York, H. W. Gray [ca. 1905]. 1 l., 22 pp., 25 cm. (Novello's Original Octavo Edition.)
Two copies.   P.N.: Bach's Cantata, "Thou Guide of Israel." – Novello, Ewer and Co.'s Octavo Edition

1076. Thou Shepherd Bountiful, Hear Us. ... [Philadelphia] Association of American Choruses [1947?]. 1 l., 20 pp., 26 cm. (Choral Series, No. 111.)
Photo-offset lithograph process. Translation by Henry S. Drinker.

CANTATA NO. 104: Vocal score

1077. "Thou Shepherd Bountiful, Hear Us". ... [Philadelphia] University of Pennsylvania, n.d. 12 pp., 27 cm. (Choral Series, No. 77.)
Edited by Henry S. Drinker.

CANTATA NO. 104: Vocal parts

1078. Kirchen-Musik von Johann Sebastian Bach, Die vier Singstimmen vom 2ten Band. Bonn, Simrock [1830?]. Soprano: 1 l., 9 pp.; Alto: 10 pp.; Tenor: 14 pp.; Bass: 11 pp.; 27 cm.; wove paper.
Edited by Adolph Bernhard Marx.   P.N.: 2901

CANTATA NO. 104: Excerpts

1079. Two Choral Numbers from Cantata No. 104 (1. Thou Guide of Israel, Hearken, Du Hirte Israel, höre; 2. The Lord My Guide Will Surely Be, Der Herr ist mein getreuer Hirt. Boston, E. C. Schirmer [c 1935]. 18 pp., 27 cm. (Vassar Choral Music, No. 880.)
Chorus parts arranged by E. Harold Geer. English version by John Troutbeck.   P.N.: E.C.S. N° 870

CANTATA NO. 105. Herr, gehe nicht ins Gericht (S. 105): Full scores

1080. Herr, gehe nicht ins Gericht...herausgegeben von Adolph Bernhard Marx. Bonn, Simrock [1830?]. [1], 2-23 pp.; 34 cm.; wove paper. (Kirchen Musik, Band 2.)
Stamp with facsimile signature on title page: August Grüters.
                          P.N.: 2885
1081. Herr, gehe nicht ins gericht. ... Based on the Bach-Gesellschaft edition. New York, Broude [ca. 1940]. 4 ll., 40 pp., frontis. (facs.), 19 cm.
Edited by Arnold Schering, whose introduction is printed in English translation. Two leaves, issued separately, contain Henry S. Drinker's translation of the text.   P.N.: 84

CANTATA NO. 105: Vocal-piano scores

1082. Cantate am 9. Sonntage nach Trinitatis. ... Leipzig, C. F. Peters [1880]. 29 pp., 27 cm. (Edition Peters, No. 1689.)
Edited by Gustav Rösler.   P.N.: 6366
1083. Dieu, ne juge point tes fils. Paroles françaises de Maurice Bouchor, partition chant et piano par A. Guilmant. Paris, Choudens [1925?]. 1 l., 41 pp., 30 cm. (Edition française de musique classique, No. 6.)   P.N.: A.C. 11708.
1084. "Herr, gehe nicht ins Gericht"...Klavierauszug von B. Todt... "Bozhe, ne vnidi v sud." Leipzig, Breitkopf & Härtel [ca. 1908]. 1 l., 30 pp., 27 cm.   P.N.: 25753
1085. "Herr, gehe nicht ins Gericht"..."Lord, Enter Not into Judgement"...English version by J. Michael Diack ... Klavier-

auszug von Günter Raphael. Leipzig, Breitkopf & Härtel [1931].
1 l., 36 pp., 27 cm. (Joh. Seb. Bach Kirchenkantaten, Klavierauszüge, No. 105.) P.N.: J.S.B.I.105.

1086. "Lord, Enter Not into Wrath." Edited and arranged by
W. G. Whittaker, the English words by C. Sanford Terry. [London]
Oxford University Press [c 1927]. 3 ll., 44 pp., 1 l., 25 cm.

1087. Lord, Weigh Us and Judge Us Not. ... [Philadelphia] Associa-
tion of American Choruses, n.d. 1 l., 30 pp., 26 cm. (Choral Series,
No. 134.)
Photo-offset lithograph process. Translation by Henry S. Drinker.

CANTATA NO. 105: Vocal score

1088. Cantata 105. ... [Philadelphia] University of Pennsylvania
[1939?]. 16 pp., 27 cm. (Choral Series, No. 42.)
Edited by Henry S. Drinker.

CANTATA NO. 105: Excerpts

1089. Herr, gehe nicht ins Gericht. Lord, enter not into wrath. ...
Two choruses for mixed voices from the church cantata No. 105...
English paraphrase by Charles Sanford Terry...edited and the piano
part arranged by H. Clough-Leighter. Boston, E. C. Schirmer
[c 1935]. 27 pp., 27 cm. (E.C.S. Sacred Music, No. 1675.)
Second chorus: Nun, ich weiss, du wirst mir stillen. Now I know
that Thou art loving. P.N.: E.C.S. No. 910.

CANTATA NO. 106. ("Actus tragicus") Gottes Zeit ist die allerbeste Zeit
(S. 106): Full scores

1090. Actus tragicus, Cantata 106...bearbeitet von Robert Franz. ...
Leipzig, F. E. C. Leuckart (Constantin Sander) [ca. 1875]. 47,
[1] pp.; 35 cm. P.N.: F.E.C.L.1856

1091. "God's Own Time"...English translation by Dr. C. Sanford
Terry, Kontinuoarbeitung von...Arthur Willner. Vienna, Wiener
Philharmonischer Verlag, A. G., 1925. 4 ll., 44 pp., frontis. (port.),
19 cm. (Philharmonia Partituren, No. 106.)
General editor is Wilhelm Fischer, who wrote the preface.
P.N.: W.Ph.V. 106.

1092. Gottes Zeit ist die allerbeste Zeit...Nach der Ausgabe der
Bach-Gesellschaft revidiert und mit Einführung versehen von Arnold
Schering. Leipzig, Vienna, Eulenburg [1927?]. 4 ll., 32 pp., 2 ll.,
19 cm. (Eulenburgs kleine Partitur-Ausgabe, No. 1007.)
P.N.: E.E.4668.

1093. Gottes Zeit Kantate...Partitur mit Cembalo- und Orgelstimme
herausgegeben von Max Seiffert. Leipzig, C. F. Peters [1924?].
32 pp., 34 cm. (Edition Peters, No. 3749c.) P.N.: 10300

1094. No. 6, Gottes Zeit ist die allerbeste Zeit, Kirchenmusik von
Johann Sebastian Bach. [Bonn, Simrock, 1830?] [1], 2-21 pp.;

1094. *(continued)*   34 cm.; wove paper.   (Kirchen Musik, Band 2.)
Stamp with facsimile signature on title page: August Grüters.
Edited by Adolph Bernhard Marx.   P.N.: 2886

CANTATA NO. 106: Vocal-piano scores

1095. Actus tragicus...Cantate nach Worten der heiligen Schrift. ...
Leipzig, C. F. Peters [1880?]. 31 pp., 27 cm. (Edition Peters, No. 42.)
Edited by Gustav Rösler.   P.N.: 6311

1096. Actus tragicus, Kantate...nach Worten der heiligen Schrift. ...
Leipzig, Breitkopf & Härtel [1893?]. 28 pp. (pp. 147-74), 27 cm.
P.N.: J.S.B.I.106.

1097. Cantata 106. ... [Philadelphia] Association of American
Choruses [1947?]. 1 l., 30 pp., 26 cm. (Choral Series, No. 112.)
Photo-offset lithograph process. Translation by Henry S. Drinker.

1098. God's Time Is the Best...Edited by Frank Damrosch. ... New
York, G. Schirmer [c 1899]. 1 l., 31 pp., 1 l., 26 cm. (Musical Art
Society of New York, No. 7.)
Two copies. A third copy, reissued in 1927 in the series "G.
Schirmer's Collection of Oratorios and Cantatas."   P.N.: 14352

1099. God's Time Is the Best...The English translation and adaptation
by the Rev. Dr. Troutbeck. London, Novello; New York, H. W. Gray
[1928?]. 1 l.; 29, [1] pp.; 26 cm. (Novello's Original Octavo
Edition.)   P.N.: Bach's "God's time is the best." –
Novello, Ewer and Co.'s Octavo edition.

1100. "Gottes Zeit ist die allerbeste Zeit"..."God's Time Is Best"...
English version by J. Michael Diack...Klavierauszug von Otto
Schröder. Leipzig, Breitkopf & Härtel [c 1932]. 1 l., 28 pp., 27 cm.
(Joh. Seb. Bach Kirchenkantaten, Klavierauszüge, No. 106.)
P.N.: N.B.XXVII.1.

1101. Johann Sebastian Bach, Vocalwerke im Clavier Auszuge be-
arbeitet von Robert Franz, Kirchen-Cantaten...[No.] 10, Gottes
Zeit ist die allerbeste Zeit (Actus tragicus). ... Leipzig, F. E. C.
Leuckart (Constantin Sander) [ca. 1890]. 33, [1] pp.; 27 cm.
P.N.: F.E.C.L.1859.

CANTATA NO. 106: Vocal score

1102. Cantata 106. ... [Philadelphia] University of Pennsylvania,
n.d. 20 pp., 27 cm. (Choral Series, No. 46.)
[Edited by Henry S. Drinker.]

CANTATA NO. 106: Excerpts

1103. Aria aus der Cantate "Gottes Zeit ist die allerbeste Zeit"...
"In deine Hände befehl' ich meinen Geist," Arrang. von W. Rust.
Berlin, Schlesinger'sche Buch- & Musikhandlung [ca. 1855]. 3 pp.,
34 cm., wove paper. (Sion, Vol. 3, No. 50.)   P.N.: 4193

1104. Sonatina from "Gottes Zeit ist die allerbeste Zeit"...Arranged
[for organ] by Harvey Grace. [London] Oxford University Press
[c 1928]. 1 l., 4 pp., 32 cm. (Ten Instrumental Movements from the
Cantatas, Nos. 1 and 2.)
    Second composition: Sinfonia to "Ich steh' mit einem Fuss im
    Grabe."

CANTATA NO. 107. Was willst du dich betrüben (S. 107): Vocal-piano
scores

1105. Cantata 107. ... [Philadelphia] Association of American
Choruses [1946?]. 1 l., 24 pp., 26 cm. (Choral Series, No. 32.)
    Photo-offset lithograph process. Translation by Henry S. Drinker.
1106. Cantate am 7. Sonntage nach Trinitatis. ... Leipzig, C. F. Peters
[1880]. 23 pp., 27 cm. (Edition Peters, No. 1685.)
    Edited by Gustav Rösler.   P.N.: 6362
1107. Kantate am siebenten Sonntage nach Trinitatis. ... Leipzig,
Breitkopf & Härtel [1893?]. 1 l., 24 pp., 27 cm. (Joh. Seb. Bach
Kirchenkantaten, No. 107.)   P.N.: J.S.B.I.107.
1108. "Why Art Cast Down Within Me?" Edited and arranged by
W. G. Whittaker, the English words by C. Sanford Terry. [London]
Oxford University Press [c 1929]. 4 ll., 28 pp., 25 cm.

CANTATA NO. 108. Es ist euch gut, dass ich hingehe (S. 108): Vocal-
piano scores

1109. For You 'tis Best That I Shall Go Hence. ... [Philadelphia]
Association of American Choruses [1946?]. 1 l., 24 pp., 26 cm.
(Choral Series, No. 50.)
    Photo-offset lithograph process. Translation by Henry S. Drinker.
1110. Kantate am Sonntage Cantate. ... Leipzig, C. F. Peters [1883].
24 pp., 27 cm. (Edition Peters, No. 2148.)
    Edited by Gustav Rösler.   P.N.: 6652
1111. Kantate am Sonntage Kantate. ... Leipzig, Breitkopf & Härtel
[1893?]. 1 l., 24 pp., 27 cm. (Joh. Seb. Bach Kirchenkantaten,
No. 108.)   P.N.: J.S.B.I.108.

CANTATA NO. 109. Ich glaube, lieber Herr, hilf meinem Unglauben
(S. 109): Vocal-piano scores

1112. Cantate am 21. Sonntage nach Trinitatis. ... Leipzig, C. F.
Peters [1880]. 29 pp., 27 cm. (Edition Peters, No. 1686.)
    Edited by Gustav Rösler.   P.N.: 6363
1113. I Doubt Not, Dearest Lord. ... [Philadelphia] Association of American Choruses [1946?]. 1 l., 30 pp., 26 cm. (Choral Series, No. 51.)
    Photo-offset lithograph process. Translation by Henry S. Drinker.
1114. Kantate am einundzwanzigsten Sonntage nach Trinitatis. ...
Leipzig, Breitkopf & Härtel [ca. 1893]. 1 l., 30 pp., 27 cm. (Joh. Seb.
Bach Kirchenkantaten, No. 109.)   P.N.: J.S.B.I.109.

CANTATA NO. 110. Unser Mund sei voll Lachens (S. 110): Vocal-piano scores

1115. Cantate am ersten Weihnachtsfesttage. ... Leipzig, C. F. Peters [1880]. 35 pp., 27 cm. (Edition Peters, No. 1681.) Edited by Gustav Rösler.   P.N.: 6327

1116. Kantate am ersten Weihnachtsfesttage. ... Leipzig, Breitkopf & Härtel [ca. 1893]. 1 l., 38 pp., 27 cm. (Joh. Seb. Bachs Kantaten, No. 110.)   P.N.: J.S.B.I.110.

1117. Then Our Mouth Filled with Laughter. ... [Philadelphia] Association of American Choruses [1946?]. 1 l., 38 pp., 1 l., 26 cm. (Choral Series, No. 52.)
Photo-offset lithograph process. Translation by Henry S. Drinker.

CANTATA NO. 111. Was mein Gott will, das g'scheh' allzeit (S. 111): Vocal-piano scores

1118. Kantate am dritten Sonntage nach Epiphanias. ... Leipzig, Breitkopf & Härtel [ca. 1893]. 1 l., 26 pp., 27 cm. (Joh. Seb. Bach Kirchenkantaten, No. 111.)   P.N.: J.S.B.I.111.

1119. What God Resolves, Will Come About. ... [Philadelphia] Association of American Choruses [1946?]. 1 l., 26 pp., 26 cm. [Choral series, No. 53.)
Photo-offset lithograph process. Translation by Henry S. Drinker.

CANTATA NO. 112. Der Herr ist mein getreuer Hirt (S. 112): Vocal-piano scores

1120. Cantate am Sonntage Misericordias Domini. ... Leipzig, C. F. Peters [1880]. 21 pp., 27 cm. (Edition Peters, No. 1682.) Edited by Gustav Rösler.   P.N.: 6359

1121. Kantate am Sonntage Misericordias Domini. ... Leipzig, Breitkopf & Härtel [ca. 1893]. 1 l., 22 pp. (pp. 27-48), 27 cm. (Joh. Seb. Bach Kirchenkantaten, No. 112.)   P.N.: J.S.B.I.112.

1122. The Lord Is My Shepherd... Edited by John Pointer, English words by Paul England. London, Novello; New York, H. W. Gray, c 1906. 1 l., 29 pp., 25 cm. (Novello's Original Octavo Edition.)   P.N.: 12195

1123. The Lord My God My Shepherd Is. ... [Philadelphia] Association of American Choruses [1949?]. 1 l., 22 pp., 26 cm. (Choral Series, No. 121.)
Photo-offset lithograph process. Translation by Henry S. Drinker.

CANTATA NO. 112: Vocal scores

1124. Cantata 112. ... [Philadelphia] University of Pennsylvania, n.d. 12 pp., 27 cm. (Choral series, No. 41.)
[Edited by Henry S. Drinker.]

1125. Cantata 112. ... [Philadelphia] University of Pennsylvania [1941?]. 12 pp., 26 cm. (Choral Series, No. 41-A.) Edited by Henry S. Drinker.

CANTATA NO. 113. Herr Jesu Christ, du höchstes Gut (S. 113): Vocal-piano scores

1126. Kantate am elften Sonntage nach Trinitatis. ... Leipzig, Breitkopf & Härtel [ca. 1893]. 1 l., 34 pp. (pp. 49-82), 27 cm. (Joh. Seb. Bachs Kantaten, Nr. 113.)   P.N.: J.S.B.I.113.

1127. Lord Jesus Christ, Thou Fount of Grace. ... [Philadelphia] Association of American Choruses [1947?]. 1 l., 34 pp., 26 cm. (Choral Series, No. 90.) Photo-offset lithograph process. Translation by Henry S. Drinker.

CANTATA NO. 114. Ach, lieben Christen, seid getrost (S. 114): Vocal-piano scores

1128. Kantate Ach, liebe Christen... Klavierauszug mit Text von Herman Roth. Leipzig, C. F. Peters [1912]. 29 pp., 28 cm. (Edition Peters, No. 3354.)   P.N.: 9614

1129. Kantate am siebzehnten Sonntage nach Trinitatis. ... Leipzig, Breitkopf & Härtel [ca. 1893]. 1 l., 28 pp. (pp. 83-110), 27 cm. (Joh. Seb. Bach Kirchenkantaten, No. 114.)   P.N.: J.S.B.I.114.

1130. Keep Up Your Courage, Christian Folk. ... [Philadelphia] Association of American Choruses [1948?]. 1 l., 28 pp., 1 l., 26 cm. (Choral Series, No. 152.) Photo-offset lithograph process. Translation by Henry S. Drinker.

CANTATA NO. 115. Mache dich, mein Geist, bereit (S. 115): Vocal-piano scores

1131. Cantate am 22. Sonntage nach Trinitatis. ... Leipzig, C. F. Peters [1880]. 21 pp., 27 cm. (Edition Peters, No. 1678.) Edited by Gustav Rösler.   P.N.: 6364

1132. "Christian Stand with Sword in Hand"... English version by Canon C. V. Gorton. ... Leipzig, Breitkopf & Härtel, c 1911. 21 pp., 27 cm. (Joh. Seb. Bach's Church Cantatas and Motets, Vocal Scores, Cantatas, No. 115.)   P.N.: 26763

1133. Come, My Soul, Today Prepare. ... [Philadelphia] Association of American Choruses [1948?]. 1 l., 20 pp., 1 l., 26 cm. (Choral Series, No. 135.) Photo-offset lithograph process. Translation by Henry S. Drinker.

1134. Kantate am zweiundzwanzigsten Sonntage nach Trinitatis. ... Leipzig, Breitkopf & Härtel [ca. 1893]. 20 pp. (pp. 111-30), 27 cm.   P.N.: J.S.B.I.115.

1135. Ready Be, My Soul, Alway... Edited by Ivor Atkins, English text by Charles Sanford Terry. London, Novello; New York,

1135. *(continued)* H.W. Gray [1925?]. 2 ll., 27 pp., 25 cm. (Novello's Original Octavo Edition.)   P.N.: 15260
CANTATA NO. 115: Vocal score
1136. Come, My Soul, Thyself Prepare. ... [Philadelphia] University of Pennsylvania [1941?]. 12 pp., 26 cm. (Choral Series, No. 125.) Edited by Henry S. Drinker.
CANTATA NO. 116. Du Friedefürst, Herr Jesu Christ (S. 116): Vocal-piano scores
1137. Kantate am fünfundzwanzigsten Sonntage nach Trinitatis. ... Leipzig, Breitkopf & Härtel, 1893. 26 pp. (pp. 131-56), 27 cm.
                                                              P.N.: J.S.B.I.116
1138. O Jesu Christ, Thou Prince of Peace...Edited by John Pointer, English version by Paul England. London, Novello, c 1913. 1 l., 33, 8 pp. (Novello's Original Octavo Edition.)   P.N.: 13801
1139. Thou Prince of Peace, to Thee We Bow. ... [Philadelphia] Association of American Choruses [1948?]. 1 l., 26 pp., 26 cm. (Choral Series, No. 154.)
       Photo-offset lithograph process. Translation by Henry S. Drinker.
CANTATA NO. 117. Sei Lob und Ehr' dem höchsten Gut (S. 117): Vocal-piano scores
1140. All Glory to the Lord of Lords. ... [Philadelphia] Association of American Choruses [1947?]. 1 l., 26 pp., 26 cm. (Choral Series, No. 91.)
       Photo-offset lithograph process. Translation by Henry S. Drinker.
1141. Cantate über Joh. Jacob Schütz's Lied: "Sei Lob und Ehr' dem höchsten Gut". ... Leipzig, C. F. Peters [1880]. 26 pp., 27 cm. (Edition Peters, No. 1690.)
       Edited by Gustav Rösler.   P.N.: 6367
1142. Kantate "Sei Lob und Ehr' dem höchsten Gut". ... Leipzig, Breitkopf & Härtel [ca. 1893]. 1 l., 26 pp., 27 cm. (Joh. Seb. Bach Kirchenkantaten, No. 117.)   P.N.: J.S.B.I.117.
CANTATA NO. 118. O Jesu Christ, mein's Lebens Licht (S. 118): Vocal-piano scores
1143. Dear Friend, the Loss We Feel this Day. ... [Philadelphia] Association of American Choruses [1948?]. 1 l., 6 pp., 26 cm. (Choral Series, No. 159.)
       Photo-offset lithograph process. Translation by Henry S. Drinker.
1144. Kantate O Jesu Christ, mein's Lebens Licht...Klavierauszug mit Text von Herman Roth. Leipzig, C. F. Peters [1911]. 11 pp., 27 cm. (Edition Peters, No. 3350.)   P.N.: 9582
1145. Kantate "O Jesu Christ, mein's Lebens Licht". ... Leipzig, Breitkopf & Härtel [ca. 1893]. 1 l., 6 pp. (pp. 183-88), 27 cm. (Joh. Seb. Bach Kirchenkantaten, No. 118.)   P.N.: J.S.B.I.118.

1146. "O Jesu Christ, mein's Lebens Licht"..."O Jesus Christ, My Life and Light"...Klavierauszug von Günter Raphael, English version by Mevanwy Roberts. Leipzig, Breitkopf & Härtel [c 1930]. 1 l., 10 pp., 27 cm. (Joh. Seb. Bach Kirchenkantaten, No. 118.)
P.N.: J.S.B.I.118.

1147. O Jesus Christ, My Life and Light, O Jesu Christ, mein's Lebens Licht...edited and accompaniment arranged by Ifor Jones, English version by J. M. Stein and Ifor Jones. New York, G. Schirmer [c 1947]. 10 pp., 26 cm. P.N.: 41549

CANTATA NO. 118: Vocal score

1148. Motet...(Cantata 118). ... [Philadelphia] University of Pennsylvania, n.d. 4 pp., 27 cm. (Choral Series, No. 38.)
[Edited by Henry S. Drinker.]

CANTATA NO. 119. Preise, Jerusalem, den Herrn (S. 119): Full score

1149. Preise Jerusalem, den Herrn...Nach der Ausgabe der Bach-Gesellschaft mit Einführung versehen von Arnold Schering. Leipzig, Eulenburg [1933?]. 1 l.; vi, 50 pp.; 3 ll.; 19 cm. (Eulenburgs kleine Partitur-Ausgabe, No. 1030.) P.N.: E.E. 4830

CANTATA NO. 119: Vocal-piano scores

1150. Cantate bei der Rathswahl zu Leipzig 1723. ... Leipzig, C. F. Peters [1880]. 28 pp., 27 cm. (Edition Peters, No. 1684.)
Edited by Gustav Rösler. P.N.: 6361

1151. Kantate bei derRathswahl zu Leipzig 1723. ... Leipzig, Breitkopf & Härtel [ca. 1893]. 30 pp. (pp. 189-218, 27 cm. P.N.: J.S.B.I.119.

1152. Praise, O Jerusalem, Thy God. ... [Philadelphia] Association of American Choruses [1946?]. 1 l., 30 pp., 26 cm. (Choral Series, No. 54.)
Photo-offset lithograph process. Translation by Henry S. Drinker.

1153. Praise Thou the Lord...Edited by John E. West, English version by Paul England. London, Novello; New York, H. W. Gray [ca. 1920]. 1 l., 42 pp., 25 cm. (Novello's Original Octavo Edition.)
P.N.: 11822

CANTATA NO. 120. Gott, man lobet dich in der Stille (S. 120): Vocal-piano scores

1154. Cantate bei der Rathswahl zu Leipzig. ... Leipzig, C. F. Peters [1880]. 28 pp., 27 cm. (Edition Peters, No. 1683.) P.N.: 6360

1155. God, Praise Waiteth Thee in the Temple. ... [Philadelphia] Association of American Choruses [1946?]. 1 l., 28 pp., 1 l. (Choral Series, No. 55.)
Photo-offset lithograph process. Translation by Henry S. Drinker.

1156. Kantate bei der Rathswahl zu Leipzig. ... Leipzig, Breitkopf & Härtel [ca. 1893]. 28 pp. (pp. 219-46), 27 cm. P.N.: J.S.B.I.

116   PUBLISHED MUSIC OF J. S. BACH

CANTATA NO. 121. Christus wir sollen loben schon (S. 121): Vocal-piano scores

1157.   Christ Jesus Praise We Every One. ... [Philadelphia] Association of American Choruses [1950?]. 1 l., 26 pp., 26 cm. (Choral Series, No. 6.)
Photo-offset lithograph process. Translation by Henry S. Drinker.

1158.   Kantate am zweiten Weihnachtsfesttage. ... Leipzig, Breitkopf & Härtel [1894?]. 1 l., 26 pp., 27 cm. (Joh. Seb. Bach Kirchen-kantaten, No. 121.)   P.N.: J.S.B.I.121.

1159.   "Lord Christ, We Now Thy Praises Sing." Edited and arranged by W. G. Whittaker, the English words by C. Sanford Terry. [London] Oxford University Press [c 1926]. 2 ll., 38 pp., 1 l., 25 cm.

CANTATA NO. 121: Vocal score

1160.   Cantata 121. ... [Philadelphia] Association of American Choruses, n.d. 15 pp., 26 cm. (Choral Series, No. 6.)
[Edited by Henry S. Drinker.]

CANTATA NO. 122. Das neugebor'ne Kindelein (S. 122): Vocal-piano scores

1161.   Kantate am Sonntage nach Weihnachten. ... Leipzig, Breitkopf & Härtel [1894?]. 20 pp. (pp. 27-46), 27 cm.   P.N.: J.S.B.I.122.

1162.   "Sing We the Birth." Edited and arranged by W. G. Whittaker, the English words by C. Sanford Terry. [London] Oxford University Press [1924]. 2 ll., 32 pp., 25 cm.

1163.   Unto the World this Happy Morn. ... [Philadelphia] Associa-tion of American Choruses [1947?]. 1 l., 20 pp., 26 cm. (Choral Series, No. 114.)
Photo-offset lithograph process. Translation by Henry S. Drinker.

CANTATA NO. 122: Vocal score

1164.   Cantata 122. ... [Philadelphia] University of Pennsylvania [1941?]. 15 pp., 26 cm. (Choral Series, No. 126.)
Edited by Henry S. Drinker.

CANTATA NO. 122: Excerpts

1165.   Trio. God Is Our Friend. From church cantata No. 122... arranged for female voices and edited by W. G. Whittaker, English words by C. S. Terry. London, Oxford University Press [c 1926]. 8 pp., 26 cm. (The Oxford Choral Songs from the Old Masters, No. 352.)

CANTATA NO. 123. Liebster Immanuel, Herzog der Frommen (S. 123): Full score

1166.   Liebster Immanuel, Herzog der Frommen...Nach der Ausgabe der Bach-Gesellschaft revidiert und mit Einführung versehen von

Arnold Schering. Leipzig, Eulenburg [1931?]. viii, 24 pp., 2 ll., 19 cm. (Eulenburgs kleine Partitur-Ausgabe, No. 1026.)

P.N.: E.E. 4826

CANTATA NO. 123: Vocal-piano scores

1167. Cantata 123. ... [Philadelphia] Association of American Choruses [1950?]. 1 l., 22 pp., 26 cm. (Choral Series, No. 5.)
Photo-offset lithograph process. Translation by Henry S. Drinker.

1168. Kantate am Feste der Erscheinung Christi. ... Leipzig, Breitkopf & Härtel [1894?]. 1 l., 22 pp. (pp. 47-68), 27 cm. (Joh. Seb. Bach Kirchenkantaten, No. 123.)   P.N.: J.S.B.I.123.

CANTATA NO. 123: Vocal score

1169. Cantata 123. ... [Philadelphia] Association of American Choruses, n.d. 11 pp., 26 cm. (Choral series, No. 5.)
Edited by Henry S. Drinker.

CANTATA NO. 124. Meinen Jesum lass' ich nicht (S. 124): Vocal-piano scores

1170. Jesus, Never Leave I Thee. ... [Philadelphia] Association of American Choruses [1946?]. 1 l., 22 pp., 26 cm. (Choral Series, No. 56.)
Photo-offset lithograph process. Translation by Henry S. Drinker.

1171. Kantate am ersten Sonntage nach Epiphanias. ... Leipzig, Breitkopf & Härtel, 1894. 22 pp. (pp. 69-90), 27 cm.   P.N.: J.S.B.I.124.

CANTATA NO. 125. Mit Fried' und Freud' ich fahr' dahin (S. 125): Vocal-piano scores

1172. In Peace and Joy I Go Away. ... [Philadelphia] Association of American Choruses [1947?]. 1 l., 28 pp., 26 cm. (Choral Series, No. 107.)
Photo-offset lithograph process. Translation by Henry S. Drinker.

1173. Kantate am Feste der Reinigung Mariae. ... Leipzig, Breitkopf & Härtel, 1894. 28 pp. (pp. 91-118), 27 cm.   P.N.: J.S.B.I.125

CANTATA NO. 125: Vocal score

1174. Cantata No. 125. ... [Philadelphia] University of Pennsylvania, n.d. 12 pp., 27 cm. (Choral Series, No. 16.)
[Edited by Henry S. Drinker.]

1175. Offertorium (Da pacem nobis Domini) für Sopran, Alt, Tenor und Bass, 2 Violinen, Viola, 1 Flöte, 1 Oboe oder Clarinett, Violoncell und Contrabass componirt von J. S. Bach, Erste Ausgabe nach dem original Manuscript. Vienna, Diabelli [1829?]. [1], 2-11 pp.; 35 cm.; wove paper. (Ecclesiasticon, No. 37.)
Signature and date on title page: Aiſe Leutner | 1829 | 2 | 2. This is the Latin version of the first chorus of Cantata 125.

P.N.: D. et C. N°. 5495

CANTATA NO. 126. Erhalt' uns, Herr, bei deinem Wort (S. 126):
Vocal-piano scores

1176. Kantate am Sonntage Sexagesimae. ... Leipzig, Breitkopf &
Härtel [1894?]. 1 l., 24 pp., 27 cm. (Joh. Seb. Bach Kirchen-
kantaten, No. 126.)   P.N.: J.S.B.I.126.
1177. Sustain Us, Lord Omnipotent. ... [Philadelphia] Association of
American Choruses [1946?]. 1 l., 24 pp., 26 cm. (Choral Series,
No. 57.)
       Photo-offset lithograph process. Translation by Henry S. Drinker.

CANTATA NO. 127. Herr Jesu Christ, wahr'r Mensch und Gott (S. 127):
Vocal-piano scores

1178. Kantate am Sonntage Esto mihi...Leipzig, Breitkopf & Härtel
[1894?] 1 l., 24 pp., 27 cm. (Joh. Seb. Bach Kirchenkantaten,
No. 127.)   P.N.: J.S.B.I.127.
1179. Thou Who, a God, as Man Yet Came. ... [Philadelphia]
Association of American Choruses [1946?]. 1 l., 24 pp., 26 cm.
[Choral Series, No. 58.)
       Photo-offset lithograph process. Translation by Henry S. Drinker.

CANTATA NO. 128. Auf Christi Himmelfahrt allein (S. 128): Vocal-
piano scores

1180. Kantate am Feste der Himmelfahrt Christi. ... Leipzig, Breitkopf & Härtel [1894?]. 24 pp. (pp. 167-90), 27 cm.
                                        P.N.: J.S.B.I.128.
1181. On Jesus Christ's Ascent on High. ... [Philadelphia] Association
of American Choruses [1946?]. 1 l., 24 pp., 1 l., 26 cm. (Choral
Series, No. 59.)
       Photo-offset lithograph process. Translation by Henry S. Drinker.

CANTATA NO. 128: Vocal score

1182. Cantata 128. ... [Philadelphia] University of Pennsylvania
[1941?]. 15 pp., 26 cm. (Choral Series, No. 141.)
       Edited by Henry S. Drinker.

CANTATA NO. 129. Gelobet sei der Herr, mein Gott (S. 129): Vocal-
piano scores

1183. All Glory to the Lord. ... [Philadelphia] Association of American
Choruses [1947?]. 1 l., 36 pp., 1 l., 26 cm. (Choral Series, No. 99.)
       Photo-offset lithograph process. Translation by Henry S. Drinker.
1184. Kantate am Trinitatisfeste. ... Leipzig, Breitkopf & Härtel
[1894?]. 1 l., 36 pp. (pp. 191-226), 27 cm. (Joh. Seb. Bach Kirchenkantaten, No. 129.)   P.N.: J.S.B.I.129.

CANTATA NO. 129: Excerpts

1185. Two Chorales by J. S. Bach. ... London, Oxford University

Press, for The Society for Promoting Christian Knowledge, 1930.
6 pp., 26 cm. (Church Music Society Reprints, No. 17B.)
Contents: I. Now Cheer our Hearts this Eventide; II. Awake, thou
Wintry Earth.

CANTATA NO. 130. Herr Gott, dich loben alle wir (S. 130): Vocal-
piano scores

1186. Kantate am Michaelisfeste. ... Leipzig, Breitkopf & Härtel
[1894?]. 28 pp. (pp. 227-54), 27 cm.   P.N.: J.S.B.I.130.
1187. Lord God, We Praise Thee, All of Us. ... [Philadelphia] Association of American Choruses [1948?]. 1 l., 28 pp., 26 cm. (Choral
Series, No. 155.)
Photo-offset lithograph process. Translation by Henry S. Drinker.

CANTATA NO. 130: Vocal score

1188. Cantata 130. ... [Philadelphia] University of Pennsylvania,
n.d. 16 pp., 26 cm. (Choral Series, No. 142.)
[Edited by Henry S. Drinker.]

CANTATA NO. 131. Aus der Tiefe rufe ich, Herr, zu dir (S. 131):
Vocal-piano scores

1189. "Aus der Tiefe rufe ich, Herr, zu dir"..."Out of Darkness"...
Klavierauszug von Günter Raphael. English version by J. Michael
Diack. Leipzig, Breitkopf & Härtel [c 1932]. 1 l., 42 pp., 27 cm.
(Joh. Seb. Bach Kirchenkantaten, No. 131.)   P.N.: J.S.B.I.131.
1190. Cantate "Aus der Tiefe rufe ich, Herr, zu dir". ... Leipzig,
C. F. Peters [1880]. 32 pp., 28 cm. (Edition Peters, No. 1688.)
Edited by Gustav Rösler.   P.N.: 6365
1191. From the Deep, Lord. ... [Philadelphia] Association of American
Choruses [1948?]. 1 l., 36 pp., 1 l., 26 cm. (Choral Series, No. 131.)
Photo-offset lithograph process. Translation by Henry S. Drinker.
1192. Kantate "Aus der Tiefe rufe ich, Herr, zu dir". ... Leipzig,
Breitkopf & Härtel [1894]. 1 l., 36 pp., 27 cm. (Gesammtausgabe für
den praktischen Gebrauch. I. Kantaten. Nr. 131.)
                                                  P.N.: J.S.B.I.131.

CANTATA NO. 131: Vocal score

1193. Cantata No. 131. ... [Philadelphia] University of Pennsylvania,
n.d. 28 pp., 27 cm. (Choral Series, No. 18.)
[Edited by Henry S. Drinker.]

CANTATA NO. 132. Bereitet die Wege, bereitet die Bahn (S. 132):
Vocal-piano score

1194. Kantate am vierten Advent. ... Leipzig, Breitkopf & Härtel
[1894?]. 1 l., 22 pp., 27 cm. (Joh. Seb. Bach Kirchenkantaten,
No. 132.)   P.N.: J.S.B.I.132.

CANTATA NO. 133. Ich freue mich in dir (S. 133): Vocal-piano scores
1195. "In Thee Do I Rejoice." Edited, arranged, and with English
text by W. G. Whittaker. [London] Oxford University Press [c 1929].
3 ll., 38 pp., 1 l., 25 cm.
1196. Kantate am dritten Weihnachtsfesttage. ... Leipzig, Breitkopf &
Härtel [1894?]. 1 l., 26 pp., 27 cm. (Joh. Seb. Bach Kirchenkantaten,
No. 133.)   P.N.: J.S.B.I.133.
1197. My Joy Is All in Thee. ... [Philadelphia, Association of American
Choruses, 1946?] 1 l., 26 pp., 26 cm. (Choral Series No. 63.)
Photo-offset lithograph process. Translation by Henry S. Drinker.

CANTATA NO. 134. Ein Herz, das seinen Jesum lebend weiss (S. 134):
Vocal-piano scores
1198. Kantate am dritten Osterfesttage. ... Leipzig, Breitkopf &
Härtel [1894?]. 36 pp. (pp. 85-120), 27 cm.   P.N.: J.S.B.I.134.
1199. The Soul That Truly Knows His Risen Lord. ... [Philadelphia]
Association of American Choruses [1946?]. 1 l., 36 pp., 26 cm.
Photo-offset lithograph process. Translation by Henry S. Drinker.

CANTATA NO. 135. Ach Herr, mich armen Sünder (S. 135): Full score
1200. [Original MS. title:] Domin. 3 post Trinit: Ach Herr mich
armen Sünder à 4 voc: 2 Hautbois 2 Violini Viola e Continuo di Sign.
I. S. Bach. Leipzig, G. Röder, 1926. 12 ll., 38 cm.
Facsimile of original MS. in the Leipzig Stadtbibliothek. Commentary by Karl Straube. Limited edition of 400 copies.

CANTATA NO. 135: Vocal-piano scores
1201. Ah Lord Spare Thou this Sinner. ... [Philadelphia] Association
of American Choruses [1947?]. 1 l., 20 pp., 1 l., 26 cm. (Choral
Series, No. 92.)
Photo-offset lithograph process. Translation by Henry S. Drinker.
1202. Kantate am dritten Sonntage nach Trinitatis. ... Leipzig, Breitkopf & Härtel [1894?]. 20 pp. (pp. 121-40), 27 cm. P.N.: J.S.B.I.135
1203. O Lord, This Grieving Spirit; Ach Herr, mich armen Sünder...
Edited and accompaniment arranged by Ifor Jones... English version
by J. M. Stein and Ifor Jones. New York, G. Schirmer [c 1947].
32 pp., 26 cm.   P.N.: 41550

CANTATA NO. 135: Excerpts
1204. Ach Herr, mich armen Sünder, O Lord, Relent, I Pray Thee.
Two choruses for mixed voices from Cantata No. 135...English
version by Charles Sanford Terry, edited, and the piano part arranged,
by H. Clough-Leighter. Boston, E. C. Schirmer, c 1936. 17 pp.,
1 l., 28 cm. (E.C.S. Sacred Music, No. 1724.)
Second chorus: Ehr' sei in's Himmels Throne; All Praise to Thy
Great Merit.   P.N.: E.C.S. No. 1028

CANTATAS 121

1205. Cantata No. 135. ... [Philadelphia, University of Pennsylvania, n.d.] 4 pp., 26 cm.
Contents: First chorus. [Edited by Henry S. Drinker.]

CANTATA NO. 136. Erforsche mich, Gott, und erfahre mein Herz (S. 136): Vocal-piano scores

1206. Examine Me, God. ... [Philadelphia] Association of American Choruses, n.d. 1 l., 28 pp., 1 l., 26 cm. (Choral Series, No. 65.) Photo-offset lithograph process. Translation by Henry S. Drinker.

1207. Kantate am achten Sonntage nach Trinitatis. ... Leipzig, Breitkopf & Härtel [1894?]. 28 pp. (pp. 141-68), 27 cm.
P.N.: J.S.B.I.136.

CANTATA NO. 137. Lobe den Herren, den mächtigen König der Ehren (S. 137): Vocal-piano scores

1208. Kantate am zwölften Sonntage nach Trinitatis. ... Leipzig, Breitkopf & Härtel [1894?]. 1 l., 26 pp. (pp. 169-94), 27 cm. (Joh. Seb. Bach Kirchenkantaten, No. 137.) P.N.: J.S.B.I.137.

1209. "Lobe den Herren, den mächtigen König der Ehren"..."Praise Him, the Lord, the Almighty, the King, and Adore Him"...Klavierauszug von Günter Raphael, English version by Mevanwy Roberts. Leipzig, Breitkopf & Härtel [c 1932]. 1 l., 30 pp., 28 cm. (Joh. Seb. Bach Kirchenkantaten, No. 137.)
Four copies. P.N.: J.S.B.I.137.

1210. Praise the Almighty. ... [Philadelphia] Association of American Choruses, n.d. 1 l., 26 pp., 26 cm. (Choral Series, No. 137.) Photo-offset lithograph process. Translation by Henry S. Drinker.

CANTATA NO. 137: Vocal score

1211. Cantata No. 137 ... with concluding chorale from Cantata No. 55. ... [Philadelphia] University of Pennsylvania, n.d. 12 pp., 27 cm. (Choral Series, No. 27.)
[Edited by Henry S. Drinker.]

CANTATA NO. 137: Excerpts

1212. Chorale from Church Cantata No. 137, Praise to the Highest... Arranged and edited by W. G. Whittaker, English text by C. S. Terry. ... London, Oxford University Press, c 1928. 6 pp., 26 cm. (The Oxford Choral Songs from the Old Masters, No. 1437.)

CANTATA NO. 138. Warum betrübst du dich, mein Herz (S. 138): Vocal-piano scores

1213. Kantate am fünfzehnten Sonntage nach Trinitatis. ... Leipzig, Breitkopf & Härtel [1894?]. 26 pp. (pp. 195-220), 27 cm.
P.N.: J.S.B.I.138

1214. What Is It Troubles Thee. ... [Philadelphia] Association of American Choruses [1947?]. 1 l., 26 pp., 26 cm. (Choral Series, No. 136.)
Photo-offset lithograph process. Translation by Henry S. Drinker.

CANTATA NO. 138: Vocal score

1215. Cantata 138. ... [Philadelphia] Association of American Choruses, n.d. 19 pp., 26 cm. (Choral Series, No. 7.)
[Edited by Henry S. Drinker.]

CANTATA NO. 139. Wohl dem, der sich auf seinen Gott (S. 139): Vocal-piano scores

1216. Kantate am dreiundzwanzigsten Sonntage nach Trinitatis. ... Leipzig, Breitkopf & Härtel [1894?]. 1 l., 28 pp. (pp. 221-48), 27 cm. (Joh. Seb. Bach Kirchenkantaten, No. 139.)
                                                                                P.N.: J.S.B.I.139.
1217. Tis Well with Him Who on the Lord. ... [Philadelphia] Association of American Choruses [1947?]. 1 l., 28 pp., 1 l., 26 cm. (Choral Series, No. 93.)
Photo-offset lithograph process. Translation by Henry S. Drinker.

CANTATA NO. 140. Wachet auf, ruft uns die Stimme (S. 140): Full scores

1218. Wachet auf Kantate...Partitur mit Cembalo- und Orgelstimme herausgegeben von Max Seiffert. Leipzig, C. F. Peters [1933?]. 36 pp., 34 cm. (Edition Peters, No. 3749a.)   P.N.: 10270
1219. Wachet auf, ruft uns die Stimme...Nach der Ausgabe der Bach-Gesellschaft revidiert und mit Einführung versehen von Arnold Schering. Leipzig, Eulenburg [1930?]. 1 l.; vii, 52 pp.; 3 ll.; 19 cm. (Eulenburgs kleine Partitur-Ausgabe, No. 1020.)   P.N.: E.E. 4820

CANTATA NO. 140: Vocal-piano scores

1220. Cantate am 27. Sonntage nach Trinitatis. ... Leipzig, C. F. Peters [1881]. 39 pp., 27 cm. (Edition Peters, No. 1691.)
Edited by Gustav Rösler.   P.N.: 6460
1221. Kantate am siebenundzwanzigsten Sonntage nach Trinitatis. ... Leipzig, Breitkopf & Härtel [1894?]. 1 l., 43 pp. (pp. 249-91), 27 cm. (Joh. Seb. Bach Kirchenkantaten, No. 140.)   P.N.: J.S.B.I.140.
1222. "Sleepers Wake, Loud Sounds the Warning"..."Lève-toi, prête l'oreille"...version française de M. Kufferath. Leipzig, Breitkopf & Härtel [c 1912]. 50 pp., 27 cm.   P.N.: 26751
1223. Sleepers, Wake!...The pianoforte accompaniment arranged by Ebenezer Prout, the English translation by Miss G. E. Troutbeck. London, Novello; New York, H. W. Gray, c 1901. 2 ll., 44 pp., 25 cm. (Novello's Original Octavo Edition.)
Four copies.   P.N.: 11246

1224. Wake Ye Maids. ... [Philadelphia] Association of American Choruses [1947?]. 1 l., 43 pp., 26 cm. (Choral Series, No. 113.) Photo-offset lithograph process. Translation by Henry S. Drinker.

CANTATA NO. 140: Vocal score

1225. Cantata 140. ... [Philadelphia] University of Pennsylvania [1940?]. 27 pp., 27 cm. (Choral Series, No. 78.) Edited by Henry S. Drinker.

CANTATA NO. 140: Excerpts

1226. Now Let All the Heavens Adore Thee. From the cantata "Sleepers, Wake"...for three-part chorus of women's voices... arranged by Norwood Hinkle...English version by Catherine Winkworth. New York, Oliver Ditson [c 1933]. 4 pp., 28 cm. (Choruses for Girls' Glee-Clubs, No. 14,573.)   P.N.: 77243-3
1227. "Sleepers, Wake"...For four-part chorus of mixed voices... English version by Milford East. New York, G. Schirmer [c 1930]. 7 pp., 27 cm. (G. S. 8vo Choruses, No. 7427.)   P.N.: 35030
1228. Wake, Awake...from Church cantata No. 140...Edited by Max T. Krone...English translation by Max T. Krone. New York, M. Witmark [c 1936]. 23 pp., 27 cm. (The Witmark Choral Library, No. 2905.)
Complimentary copy, with inscription to Albert Riemenschneider from Max Krone.   P.N.: M.W. & Sons 19746-22

CANTATA NO. 141. Das ist je gewisslich wahr (S. 141): Vocal-piano scores

1229. Cantata 141. ... [Philadelphia] Association of American Choruses [1946?]. 1 l., 14 pp., 26 cm. (Choral Series, No. 30.) Photo-offset lithograph process. Translation by Henry S. Drinker.
1230. Kantate am dritten Advent. ... Leipzig, Breitkopf & Härtel [1894?]. 1 l., 14 pp., 27 cm. (Joh. Seb. Bach Kirchenkantaten, No. 141.)   P.N.: J.S.B.I.141.

CANTATA NO. 142. Uns ist ein Kind geboren (S. 142): Vocal-piano scores

1231. For Us a Child Is Born (Uns ist ein Kind geboren)...the English version by Sydney Biden. New York, Galaxy [c 1939]. 33 pp., 27 cm.   P.N.: G.M. 1012-31
1232. Kantate am ersten Weihnachtsfesttage...Klavierauszug von Otto Schröder. Leipzig, Breitkopf & Härtel [1924]. 1 l., 22 pp., 27 cm. (Joh. Seb. Bach Kirchenkantaten, No. 142.) P.N.: N.B.XXV.1.
1233. To Us a Child Is Given. ... [Philadelphia] Association of American Choruses [1947?]. 1 l., 22 pp., 26 cm. (Choral Series, No. 115.)
Photo-offset lithograph process. Translation by Henry S. Drinker.

124 PUBLISHED MUSIC OF J. S. BACH

CANTATA NO. 142: Vocal score

1234. Cantata No. 142. ... [Philadelphia, University of Pennsylvania, n.d.] 12 pp., 27 cm.

CANTATA NO. 143. Lobe den Herrn, meine Seele (S. 143): Vocal-piano scores

1235. Kantate am Neujahrstage. ... Leipzig, Breitkopf & Härtel [1894?]. 1 l., 20 pp., 27 cm. (Joh. Seb. Bach Kirchenkantaten, No. 143.)   P.N.: J.S.B.I.143.

1236. Praise Thou the Lord, O My Spirit. ... [Philadelphia] Association of American Choruses [1948?]. 1 l., 20 pp., 26 cm. (Choral Series, No. 163.)
Photo-offset lithograph process. Translation by Henry S. Drinker.

CANTATA NO. 143: Vocal score

1237. Cantata 143. ... [Philadelphia] Association of American Choruses, n.d. 11 pp., 26 cm. (Choral Series, No. 3.) [Edited by Henry S. Drinker.]

CANTATA NO. 144. Nimm, was dein ist, und gehe hin (S. 144): Vocal-piano scores

1238. Cantata 144. ... [Philadelphia] Association of American Choruses, n.d. 1 l., 18 pp., 26 cm. (Choral Series, No. 31.)
Photo-offset lithograph process. Translation by Henry S. Drinker.

1239. Kantate am Sonntage Septuagesimae. ... Leipzig, Breitkopf & Härtel [1894?]. 1 l., 18 pp. (pp. 57-74), 27 cm. (Joh. Seb. Bach Kirchenkantaten, No. 144.)   P.N.: J.S.B.I.144.

1240. "Take What Thine Is, and Go Thy Way." Edited and arranged by W. G. Whittaker, the English words by C. Sanford Terry. [London] Oxford University Press [c 1929]. 2 ll., 24 pp., 25 cm.

CANTATA NO. 145. Auf, mein Herz, des Herren Tag (S. 145): Vocal-piano scores

1241. If Thou, with True Devotion. ... [Philadelphia] Association of American Choruses [1946?]. 1 l., 24 pp., 1 l., 26 cm. (Choral Series, No. 66.)
Photo-offset lithograph process. Translation by Henry S. Drinker.

1242. Kantate am Osterfeste. ... Leipzig, Breitkopf & Härtel [1894?]. 24 pp. (pp. 75-98), 27 cm.   P.N.: J.S.B.I.145.

CANTATA NO. 146. Wir müssen durch viel Trübsal in das Reich Gottes eingehen (S. 146): Vocal-piano scores

1243. Kantate am Sonntage Jubilate. ... Leipzig, Breitkopf & Härtel [1894?]. 46 pp. (pp. 99-144), 27 cm.   P.N.: J.S.B.I.146.

1244. Thru Bitter Tribulation. ... [Philadelphia] Association of American Choruses [1946?]. 1 l., 46 pp., 26 cm. (Choral Series, No. 67.)
Photo-offset lithograph process. Translation by Henry S. Drinker.

1245. We Must through Great Tribulation; Wir müssen durch viel Trübsal...Edited and accompaniment arranged by Ifor Jones, English version by J. M. Stein and Ifor Jones. New York, G. Schirmer [c 1942]. 64 pp., 26 cm.   P.N.: 39779

CANTATA NO. 147. Herz und Mund und Tat und Leben (S. 147): Vocal-piano scores

1246. Jesus, Thou My Constant Gladness [Herz und Mund und Tat und Leben]...Edited by William A. Goldsworthy, the English text by Nadine M. and W. A. Goldsworthy. New York, H. W. Gray, c 1950. 63 pp., 27 cm.
Two copies.   P.N.: Bach – Jesus, Thou My etc.-(63)

1247. Kantate am Feste der Maria Heimsuchung. ... Leipzig, Breit-kopf & Härtel [1894?]. 1 l., 44 pp., 27 cm. (Joh. Seb. Bach Kirchen-kantaten, No. 147.)   P.N.: J.S.B.I.147.

1248. Word and Deed. ... [Philadelphia] Association of American Choruses [1949?]. 1 l., 44 pp., 1 l., 26 cm. (Choral Series, No. 158.) Photo-offset lithograph process. Translation by Henry S. Drinker.

CANTATA NO. 147: Vocal score

1249. Cantata 147. ... [Philadelphia] University of Pennsylvania, n.d. 27 pp., 26 cm. (Choral Series, No. 143.)
[Edited by Henry S. Drinker.]

CANTATA NO. 147: Excerpts

1250. Chorale from Church Cantata No. 147...[Jesus Makes My Soul to Flourish; Wohl mir, dass ich Jesum habe]...for four-part chorus of mixed voices with organ accompaniment...arranged by Bryceson Treharne, English version by Willis Wager. New York, G. Schirmer, c 1939. 10 pp., 27 cm. (G. Schirmer, Octavo No. 8387.)
P.N.: 38609

1251. Jesu, Joy of Man's Desiring (Iesu, drud ddifyrrwch dynion)... Arranged and edited by A.L. [two-part female voices], Welsh version by R. Williams Parry and E. T. Davies. London, Oxford University Press, c 1931. 6 pp., 26 cm. (The Oxford Choral Songs from the Old Masters, No. 1518.)

1252. 'Jesu, Joy of Man's Desiring' ('Iesu, drud ddifyrrwch dynion')... Arranged and edited by W. Gillies Whittaker [three-part female voices], Welsh version by R. Williams Parry and E. T. Davies. London, Oxford University Press, c 1931. 8 pp., 26 cm. (The Oxford Choral Songs from the Old Masters, No. 1519.)

1253. Jesu, Joy of Man's Desiring...Arranged for organ by Harvey Grace. New York, Oxford University Press [c 1927]. 1 l., 5 pp., 32 cm.

1254. Jesu, Joy of Man's Desiring ('Iesu, drud ddifyrrwch dynion') ... Arranged for treble voices in unison and edited by W. Gillies Whittaker, Welsh version by R. Williams Parry and E. T. Davies.

1254. *(continued)* London, Oxford University Press, c 1930. 6 p.p, 26 cm. (The Oxford Choral Songs from the Old Masters, No. 1495.)
1255. Jesu, Joy of Man's Desiring... Chorus for men's voices, 3-part... Arranged by Richard G. Appel. Boston, Oliver Ditson, c 1934. 7 pp., 28 cm. (Octavo No. 14, 706.)   P.N.: 77474-5
1256. Jesu, Joy of Man's Desiring... Chorus for women's voices, 3-part... Arranged by Richard G. Appel. Boston, Oliver Ditson, c 1934 7 pp., 28 cm. (Octavo No. 14, 727.)   P.N.: 77475-5
1257. Jesu, Joy of Man's Desiring... Edited by H. P. Allen.... London, Oxford University Press, for the Society for Promoting Christian Knowledge, 1930. 8 pp., 26 cm. (Church Music Society Reprints, No. 16A.)
1258. "Jesu, Joy of Man's Desiring"... Edited by W. G. Whittaker, mixed voices. New York, Oxford University Press, c 1928. 3 pp., 26 cm. (Oxford Choral Songs from the Old Masters, No. 1443.)

CANTATA NO. 148. Bringt dem Herrn Ehre seines Namens (S. 148): Vocal-piano scores

1259. Give to the Lord |Glory. ... [Philadelphia] Association of American Choruses [1946?]. 1 l., 24 pp., 1 l., 26 cm. (Choral Series, No. 68.)
    Photo-offset lithograph process. Translation by Henry S. Drinker.
1260. Kantate am siebenzehnten Sonntage nach Trinitatis. ... Leipzig, Breitkopf & Härtel [1894?]. 24 pp. (pp. 189-212), 27 cm.
                                                        P.N.: J.S.B.I.148.

CANTATA NO. 149. Man singet mit Freuden vom Sieg (S. 149): Vocal-piano scores

1261. Kantate am Michaelisfeste. ... Leipzig, Breitkopf & Härtel [1894?]. 28 pp. (pp. 213-40), 27 cm.   P.N.: J.S.B.I.149
1262. Let Songs of Rejoicing Be Raised... Edited by John Pointer, English version by Paul England. London, Novello; New York, H. W. Gray, c 1910. 1 l., 45 pp., 8 pp., 25 cm. (Novello's Original Octavo Edition.)   P.N.: 12740
1263. The Voice of Rejoicing and Hope. ... [Philadelphia] Association of American Choruses [1946?]. 1 l., 28 pp., 1 l., 26 cm. (Choral Series, No. 69.).
    Photo-offset lithograph process. Translation by Henry S. Drinker.

CANTATA NO. 150. Nach dir, Herr, verlanget mich (S. 150): Vocal-piano scores

1264. Kantate "Nach dir, Herr, verlanget mich". ... Leipzig, Breitkopf & Härtel [1895?]. 1 l., 27 pp. (pp. 241-67), 27 cm. (Joh. Seb. Bach Kirchenkantaten, No. 150.)   P.N.: J.S.B.I.150.
1265. Lord, to Thee. ... [Philadelphia] Association of American Choruses [1948?]. 1 l., 27 pp., 1 l., 26 cm. (Choral Series, No. 130.)
    Photo-offset lithograph process. Translation by Henry S. Drinker.

1266. "Nach dir, Herr, verlanget mich"..."Lord, My Soul Doth Thirst for Thee"... Klavierauszug von Günter Raphael, English version by Stewart Wilson. Leipzig, Breitkopf & Härtel [c 1932]. 1 l., 38 pp. 27 cm. (Joh. Seb. Bach Kirchenkantaten, No. 150.)
P.N.: J.S.B.I.150.

CANTATA NO. 150: Vocal score

1267. Cantata No. 150. ... [Philadelphia] University of Pennsylvania, n.d. 20 pp., 27 cm. (Choral Series, No. 19.) [Edited by Henry S. Drinker.]

CANTATA NO. 151. Süsser Trost, mein Jesus kommt (S. 151): Vocal-piano score

1268. "Süsser Trost, mein Jesus kömmt"..."Blessed Morn, When Jesus Was Born"... Klavierauszug von Günter Raphael, English version by J. Michael Diack. Leipzig, Brcitkopf & Härtel [c 1929]. 1 l., 16 pp., 27 cm. (Joh. Seb. Bach Kirchenkantaten, No. 151.) Two copies.
P.N.: J.S.B.I.151.

CANTATA NO. 152. Tritt auf die Glaubensbahn (S. 152): Vocal-piano scores

1269. Kantate am Sonntage nach Weihnachten. ... Leipzig, Breitkopf & Härtel [1895?]. 20 pp. (pp. 17-36), 27 cm.   P.N.: J.S.B.I.152.
1270. "O Walk the Heavenly Way." Edited and arranged by Charles Kennedy Scott, the English words by Beatrice E. Bulman. [London] Oxford University Press [c 1928]. 2 ll., 26 pp., 1 l., 25 cm.
1271. "Walk in the Way of Faith"... Vocal score by B. Todt, English version by F. S. Copeland. ... Leipzig, Breitkopf & Härtel [c 1908]. 20 pp., 27 cm.   P.N.: 26137

CANTATA NO. 153. Schau, lieber Gott, wie meine Feind (S. 153): Vocal-piano score

1272. Kantate am Sonntage nach der Beschneidung Christi. ... Leipzig, Breitkopf & Härtel [1895?]. 1 l., 18 pp. (pp. 37-54), 27 cm. (Joh. Seb. Bach Kirchenkantaten, No. 153.)   P.N.: J.S.B.I.153.

CANTATA NO. 154. Mein liebster Jesus ist verloren (S. 154): Vocal-piano scores

1273. "Mein liebster Jesus ist verloren"..."Mon bien-aimé, tu m'abandonnes"... traduction française de G. Bret. ... Leipzig, Breitkopf & Härtel [1895?]. 24 pp., 27 cm.   P.N.: J.S.B.I.154.
1274. My Dearest Jesu Now Hath Left Me (Mein liebster Jesu ist verloren)... Edited by Christopher O. Honaas, English translation by Emilie Goodman Wright. New York, H. W. Gray [c 1941]. 2 ll., 32 pp., 27 cm.   P.N.: Bach – My Dearest Jesu (32)

128   PUBLISHED MUSIC OF J. S. BACH

CANTATA NO. 155. Mein Gott, wie lang', ach lange (S. 155): Vocal-piano scores

1275.   Kantate am zweiten Sonntage nach Epiphanias. ... Leipzig, Breitkopf & Härtel [1895?]. 14 pp. (pp. 77-90), 27 cm.
                                                                    P.N.: J.S.B.I.155.
1276.   Kantate Mein Gott, wie lang...Klavierauszug mit Text von Herman Roth. Leipzig, C. F. Peters [1912]. 20 pp., 27 cm. (Edition Peters, No. 3356.)   P.N.: 9645

CANTATA NO. 156. Ich steh' mit einem Fuss im Grabe (S. 156): Vocal-piano score

1277.   Kantate am dritten Sonntage nach Epiphanias. ... Leipzig, Breitkopf & Härtel [1895?]. 18 pp. (pp. 91-108), 27 cm.
                                                                    P.N.: J.S.B.I.156.
CANTATA NO. 157. Ich lasse dich nicht, du segnest mich denn (S. 157): Vocal-piano score

1278.   Kantate am Feste der Reinigung Mariae. ... Leipzig, Breitkopf & Härtel [1895?]. 26 pp. (pp. 109-34), 27 cm.   P.N.: J.S.B.I.157.

CANTATA NO. 158. Der Friede sei mit dir (S. 158): Vocal-piano score

1279.   Kantate am Feste der Reinigung Mariae oder am dritten Oster-festtage. ... Leipzig, Breitkopf & Härtel [1895?]. 1 l., 14 pp., 27 cm. (Joh. Seb. Bach Kirchenkantaten, No. 158.)   P.N.: J.S.B.I.158.

CANTATA NO. 159. Sehet, wer geh'n hinauf gen Jerusalem (S. 159): Vocal-piano scores

1280.   Kantate am Sonntage Esto mihi. ... Leipzig, Breitkopf & Härtel [1895?]. 14 pp. (pp. 149-62), 27 cm.   P.N.: J.S.B.I.159.
1281.   Kantate Sehet, wir gehn hinauf...Klavierauszug mit Text von Herman Roth. Leipzig, C. F. Peters [1912]. 19 pp., 27 cm. (Edition Peters, No. 3355.)   P.N.: 9632
1282.   "Sehet, wir geh'n hinauf gen Jerusalem"..."Come and Let Us Go up to Jerusalem"...Klavierauszug von Günter Raphael, English version by J. Michael Diack. Leipzig, Breitkopf & Härtel [c 1931]. 1 l., 15 pp., 27 cm. (Joh. Seb. Bach Kirchenkantaten, No. 159.)
                                                                    P.N.: J.S.B.I.159.
CANTATA NO. 160. Ich weiss, dass mein Erlöser lebt (S. 160): Vocal-piano score

1283.   Solo-Kantate für Tenor am ersten Osterfesttage...Klavierauszug von Otto Schröder. Leipzig, Breitkopf & Härtel [1923]. 1 l., 14 pp., 27 cm. (Joh. Seb. Bach Kirchenkantaten, No. 160.) P.N.: N.B.XXIII.1.

CANTATA NO. 161. Komm, du süsse Todesstunde (S. 161): Full scores

1284.   Komm, du süsse Todesstunde...Nach der Ausgabe der Bach-Gesellschaft revidiert und mit Einführung versehen von Arnold

Schering. Leipzig, Vienna, Eulenburg [1926?]. 3 ll., 30 pp., 2 ll., 19 cm. (Eulenburgs kleine Partitur-Ausgabe, No. 1005.)   P.N.: E.E. 4600.

CANTATA NO. 161: Vocal-piano scores

1285.   Come, O Death, Thou Blessed Healer. ... [Philadelphia] Association of American Choruses [1947?]. 1 l., 20 pp., 1 l., 26 cm. (Choral Series, No. 85.)
   Photo-offset lithograph process. Translation by Henry S. Drinker.

1286.   "Come, Thou Lovely Hour of Dying." Edited and arranged by Charles Kennedy Scott, the English words by Beatrice E. Bulman. [London] Oxford University Press [c 1928]. 3 ll.; 29, [1] pp.; 25 cm.

1287.   Kantate am sechzehnten Sonntage nach Trinitatis. ... Leipzig, Breitkopf & Härtel [1895?]. 1 l., 20 pp., 27 cm. (Joh. Seb. Bach Kirchenkantaten, No. 161.)   P.N.: J.S.B.I.161.

1288.   Kantate: Dominica 16 post Trinitatis. ... Leipzig, C. F. Peters [1913]. 28 pp., 27 cm. (Edition Peters, No. 3359.)
   Edited by Herman Roth.   P.N.: 9735

1289.   "Komm, du süsse Todesstunde"..."Come, Thou Blessed Hour" ...Klavierauszug von Günter Raphael, English version by J. Michael Diack. Leipzig, Breitkopf & Härtel [c 1930]. 1 l., 23 pp., 27 cm. (Joh. Seb. Bach Kirchenkantaten, No. 161.)   P.N.: J.S.B.I.161.

CANTATA NO. 161: Excerpts

1290.   Wenn es meines Gottes Wille, If It Be God's Will and Pleasure, two choruses for mixed voices from Cantata No. 161...English version by Charles Sanford Terry...edited and the piano part arranged by H. Clough-Leighter. Boston, E. C. Schirmer, c 1936. 17 pp., 1 l., 28 cm. (E.C.S. Sacred Music, No. 1725.)
   Second chorus: Der Leib zwar in der Erden; Though Worms Destroy My Body.   P.N.: E.C.S. No. 1029

CANTATA NO. 162. Ach, ich sehe, itzt, da ich zur Hochzeit gehe (S. 162): Vocal-piano score

1291.   Kantate am zwanzigsten Sonntage nach Trinitatis. ... Leipzig, Breitkopf & Härtel [1895?]. 20 pp. (pp. 21-40), 27 cm.
                                                        P.N.: J.S.B.I.162.

CANTATA NO. 163. Nur jedem das Seine (S. 163): Vocal-piano score

1292.   Kantate am dreiundzwanzigsten Sonntage nach Trinitatis. ... Leipzig, Breitkopf & Härtel [1895?]. 1 l., 20 pp. (pp. 41-60), 27 cm. (Joh. Seb. Bach Kirchenkantaten, No. 163.)   P.N.: J.S.B.I.163

CANTATA NO. 164. Ihr, die ihr euch von Christo nennet (S. 164): Vocal-piano score

1293.   Kantate am dreizehnten Sonntage nach Trinitatis. ... Leipzig, Breitkopf & Härtel [1895?]. 1 l., 20 pp., 27 cm. (Joh. Seb. Bach Kirchenkantaten, No. 164.)   P.N.: J. S. B. I. 164.

130 PUBLISHED MUSIC OF J. S. BACH

CANTATA NO. 165. O heil'ges Geist- und Wasserbad (S. 165): Vocal-piano score

1294. Cantate am Trinitatisfeste. ... Leipzig, Breitkopf & Härtel [1895?]. 1 l., 14 pp., 27 cm. (Joh. Seb. Bach Kirchenkantaten, No. 165.)　　　　　　　　　P.N.: J.S.B.I.165.

CANTATA NO. 166. Wo gehest du hin? (S. 166): Vocal-piano score

1295. Kantate am Sonntage Kantate. ... Leipzig, Breitkopf & Härtel [1895?]. 1 l., 18 pp., 27 cm. (Joh. Seb. Bach Kirchenkantaten, No. 166.)　　　　　　　　　P.N.: J.S.B.I 166.

CANTATA NO. 166: Excerpts

1296. Chorale 'Lord Christ Above'...From church cantata No. 166... arranged and edited by W. G. Whittaker, English text by C. S. Terry. London, Oxford University Press, c 1928. 5 pp., 26 cm. (The Oxford Choral Songs from the Old Masters, No. 1438.)

CANTATA NO. 167. Ihr Menschen, rühmet Gottes Liebe (S. 167): Vocal-piano scores

1297. Kantate am Feste Johannis des Täufers. ... Leipzig, Breitkopf & Härtel [1895?]. 1 l., 22 pp. (pp. 113-34), 27 cm. (Joh. Seb. Bach Kirchenkantaten, No. 167.)　　　　　P.N.: J.S.B.I.167.
1298. "Ye Mortals Extol the Love of the Father"...Vocal score by B. Todt, English version by Morton Latham. ... Leipzig, Breitkopf & Härtel [c 1911]. 22 pp., 27 cm.　　　　　P.N.: 26656
1299. Ye Mortals, Praise Ye God's Affection. ... [Philadelphia] Association of American Choruses [1947?]. 1 l., 22 pp., 26 cm. (Choral Series, No. 102.)
Photo-offset lithograph process. Translation by Henry S. Drinker.

CANTATA NO. 168. Tue Rechnung! Donnerwort (S. 168): Vocal-piano score

1300. Cantate am neunten Sonntage nach Trinitatis. ... Leipzig, Breitkopf & Härtel [1895?]. 1 l., 22 pp. (pp. 135-56), 27 cm. (Joh. Seb. Bach Kirchenkantaten, No. 168.)　　　　P.N.: J.S.B.I.168.

CANTATA NO. 169. Gott soll allein mein Herze haben (S. 169): Vocal-piano score

1301. Kantate am achtzehnten Sonntage nach Trinitatis. ... Leipzig, Breitkopf & Härtel [1895?]. 1 l., 24 pp. (pp. 157-80), 27 cm. (Joh. Seb. Bach Kirchenkantaten, No. 169.)　　　　P.N.: J.S.B.I.169.

CANTATA NO. 170. Vergnügte Ruh', beliebte Seelenlust (S. 170): Vocal-piano score

1302. Kantate am sechsten Sonntage nach Trinitatis. ... Leipzig, Breitkopf & Härtel [1895?]. 1 l., 21 pp. (pp. 181-201), 27 cm. (Joh. Seb. Bach Kirchenkantaten, No. 170.)　　　　P.N.: J.S.B.I.170

CANTATA NO. 171. Gott, wie dein Name, so ist auch dein Ruhm (S. 171): Vocal-piano scores

1303. God, as Thy Name Is. ... [Philadelphia] Association of American Choruses [1946?]. 1 l., 24 pp., 1 l., 26 cm. (Choral Series, No. 70.) Photo-offset lithograph process. Translation by Henry S. Drinker.

1304. Kantate am Feste der Beschneidung Christi. ... Leipzig, Breitkopf & Härtel [1895?]. 1 l., 24 pp., 27 cm. (Joh. Seb. Bach Kirchenkantaten, No. 171.) P.N.: J.S.B.I.171.

1305. Kantate: Gott, wie dein Name, so ist auch dein Ruhm. ... Leipzig, C. F. Peters [1912]. 32 pp., 27 cm. (Edition Peters, No. 3358.)
Edited by Herman Roth. P.N.: 9708

CANTATA NO. 172. Erschallet, ihr Lieder (S. 172)

1306. Kantata am ersten Pfingstfesttage. ... Leipzig, Breitkopf & Härtel [1895?]. 1 l., 22 pp., 27 cm. (Joh. Seb. Bach Kirchenkantaten, No. 172.) P.N.: J.S.B.I.172.

1307. Kantate: Erschallet, ihr Lieder. ... Leipzig, C. F. Peters [1911]. 26 pp., 27 cm. (Edition Peters, No. 3352.)
Edited by Herman Roth. P.N.: 9584

1308. Ye Voices, Resounding. ... [Philadelphia] Association of American Choruses [1946?]. 1 l., 22 pp., 26 cm. (Choral Series, No. 71.)
Photo-offset lithograph process. Translation by Henry S. Drinker.

CANTATA NO. 173. Erhöhtes Fleisch und Blut (S. 173): Vocal-piano scores

1309. Exalted Flesh and Blood. ... [Philadelphia] Association of American Choruses [1946?]. 1 l., 22 pp., 26 cm. (Choral Series, No. 72.)
Photo-offset lithograph process. Translation by Henry S. Drinker.

1310. Kantate am zweiten Pfingstfesttage. ... Leipzig, Breitkopf & Härtel [1895?]. 22 pp. (pp. 47-68), 27 cm. P.N.: J.S.B.I.173.

CANTATA NO. 174. Ich liebe den Höchsten von ganzem Gemüte (S. 174): Vocal-piano score

1311. Kantate am zweiten Pfingstfesttage. ... Leipzig, Breitkopf & Härtel, 1895. 1 l., 26 pp. (pp. 69-94), 27 cm. (Joh. Seb. Bach Kirchenkantaten, No. 174.) P.N.: J.S.B.I.174.

CANTATA NO. 175. Er rufet seinen Schafen mit Namen (S. 175): Vocal-piano score

1312. Kantate am dritten Pfingstfesttage. ... Leipzig, Breitkopf & Härtel [1896?]. 1 l., 18 pp., 27 cm. (Joh. Seb. Bach Kirchenkantaten, No. 175.) P.N.: J.S.B.I.175.

CANTATA NO. 176. Es ist ein trotzig und verzagt Ding (S. 176): Full score

1313. Es ist ein trotzig und verzagt Ding...Nach der Ausgabe der Bach-Gesellschaft mit einführung versehen von Arnold Schering. Leipzig, Eulenburg [1934?]. 3 ll., 26 pp., 2 ll., 19 cm. (Eulenburgs kleine Partitur-Ausgabe, No. 1032.)   P.N.: E.E. 4832

CANTATA NO. 176: Vocal-piano scores

1314. The Heart Is Wicked and Deceitful. ... [Philadelphia] Association of American Choruses [1947?]. 1 l., 18 pp., 26 cm. (Choral Series, No. 73.)
    Photo-offset lithograph process. Translation by Henry S. Drinker.

1315. Kantate am Trinitatisfeste. ... Leipzig, Breitkopf & Härtel [1896?]. 1 l., 18 pp. (pp. 113-30), 27 cm. (Joh. Seb. Bach Kirchenkantaten, No. 176.)   P.N.: J.S.B.I.176.

CANTATA NO. 177. Ich ruf' zu dir, Herr Jesu Christ (S. 177): Vocalpiano scores

1316. Cantate am vierten Sonntage nach Trinitatis. ... Leipzig, Breitkopf & Härtel [1896?]. 34 pp. (pp. 131-64), 27 cm.
          P.N.: J.S.B.I.177.

1317. I Cry to Thee. ... [Philadelphia] Association of American Choruses, n.d. 1 l., 34 pp., 26 cm. (Choral Series, No. 74.)
    Photo-offset lithograph process. Translation by Henry S. Drinker.

CANTATA NO. 178. Wo Gott, der Herr, nicht bei uns hält (S. 178): Vocal-piano scores

1318. Kantate am achten Sonntage nach Trinitatis. ... Leipzig, Breitkopf & Härtel [1896?]. 1 l., 34 pp., 27 cm. (Joh. Seb. Bach Kirchenkantaten, No. 178.)   P.N.: J.S.B.I.178.

1319. Were God the Lord Not on Our Side. ... [Philadelphia] Association of American Choruses [1948?]. 1 l., 34 pp., 26 cm. (Choral Series, No. 153.)
    Photo-offset lithograph process. Translation by Henry S. Drinker.

CANTATA NO. 179. Siehe zu, dass deine Gottesfurcht nicht Heuchelei sei (S. 179): Vocal-piano scores

1320. Kantate am elften Sonntage nach Trinitatis. ... Leipzig, Breitkopf & Härtel [1896?]. 1 l., 20 pp., 27 cm. (Joh. Seb. Bach Kirchenkantaten, No. 179.)   P.N.: J.S.B.I.179.

1321. Trust the Lord. ... [Philadelphia] Association of American Choruses [1947]. 1 l., 20 pp., 1 l., 26 cm. (Choral Series, No. 75.)
    Photo-offset lithograph process. Translation by Henry S. Drinker.

CANTATA NO. 180. Schmücke dich, o liebe Seele (S. 180): Vocalpiano scores

1322. Beautify Thyself, My Spirit...Schmücke dich, O liebe Seele...

edited and accompaniment arranged by Ifor Jones...English version
by J. M. Stein and Ifor Jones. New York, G. Schirmer [c 1942].
44 pp., 26 cm.   P.N. 39747
1323. Deck Thyself, My Soul, with Gladness. ... [Philadelphia]
Association of American Choruses [1947?]. 1 l., 28 pp., 1 l., 26 cm.
(Choral Series, No. 116.)
    Photo-offset lithograph process. Translation by Henry S. Drinker.
1324. Kantate am zwanzigsten Sonntage nach Trinitatis. ... Leipzig,
Breitkopf & Härtel [1896?]. 28 pp. (pp. 219-46), 27 cm.
                                              P.N.: J.S.B.I.180.
1325. Kantate Schmücke dich, o liebe Seele...Klavierauszug mit Text
von Herman Roth. Leipzig, C. F. Peters [1911]. 34 pp., 27 cm.
(Edition Peters, No. 3353.)   P.N.: 9585
1326. Rise, O Soul, This Happy Morning...Edited by John E. West,
English version by A. H. Fox Strangways. London, Novello; New
York, H. W. Gray [1925?]. 2 ll., 38 pp., 1 l. (Novello's Original
Octavo Edition.)   P.N.: 15161
1327. "Soul, Array Thyself with Gladness"...Vocal score by B. Todt,
English version by Muriel Davenport. Leipzig, Breitkopf & Härtel,
c 1905. 1 l., 28 pp., 27 cm. (Joh. Seb. Bach Vocal Scores, Cantatas,
No. 180.)   P.N.: 25142.

CANTATA NO. 180: Vocal score

1328. Cantata 180. ... [Philadelphia] University of Pennsylvania
[1940?]. 16 pp., 26 cm. (Choral Series, No. 98.)
    Edited by Henry S. Drinker.

CANTATA NO. 180: Excerpts

1329. Deck Thyself, My Soul, with Gladness, Schmücke dich, O liebe
Seele. Two choruses for mixed voices from Cantata No. 180...
English version by Catherine Winkworth...modified by Miriam
Chase, edited by H. Clough-Leighter. Boston, E. C. Schirmer
[1931]. 21, [3] pp., 27 cm. (E. C. Schirmer's Sacred Music, No.
1197.)   P.N.: E.C.S. N°. 606
    Second chorus: Jesus, Bread of Life; Jesu, wahres Brot des Lebens.

CANTATA NO. 181. Leichtgesinnte Flattergeister (S. 181): Vocal-piano
scores

1330. Kantate am Sonntage Sexagesimae. ... Leipzig, Breitkopf &
Härtel [1896?]. 1 l., 20 pp., 27 cm. (Joh. Seb. Bach Kirchenkantaten,
No. 181.)   P.N.: J.S.B.I.181.
1331. Scatterbrained and Shallow People. ... [Philadelphia] Associa-
tion of American Choruses [1947?]. 1 l., 20 pp., 1 l., 26 cm. (Choral
Series, No. 76.)
    Photo-offset lithograph process. Translation by Henry S. Drinker.

134   PUBLISHED MUSIC OF J. S. BACH

CANTATA NO. 182. Himmelskönig, sei willkommen (S. 182): Full score

1332. Himmelskönig, sei willkommen...nach der Ausgabe der Bach-
Gesellschaft und auf Grund des Autographs und der Originalstimmen
revidiert und mit Einführung versehen von Arnold Schering. Leipzig,
Eulenburg [1931?]. ix, 44 pp., 3 ll., 19 cm. (Eulenburgs kleine
Partitur-Ausgabe, No. 1024.)   P.N.: E.E.4824

CANTATA NO. 182: Vocal-piano scores

1333. "Himmelskönig, sei willkommen"..."Divin Maître, sur nous
règne," traduction française de G. Bret. ... Leipzig, Breitkopf &
Härtel [1896?]. 1 l., 44 pp., 27 cm. (Joh. Seb. Bach Kirchenkantaten,
No. 182.)   P.N.: J.S.B.I.182

1334. "King of Heaven, Be Thou Welcome." Edited, arranged, and
with English text by W. G. Whittaker. [London] Oxford University
Press [c 1928]. 3 ll., 55 pp., 1 l., 25 cm.

1335. King of Heaven, Ever Welcome. ... [Philadelphia] Association
of American Choruses [1947?]. 1 l., 44 pp., 1 l., 26 cm. (Choral
Series, No. 103.)
     Photo-offset lithograph process. Translation by Henry S. Drinker.

CANTATA NO. 182: Vocal score

1336. Cantata 182. ... [Philadelphia] University of Pennsylvania, n.d.
19 pp., 27 cm. (Choral Series, No. 36.)
[Edited by Henry S. Drinker.]

CANTATA NO. 182: Vocal parts

1337. Kirchengesänge von Johann Seb. Bach. I., II. Berlin, Traut-
wein [1843?]. 4 part-books, obl. fol., 18×27 cm., wove paper.
(Klassische Werke alterer und neuerer Kirchenmusik in ausgesetzen
Chorstimmen.)
     Stamp of former owner on wrapper: Koen. Schullehrer Seminar zu
Potsdam.   P.N.: 820

CANTATA NO. 182: Excerpts

1338. King of Heaven, Come in Triumph; Himmelskönig, sei willkommen. Three choruses for mixed voices from Cantata No. 182...
English version by Henry Wilder Foote, edited by H. Clough-
Leighter. Boston, E. C. Schirmer [c 1931]. 39, [1] pp.; 27 cm.
(E. C. Schirmer's Sacred Music, No. 1196.)
     Second chorus: Jesu, By Thy Suffering; Jesu, deine Passion. Third
chorus: With Joy We March Onward to Zion, So lasset uns gehen
in Salem.   P.N.: E.C.S. No. 586.

1339. King of Heaven [Himmelskönig, sei willkommen]. Chorus from
the church cantata No. 182... English translation by Max T. Krone. ...
edited by M.T.K. New York, Witmark, c 1933. 11 pp., 27 cm. (The
Witmark Choral Library, No. 2704.)   P.N.: M.W. & Sons 19308.

CANTATA NO. 183. Sie werden euch in den Bann tun (S. 183): Vocal-piano score

1340. Kantate am Sonntage Exaudi...Zweite Composition. ... Leipzig, Breitkopf & Härtel [1896?]. 12 pp. (pp. 55-66), 27 cm.
P.N.: J.S.B.I.183.

CANTATA NO. 184. Erwünschtes Freudenlicht (S. 184): Vocal-piano scores

1341. Kantate am dritten Pfingstfesttage. ... Leipzig, Breitkopf & Härtel [1896?]. 28 pp. (pp. 67-94), 27 cm.   P.N.: J.S.B.I.184.

1342. O Welcome Joyous Light. ... [Philadelphia] Association of American Choruses [1947?]. 1 l., 28 pp., 1 l., 26 cm. (Choral Series, No. 77.)
Photo-offset lithograph process. Translation by Henry S. Drinker.

CANTATA NO. 185. Barmherziges Herze der ewigen Liebe (S. 185): Vocal-piano score

1343. Kantate am vierten Sonntage nach Trinitatis. ... Leipzig, Breitkopf & Härtel [1896?]. 1 l., 18 pp., 27 cm. (Joh. Seb. Bach Kirchenkantaten, No. 185.)   P.N.: J.S.B.I.185.

CANTATA NO. 186. Ärgre dich, o Seele, nicht (S. 186): Vocal-piano scores

1344. Fret Thee Not, Thou Mortal Soul. ... [Philadelphia] Association of American Choruses [1947?]. 1 l., 41 pp., 26 cm. (Choral Series, No. 76.)
Photo-offset lithograph process. Translation by Henry S. Drinker.

1345. Kantate am siebenten Sonntage nach Trinitatis. ... Leipzig, Breitkopf & Härtel [1896?]. 36 pp. (pp. 113-48), 27 cm.
P.N.: J.S.B.I.186.

CANTATA NO. 187. Es wartet alles auf dich (S. 187): Vocal-piano scores

1346. Kantate am siebenten Sonntage nach Trinitatis. ... Leipzig, Breitkopf & Härtel [1896?]. 32 pp. (pp. 148-80), 27 cm.
P.N.: J.S.B.I.187.

1347. They All Are Waiting on Thee. ... [Philadelphia] Association of American Choruses [1948?]. 1 l., 32 pp., 26 cm. (Choral Series, No. 156.)
Photo-offset lithograph process. Translation by Henry S. Drinker.

CANTATA NO. 187: Vocal score

1348. Cantata 187. ... [Philadelphia] University of Pennsylvania, n.d. 20 pp., 26 cm. (Choral Series, No. 136.)
[Edited by Henry S. Drinker.]

CANTATA NO. 188. Ich habe meine Zuversicht (S. 188): Vocal-piano scores

1349. In God I Place My Faith and Trust; Ich habe meine Zuversicht

1349. *(continued)* ... Edited and accompaniment arranged by Ifor Jones. ...English version by J. M. Stein and Ifor Jones. New York, G. Schimer [c 1941]. 24 pp., 26 cm. P.N.: 39306
1350. Kantate am einundzwanzigsten Sonntage nach Trinitatis. ... Leipzig, Breitkopf & Härtel [1896?]. 18 pp. (pp. 181-98), 27 cm. P.N.: J.S.B.I.188.

CANTATA NO. 189. Meine Seele rühmt und preist (S. 189): Vocal-piano score

1351. Kantate "Meine Seele rühmt und preist". ... Leipzig, Breitkopf & Härtel [1896?]. 1 l., 12 pp., 27 cm. (Joh. Seb. Bach Kirchenkantaten, No. 189.) P.N.: J.S.B.I.189.

CANTATA NO. 190. Singet dem Herrn ein neues Lied (S. 190): Vocal-piano scores

1352. Kantate am Feste der Beschneidung Christi. ... Leipzig, Breitkopf & Härtel [1896?]. 1 l., 29 pp. (pp. 211-39), 27 cm. (Joh. Seb. Bach Kirchenkantaten, No. 190.) P.N.: J.S.B.I.190.
1353. Sing a New Song to God the Lord. ... [Philadelphia] Association of American Choruses [1947?]. 1 l., 29 pp., 26 cm. (Choral Series, No. 79.)
Photo-offset lithograph process. Translation by Henry S. Drinker.
1354. "Sing to the Lord a Glad New Song" (Praise Thy God, O Zion"). Vocal score by B. Todt, English version by F. J. Read. Leipzig, Breitkopf & Härtel, c 1904. 29 pp., 27 cm. (Joh. Seb. Bach's Works, Cantata No. 190.) P.N.: 24159

CANTATA NO. 191. Gloria in excelsis Deo (S. 191): Vocal-piano score

1355. Kantate am Weihnachtsfeste. ... Leipzig, Breitkopf & Härtel [1896?]. 46 pp., 27 cm.   ·   P.N.: J.S.B.I.190.

CANTATA NO. 192. Nun danket alle Gott (S. 192): Vocal-piano scores

1356. Kantate "Nun danket alle Gott". ... Leipzig, Breitkopf & Härtel [1896?]. 28 pp. (pp. 47-74), 27 cm. P.N.: J.S.B.I.192.
1357. Now Thank We All Our God, Nun danket alle Gott...edited by Ifor Jones...English version by J. M. Stein and Ifor Jones. New York, G. Schirmer [c 1940]. 47 pp., 26 cm. P.N.: 39157
1358. Now Thank We All Our God. ... [Philadelphia] Association of American Choruses [1948?]. 1 l., 28 pp., 1 l., 26 cm. (Choral Series, No. 157.)
Photo-offset lithograph process. Translation by Henry S. Drinker.

CANTATA NO. 192: Vocal score

1359. Cantata No. 192. ... [Philadelphia] University of Pennsylvania, n.d. 20 pp., 27 cm. (Choral Series, No. 31.)
[Edited by Henry S. Drinker.]

CANTATAS 137

CANTATA NO. 193. Ihr Tore (Pforten) zu Zion (S. 193): Vocal-piano scores

1360. Kantate "Ihr Pforten zu Zion". ... Leipzig, Breitkopf & Härtel [1896?]. 20 pp. (pp. 75-94), 27 cm.   P.N.: J.S.B.I.193.
1361. Ye Portals of Zion. ... [Philadelphia] Association of American Choruses [1947?]. 1 l., 22 pp., 26 cm. (Choral Series, No. 81.)
Photo-offset lithograph process. Translation by Henry S. Drinker.

CANTATA NO. 194. Höchsterwünschtes Freudenfest (S. 194): Vocal-piano scores

1362. Kantate für das Trinitatisfest. ... Leipzig, Breitkopf & Härtel [1897?]. 48 pp. (pp. 95-142), 27 cm.   P.N.: J.S.B.I.194.
1363. Welcome Joyous Festal Day. ... [Philadelphia] Association of American Choruses [1947?]. 2 ll., 48 pp., 26 cm. (Choral Serics, No. 82.)
Photo-offset lithograph process. Translation by Henry S. Drinker.

CANTATA NO. 195. Dem Gerechten muss das Licht (S. 195): Vocal-piano scores

1364. For the Righteous. ... [Philadelphia] Association of American Choruses [1947?]. 1 l., 40 pp., 1 l., 26 cm. (Choral Series, No. 83.)
Photo-offset lithograph process. Translation by Henry S. Drinker.
1365. "For the Righteous"...Vocal score by B. Todt, English version by the Rev. G. W. Daisley. Leipzig, Breitkopf & Härtel [ca. 1905]. 40 pp., 27 cm. (Joh. Seb. Bach's Works, Cantata No. 195.)   P.N.: 24163
1366. Trauungs Cantate (No. 1). ... Leipzig, C. F. Peters [1877]. 33 pp., 27 cm. (Edition Peters, No. 1662.)
Edited by Gustav Rösler.   P.N.: 5931
1367. Trauungs-Kantate "Dem Gerechten muss das Licht".... Leipzig, Breitkopf & Härtel [1897?]. 1 l., 40 pp., 27 cm. (Joh. Seb. Bach Kirchenkantaten, No. 195.)   P.N.: J.S.B.I.195.

CANTATA NO. 195: Excerpts

1368. The Hundredth Psalm...Arranged by Ivor Atkins and J. Michael Diack. Glasgow, Paterson, Sons & Co., c 1924. 1 l., 32 pp., 27 cm.

CANTATA NO. 196. Der Herr denket an uns (S. 196): Vocal-piano scores

1369. Cantate "Der Herr denket an uns"...Trauungs-Cantate No. 20 ... Leipzig, C. F. Peters [1877]. 23 pp., 27 cm. (Edition Peters, No. 1653.)
Edited by Gustav Rösler.   P.N.: 5922
1370. The Lord Careth For Us, Wedding Cantata. ... [Philadelphia] Association of American Choruses [1947?]. 1 l., 20 pp., 26 cm. (Choral Series, No. 104.)
Photo-offset lithograph process. Translation by Henry S. Drinker.

138   PUBLISHED MUSIC OF J. S. BACH

1371. Trauungs-Kantate "Der Herr denket an uns". ... Leipzig, Breitkopf & Härtel [1897?]. 1 l., 20 pp. (pp. 183-202), 27 cm. (Joh. Seb. Bach Kirchenkantaten, No. 196.) P.N.: J.S.B.I.196.

CANTATA NO. 196: Vocal score

1372. Trauungs-Kantate "Der Herr denket an uns". ... n.p., n.d. 11 pp., 25 cm. Photo-offset lithograph process, with English translation between scores.

CANTATA NO. 197. Gott ist unsre Zuversicht (S. 197): Vocal-piano scores

1373. Put Thy Faith in God the Lord, Wedding Cantata. ... [Philadelphia] Association of American Choruses [1947?]. 1 l., 36 pp., 1 l., 26 cm. (Choral Series, No. 84.) Photo-offset lithograph process. Translation by Henry S. Drinker.
1374. Trauungs-Kantate "Gott ist unsre Zuversicht". ... Leipzig, Breitkopf & Härtel [1897]. 36 pp. (pp. 203-38), 27 cm. (Joh. Seb. Bach Kirchenkantaten, No. 197.) P.N.: J.S.B.I.197.
1375. Trauungs-Kantate "Gott ist uns're Zuversicht"...No. 3 der Trauungs-Kantaten. ... Leipzig, C. F. Peters [1877]. 35 pp., 27 cm. (Edition Peters, No. 1654.)
Edited by Gustav Rösler.   P.N.: 5923

CANTATA NO. 198. Lass, Fürstin, lass noch einen Strahl (S. 198): Vocal-piano scores

1376. Lass, Höchster, lass der Hoffnung Strahl..."Grant, Lord God, Grant That Hope's Bright Ray," Bearbeitet von Phillipp Wolfrum, English translation by A. Kalish, Klavier-Auszug mit Text von Otto Taubmann. Leipzig, Breitkopf & Härtel [c 1903]. 1 l., 68 pp., 27 cm. (Edition Breitkopf, No. 1942.) P.N.: V.A. 1942
1377. Lord, Rebuke Me Not...Edited by E. H. Thorne, English version by J. Michael Diack. London, Novello; New York, H. W. Gray, c 1910. 1 l., 58 pp., 25 cm. (Novello's Original Octavo Edition.) P.N.: 13293
1378. Ode of Mourning...English version by George L. Osgood. Edited by Frank Damrosch. ... New York, G. Schirmer [c. 1900]. 48 pp., 26 cm. P.N.: 15168
1379. The Trauerode. ... [Philadelphia] Association of American Choruses [1947?]. 48 pp., 26 cm. (Choral Series, No. 105.) Photo-offset lithograph process. Translation by Henry S. Drinker.
1380. Trauer-Ode auf das Ableben der Gemahlin August des Starken "Christine Eberhardine"...Ode funèbre pour la mort de la reine Chrétienne Gérardine, traduction française (d'après l'adaptation de W. Rust) de Gustave Bret. Leipzig, Breitkopf & Härtel [ca. 1897]. 50 pp., 27 cm. P.N.: J.S.B.I.198.

1381.   Trauer-Ode aus den Tag aller Seelen. ... Leipzig, C. F. Peters
[ca. 1916]. 47 pp., 27 cm. (Edition Peters, No. 1014.)
  Edited by Gustav Rösler. Two copies.   P.N.: 10014
note: No editions of Cantatas 199 and 200 in Library.

cantata no. 201. Geschwinde, geschwinde, ihr wirbelnde Winde
(Der Streit zwischen Phoebus und Pan) (S. 201): Vocal-piano scores

1382.   Le défi de Phoebus et de Pan...Version française de Victor
Wilder, réduction pour piano et chant par Auguste Chapuis. ... Paris,
J. Hamelle, c 1905. 2 ll., 83 pp., 29 cm.   P.N.: J.3395.H.

1383.   Phoebus and Pan...edited, with pianoforte accompaniment, by
John E. West, the English version by J. Michael Diack. London,
Novello; New York, H. W. Gray [c 1912]. 4 ll., 76 pp., 8 pp., 26 cm.
(Novello's Original Octavo Edition.)   P.N.: 13568

1384.   Der Streit zwischen Phöbus und Pan, Dramma per Musica...im
Klavierauszuge mit Text bearbeitet von Selmar Bagge. Leipzig,
C. F. Peters [ca. 1896]. 52 pp., 27 cm. (Edition Peters, No. 2226.)
                                                      P.N.: 8384

1385.   Der Streit zwischen Phoebus und Pan...Dramma per Musica,
Klavierauszug nach dem Arrangement von Felix Mottl eingerichtet
von Otto Taubmann, English translation by Percy Pinkerton.
Leipzig, Breitkopf & Härtel, c 1903. 1 l., 62 pp., 27 cm. (Edition
Breitkopf, No. 1951.)   P.N.: V.A.1951.

1386.   Der Streit zwischen Phoebus und Pan, Dramma per Musica. ...
Leipzig, Breitkopf & Härtel [1897?]. 1 l., 62 pp., 27 cm. (Johann
Sebastian Bachs Werke...Gesammtausgabe für den praktischen
Gebrauch, I. Kantaten, Nr. 201.)   P.N.: J.S.B.I.201.

cantata no. 202. Weichet nur, betrübte Schatten (S. 202): Vocal-
piano scores

1387.   Kantate "Weichet nur, betrübte Schatten". ... Leipzig,
Breitkopf & Härtel [1897?]. 1 l., 22 pp. (pp. 63-84), 27 cm. (Joh. Seb.
Bachs Kantaten, No. 202.)   P.N.: J.S.B.I.202.

1388.   Vanish Now, Ye Winter Shadows. [Philadelphia] Association
of American Choruses [1945?]. 1 l., 22 pp., 26 cm. (Solo Series,
No. 56.)
  Photo-offset lithograph process. Translation by Henry S. Drinker.

cantata no. 203. Amore traditore (S. 203): Vocal-piano score

1389.   Kantate "Amore traditore" [Cupido Veräther]. ... Leipzig, Breitkopf & Härtel [1897?]. 19 pp. (pp. 85-102), 27 cm. P.N.: J.S.B.I.203.

cantata no. 204. Ich bin in mir vergnügt (S. 204): Vocal-piano score

1390.   Von der Vergnügsamkeit "Ich bin in mir vergnügt". ... Leipzig,
Breitkopf & Härtel [1898?]. 42 pp. (pp. 103-44), 27 cm.
                                                      P.N.: J.S.B.I.204.

CANTATA NO. 205. Zerreisset, zersprenget, zertrümmert die Gruft (Der zufriendengestellte Aeolus) (S. 205): Full score

1391. Der zufriedengestellte Aeolus...nach dem Autograph revidiert und mit Einführung versehen von Arnold Schering. Leipzig, Vienna, Eulenburg [1924?]. 1 l.; vii, 112 pp.; 2 ll.; 19 cm. (Eulenburgs kleine Partitur-Ausgabe, No. 967.)   P.N.: E.E.4425

CANTATA NO. 205: Vocal-piano score

1392. Der zufriedengestellte Aeolus..."Zerreisset, zersprenget, zertrümmert die Gruft"...Eole apaisé..."Qu'éclate la rage de notre courroux"...traduction française de G. Bret. Leipzig, Breitkopf & Härtel [1898?]. 1 l., 68 pp., 27 cm. (Joh. Seb. Bach weltliche Kantaten, No. 205.)   P.N.: J.S.B.I.205.

CANTATA NO. 206. Schleicht, spielende Wellen (S. 206): Vocal-piano score

1393. Drama auf das Geburtsfest Augusts III Königs von Polen, Churfürsten von Sachsen etc., "Schleicht, spielende Wellen". ... Leipzig, Breitkopf & Härtel [1898?]. 48 pp. (pp. 207-54), 27 cm.
          P.N.: J.S.B.I.206.

CANTATA NO. 206: Excerpts

1394. Cantata: Flow, Sparkling Blue Waters; "Schleicht, spielende Wellen," opening chorus...English version by Martha Martin, edited by W. H. Humiston. Boston, E. C. Schirmer, c 1922. 19 pp., 27 cm.   P.N.: A.B.P.S. No. 5-19

CANTATA NO. 207. Auf, schmetternde Töne der muntern Trompeten (S. 207a): Vocal-piano scores

1395. "Auf, schmetternde Töne der muntern Trompeten," Dramma per Musica zum Namenstage des Königs Augusts, Churfürsten von Sachsen. ... Leipzig, Breitkopf & Härtel [1898?]. 46 pp. (pp. 255-300), 27 cm.   P.N.: J.S.B.I.207.

1396. Ring Out, All Ye Trumpets. ... [Philadelphia] Association of American Choruses [1949?]. 40 pp., 26 cm. (Choral Series, No. 172.)
          Photo-offset lithograph process. Translation by Henry S. Drinker.

CANTATA NO. 207: Vocal score

1397. Cantata No. 207..."Ring Out All Ye Trumpets". ... [Philadelphia] University of Pennsylvania [1939?]. 20 pp., 27 cm. (Choral Series, No. 64.)
          Edited by Henry S. Drinker.

CANTATA NO. 207: Excerpts

1398. First chorus from "Auf, schmetternde Töne" ["Rejoice and Give Welcome"]. ... Leipzig, Breitkopf & Härtel [ca. 1910]. 11 pp., 27 cm.   P.N.: 26514

1399. March from "Dramma per Musica"...Arranged [for organ] by
Harvey Grace. [London] Oxford University Press [c 1928]. 1 l.,
4 pp., 32 cm. (Ten Instrumental Movements from the Cantatas,
No. 6.)

CANTATA NO. 208. Was mir behagt, ist nur die muntre Jagd (S. 208):
Vocal-piano scores

1400. Birthday Cantata (The Chase) composed for the birthday of
Herzog Christian zu Sachsen Weissenfels...English version by
J. Michael Diack. Leipzig, Breitkopf & Härtel, c 1910. 53 pp.,
27 cm.   P.N.: 26493
1401. Kantate zum Geburtstage des Herzogs Christian zu Sachsen-
Weissenfels "Was mir behagt, ist nur die muntre Jagd". ... Leipzig,
Breitkopf & Härtel [1898?]. 1 l., 46 pp., 27 cm. (Joh. Seb. Bach
weltlichen Kantaten, No. 208.)   P.N.: J.S.B.I.208.

CANTATA NO. 208: Excerpts

1402. Sheep May Safely Graze. For chorus of women's voices, three
part...choral arrangement by Katherine K. Davis, English words by
K.K.D., sacred words by C. R. W. Robertson. New York, Galaxy,
c 1942. 8 pp., 27 cm.   P.N.: G.M.1279-7
1403. Trio from the secular cantata "Was mir behagt" ("'Tis My
Pleasure") ... arranged [for organ] by Harvey Grace. ... [London]
Oxford University Press [c 1928]. 1 l., 4 pp., 32 cm. (Ten Instrumental Movements from the Cantatas, Nos. 3 and 4.)
Second excerpt: Sinfonia (Trio) to "Nach dir, Herr, verlanget
mich."

CANTATA NO. 209. Non sa che sia dolore (S. 209): Vocal-piano score

1404. "Non sa che sia dolore" [Was Schmerz sei und was Leiden]. ...
Leipzig, Breitkopf & Härtel [1898?]. 1 l., 22 pp., 27 cm. (Joh. Seb.
Bach weltliche Kantaten, No. 209.)   P.N.: J.S.B.I.209.

CANTATA NO. 210. O holder Tag, erwünschte Zeit (S. 210): Vocal-
piano score

1405. "O holder Tag, erwünschte Zeit"..."O Jour heureux, ô temps
béni"...traduction française par G. Bret. ... Leipzig, Breitkopf &
Härtel, 1898. 40 pp. (pp. 69-108), 27 cm.   P.N.: J.S.B.I.210.

CANTATA NO. 211. Schweigt stille, plaudert nicht (Kaffee-Kantate)
(S. 211): Full scores

1406. "Be Silent, Silent All"...The English translation is published
by Weekes & Co., London, by whose kind permission that translation
is used in this edition. Vienna, Wiener Philharmonischer Verlag,
A.G., 1924. 4 ll., 52 pp., frontis., 19 cm. (Philharmonia Partituren,
No. 103.)
Edited by Wilhelm Fischer.   P.N.: W.Ph.V.103.

1407. J. S. Bach | Kaffeekantate Faksimile Reproduction...Original:
Preussische Staatsbibliothek Berlin. Vienna, Philharmonischer Verlag,
A.G., 1923. [23] pp., 1 l., 38 cm. (Philharmonia-Facsimiledrucke,
No. 1.)
     This is numbered copy 300.
1408. Komische Cantaten No. I, Schlendrian mit seiner Tochter
Liessgen...Herausgegeben von S. W. Dehn, Interdum et Socrates
equitabat arundine longa. Berlin, bei Gustav Crantz; Vienna, bei
T. Haslinger; Leipzig, bei Fr. Hofmeister [1837]. 31 pp., 34 cm.,
wove paper.   P.N.: 29
1409. Schweigt stille, plaudert nicht...Nach dem Autograph revidiert
und mit Einführung versehen von Arnold Schering. Leipzig, Vienna,
Eulenburg [1925?]. 3 ll., 42 pp., 2 ll., 19 cm. (Eulenburgs kleine
Partitur-Ausgabe, No. 971.)   P.N.: E.E.4528

CANTATA NO. 211: Vocal-piano scores
1410. Bach's Comic Cantatas. Edited by Samuel Reay. ... London,
Weekes [1882?]. 4 ll., 38 pp., 2 ll., 50 pp., 28 cm.
     Contents: Cantata 211 (Coffee Cantata) and Cantata 212 (Peasant's
Cantata).   P.N.: W 1671 [and] W 1666
1411. Coffee and Cupid...Edited by Charles Sanford Terry. London,
Stainer & Bell [1924?]. 50 pp., 1 l., 26 cm.   P.N.: S. & B. 2850
1412. The Coffee Cantata. ... [Philadelphia] Association of American
Choruses [1947?]. 39 pp., 26 cm. (Choral Series, No. 118.)
     Photo-offset lithograph process. Translation by Henry S. Drinker.
1413. The Coffee Cantata. Arranged for soli and chorus by J. Michael
Diack and Harry Edgar Baker. ... Glasgow, Paterson, Sons & Co.,
c 1924. 2 ll., 51 pp., 27 cm.
     Also included, as Numbers 1-3: Chorus and No. 10 (recitative) from
Cantata 207a and final chorus from Cantata 205. Two copies.
1414. "Schweigt stille, plaudert nicht"..."Silence, Ecoutez"...
Traduction française de G. Bret et Albert Schweitzer. ... Leipzig,
Breitkopf & Härtel [1898?]. 1 l., 36 pp. (pp. 109-44), 27 cm. (Joh.
Seb. Bach weltliche Kantaten, No. 211.)   P.N.: J.S.B.I.211.

CANTATA NO. 211: Vocal score
1415. The Coffee Cantata. ... [Philadelphia] University of Pennsylvania [1939?]. 19 pp., 27 cm. (Choral Series, No. 50.)
     Edited by Henry S. Drinker.

CANTATA NO. 212. Mer hahn en neue Oberkeet (S. 212): Full scores
1416. Komische Cantaten, No. II für 1 Waldhorn, 1 Flöte trav.
2 Violinen, Bratsche, Discant, Bass und Fundament herausgegeben
von S. W. Dehn. Berlin, bei Gustav Crantz; St. Petersburg, bei
M. Bernard; London, bei G. André [1837]. 31 pp., 34 cm., wove
paper.   P.N.: G.C. 138.

1417.   Mer hahn en neue Oberkeet...Neue Instrumentation von Felix Mottl. ... Leipzig, Eulenburg [1926?]. 1 l., 54 pp., 2 ll., 19 cm. (Eulenburgs kleine Partitur-Ausgabe, No. 1006.)   P.N.: E.E.3513

CANTATA NO. 212: Vocal-piano scores

1418.   "Mer hahn en neue Oberkeet". ... Leipzig, Breitkopf & Härtel [1898?]. 38 pp. (pp. 145-82), 27 cm.   P.N.: J.S.B.I.212.

1419.   The Peasant Cantata, English version by J. Michael Diack. Arranged for soli and chorus by Harry Edgar Baker. ... London and Edinburgh, Paterson's Publications, c 1923. 44 pp., 28 cm.
P.N.: P.C.

1420.   The Peasant Cantata, English version by J. Michael Diack. Arranged for soli and chorus by Harry Edgar Baker. ... Glasgow and London, Paterson's Publications, c 1923. 59 pp., 19 cm. Different arrangement from edition with same title, date, and P.N.
P.N.: P.C.

1421.   The Peasants' Cantata. ... [Philadelphia] Association of American Choruses [1947?]. 1 l., 38 pp., 26 cm. (Choral Series, No. 119.)
Photo-offset lithograph process. Translation by Henry S. Drinker.

1422.   "We Have a Fine New Master Here"...vocal score by B. Todt, English translation by Lucy E. Broadwood. Leipzig, Breitkopf & Härtel, c 1905. 1 l., 38 pp., 27 cm. (Joh. Seb. Bach Cantatas, No. 212.)   P.N.: 25262

CANTATA NO. 212: Vocal scores

1423.   The Peasant's Cantata. ... [Philadelphia] University of Pennsylvania, n.d. 20 pp., 27 cm. [Edited by Henry S. Drinker.]

1424.   The Peasants' Cantata. ... [Philadelphia] Association of American Choruses [1943?]. 20 pp., 26 cm. (Choral Series, No. 2.) Edited by Henry S. Drinker.

CANTATA NO. 213. Lasst uns sorgen, lasst uns wachen (Hercules auf dem Scheidewege) (S. 213): Vocal-piano scores

1425.   Dramma per musica, Die Wahl des Herkules..."Lasst uns sorgen, lasst uns wachen"..."Environnons de tendresse l'enfant béni"...traduction française par G. Bret. ... Leipzig, Breitkopf & Härtel [1898?]. 57 pp., 27 cm.   P.N.: J.S.B.I.213.

NOTE: No editions of Cantatas 214 and 215 in Library.

CANTATA NO. 216. Vergnügte Pleissen-Stadt (S. 216): Full score

1426.   Vergnügte Pleissen-Stadt...Als Fragment aufgefunden und herausgegeben von Werner Wolffheim, Vollendet und für zwei Flöten, Oboe, Violoncello und Klavier gesetzt von Georg Schumann, English translation by C. Sanford Terry. ... Berlin-Lichterfelde,

1426. *(continued)* Schlesingersche Buch- und Musikhandlung, Rob. Lienau; Vienna, Carl Haslinger [c 1924]. Score: 3 ll., 33 pp.; Oboe: 3 pp.; 1st & 2nd flute: 7 pp.; Violoncello: 4 pp.; 31 cm.   P.N.: S. 10346
NOTE: No. editions of Cantatas 217-24 in Library.

CAPRICCIO (B FLAT) SOPRA LA LONTANANZA DEL SUO FRATELLO DILETTISSIMO (S. 992)

1427.   Capriccio on the Departure of His Beloved Brother, Johann Jacob Bach (1704)...With facsimile and introduction by Stainton de B. Taylor. London, Peters Edition & Hinrichsen Edition, 195? 2 ll., 7 pp., 31 cm. (Edition Peters, No. 208c.)   P.N.: 8242
1428.   Capriccio sur le départ de son frère bien-aimé...Nouvelle edition revue par I. Philipp. Paris, Durand [ca. 1900]. 8 pp., 32 cm. (Édition classique A. Durand & Fils, No. 11106.)
                                                        P.N.: D. & F.11,106
1429.   Heinrich Germer's akademische Ausgabe klassischer Pianoforte-Werken für den Unterricht...J. S. Bach, Capriccio "Die Abreise"... Leipzig, Hug [c 1903]. 9, [1] pp., 34 cm.   P.N.: G. 92
1430.   Capriccio in B-dur sopra la lontananza del suo fratello diletissimo, nebst einer sonate aus Johann Kuhnaus, Musikalische Verstellung einiger biblischer Historien als Zugabe, Eingeleitet und herausgegeben von Herman Roth. Munich, Drei Masken Verlag, 1920. xix, 31 pp.; 4 ll.; frontis.; 19 cm.
1431.   Oeuvres originales J. S. Bach, Capriccio sur le départ de son frère bien-aimé. Paris, Maurice Senart [ca. 1910]. 7 pp., 35 cm. (Nouvelle édition française de musique classique, No. 28.) Series published under the general editorship of Vincent D'Indy. Revision by Blanche Selva.   P.N.: 28

CHORALES (S. 253-438)

Collections

1432.   Anniversary Collection of Bach Chorales...Compiled and edited by Walter E. Buszin. Chicago, Hall & McCreary, c 1935. Nos. 1-3 (no pagination), 23 cm. (H. & M. Auditorium Series,No. 5.)
1433.   The Bach Chorale Book, A Collection of Hymns Set Exclusively to Chorales...Selected and edited by the Rev. J. Herbert Barlow. New York, H. W. Gray; sole agents for Novello, London; 1922. ix, 132 pp., 22 cm.
1434.   Der Bach-Choralist, Vierstimmige Choralgesänge von Joh. Seb. Bach nach ihrer Gottesdienstlichen Verwendbarkeit auf Grund der Evangelien ausgewählt, geordnet und den evangelischen Kirchenchören dargeboten von Fritz Lubrich. Leipzig, Karl Klinner [1909]. 3 ll.; iv, 28 pp.; 19 cm.   P.N.: C.K.2038

1435. Bach's Extended Chorales, with English and Welsh translations. Arranged and edited by W. G. Whittaker. London, Oxford University Press, c 1927-29. 20 parts in 1, each paginated separately. 25 cm.

1436. 100 Chorals, version française par Augustin Mahot avec une préface de Vincent D'Indy. ... Leipzig, Breitkopf & Härtel [ca. 1915]. 4 pts. in 1. 27 cm. (Edition Breitkopf, Nos. 2121-2124.)
P.N.'s: V.A. 2121 – V.A. 2124

1437. Chorales Harmonized by Johann Sebastian Bach. Collected and arranged in melodic order by H. Elliot Button. ... London, Novello; New York, H. W. Gray [ca. 1920]. xv, 181 pp.; 28 cm.   P.N.: 14968

1438. Chorales... selected and edited by Charles N. Boyd and Albert Riemenschneider; Book I: Chorales 1-91, Book II: Chorales 92-120. ... New York, G. Schirmer [c 1939] c 1941. 2 vols. 31 cm.
P.N.: Bk. I: 37623, Bk. II: 39259
Book I has chorales in open score with figured bass; Book II has full score with continuo with figured bass. Vocal score and parts for Book II published separately, plate numbers 39260 [and] 39261. Parts: 2 flutes, 3 oboes, 2 clarinets, 2 cornets, 3 trumpets, 3 trombones, timpani, piano and strings. Vocal score copyright 1941.

1439. 371 vierstimmige Choralgesänge von Johann Sebastian Bach. Dritte Auflage. Leipzig, Breitkopf & Härtel [1832]. 3 ll., 5-211 pp., 20 cm., wove paper.
Vorwort signed by C. F. Becker and dated 9 December, 1831. Becker calls this the third edition, counting the two editions published by C. P. E. Bach as first and second.   P.N.: 5089

1440. 371 vierstimmige Choralgesänge von Johann Sebastian Bach. Vierte Auflage. Leipzig, Breitkopf & Härtel [ca. 1875]. 3 ll., 178 pp., obl. 8°, 18 × 27 cm.
This is Dörffel's revision of Becker's original edition.   P.N.: V.A. 10

1441. 371 vierstimmige Choralgesänge. Leipzig, Breitkopf & Härtel [ca. 1915]. 3 ll., 178 pp., obl. 8°, 19 × 27 cm. (Edition Breitkopf, No. 10.)
This is the 4th edition, with new plates, but the same plate number.
P.N.: V.A. 10

1442. Eight Chorales (Bach Memorial Collection)... Selected and edited by Walter E. Buszin. St. Louis, Concordia, c 1950. 10 pp., 27 cm. (Anthology of Sacred Music, No. BA 26.)
P.N.: BA 26 – Eight Chorales

1443. Eight Chorales with Original Melodies. ... [Philadelphia] University of Pennsylvania, n.d. 11 pp., 26 cm. (Choral Series, No. 101.)

1444. Eleven Easter Chorales. ... [Philadelphia] University of Pennsylvania [1939?]. 12 pp., 28 cm. (Choral Series, No. 37.)
Edited by Henry S. Drinker.

146   PUBLISHED MUSIC OF J. S. BACH

1445.   Eleven Unison Chorales for Soprano and Alto from the Cantatas of J. S. Bach. ... [Philadelphia, University of Pennsylvania] n.d. 11 pp., 27 cm.
1446.   Four Chorals as Arranged by Johann Sebastian Bach: 1. Blessed Jesu, at Thy Word; 2. In Death's Strong Grasp the Savior Lay; 3. O Man, Thy Grievous Loss Bemoan; 4. In Thee is Gladness. Cleveland, Greater Cleveland Lutheran Chorus, n.d. 3 pp., 27 cm.
1447.   The Four-Part Chorals of J. S. Bach, with the German text of the hymns and English translations. Edited, with an historical introduction, notes, and critical appendices, by Charles Sanford Terry. London, Oxford University Press, 1929. 3 ll., xii, 539 pp., frontis., illus. (facs).
1448.   Hark, a Voice Saith, All Are Mortal; Out of the Depths I Cry to Thee; Be Thou Content. As arranged by Johann Sebastian Bach. Cleveland, Bach Chorus of Cleveland, n.d. 3 pp., 27 cm. Translation by Catherine Winkworth.
1449.   Joh. Seb. Bach ausgewählte Choräle herausgegeben von Siegfried Ochs. Heft 1. Berlin, Ed. Bote & G. Bock, c 1928. 15 pp., 29 cm.   P.N.: B. & B. 19881
1450.   Joh. Seb. Bach's vierstimmige Kirchengesänge. Geordnet und mit einem Vorwort begleitet von C. F. Becker... Mit Johann Sebastian Bach's Portrait. Leipzig, Verlag von Robert Friese, 1843. x, 279 pp.; frontis. (engraved by Kluge), 24 cm., wove paper, printed music. Signature on front pastedown: Julius Klengel.
1451.   Joh. Seb. Bach's vierstimmige Kirchengesänge herausgegeben von Woldemar Bargiel. Heft I [to Heft VIII]. Berlin, Ed. Bote & G. Bock [1891-93]. 8 pts. in 2 vols. 27 cm., printed music.   P.N.: 13591-13598
1452.   Joh. Seb. Bach's vierstimmige Kirchengesänge [Heft I] herausgegeben von Woldemar Bargiel. ... Berlin, Ed. Bote & G. Bock [1891?]. 1 l., 38 pp., 2 ll.
      Text and plates entirely recast, although pagination and plate numbers are the same as in the eight-volume edition. P.N.: 13591
1453.   Johann Sebastian Bach Mehrstimmige Choräle zum ersten Mal mit den zugehörigen Texten und den Quellen-Nachweisen herausgegeben von Ludwig Erk. Völlig neu durchgesehene und berichtigte Ausgabe, besorgt von Friedrich Smend. Leipzig, C. F. Peters [1932]. 2 vols. Obl. fol., 23 × 30 cm. (Edition Peters, No. 4264a, b.)
                                              P.N.'s: 10993, 10994
1454.   Johann Sebastian Bach's Choralgesänge und geistliche Arien. Zum ersten Mal unverändert nach authentischen Quellen mit ihren ursprünglichen Texten und mit den nöthigen kunsthistorischen Nachweisungen herausgegeben von Ludwig Erk. Neue Ausgabe. Leipzig, C. F. Peters [ca. 1895]. 2 vols. in 1. Obl. fol., 23 × 31 cm.
      Reprint of Erk's first edition, including the prefaces, dated 1850 and 1865.   P.N.: 8420, 8421

1455. Johann Sebastian Bach's mehrstimmige Choralgesänge und geistliche Arien. Zum erstenmal unverändert nach authentischen Quellen mit ihren ursprunglichen Texten und mit den nöthigen kunsthistorischen Nachweisungen herausgegeben von Ludwig Erk. ... Leipzig, im Bureau de musique von C. F. Peters [1851, 1866]. 2 vols. in 1. Obl. 8°, 22 × 27 cm., wove paper.

Signature on recto of front flyleaf and title page: A. E. Rouse. Preface to Vol. 1 dated 8 December, 1850; to Vol. 2, 8 October, 1865. P.N.'s: 3339, 4457

1456. Johann Sebastian Bachs vierstimmige Choralgesänge. Erster [Zweyter, Dritter, Vierter] Theil. Leipzig, Johann Gottlob Immanuel Breitkopf, 1784-1787. 4 vols. in 1. 26 cm., laid paper, original pictorial boards, printed music.

Page 152 misnumbered 153. Frequent MS. corrections throughout.

1457. Johann Sebastian Bachs vierstimmige Choralgesänge gesammlet von Carl Philipp Emanuel Bach. Erster [and Zweyter] Theil. Berlin and Leipzig, Friedrich Wilhelm Birnstiel, 1765, 1769. 2 vols. in 1. Obl. fol., 20 × 33 cm., mottled boards, printed music.

Imperfect: most inner margins reinforced or repaired or both; both title pages repaired with new paper (some loss of text of title page of part 2); outer margins of some leaves and many outer corners repaired or reinforced. Stamp and shelf-mark of Prussian State Library on title page of part 1 and stamp also on p. 99; stamp of Akademie für Kirchen- und Schulmusik in Berlin on title page of part 1. Signature of [Ludwig Christian] Erk on title page of part 1.

1458. Johann Sebastian Bach's Werke. Für Gesang. Gesammt-ausgabe für den praktischen Gebrauch. VII, Choralgesänge. Leipzig, Breitkopf & Härtel [1898]. viii, 261 pp., 27 cm.

Edited by Bernhard F. Richter.

P.N.'s: J.S.B.VIII (music) E.B. 3765 (prelim. ll.)

1459. Lord, Hear the Voice of My Complaint; Jesus, Thou Who Knewest Death; O Thou, of God the Father; O Darkest Woe. As arranged by Johann Sebastian Bach. Cleveland, Bach Chorus of Cleveland, n.d. [3] pp., 27 cm.

Translation by Catherine Winkworth.

1460. O Thou, of God the Father; O Darkest Woe. Cleveland, The Greater Cleveland Lutheran Chorus, n.d. 1 p., 27 cm.

Translation by Catherine Winkworth.

1461. 60 ausgewählte vierstimmige Choräle. ... Leipzig, Breitkopf & Härtel [ca. 1915]. 2 ll., 34 pp., obl. 8°, 19 × 28 cm. (Edition Breitkopf, No. 3747.)

Foreword by A. Gessner. P.N.: V.A. 3747

1462. A Second Book of Chorals by Johann Sebastian Bach. Selected and provided with suitable English texts by Thomas Whitney Surette.

1462. *(continued)*   Boston, E. C. Schirmer, c 1932. iv, 31 pp., 28 cm.
(Concord Series, No. 615.)   P.N.: E.S.S. N° 751
1463. Sixty Chorales Harmonized by Johann Sebastian Bach (with
English text). Selected and edited by Percy Goetschius. ... Boston,
Oliver Ditson, c 1934. 5 ll., 62 pp., 28 cm.
1464. Ten Bach Chorales, arranged for men's voices (four parts) by
Bryceson Treharne, with the original texts and new English trans-
lations by Willis Wager. New York, G. Schirmer, c 1939. 39 pp.,
27 cm.   P.N.: 38032
1465. Three Chorals as Arranged by Johann Sebastian Bach: 1. The
Blessed Christ is Ris'n Today; 2. Ere Yet the Dawn Hath Filled the
Skies; 3. Today God's Only 'Gotten Son. Cleveland, Greater
Cleveland Lutheran Chorus, n.d. 2 pp., 27 cm.
Translation by Catherine Winkworth.
1466. The 389 Chorales of Johann Sebastian Bach with English texts
by Henry S. Drinker. [Princeton, N.J., Association of American
Choruses, 1944.] xx, 284 pp., 26 cm. (Choral Series, No. 1.)
Melodic index to the 389 chorales on pp. 262-84.
1467. 371 Harmonized Chorales and 69 Chorale Melodies with
Figured Bass...entirely revised, corrected, edited, and annotated by
Albert Riemenschneider. New York, G. Schirmer, c 1941. xvi,
[2], 165 pp.; 30 cm.   P.N.: 39105c (on p. 1 only)
1468. Twelve Embellished Chorales and Two Extended Chorales from
the Cantatas of J. S. Bach. ... [Philadelphia] University of Pennsylvania, n.d. 23 pp., 27 cm. (Choral Series, No. 14.)
[Edited by Henry S. Drinker.]
1469. Twenty-Five Chorales ... selected, edited and provided with
suitable English texts by Berta Elsmith and Thomas Whitney Surette.
Boston, E. C. Schirmer, c 1921. 2 ll., 31 pp., 28 cm. (The Concord
Series.)   P.N.: E.C.S.M. Co. No. 1 (31) (on pp. 1 & 2 only)
1470. Twenty-Five Chorales...Selected, edited, and provided with
suitable English texts by Thomas Whitney Surette and Berta Elsmith.
Boston, The Boston Music Company, c 1919. 2 ll., 31 pp., 27 cm.
(The Concord Music Series.)
Identical with the E. C. Schirmer edition c 1921.
                                                  P.N.: B.M.Co.6176
1471. Twenty-Four English Hymns Adapted to Bach's Chorales.
Edited by J. Michael Diack. Glasgow, Paterson's Publications
[ca. 1920]. 27 pp., 26 cm.
1472. Two Chorales from the "Ode of Mourning": 1. Was mein Gott
will (Have I To Tread the Road of Death), 2 .Jesus, meine Zuversicht
(Up, My Soul): for four-part chorus of mixed voices with organ
accompaniment ad lib. Edited by Frank Damrosch, English version
by George L. Osgood. New York, G. Schirmer, c 1900, c 1927.

5 pp., 27 cm. Polyphonic choruses of the early masters; G.S.8vo Choruses, No. 7572.) P.N.: 35573

1473. 263 Settings of 73 Chorale Melodies. Edited for analysis and comparison by Mary Phillips Webster. Cambridge (Mass.) [Edwards Bros., Ann Arbor, Michigan] 1942. 2 ll.; [1], 104 pp.; 37 cm.
Associate editor: Raymond C. Robinson. Autograph inscription on front flyleaf: This book is one of the first edition | of two hundred copies. | Mary Phillips Webster. | April 4, 1942.

Arrangement

1474. 101 Chorals à 4 parties de J. S. Bach réduits pour l'orgue (ou piano). ... Paris, A. Durand [1933?]. 2 ll., 38 pp., 1 l., 31 cm. (Édition classique A. Durand & Fils, No. 988.) P.N.: D. & F. 988

Single Works

HERZLICH TUT MICH VERLANGEN

1475. The Passion Chorale "Herzlich thut mich verlangen," in the choral works of J. S. Bach. [Philadelphia, University of Pennsylvania] n.d. 27 pp., 27 cm.

KOMM SÜSSER TOD

1476. Come, Sweet Death. For organ...Transcribed by Bryceson Treharne. Boston, The Boston Music Company [c 1937]. 3, [1] pp.; 31 cm. (Organ Series IV.) P.N.: B.M.Co. 9385

NUN KOMM DER HEIDEN HEILAND

1477. The Chorale "Nun komm, der Heiden Heiland," in the choral works of J. S. Bach. ... [Philadelphia] University of Pennsylvania, n.d. 16 pp., 27 cm. (Choral Series, No. 29.)
[Edited by Henry S. Drinker.]

O GOTT, DU FROMMER GOTT

1478. The Chorale "O Gott, du frommer Gott," in the choral works of J. S. Bach. [Philadelphia] University of Pennsylvania, n.d. 24 pp., 27 cm. (Choral Series, No. 34.)
[Edited by Henry S. Drinker.]

O HAUPT, VOLL BLUT UND WUNDEN

1479. O Sacred Head Surrounded, hymn for Lent and Passiontide. Melody by Hasler, varied harmonizations by J. S. Bach. London, Novello; New York, H. W. Gray, 1934. 3 pp., 26 cm. (Novello's Parish Choir Book, No. 1189.)
Issued as "Extra Supplement" to the *Musical Times*, February, 1934.
P.N.: 15902.

SCHMÜCKE DICH, O LIEBE SEELE

1480. Deck Thyself, My Soul, with Gladness (Schmuecke dich, o liebe Seele). Cleveland, The Greater Cleveland Lutheran Chorus, n.d. 1 p., 26 cm.

SOLLT ICH MEINEM GOTT NICHT SINGEN

1481. Shall I Not to God Sing Praises...Edited by Walter E. Buszin. St. Louis, Concordia, c 1945. 6 pp., 26 cm. (Anthologia Lutherana, No. B 2.)   P.N.: Shall I not to God sing Praises, 5

WAS GOTT TUT, DAS IST WOHLGETAN

1482. Choral Works of J. S. Bach Using the Choral Melody "Was Gott thut das ist wohlgethan". ... [Philadelphia] University of Pennsylvania, n.d. 16 pp., 27 cm. (Choral Series, No. 49.) [Edited by Henry S. Drinker.]

WER NUR DEN LIEBEN GOTT LÄSST WALTEN

1483. If Thou But Suffer God to Guide Thee, chorale for mixed voices. Harmonized by John Sebastian Bach, edited by Augustus D. Zanzig, translated by Catherine Winkworth. Boston, Oliver Ditson Company, c 1930. 4 pp., 28 cm. (Vocal Chamber Music for Small Groups and for A Capella Choruses, First Series, No. 14, 403.)
P.N.: 76814-3

WERDE MUNTER, MEIN GEMÜTE

1484. At the Lamb's High Feast We Sing...Melody by Johann Schop, varied harmonizations by J. S. Bach. London, Novello; New York, H. W. Gray, 1934. 3 pp., 26 cm. (Novello's Parish Choir Book, No. 1190.)
Issued as "Extra Supplement" to the *Musical Times*, February, 1934.
P.N.: 15902

WIE SCHÖN LEUCHTET DER MORGENSTERN

1485. The Chorale "Wie schön leuchtet der Morgenstern," in the choral works of J. S. Bach. [Philadelphia] University of Pennsylvania [ca. 1935]. 28 pp., 27 cm. (Choral Series, No. 12.) Edited by Henry S. Drinker.

CHORALE PRELUDES (S. 599-765)

Collections

1486. J. S. Bachs Choral-Vorspiele für die Orgel mit einem und zwey Klavieren und Pedal. Erstes [and Zweytes, Dritter, Vierte] Heft. Leipzig, Breitkopf & Härtel [1802?-05?]. 4 vols. in 1. 31 cm., laid paper.
Edited by Johann Gottfried Schicht. Signature on front flyleaf: Dr. Emil Vogel.

1487. Joh. Seb. Bach, Choralvorspiele in authentischer Folge zusammengestellt auf Grund der Bach-Ausgabe von Griepenkerl und Roitzsch. Band I. Orgelbüchlein; Band II. Sechs Choräle und achtzehn Choräle; Band III. Clavierübung Teil 3. Leipzig, C. F. Peters [ca. 1927]. 3 vols. in 1. Obl. fol., 26 × 33 cm. (Edition Peters, Nos. 3946-48.)   P.N.'s: 10635 [to] 10637

1488. Joh. Seb. Bach, Choralvorspiele in authentischer Folge zusammengestellt auf Grund der Bach-Ausgabe von Griepenkerl und Roitzsch. Band I. Orgelbüchlein; Band II. Sechs Choräle und achtzehn Choräle; Band III. Clavierübung Teil 3. Frankfurt, New York, London, C. F. Peters [c 1951]. 3 vols. Obl. fol., 23 × 31 cm. (Edition Peters, Nos. 3946-48.)
Imperfect: Vol. 1 wanting. This is same as edition in entry above, except for a new title page and indexes.   P.N.'s: 10635 [to] 10637

1489. The Organ Works of John Sebastian Bach, The Chorale Preludes with an Introduction by Ernest Newman. Book XV [to XX], edited by Ivor Atkins. London, Novello; New York, H. W. Gray [1923?-27?]. 6 vols. Obl. fol., 25 × 35 cm.
Two copies.   P.N.'s: 13884-13886, 14324-14325, 14400

Selections

1490. 15 grosse Choral-Vorspiele für die Orgel von Johann Sebastian Bach. Leipzig, Breitkopf & Härtel; London, Coventry & Hollier [1846?]. 48 pp., 1 l., obl. fol., 27 × 34 cm., wove paper.
Same as Books 3 and 4 of Mendelssohn's London edition of Bach's organ compositions on chorales.   P.N.: 7492

1491. 15 grosse Choral-Vorspiele für die Orgel von Johann Sebastian Bach. Leipzig, Breitkopf & Härtel [ca. 1895]. 1 l., 48 pp., obl. fol., 23 × 21 cm.
Lithographed edition of Mendelssohn's original edition. Presentation bookplate from the daughters of the former owner, Charles Edwin Clemens.   P.N.: V.A.1237

1492. Johann Sebastian Bach Memorial Collection. Selected and edited by Walter E. Buszin. ... St. Louis, Concordia, c 1950. 103 pp., 32 cm. (Organ Series, Vol. III.)   P.N.: Buszin, Anthology III

1493. John Sebastian Bach's Organ Compositions on Corales (Psalm Tunes). Edited from the original manuscripts by Felix Mendelssohn Bartholdy. London, Coventry & Hollier; Leipzig, Breithopf [sic] and Härtel [1845]. 5 vols. in 1. Obl. fol., 25 × 35 cm., wove paper.
Signature on title pate of Book I: Charles Steggall.
P.N.: BACH's Organ Music N°.
[numberfilled in only for books 3 & 4]

1494. Neunzehn bis jetzt unbekannte Choralvorspiele von J. S. Bach. Erfurt, Gotthilf Wilhelm Körner [1849?]. 12 pp., obl. 4°, 23 × 27 cm. (Sämmtliche Compositionen für die Orgel, Heft 4.) Edited by Gotthilf Wilhelm Körner.   P.N.: 84

1495. Twelve Chorale Preludes for Organ by Johann Sebastian Bach, selected and edited by Franklin Glynn. New York, G. Schirmer [c 1931]. 1 l., vii, 2-47 pp., obl. fol., 27 × 35 cm.   P.N.: 35361

1496. Zwölf Choräle von Sebastian Bach, umgearbeitet von Vogler, zergleidert von Carl Maria von Weber, Nebst 1 Bogen Text. ... Leipzig, C. F. Peters [1815?]. 1 l.; 4-15 pp. (text); [2], 3-8 pp. (Zergleiderung); obl. fol.; 26 × 37 cm. (text); 26 × 17 cm. (Zergleiderung).   P.N.: 843 (text only)

1497. 2 Chorale Preludes manualiter, Allein Gott in der Höh'—To God on High Above; Aus tiefer Noth—In My Despair I Cry to Thee; arranged for one manual and pedal by Stainton de B. Taylor. London, Hinrichsen Edition, c 1954. 7 pp., 31 cm. (Hinrichsen Edition, No. 376a.)   P.N.: 376

Achtzehn Choräle von verschiedener Art (S. 651-68)

1498. Eighteen Large Chorales for the Organ by Johann Sebastian Bach. Edited by Albert Riemenschneider. Bryn Mawr, Pennsylvania, Oliver Ditson [c 1952]. xi, 2-103 pp., illus. (music facs.), 31 cm.

Clavier-Übung III (S. 552, 669-89)

1499. Dritter Theil der Clavier Übung...vor die Orgel. ... [Leipzig] In Verlegung des Authoris [1739]. 1 l., 77 pp., obl. fol., 20 × 34 cm. Positive and negative photostats of copy now in Library of Congress.

1500. Exercices pour le clavecin par J. S. Bach, Oeuvre III. Vienna, chez Hoffmeister & comp.; Leipzig, au Bureau de musique [ca. 1804?]. 63 pp., obl. fol., 24 × 34 cm., wove paper.   P.N.: 307

1501. Exercices pour le clavecin par J. S. Bach, Oeuv. III, Partie I. Leipzig, au Bureau de musique de C. F. Peters [1817?]. 63 pp., obl. fol., 25 × 33 cm., wove paper.
        Reengraved, although plate number is the same as that of Hoffmeister edition [ca. 1804?]. Formerly the property of Clara Wieck Schumann.   P.N.: 307

Orgel-Büchlein [für Wilhelm Friedemann Bach?] (S. 599-644)

1502. Johann Sebastian Bach Orgelbüchlein und andere kleine Choralvorspiele herausgegeben von Hermann Keller. ... Kassel, Bärenreiter [1928]. 40 unnumbered ll., obl. fol., 24 × 31 cm. (Bärenreiter Ausgabe, No. 145.)

1503. The Liturgical Year (Orgelbüchlein)...Forty-five organ chorals edited by Albert Riemenschneider. Boston, Oliver Ditson [c 1933]. xvi, 138 pp., 31 cm.

Sechs (schübler) Choräle von verschiedener Art (S. 645-650)

1504. Sechs Chorale von verschiedener Art auf einer Orgel mit 2 Clavieren und Pedal vorzuspielen verfertiget von Johann Sebastian Bach. ... Zella, In Verlegung Joh. Georg Schüblers [1747?]. 1 l., 14 pp., obl. 8°.
Photostat of Van Hoboken copy.

1505. Six Organ Chorals (Schübler)...Edited by Albert Riemenschneider. Philadelphia, Oliver Ditson [c 1942]. ix, 97 pp., illus. (facs.), 31 cm.
Two copies.   P.N.: 78332-97

Single Works

1506. Blessed Jesu, We Are Here; Liebster Jesu, wir sind hier, chorale prelude...Edited by Clark B. Angel. New York, G. Schirmer, c 1949. Pp. 3-4 (3 ll.), 31 cm. (Compositions for the Organ with Registration for both Hammond and Pipe Organ.)   P.N.: 41989

1507. J. S. Bach Choralvorspiel: "Aus tiefer Noth schrei ich zu dir," bearbeitet von K. H. David. Regensburg, Gustav Bosse, 1930. 4 pp., 31 cm.
Notenbeilage No. 10 for Zeitschrift für Musik, Vol. 97, No. 10 (1930).

1508. Johann Sebastian Bach, Fantasia super Komm heiliger Geist. Faksimileausgabe mit erläuternden Worten von Peter Wackernagel. Leipzig, [Carl] Merseburger, 1950. 8 unnumbered ll., frontis., 34 cm. (Edition Merseburger, No. 808.)
Facsimile of 3 leaves from MS. p. 271 in the Berlin Bibliothek.

1509. O Father, Almighty God, by Johann Sebastian Bach (?). Edited by Walter E. Buszin. St. Louis, Concordia [ca. 1950]. 4 pp., 32 cm. (Anthology of Sacred Music.)   P.N.: Buszin, Anthology

1510. Three Preludes on 'In dulci jubilo.' Arranged as a suite or chorale-partita for organ solo, preceded by Bach's choral setting of the tune [by Stainton de B. Taylor]. London, Hinrichsen Edition and Peters Edition, c 1953. 10 pp., 1 l., 31 cm. (Edition Peters, No. 356.)
P.N.: Edition Peters, No. 356

CHORALE VARIATIONS

SEI GEGRÜSSET, JESU GÜTIG (S. 768)

1511. John Sebastian Bach's Eleven Variations on the Corale Sey gegrusset Jesu gutig (All Hail Good Jesus). Edited from the original

154   PUBLISHED MUSIC OF J. S. BACH

1511. *(continued)*   manuscript by Felix Mendelssohn Bartholdy. London,
Coventry & Hollier [1846?]. 1 l., 18 pp., obl. fol., 25×35 cm.,
wove paper.   P.N.: Bach's Organ Music. Bk.

VOM HIMMEL HOCH, DA KOMM ICH HER (S. 769)

1512.   Einige canonische Veraenderungen über das Weynacht-Lied:
Vom Himmel hoch da komm ich her, vor die Orgel mit 2. Clavieren
und dem Pedal von Iohann Sebastian Bach Königl. Pohl. und Chur-
Saechss. Hoff Compositeur Capellm. u. Direct. Chor. Mus. Lips.
Nurnberg, Balthasar Schmid [ca. 1747]. [1], 1-6 pp.; 34 cm., laid
paper, ¾ calf.

   MS. inscription on title page: Ex collectione G. Poelchau. MS.
   inscription on verso of leaf 4: Werke. Orgelcompositionen von
   J.-Seb. Bach. Nach den Originalhandschriften herausgegeben von
   Georg Poelchau.   P.N.: XXVIII; on title page it is N. XXVIII
1513.   Sämmtliche Orgel-Werke von Joh. Seb. Bach. No. 2. ... Vienna,
Tobias Haslinger [1832?]. 1 l., 14 pp., 1 l., 32 cm. (Saemmtliche
Werke von J. S. Bach. No. 2.)

   Caption title: Canonische Veränderungen, über das Weihnachts-
   Lied: "Vom Himmel hoch, da komm ich her."   P.H.: T.H.5802

CHROMATISCHE FANTASIE UND FUGE D-MOLL (S. 903)

1514.   Chromatic Fantasia and Fugue, edited by Richard Burmeister.
Boston, Oliver Ditson, c 1925. 23 pp., 31 cm. (Ditson Edition,
No. 370.)   P.N.: 74936-21
1515.   Chromatic Fantasy and Fugue...Edited by John Kirkpatrick.
16 pp., 36 cm.

   This is a photographic reproduction of a MS. study by Mr. Kirkpatrick, sent to Mr. Riemenschneider in September, 1943.
1516.   Chromatische Fantasie für das Pianoforte von Johann Sebastian
Bach. Neue Ausgabe mit einer Bezeichnung ihres wahren Vortrags,
wie derselbe von J. S. Bach auf W. Friedemann Bach, von diesem auf
Forkel und von Forkel aus seine Schüler gekommen. Leipzig, im
Bureau de Musique von C. F. Peters [1819?]. iv, 15 pp., obl. fol.,
25×34 cm.

   Three copies. Copy 2 formerly the property of Clara Wieck
   Schumann, who annotated it extensively. Introduction (pp. i-iv)
   missing.   P.N.: 74, 1512
1517.   Chromatische Fantasie und Fuge. Herausgegeben von Edwin
Fischer. ... Berlin, Ullstein [c 1928]. 24 pp., 31 cm. (Tonmeister
Ausgabe, No. 7.)   P.N.: T.A. Nr. 7.
1518.   Chromatische Fantasie und Fuge...Kritische Ausgabe mit
Anhang von Heinrich Schenker. ... Vienne, Leipzig, Universal-

Edition (Aktiengesellschaft), c 1910. 50 pp., 31 cm. (Universal-Edition, No. 2540.)

Pages 47-50 contain a variant reading of the fantasia.

P.N.: U.E.2540.

1519. Chromatische Phantasie und Fuge...nach eigenem Gebrauch beim Vortrag und Unterricht herausgegeben von Emil von Sauer. Leipzig, C. F. Peters [1930?]. 16 pp., 31 cm. (Edition Peters, No. 3514.) P.N.: 9979

1520. Fantaisie chromatique composée par J. S. Bach. Leipzig, au Bureau de musique, d'A. Kühnel [1806?]. 15 pp., obl. fol., 23 × 32 cm., wove paper, original blue boards. P.N.: 74

1521. Fantaisie chromatique & fugue. Nouvelle édition revue, doigtée et annotée d'après les textes originaux par Adolphe F. Wouters. ... 4ᵐᵉ Édition. Brussels, Éditions Antoine Ysaye & Co. [ca. 1885]. 1 l.; 15, [1] pp.; 35 cm.

At head of title: Répertoire des Conservatoires Royaux de Bruxelles et d'Anvers. Wrapper bears imprint of Schott Frères, who bought out Ysaye & Co. P.N.: J.B.K.2873

1522. Fantaisie chromatique et fuge en Ré mineur...Nouvelle édition soigneusement revue corrigée et doigtée...Oeuvres complets, Liv. V. Offenbach s/M., chez Jean André [1847?]. 15 pp., 1 l., 31 cm.

At head of title: Oeuvres pour le pianoforte composés par J. S. Bach.

P.N.: 6605

1523. Fantaisie chromatique et fugue pour piano. Edition revue et doigtée par H. Dallier. ... Paris, Henry Lemoine, c 1922. 1 l., 16 pp., 1 l., 30 cm. (Edition nationale française Panthéon des pianistes, No. 1223.) P.N.: HL. 21,464. P. 1223

1524. Fantaisie chromatique et fugue pour piano revue par A. Siloti. ... Moscow, Petrograd, Rossiiskoe musykal'nee isdatel'stve, c 1916. 19 pp., 35 cm. P.N.: P.M.N.311

1525. Oeuvres originales J. S. Bach, Fantaisie chromatique et fugue. 1ʳᵉ partie [and 2ᵉ partie]. Paris, Maurice Sénart [ca. 1910]. 2 parts. 35 cm. (Nouvelle édition française de musique classique, Nos. 213-214.)

General editor of series: Vincent D'Indy. Révision par Blanche Selva. P.N.: Pt. I: 213; Pt. II: S. & Cⁱᵉ 214.

CLAVIER WORKS

Collections

1526. Bearbeitungen, Übertragungen, Studien und Kompositionen für das Pianoforte nach Johann Sebastian Bach von Ferruccio Busoni. Vollständige und vervollkommnete Ausgabe. Leipzig, Breitkopf & Härtel [c 1894-c 1920]. 7 vols. Illus., facs. (incl. music), 34 cm. P.N.'s: B.B.I.-B.B.VII

1527. Joh. Seb. Bach Klavierwerke. Neue Ausgabe von Ferruccio
Busoni, Egon Petri und Bruno Mugellini. ... Leipzig, Breitkopf &
Härtel [c 1894-c 1923]. 25 parts in 8 vols. Illus., facs. (incl.
music), 30 cm. (Edition Breitkopf, Nos. 4301-4325.)
P.N.'s: 19274-75, 27451-73;
Introductions: E.B. 4306-E.B.4318;
E.B.4322-E.B.4323; E.B.4325
1528. Joh. Seb. Bach Klavierwerke, Oeuvres pour piano; Piano works
...Nach den Urtexten revidiert von Julius Röntgen. ... Vienna,
Leipzig, Universal-Edition, A.G. [ca. 1902]. 10 vols. in 3. 30 cm.
(Universal Edition, Nos. 323-30, 520, 1547-48.)
P.N.'s: U.E. 323 to U.E. 330; U.E. 520; 1547; 1548
1529. Joh. Seb. Bach Klavier-Werke, Pianoforte compositions,
Oeuvres de piano, Mit Fingersatz und Vortragszeichen versehen von
Carl Reinecke. Band XI. 16 Konzerte nach Konzerten von Benedetto
Marcello, G. Ph. Telemann, A. Vivaldi u.a. ... Leipzig, Breitkopf &
Härtel [ca. 1905]. 71 pp., 33 cm. (Volksausgabe, No. 1922.)
Vol. XI of this edition only. This copy unopened.   P.N.: V.A.1922
1530. Joh. Seb. Bach Klavier-Werke, Pianoforte compositions,
Oeuvres de piano, Mit Fingersatz und Vortragszeichen zum Gebrauch
in Konservatorium der Musik zu Leipzig versehen von Carl Reinecke.
... Leipzig, Breitkopf & Härtel [1877?]. 7 vols. 32 cm. (Volksaus-
gabe, Nos. 2-8.)   P.N.'s: V.A. 2 to V.A. 8
1531. Joh. Seb. Bach Klavier-Werke vollständig neue, für Vortrag,
Studium und Unterricht sorgfältig bezeichnete Bach-Ausgabe von
Max Reger und Aug. Schmid-Lindner. Mainz, Leipzig, Schott
[c 1916, c 1915]. 9 parts in 3 vols. 33 cm. (Ausgabe der Musik-
freunden.)
Vols. 8 and 9 wanting (apparently never published).
P.N.'s: 30255-30259^{1+2}, 30600^{1+2}, 30274
1532. Joh. Seb. Bach's Klavierwerke...Kritische Ausgabe mit Fingersatz und Vortragsbezeichnungen versehen von Dr. Hans Bischoff.
Leipzig, Steingräber [1880-88]. 7 vols. in 6. 33 cm. (Edition Stein-
gräber, Nos. 111-17.)   P.N.'s: 149, 150a & b, 151-153, 232, 327
1533. Johann Sebastian Bach's Klavierwerke mit Fingersatz und
Vortragszeichen zum Gebrauch im Conservatorium der Musik zu
Leipzig versehen von Carl Reinecke. ... Leipzig, Breitkopf & Härtel
[ca. 1870]. 4 parts in 2 vols. 31 cm.   P.N.'s: 12546, 12571-12573
1534. Johann Sebastian Bach's Klavierwerke mit Fingersatz und
Vortragszeichen zum Gebrauch im Conservatorium der Musik zu
Leipzig versehen von Carl Reinecke. Achter Band. ... Leipzig,
Breitkopf & Härtel [1912?]. 119 pp., 31 cm. (Volksausgabe, No.
1484.)
Vol. 8 of Reinecke's edition of the complete keyboard works.
P.N.: V.A.1484

1535. Klavierwerke von Joh. Seb. Bach herausgegeben von Czerny, Griepenkerl und Roitzsch. Leipzig, C. F. Peters [ca. 1906]. 24 parts in 8 vols. Illus., facs., 31 cm.
P.N.'s: 3338 (new), 6383, 6734, 6868, 7916-17, 7942, 8036-40, 8216, 8242, 8274-75, 8402-03, 8462, 8605, 8854-57
1536. Metodo per lo studio del pianoforte di Beniamino Cesi, Composizioni di Gio. Seb. Bach raccolte, ordinate e digitate. ... Milan, Ricordi [ca. 1890]. 9 vols. in 4. 32 cm. (Biblioteca del pianista.)
P.N.'s: 100517-100523, 100529-100530
1537. Sammlung der Clavier-Compositionen von Johann Sebastian Bach, Herausgegeben von Friedrich Chrysander. ... Wolfenbuettel, L. Holle [1856-57]. 27 parts in 4 vols. Illus., 34 cm.
P.N.'s: 341-366

Selections

1538. Bach Two-Part Pianoforte Music Selected from the Kleine Preludien (VI petits préludes), Französische Suiten (Suites françaises) and Zweistimmige Inventionen (Quinze inventions à 2 voix). Edited by John Farmer. Book I: Two-part pianoforte music. ... London, Joseph Williams [1887]. 2 ll., 61 pp., 35 cm. (High School Edition.)
P.N.: Bach's Works Bk. 1 ed: J. Farmer. N.7684
1539. Classische Hochschule für Pianisten redigirt von L. Köhler; Fünfte Abtheilung: 24 Praeludien, Inventionen etc., 16 Symphonien und Phantasiestücke, 24 Fugen (Wohltemperirtes Clavier) von Joh. Seb. Bach. Mit Biographie, Anleitung zum Studium und Gebrauch der Bachschen Clavier-Werke beim Unterricht. Leipzig & New York, J. Schuberth [1864?]. 4 ll., pp. 177-283, 1 l., 32 cm.
P.N.'s: 3781 to 3783
1540. Collection complète pour le piano des oeuvres de J. S. Bach. Edition publiée par souscription revue corrigée et doigtée par C. Czerny et un comité d'artistes du plus grand mérite. [Paris] chez Mme. Vve. Launer [ca. 1840]. 4 vols. in 1. 34 cm.
Front cover has statement stamped in gold: Conservatoire de Musique | & Déclamation | *Concours de* 1851 | 2me Prix de Piano | Décerné à Mr. Bizet. P.N.'s: VeL. 3271-VeL. 3274
1541. Compositions pour le clavecin seul par J. Seb. Bach. Edition nouvelle, revue et corrigée critiquement, doigtée, métronomisée et enrichie de notes sur l'exécution par C. Czerny, G. C. Griepenkerl et F.A. Roitzsch. Leipzig & Berlin, C. F. Peters [1867]. 2 ll., 5-63 pp., 33 cm., wove paper. (Oeuvres de Bach, Série I, Cahier 13.)
P.N.: 4558
1542. Compositions pour le piano-forte sans et avec accompagnement par Jean Sebastien Bach. Edition nouvelle, soigneusement revue, corrigée et doigtée, ainsi que pourvue de notifications sur l'exécution et sur les mesures des temps (d'après le Métronome de Maelzel) et

158   PUBLISHED MUSIC OF J. S. BACH

1542. *(continued)* accompagnée d'une préface par Charles Czerny. ... Leipzig, au Bureau de Musique de C. F. Peters [1839?] 1 l., 99 pp., 33 cm., wove paper. (Oeuvres complets, Livre 4.) Inserted between title and table are 3 separate publications of 3 items in this collection, with the same plate number, but different pagination, and edited by F. C. Griepenkerl with significant differences. They are Nos. 2, 3, and 11 of the series: Pièces détachées de la 4me livraison.   P.N.: 2696

1543. Compositions pour le piano-forte sans et avec accompagnement par Jean Sebastien Bach. Edition nouvelle, soigneusement revue, corrigée et doigtée, ainsi que pourvue de notifications sur l'exécution et sur les mesures des temps (d'après le Métronome de Maelzel) et accompagnée d'une préface par Charles Czerny. Leipzig, au Bureau de Musique de C. F. Peters [1840?]. 1 l.; [1], 4-83 pp.; 33 cm.; wove paper. (Oeuvres complets, Livre 6.)   P.N.: 2747

1544. Compositions pour le piano-forte sans et avec accompagnement par Jean Sebastien Bach. Edition nouvelle, soigneusement revue, corrigée, métronomisée et doigtée; enrichie de notes sur l'exécution et accompagnée d'une préface par Fréd. Conr. Griepenkerl. ... Leipzig, au Bureau de Musique de C. F. Peters [1840?]. 1 l.; [1], 4-85 pp.; 33 cm.; wove paper. (Oeuvres complettes, Livre 7.)   P.N.: 2748

1545. Compositions pour le piano-forte sans et avec accompagnement par Jean Sebastien Bach. Edition nouvelle, soigneusement revue, corrigée, métronomisée et doigtée; enrichie de notes sur l'exécution et accompagnée d'une préface par Fréd. Conr. Griepenkerl. ... Leipzig, au Bureau de Musique de C. F. Peters [1843]. 1 l.; i-vii, 4-89 pp.; 33 cm.; wove paper. (Oeuvres complettes, Livre 9.)   P.N.: 2838

1546. Compositions pour piano de J. S. Bach, Vol. I [and II]. Braunschweig [Brunswick] Henry Litolff [ca. 1885]. 2 vols. 30 cm. (Collection Litolff, Nos. 169-70.)

                    P.N.'s: Vol. I: COLLECTION LITOLFF No. 868;
                              COLLECTION LITOLFF No. 869;
                              COLLECTION LITOLFF No. 169;
                  Vol. II: COLLECTION LITOLFF No. 170;
                              COLLECTION LITOLFF No. 870

1547. G. S. Bach, Ventitre pezzi facili per pianoforte scelti, ordinati e diteggiati, con note illustrative e la maniera d'esecuzione di tutti gli abbellimenti da Bruno Mugellini. ... Milan, Ridordi [ca. 1910]. 3 ll., 42 pp., 30 cm. (Edition Ricordi, No. 451.)   P.N.: E.R.451

1548. J. S. Bach, Concerto Italien et Fantaisie chromatique. Révision par Maurice Emmanuel, doigté par I. Philipp. ... Paris, Durand [1930?]. 1 l.; iii, 2-33, [1] pp.; 30 cm. (Edition classique A. Durand & Fils, No. 9408.) Printed at Imp. Delanchy, Dupré – Paris – Asnières, 1930, but copyright date is 1916.   P.N.: D. & F. 9408

1549. J. S. Bach, 24 Praeludien, Inventionen und Tanzstücke, Louis Köhler. ... Leipzig, J. Schuberth [1877?]. 1 l., 31 pp., 33 cm. (Edition Schuberth, No. 66.)
This is Section VI of the Classische Hochschule edited by Köhler.
P.N.: 4263
1550. Joh. Seb. Bach, Piano works...Italien concerto, Chromatic fantasia & fuge, Fantasia in C minor and Prelude and fugue in A minor. ... London, Augener [ca. 1910]. 48 pp., 31 cm. (Augener's Edition, No. 8022.) P.N.'s: 12550; 12617; 11514; 14934; 10633
1551. Joh. Sebastian Bach, Das Italienische Konzert...Chromatische Fantasie und Fuge...Fantasie und Fuge in C-moll...Fuge in A-moll ...Praeludium, Fuge und Allegro...Fuge in D-moll...Fantasie und Fuge in A-moll...Piano solo. Magdeburg, Heinrichshofen, c 1919. 70 pp., 30 cm. (Neue instruktive Ausgabe von Theodor Wiehmayer, No. 30.) P.N.: H.V.11627
1552. Johann Sebastian Bach, Chromatic fantasy and fugue; Concerto in the Italian style; Fantasy in C minor; Prelude and fugue in A minor. Edited and revised by Hans von Bülow and Max Vogrich. New York, G. Schirmer, c 1896. 1 l.; 55, [1] pp.; 30 cm. (Schirmer's Library of Musical Classics, Vol. 22.) P.N.: 12661
1553. Klavierwerke von Joh. Seb. Bach herausgegeben von Adolf Ruthardt. Revidierte Ausgabe. Leipzig, C. F. Peters [ca. 1930]. 55 pp., 30 cm. (Edition Peters, No. 2798.)
This is Band 10 of Ruthardt's collected edition. P.N.: 7753
1554. Das kleine Konzert Johann Sebastian Bach, "Chromatische Fantasie und Fugue," "Italienisches Konzert," Sonderband der Reihe "Das kleine Konzert" für die Oberstufe herausgegeben von Heinz Schüngeler. Magdeburg, Heinrichshofen [1942?]. 40 pp. ,31 cm.
Autographed inscription on title page reads: Seiner sehr geschätzten | Schülerin, sowie dem befreun- | deten Hause Kevekordis | in herzlichen Gedenken überricht. | Heinz Schüngler | Hagen, 19.9.42. P.N.: H.V. 13457
1555. Piano Compositions, Johann Sebastian Bach, Ebenezer Prout. Volume I: Shorter Compositions [and Volume II: Larger Compositions]. ... Boston, Oliver Ditson [1907, 1908]. 2 vols. 32 cm. (The Musicians Library.)
1556. Unsere Meister, Our Masters, Nos Maîtres. Sammlung auserlesener Werke für Pianoforte. ... Leipzig, Breitkopf & Härtel [1919?]. 1 l., 99 pp., 27 cm. (Volksausgabe, No. 1.)
Breitkopf catalog of 1885 asserts this collection was edited by Carl Reinicke. P.N.: V.A. 1

Selections, Arranged

1557. Auslese aus Johann Sebastian Bach's instruktiven Klavierwerken in erleichterter Partiturmässiger Darstellung für vier, drei oder zwei

1557. *(continued)* Hände bearbeitet von Karl Eichler mit kurzen thematischen und Vortragserläuterungen von Prof. W. Weber. Volls-tändig in 3 Bände noder in 7 Heften. ... Stuttgart, Deutsche Verlags-Anstalt [ca. 1910]. 7 parts in 3 vols. 35 cm.   P.N.'s: I; II

CONCERTOS

Brandenburg, Collections

FULL SCORES

1558. Brandenburg Concertos, No. 1 in F and No. 2 in F. With a biographical note by Frank Howes and an introduction by Gordon Jacob. Harmondsworth, Penguin Books, 1950. 119 pp., obl. 8°, 13×20 cm. (The Penguin Scores, Edited by Gordon Jacob, 7.)
P.N.: P7

Brandenburg, Single Works

BRANDENBURG CONCERTO NO. 1 (S. 1046): Full scores

1559. Brandenburgisches Konzert No. 1...Nach der Ausgabe der Bach-Gesellschaft revidiert und mit Vorwort versehen von Arnold Schering. Leipzig, Eulenburg [1928?]. 4 ll., 40 pp., 2 ll., 19 cm. (Eulenburgs kleine Partitur-Ausgabe, No. 280.)   P.N.: E.E. 3311

1560. Brandenburgisches Konzert Nr. 1. Partitur nach dem Autograph der Preussischen Staatsbibliothek zu Berlin herausgegeben von Kurt Soldan. Leipzig, C. F. Peters [1934?]. vi, 30 pp., 33 cm. (Edition Peters, No. 4410.)
Realization of continuo part by Ludwig Landshoff.   P.N.: 11163

1561. Premier concerto pour violino piccolo, 3 Hautbois et deux cors de chasse avec accompagnement de 2 violons, alto, violoncelle et basse... [secondary title]. Leipzig, au Bureau de Musique de C. F. Peters, 1850. Score and 12 parts. 33 cm., wove paper, facs.
General title page reads: Six concertos composés par Jean Sebastien Bach publiés pour la première fois d'après les manuscrits origineaux par S. W. Dehn. Facsimile of dedicatory letter to the Margrave of Brandenburg on leaf 2.   P.N.: Score: 3301; Parts: 3302

BRANDENBURG CONCERTO NO. 1 (S. 1046): Excerpts, Arrangements

1562. Brandenburgisches Konzert No. I, 4: Menuetto, Polacca & 2 Trios...Pianoforte. London, Hinrichsen Edition, c 1955. 4 pp., 31 cm. (Hinrichsen Edition, No. 304.)
Edited by Thomas A. Johnson.   P.N.: Hinrichsen Edition No. 304.

BRANDENBURG CONCERTO NO. 2 (S. 1047): Full scores

1563. Brandenburgisches Konzert No. 2...Nach der Ausgabe der Bach-Gesellschaft revidiert und mit Vorwort versehen von Arnold

Schering. Leipzig, Eulenburg [1929?]. 5 ll., 36 pp., 2 ll., 19 cm.
(Eulenburgs kleine Partitur-Ausgabe, No. 257.) P.N.: E.E.1341
1564. Brandenburgisches Konzert Nr. 2. Partitur nach dem Autograph
der Preussischen Staatsbibliothek zu Berlin herausgegeben von Kurt
Soldan. Leipzig, C. F. Peters [1934?]. vi, 24 pp., 33 cm. (Edition
Peters, No. 4411.)
Realization of continuo part by Ludwig Landshoff. P.N.: 11165
1565. Concerto No. 2...Kontinuobearbeitung von...E. Mandyczewski. ... Vienna, Wiener Philharmonischer Verlag, A.G. [1936?].
5 ll., 36 pp., frontis., 19 cm. (Philharmonia Partituren, No. 94.)
P.N.: W.Ph.V.94
1566. Second concerto pour violon, flûte, hautbois et trompette
concertans avec accompagnement de 2 violons, alto, violoncelle et
basse...[secondary title]. Leipzig, au Bureau de Musique de C. F.
Peters, 1850. Score and 9 parts. 33 cm., wove paper.
General title reads: Six concertos composés par Jean Sebastien Bach
publiés pour la première fois d'après les manuscrits origineaux par
S. W. Dehn. P.N.: Score: 3396; Parts: 3397
1567. Zweites Brandenburgisches Concert für concertirende Violine,
Flöte, Hoboe und Trompete mit Begleitung von Streichorchester und
Cembalo...Zum stilgemässen, Vortrag eingerichtet von Hermann
Kretzschmar. Leipzig, C. F. Peters [ca. 1900]. 73 pp., 28 cm.
Edition Peters, No. 3072.) P.N.: 8892

BRANDENBURG CONCERTO NO. 3 (S. 1048): Full scores

1568. Brandenburg Concerto No. 3. ... With a biographical note by
Frank Howes and an introduction by Gordon Jacob. London,
Penguin Books, 1953. 50 pp., 1 l., obl. 8°, 13 × 20 cm. (The Penguin
Scores, Edited by Gordon Jacob, 2.) P.N.: P2
1569. Brandenburgisches Konzert No. 3...Nach der Ausgabe der
Bach-Gesellschaft revidiert und mit Vorwort versehen von Arnold
Schering. Leipzig, Eulenburg [1929?]. 5 ll., 34 pp., 2 ll., 19 cm.
(Eulenburgs kleine Partitur-Ausgabe, No. 254.) P.N.: E.E.1138.
1570. Brandenburgisches Konzert Nr. 3. Partitur nach dem Auto-
graph der Preussischen Staatsbibliothek zu Berlin herausgegeben
von Kurt Soldan. Leipzig, C. F. Peters [1934?]. vi, 24 pp., 33 cm.
(Edition Peters, No. 4412.)
Realization of continuo part by Ludwig Landshoff. P.N.: 11167
1571. Concerto No. 3...Kontinuobearbeitung von...Hans Gál. ...
Vienna, Wiener Philharmonischer Verlag, A.G. [1935?]. 5 ll., 35 pp.,
frontis., 19 cm. (Philharmonia Partituren, No. 95.)
Preface by Karl Geiringer. P.N.: W.Ph.V.95.
1572. Troisième concerto pour trois violons, trois altos, et trois violon-
celles avec basse composé par Jean Sebastien Bach. ... [Leipzig, au

1572. *(continued)*   Bureau de Musique de C. F. Peters, 1850.] Score
and 10 parts. 33 cm., wove paper.
Missing general title: Six concertos composés par Jean Sebastien
Bach publiés...par S. W. Dehn.   P.N.: Score: 3406; Parts: 3407

BRANDENBURG CONCERTO NO. 3 (S. 1048): Arrangements

1573. Brandenburgisches Konzert No. III...Pianoforte. Übertragen
von Thomas A. Johnson. London, Hinrichsen Edition & Peters
Edition, c 1955. 15 pp., 31 cm. (Hinrichsen Edition, No. 305.)
                                    P.N.: Hinrichsen Edition No. 305.

BRANDENBURG CONCERTO NO. 4 (S. 1049): Full scores

1574. Brandenburg Concerto No. 4...With a biographical note by
Frank Howes and an introduction by Gordon Jacob. London,
Penguin Books, 1954. 96 pp., obl. 8°, 13 × 20 cm. (Penguin Scores,
Edited by Gordon Jacob, 22.)   P.N.: P23
1575. Brandenburgisches Konzert No. 4...Nach der Ausgabe der
Bach-Gesellschaft revidiert und mit Vorwort versehen von Arnold
Schering. Leipzig, Eulenburg [1928?]. 4 ll., 52 pp., 2 ll., 19 cm.
(Eulenburgs kleine Partitur-Ausgabe, No. 281.)   P.N.: E.E.3312
1576. Brandenburgisches Konzert No. 4. Partitur nach dem Auto-
graph der Preussischen Staatsbibliothek zu Berlin herausgegeben von
Kurt Soldan. Leipzig, C. F. Peters [1934?]. vi, 40 pp., 33 cm.
(Edition Peters, No. 4413.)
Realization of continuo by Ludwig Landshoff.   P.N.: 11169
1577. Concerto No. 4...Neu herausgegeben von...Karl Geiringer,
Kontinuobearbeitung von...E. Mandyczewski. ...Vienna, Wiener
Philharmonischer Verlag, A.G. [1928?]. 5 ll., 59 pp., frontis.,
19 cm. (Philharmonia Partituren, No. 96.)   P.N.: W.Ph.V.96.
1578.   Quatrième concerto pour violon et deux flûtes concertants avec
accompagnement de 2 violons, alto, violoncelle et basse composé par
Jean Sebastien Bach. ... [Leipzig, au Bureau de Musique de C. F.
Peters, 1850.] Score and 8 parts. 33 cm., wove paper.
Missing general title: Six concertos composés par Jean Sebastien
Bach publiés...par S. W. Dehn.   P.N.: Score: 3429; Parts: 3430

BRANDENBURG CONCERTO NO. 5 (S. 1050): Full scores

1579. Brandenburgisches Konzert No. 5...Nach der Ausgabe der
Bach-Gesellschaft revidiert und mit Vorwort versehen von Arnold
Schering. Leipzig, Eulenburg [1928?]. 4 ll., 58 pp., 3 ll., 19 cm.
(Eulenburgs kleine Partitur-Ausgabe, No. 282.)   P.N.: E.E.3313
1580. Brandenburgisches Konzert Nr. 5. Partitur nach dem Auto-
graph der Preussischen Staatsbibliothek zu Berlin herausgegeben
von Kurt Soldan. Leipzig, C. F. Peters [1934?]. vi, 31 pp., 33 cm.
(Edition Peters, No. 4414.)
Realization of continuo by Ludwig Landshoff.   P.N.: 11171

1581. Cinquième concerto pour clavecin, flûte et violon concertans avec accompagnement de violon, alto, violoncelle et basse composé par Jean Sebastien Bach. ... [Leipzig, au Bureau de Musique de C. F. Peters, 1850.] Score and 7 parts. 33 cm., wove paper. Missing general title: Six concertos composés par Jean Sebastien Bach publiés...par S. W. Dehn. P.N.: Score: 3445; Parts: 3446
1582. Concerto No. 5...Neu herausgegeben von...Karl Geiringer, Kontinuobearbeitung von...E. Mandyczewski. ... Vienna, Wiener Philharmonischer Verlag, A.G. [1936?]. 5 ll., 59 pp., frontis., 19 cm. (Philharmonia Partituren, No. 97.) P.N.: W.Ph.V.97.
1583. Konzert D dur Brandenburgisches Nr. 5...bearbeitet von Max Reger, Partitur. Leipzig, Breitkopf & Härtel [c 1915]. 1 l., 33 pp., 34 cm. (Edition Breitkopf, No. 2343.) P.N.: Part.B.2343

BRANDENBURG CONCERTO NO. 5. (S. 1050): Arrangements
1584. Klavier-Konzert D dur mit Begleitung eines zweiten Klaviers herausgegeben von Dr. Hugo Riemann. Leipzig, Steingräber [ca. 1895]. 36 pp., 33 cm. (Edition Steingräber, No. 98.) Two-piano arrangement. P.N.: 478

BRANDENBURG CONCERTO NO. 6 (S. 1051): Full scores
1585. Brandenburgisches Konzert No. 6...Nach der Ausgabe der Bach-Gesellschaft revidiert und mit Vorwort versehen von Arnold Schering. Leipzig, Eulenburg [1929?]. 4 ll., 36 pp., 2 ll., 19 cm. (Eulenburgs kleine Partitur-Ausgabe, No. 255.) P.N.: E.E.1339
1586. Brandenburgisches Konzert Nr. 6. Partitur nach dem Autograph der Preussischen Staatsbibliothek zu Berlin herausgegeben von Kurt Soldan. Leipzig, C. F. Peters [1934?]. vi, 24 pp., 33 cm. (Edition Peters, No. 4415.) Realization of continuo by Ludwig Landshoff. P.N.: 11173
1587. Sixième concerto pour deux altos, deux violes da gamba, avec violoncelle et basse composé par Jean Sebastien Bach...[secondary title]. Leipzig, au Bureau de Musique de C. F. Peters, 1850. Score and 6 parts. 33 cm., wove paper. General title: Six concertos composés par Jean Sebastien Bach publiés pour la première fois d'après les manuscrits origineaux par S. W. Dehn. P.N.: Score: 3528; Parts: 3529

Clavier

CONCERTO IN D MINOR (S. 1052): Full scores
1588. Concert en Ré mineur pour le clavecin avec accompagnement de deux violons, viola et basse composé par Jean Sebastien Bach publié d'après le manuscrit original par S. W. Dehn et F. A. Roitzsch. Leipzig, au Bureau de Musique de C. F. Peters...[1854?]. Score and

1588. *(continued)*   5 parts.   33 cm., wove paper.   (Oeuvres complettes, Livre 22).   P.N.: Score: 3717; Parts: 3718

1589.   Konzert D moll für Klavier mit Begleitung von 2 Violinen, Viola, Violoncell und Bass von Joh. Seb. Bach. Nach der Ausgabe der Bach-Gesellschaft revidiert und mit Vorwort versehen von Arnold Schering. Leipzig, Eulenburg [1925?]. 2 ll., 66 pp., 2 ll., 19 cm. (Eulenburgs kleine Partitur-Ausgabe, No. 744.)   P.N.: E.E.4467

CONCERTO IN D MINOR (S. 1052): Arrangements for 4 hands

1590.   Concerto in D minor for piano...Edited by Edwin Hughes. New York, G. Schirmer, c 1928. 1 l., 67 pp., 1 l., 30 cm. (Schirmer's Library of Musical Classics, Vol. 1527.)
Two copies.   P.N.: 34028

1591.   D moll Konzert für Pianoforte...mit Begleitung eines zweiten Pianoforte von Adolf Ruthardt. Leipzig, C. F. Peters [1930?]. 42 pp., 30 cm. (Edition Peters, No. 2912.)
Two copies.   P.N.: 8492

1592.   Klavier-Konzert, D moll freie Bearbeitung von F. B. Busoni, Solostimme mit hinzufügter 2. Klavierstimme an Stelle des Orchesters. Leipzig, Breitkopf & Härtel [c 1900]. 41 pp., 30 cm. (Edition Breitkopf, No. 2956.)
Two copies.   P.N.: V.A.2956

1593.   Konzert für Cembalo in D-moll...Unter Beibehaltung des von der Bach-Gesellschaft übermittelten Originals für den modernen Flügel bearbeitet und die Begleitstimmen auf ein zweites Klavier übertragen von Willy Eickemeyer. Leipzig, Steingräber, c 1928. 44 pp., 33 cm. (Edition Steingräber, No. 118.)   P.N.: 2409

CONCERTO IN D MINOR (S. 1052): Arrangement for violin and piano

1594.   Violin-Konzerte...Concerto d moll – ré mineur (Sauret). ... Mainz, Schott [c 1920]. Score and 1 part. 30 cm. (Edition Schott, No. 1203.)   P.N.: 31303

CONCERTO IN E MAJOR (S. 1053): Full scores

1595.   Concert en Mi majeur pour le clavecin avec accompagnement de deux violons, viola et basse composé par Jean Sebastien Bach publié pour la première fois d'après le manuscrit original par S. W. Dehn et F. A. Roitzsch. Leipzig, au Bureau de Musique de C. F. Peters [1854?]. Score and 5 parts. 33 cm., wove paper. (Oeuvres complettes, Livre 21.)   P.N.: Score: 3710; Parts: 3711

1596.   Konzert E dur für Cembalo und Streichorchester nach dem Autograph der Preussischen Staatsbibliothek zu Berlin herausgegeben von Kurt Soldan. Leipzig, C. F. Peters [1938?]. 1 l.; 38, [1] pp.; 34 cm. (Edition Peters, No. 4468.)   P.N.: 11378

CONCERTO IN E MAJOR (S. 1053): Arrangements for 4 hands

1597. Klavier-Konzert E dur mit Begleitung eines zweiten Klaviers
herausgegeben von Dr. Hugo Riemann. Leipzig, Steingräber
[ca. 1895]. 35, [1] pp.; 33 cm. (Edition Steingräber, No. 99.)
                                                        P.N.: 479
1598. Konzert E dur für Cembalo...nach dem Autograph der
Preussischen Staatsbibliothek zu Berlin. Herausgegeben von Kurt
Soldan, Ausgabe für zwei Klaviere mit Fingersatz von Hans Beltz.
Leipzig, C. F. Peters [1938?]. 1 l., 37 pp., 31 cm. (Edition Peters,
No. 4469.)   P.N.: 11389

CONCERTO IN D MAJOR (S. 1054): Full score

1599. Concert en Ré majeur pour le clavecin avec accompagnement
de deux violons, viola et basse composé par Jean Sebastien Bach
publié pour la première fois d'après le manuscrit original par S. W.
Dehn et F. A. Roitzsch. Leipzig, au Bureau de Musique de C. F.
Peters [1853?]. Score and 5 parts. Wove paper, 33 cm. (Oeuvres
complettes, Livre 19.)   P.N.: Score: 3660; Parts: 3661

CONCERTO IN A MAJOR (S. 1055): Full scores

1600. Concert en La majeur pour le clavecin avec accompagnement de
deux violons, viola, violoncelle et basse composé par Jean Sebastien
Bach publié pour la première fois d'après le manuscrit original par
S. W. Dehn et F. A. Roitzsch. Leipzig, au Bureau de Musique de
C. F. Peters [1853?]. Score and 5 parts. 33 cm. (Oeuvres complettes,
Livre 20.) Wove paper.   P.N.: Score: 3666; Parts: 3667
1601. Konzert A dur für Cembalo...nach dem Autograph der
Preussischen Staatsbibliothek zu Berlin. Herausgegeben von Kurt
Soldan. Leipzig, C. F. Peters [1938?]. 1 l., 24 pp., 1 l., 34 cm.
(Edition Peters, No. 4466.)   P.N.: 11379

CONCERTO IN A MAJOR (S. 1055): Arrangement for 4 hands

1602. Konzert A dur für Cembalo...nach dem Autograph der Preus-
sischen Staatsbibliothek zu Berlin herausgegeben von Kurt Soldan.
Ausgabe für zwei Klaviere mit Fingersatz von Hans Beltz. Leipzig,
C. F. Peters [1938]. 1 l., 23 pp., 31 cm. (Edition Peters, No. 4467.)
                                                        P.N.: 11388

CONCERTO IN F MINOR (S. 1056): Full scores

1603. Concert en Fa mineur pour le clavecin avec accompagnement de
deux violons, viola et basse composé par Jean Sebastien Bach publié
pour la première fois d'après le manuscrit original par S. W. Dehn
et F. A. Roitzsch. Leipzig, au Bureau de Musique de C. F. Peters
[1852?]. Score and 5 parts. 33 cm., wove paper.
                                    P.N.: Score: 3539; Parts: 3540

1604. Konzert F moll für Klavier...Nach der Ausgabe der Bach-Gesellschaft revidiert und mit Vorwort versehen von Arnold Schering. Leipzig, Eulenburg [1925?]. 2 ll., 26 pp., 3 ll., 19 cm. (Eulenburgs kleine Partitur-Ausgabe, No. 745.)   P.N.: E.E.4474

CONCERTO IN F MINOR (S. 1056): Arrangement for 4 hands

1605. Klavier-Konzert F-moll Ausgabe für 2 Klaviere herausgegeben von Edwin Fischer. ... Berlin, Ullstein [ca. 1930]. 28 pp., 31 cm. (Tonmeister Ausgabe, No. 10.)   P.N.: T.A. Nr. 10

1606. Klavier-Konzert F moll mit Begleitung eines zweiten Klaviers herausgegeben von Dr. Hugo Riemann. Leipzig, Steingräber [ca. 1895]. 19, [1] pp.; 33 cm. (Edition Steingräber, No. 108.) P.N.: 467

1607. Konzert F moll für Klavier und Orchester von Joh. Seb. Bach herausgegeben von Robert Teichmüller. ... Leipzig, C. F. Peters [c 1925]. 27 pp., 30 cm. (Edition Peters, No. 3830.)   P.N.: 10439

CONCERTO IN F MINOR (S. 1056): Arrangement for violin and piano

1608. Violin-Konzerte...bearbeitet von Gustav Schreck. Leipzig, C. F. Peters [1932?]. Score and 2 parts. 30 cm. (Edition Peters, No. 3069.)

Transposed to G minor. There are two separate versions of the violin part.   P.N.'s: 8980, 8980ᵃ

CONCERTO IN F MAJOR (S. 1057): Full score

1609. Concert in Fa majeur pour le clavecin et deux flûtes concertantes avec accompangement de deux violons, viola, et basse composé par Jean Sebastien Bach publié pour la première fois d'après la partition originale par S. W. Dehn et F. A. Roitzsch. Leipzig, au Bureau de Musique de C. F. Peters [1850?]. Score and 7 parts. 33 cm., wove paper. (Oeuvres complettes, Livre 16.)
          P.N.: Score: 3434; Parts: 3435

CONCERTO IN F MAJOR (S. 1057): Arrangement for 4 hands

1610. Klavier-Konzert F dur mit Begleitung eines zweiten Klaviers herausgegeben von Dr. Hugo Riemann. Leipzig, Steingräber [ca. 1895]. 31, [1] pp.; 33 cm. (Edition Steingräber, No. 119.)
          P.N.: 457

CONCERTO IN G MINOR (S. 1058): Full score

1611. Concert in Sol mineur pour le clavecin avec accompagnement de deux violons, viola, violoncelle et basse composé par Jean Sebastien Bach publié pour la première fois d'après le manuscrit original par S. W. Dehn et F. A. Roitzsch. Leipzig, au Bureau de Musique de C. F. Peters [1850?]. Score and 5 parts. 33 cm., wove paper. (Oeuvres complettes, Livre 17.)   P.N.: Score: 3410; Parts: 3411

Two Claviers

CONCERTO IN C MINOR (S. 1060): Full scores

1612. Concert (en Ut mineur) pour deux clavecins avec deux violons,
viola et basse par Jean Sebast. Bach. Première édition...par Fréd.
Conr. Griepenkerl Se. Leipzig, au Bureau de Musique de C. F. Peters;
London, J. J. Ewer; St. Petersbourg, M. Bernard [1849?]. Score and
6 parts. 33 cm. (Oeuvres complettes, Livre 13.)
General title: Compositions pour le pianoforte sans et avec accompagnement par Jean Sebastien Bach. Edition nouvelle,
soigneusement revue, corrigée, métronomisée et doigtée; enrichie
de notes sur l'exécution et accompagnée d'une préface par Fréd.
Conr. Griepenkerl.   P.N.: Score: 3120; Parts: 3121
1613. Deux concerts en Ut majeur et Ut mineur pour deux clavecins
avec accompagnement de deux violons, viola et basse par Jean
Sebastien Bach publiés pour la première fois par Fréd. Conr. Griepenkerl. Leipzig & Berlin, C. F. Peters [ca. 1865]. Score and 5 parts.
35 cm., wove paper. (Oeuvres complètes, Série II, cahier 10.)
P.N.: Score: 3120; Parts: 3121
1614. Konzert C moll für zwei Klaviere. ... Leipzig, Eulenburg [ca.
1925]. 2 ll., 48 pp., 2 ll., 19 cm. (Eulenburgs kleine Partitur-Ausgabe,
No. 731.)
Preface signed by Arnold Schering.   P.N.: E.E.3821

CONCERTO IN C MINOR (S. 1060): Arrangements for 4 hands

1615. Concerto in C minor for Two Pianos. Arranged by Harold
Bauer. New York, G. Schirmer [c 1926]. 35 pp., 31 cm.
P.N.: 32782
1616. Konzert in C-moll für 2 Klaviere...Ausgabe mit einbezogenem
Orchesterpart, Fingersatz, Vortragszeichen und Phrasierung herausgegeben von Willy Rehberg. Leipzig, Steingräber [ca. 1925]. 23,
[1] pp.; 34 cm. (Edition Steingräber, No. 2437.)   P.N.: 2288
1617. Konzert C moll für zwei Klaviere herausgegeben von F. C.
Griepenkerl. Neurevidierte Ausgabe. Leipzig, C. F. Peters [1935?].
27 pp., 30 cm. (Edition Peters, No. 2200b.)
Two copies.   P.N.: 8639
1618. Konzerte für zwei Klaviere...bearbeitet von Max Reger,
Nr. 1. C moll. ... Leipzig, Breitkopf & Härtel [c 1915]. 30 pp.,
30 cm. (Edition Breitkopf, No. 4774.)
Two copies.   P.N.: 27687

CONCERTO IN C MINOR (S. 1060): Arrangements for 2 violins and piano
or oboe, violin and piano

1619. Violin-Konzerte, Concerto de violon. ... (Berner). Mainz,
Schott [c 1916]. Score and 2 parts. 30 cm. (Edition Schott, No. 907.)
P.N.: 30231

1620.   Konzert C moll für Violine und Oboe oder für zwei Violinen
mit Klavierbegleitung...Bearbeitet von Max Seiffert. Leipzig,
C. F. Peters [1935?]. Score and 3 parts 31 cm. (Edition Peters,
No. 3722.)   P.N.: 10256

CONCERTO IN C MAJOR (S. 1061): Full scores

1621.   Concert (en Ut majeur) pour deux clavecins avec deux violons,
viola et basse par Jean Sebast. Bach. Première édition...par Fréd.
Griepenkerl Sen. Leipzig, au Bureau de Musique de C. F. Peters;
London, J. J. Ewer [1847?]. Score and 6 parts. 33 cm., wove paper.
(Oeuvres complètes, Livre 12.)
        General title: Compositions pour le pianoforte sans et avec ac-
        compagnement par Jean Sebastien Bach. Edition nouvelle,
        soigneusement revue, corrigée, métronomisée et doigtée; enrichie
        de notes sur l'exécution et accompagnée d'une préface par Fréd.
        Conr. Griepenkerl....   P.N.: Score: 3026; Parts: 3027
1622.   Konzert C dur für zwei Klaviere. ... Leipzig, Eulenburg [ca.
1925]. 2 ll., 48 pp., 2 ll., 19 cm. (Eulenburgs kleine Partitur-Ausgabe,
No. 730.)
        Preface signed by Arnold Schering.   P.N.: E.E. 3820

CONCERTO IN C MAJOR (S. 1061): Arrangements for 4 hands

1623.   Konzert in C-moll [i.e., C-dur] für 2 Klaviere...Ausgabe für 2
Klaviere allein, mit Fingersatz, Vortragszeichen und Phrasierung
versehen von Willy Rehberg. Leipzig, Steingräber [ca. 1925]. 31,
[1] pp.; 34 cm. (Edition Steingräber, No. 2438.)   P.N.: 2289
1624.   Konzert in C dur für 2 Klaviere...herausgegeben von F. C.
Griepenkerl. Neu revidierte Ausgabe. Leipzig, C. F. Peters [1933?].
33 pp., 30 cm. (Edition Peters, No. 2200a.)
        Two copies.   P.N.: 8638
1625.   Konzerte für zwei Klaviere...bearbeitet von Max Reger...
Nr. 2. C dur. ... Leipzig, Breitkopf & Härtel [c 1915]. 41 pp.,
30 cm. (Edition Breitkopf, No. 4775.)
        Two copies.   P.N.: 27688

Three Claviers

CONCERTO IN D MINOR (S. 1063): Full scores

1626.   Concert (en Ré mineur) pour trois clavecins avec deux violons,
viola et basse...première edition...par Fréd. Conr. Griepenkerl Sen.
Leipzig, C. F. Peters; London, J. J. Ewer [1846?]. Score and 7 parts.
33 cm., wove paper. (Oeuvres complettes, Livre 11.)
                            P.N.: Score: 2983; Parts: 2984
1627.   Konzert D moll für 3 Cembali...Nach der Ausgabe der Bach-
Gesellschaft revidiert und mit Vorwort versehen von Arnold Schering.

Leipzig, Eulenburg [1923?]. 2 ll., 56 pp., 2 ll., 19 cm. (Eulenburgs kleine Partitur-Ausgabe, No. 732.)   P.N.: E.E.3822

CONCERTO IN C MAJOR (S. 1064): Full scores

1628. Concert en Ut majeur pour trois clavecins avec deux violons, viola et basse par Jean Sebast. Bach, première édition, ... par Fréd. Conr. Griepenkerl Sen. Leipzig, au Bureau de Musique de C. F. Peters; London, J. J. Ewer; St. Petersburg, M. Bernard [1850?]. Score and 7 parts. 33 cm., wove paper. (Oeuvres complettes, Livre 14.)
  General title: Compositions pour le pianoforte sans et avec accompagnement par Jean Sebastien Bach. Édition nouvelle, soigneusement revue, corrigée, métronomisée et doigtée; enrichie de notes sur l'exécution et accompagnée d'une préface par Fréd. Conr. Griepenkerl.   P.N.: Scores 3292; Parts: 3293
1629. Konzert C dur für drei Cembali... Nach der Ausgabe der Bach-Gesellschaft revidiert und mit Vorwort versehen von Arnold Schering. Leipzig, Eulenburg [1923?]. 2 ll., 60 pp., 2 ll., 19 cm. (Eulenburgs kleine Partitur-Ausgabe, No. 733.)   P.N.: E.E.3823

CONCERTO IN C MAJOR (S. 1064): Arrangement for 6 hands

1630. Concerto in C Major for three harpsichords with accompaniment of stringed orchestra arranged for three pianos by Harold Bauer. New York, G. Schirmer [c 1929]. 47 pp., 23 cm.   P.N.: 34287

Four Claviers

CONCERTO IN A MINOR (S. 1065): Full scores

1631. Concerto en La mineur pour quatre clavecins avec accompagnement de deux violons, viola, et basse d'après un Concerto pour quatre violons d'Ant. Vivaldi par Jean Sebastien Bach publié pour la première fois par F. A. Roitzsch. Leipzig, au Bureau de Musique de C. F. Peters [ca. 1860]. Score and 8 parts. 33 cm., wove paper. (Oeuvres complettes, Livre 24.)   P.N.: Score: 4519; Parts: 4520
1632. Konzert A moll für vier Cembali...nach dem Konzert für 4 Violinen und Streichorchester...von Antonio Vivaldi...von Johann Sebastian Bach. Nach der Ausgabe der Bach-Gesellschaft revidiert und mit Vorwort versehen von Arnold Schering. Leipzig, Eulenburg [1931?]. 3 ll., 58 pp., 2 ll., 19 cm. (Eulenburgs kleine Partitur-Ausgabe, No. 759.)   P.N.: E.E. 4865

Clavier, Violin, and Flute

CONCERTO IN A MINOR (S. 1044): Full scores

1633. Concert en La mineur pour le clavecin, flûte et violon concertans avec accompagnement de deux violons, viola, violoncelle et

1633. *(continued)* basse composé par Jean Sebastien Bach publié par S. W. Dehn et F. A. Roitzsch. Leipzig, au Bureau de Musique de C. F. Peters [1854?]. Score and 7 parts. 33 cm., wove paper. (Oeuvres complettes, Livre 23.)   P.N.: Score: 3731; Parts: 3732

1634. Concerto per cembalo con violine e flauto obligati e con ripiene di violini. viola. violoncello et contrabasso composto da Giovanni Sebastiano Bach. Mainz, Antwerp & Brussels, B. Schott Filiorum [1848?]. 2 ll., 75 pp., 26 cm., wove paper.   P.N.: 7848

1635. Konzert A moll für Klavier, Violine und Flöte...nach der Ausgabe der Bach-Gesellschaft revidiert und mit Vorwort versehen von Arnold Schering. Leipzig, Eulenburg [1930?]. 4 ll., 74 pp., 2 ll., 19 cm. (Eulenburgs kleine Partitur-Ausgabe, No. 757.)
P.N.: E.E.4857

CONCERTO IN A MINOR (S. 1044): Arrangement for 4 hands

1636. Klavier-Konzert A moll mit Begleitung eines zweiten Klaviers herausgegeben von Dr. Hugo Riemann. Leipzig, Steingräber [ca. 1895]. 35, [1] pp.; 33 cm. (Edition Steingräber, No. 109.)
P.N.: 458

Organ

CONCERTO IN D MINOR (S. 596): Full score

1637. Konzert für die Orgel mit zwei Manualen und Pedal von J. S. Bach nach Vivaldi. Erste Ausgabe von Friedrich Konrad Griepenkerl. Leipzig, C. F. Peters [1912]. 19 pp., obl. fol., 24×31 cm. (Edition Peters, No. 3002.)

Original preface dated 1844, reprinted, and with a note added, dated November, 1912, identifying source of this composition as Vivaldi's concerto grosso, Op. 3, No. 11.   P.N.: 8722

Violin

CONCERTO IN A MINOR (S. 1041): Full scores

1638. Konzert A moll für Violine. ... Leipzig, Eulenburg [ca. 1895]. 1 l., 32 pp. (Eulenburgs kleine Partitur-Ausgabe, No. 11.)
P.N.: E.E.2808

1639. Premier concerto en La mineur pour le violon avec accompagnement de deux violons, viola et basse composé par Jean Sebastien Bach publié pour la première fois d'après le manuscrit original par S. W. Dehn. Leipzig, au Bureau de Musique de C. F. Peters [1850?]. Score and 5 parts. 33 cm., wove paper.
P.N.: Score: 3408; Parts: 3409

CONCERTO IN A MINOR (S. 1041): Violin-piano scores

1640. Concerto in A minor for violin...Fingered and arranged with piano accompaniment by Eduard Herrmann. New York, G. Schirmer, c 1920. Score and 1 part. 30 cm. (Schirmer's Library of Musical Classics, Vol. 1401.)   P.N.: 29245

1641. Concertos célèbres pour violon avec accompagnement de piano...Bach, J. S. Concerto No. 1 La mineur (Leo Portnoff). ... Leipzig, Aug. Cranz [1915?]. Score and 1 part. 30 cm. (Edition Cranz, No. 557.)
Caption title: Arrangiert u. bezeichnet von Leo Portnoff.
                                                                        P.N.: C.43526

1642. Henri Marteau Studienausgabe für Violine...Bach, Joh. Seb., Konzert A-moll (La mineur) [II Violine von Marteau]. ... Leipzig, Steingräber [c 1910]. Score and 2 parts. 34 cm. (Edition Steingräber, No. 1815.)   P.N.: 1686

1643. Konzert in a moll für Violine...Ausgabe für Violine und Klavier bezeichnet von Joseph Joachim. ... Leipzig, Simrock [c 1905]. Score and 1 part. 30 cm. (Elite Edition, No. 651 (S).)
Title, half-title, and wrapper each bears autograph: Walter Höchner 1936.   P.N.: 12730.12061

1644. Violin-Konzerte, Concertos de violon...Concerto No. 1 a moll— la mineur (Sauret). ... Meinz, Schott [c 1915]. Score and 1 part. 30 cm. (Edition Schott, No. 1201.)   P.N.: 31301

1645. Violin-Konzerte...mit Klavierbegleitung bearbeitet von Paul Klengel, Violonstimme bezeichnet von Walther Davisson, Nr. 1. A moll. ... Leipzig, Breitkopf & Härtel [c 1921]. Score and 1 part. 30 cm. (Edition Breitkopf No. 919.)   P.N.: 28566

1646. Violin-Konzerte von Joh. Seb. Bach für Pianoforte u. Violine herausgegeben von Gustav Schreck. Violinstimme bezeichnet von Andreas Moser. No. 1 Konzert A moll. ... Leipzig, C. F. Peters [1934?]. Score and 1 part. 30 cm. (Edition Peters, No. 229.)
                                                                        P.N.: 6781

1647. Violin-Konzerte von Joh. Seb. Bach. Neu bearbeitet von Henri Petri. Vienna, Universal-Edition (Aktiengesellschaft) [ca. 1926]. Score and 1 part. 30 cm. (Universal-Edition, No. 701.)
                                                 P.N.'s: U.E.701; U.E.701ª

CONCERTO IN A MINOR (S. 1041): Excerpts

1648. Cadence du Concert en La mineur pour le violon de J. S. Bach composé par J. Hellmesberger. ... Leipzig & Berlin, C. F. Peters [ca. 1867]. 3 pp., 34 cm. (Oeuvres complètes, Série III, Cahier 1.)
General title: Compositions pour violon et pour flûte par Jean Sebastien Bach. ... Edition nouvelle, revue et corrigée critiquement par Ferd. David, J. Hellmesberger et Fr. Hermann.   P.N.: 4567

CONCERTO IN E MAJOR (S. 1042): Full scores

1649. Deuxième concerto en Mi majeur pour le violon avec ac-

1649. *(continued)* compagnement de deux violons, viola et basse composé par Jean Sebastien Bach publié pour la première fois par S. W. Dehn. Leipzig, au Bureau de Musique de C. F. Peters [1855?]. Score and 5 parts. 33 cm., wove paper.
P.N.: Score: 3888; Parts: 3889
1650. Konzert E dur für Violine. ... Leipzig, Vienna, Eulenburg [ca. 1905]. 1 l., 40 pp., 2 ll., 19 cm. (Eulenburgs kleine Partitur-Ausgabe, No. 712.)   P.N.: E.E. 2815

CONCERTO IN E MAJOR (S. 1042): Violin-piano scores

1651. Concerto in E Major for violin and piano. Arranged and fingered by Eduard Herrmann. New York, G. Schirmer, c 1919. Score and 1 part. 30 cm. (Schirmer's Library of Musical Classics, Vol. 1111.)   P.N.: 25060
1652. Concertos célèbres pour violon avec accompagnement de piano...Bach, J. S. Concerto No. 2 Mi majeur (Hugo von Steiner). ... Brussels, A. Cranz [ca. 1920]. Score and 1 part. 30 cm. (Edition Cranz, No. 709.)   P.N.: C. 45681
1653. Henri Marteau Studienausgabe für Violine...Bach, Joh. Seb., Konzert E-dur (Mi majeur) [II Violine von Marteau]. ... Leipzig, Steingräber [c 1910]. Score and 2 parts. 34 cm. (Edition Steingräber, No. 1816.)   P.N.: 1687
1654. Violin-Konzerte...Concerto No. 2 E dur – mi majeur (Sauret). ... Mainz, Schott [c 1915]. Score and 1 part. 30 cm. (Edition Schott, Nos. 09208-09210.)   P.N.: 31302
1655. Violinkonzert E-dur, Concerto pour violon mi majeur, Violin concerto E Major. Violino e pianoforte...Revidiert von Henri Petri. Vienna, Universal-Edition, A.G. [1935?]. Score and 1 part. 30 cm. (Universal-Edition, No. 702.)   P.N.'s: U.E.702; U.E.702^a
1656. Violin-Konzerte...mit Klavierbegleitung bearbeitet von Paul Klengel, Violinstimme bezeichnet von Walther Davisson...Nr. 2 E dur. ... Leipzig, Breitkopf & Härtel [c 1921]. Score and 1 part. 30 cm. (Edition Breitkopf, No. 920.)   P.N.: 28576
1657. Violin-Konzerte von Joh. Seb. Bach für Pianoforte u. Violine herausgegeben von Gustav Schreck. Violinstimme bezeichnet von Andreas Moser...No. 2 Konzert. E dur. ... Leipzig, C. F. Peters [1933?]. Score and 1 part. 30 cm. (Edition Peters, No. 230.)
P.N.: 6782

CONCERTO IN D MAJOR (FRAGMENT) (S. 1045): Violin-piano score

1658. Violin-Konzerte...für Violine mit Klavierbegleitung bearbeitet von Paul Klengel, Violinstimme bezeichnet von Walther Davisson... No. 3 D dur...bearbeitet von August Saran. ... Leipzig, Breitkopf & Härtel [ca. 1925]. Score and 1 part. 30 cm. (Edition Breitkopf, No. 921.)   P.N.: V.A.921

Two Violins

CONCERTO IN D MINOR (S. 1043): Full scores

1659.   Concerto en Ré mineur pour deux violons principaux avec accompagnement de deux violons, viola et basse composé par Jean Sebastien Bach publié pour la première fois d'après le manuscrit original des parties principaux et du continuo par S. W. Dehn. Leipzig, au Bureau de Musique de C. F. Peters [1850?]. Score and 6 parts. 33 cm., wove paper.   P.N.: Score: 3394; Parts: 3395
1660.   Konzert D moll für zwei Violinen...nach der Ausgabe der Bach-Gesellschaft revidiert. Leipzig, Eulenburg [ca. 1905]. 1 l., 32 pp., 2 ll., 19 cm. (Eulenburgs kleine Partitur-Ausgabe, No. 727.)
P.N.: E.E.3817

CONCERTO IN D MINOR (S. 1043): Violin-piano scores

1661.   Concerto d moll—ré mineur für 2 Violinen und Piano... Bearbeitet von A. Wilhelmj. Mainz, Schott [c 1904]. Score and 2 parts. 31 cm. (Edition Schott, No. 906.)   P.N.: 27493
1662.   Concerto in D minor for Two violins and Piano. Edited and fingered by Eduard Herrmann. New York, G. Schirmer, c 1907. Score and 2 parts. 31 cm. (Schirmer's Library of Musical Classics, Vol. 899.)   P.N.: 18900
1663.   Doppelkonzert D-moll. Concerto pour deux violons Ré mineur. Concerto for two violins D minor. 2 Violini e pianoforte. Revidiert von Henri Petri. Vienna, Universal-Edition, A.G. [1933?]. Score and 2 parts. 31 cm. (Universal-Edition, No. 703.)
P.N.'s: U.E.703; U.E.703ᵃ, 703ᵇ
1664.   Konzert in D moll für zwei Violinen...Neue Ausgabe für 2 Violinen und Pianoforte bearbeitet von Waldemar Meyer und Robert Schwalm. Leipzig, Steingräber [ca. 1900]. Score and 2 parts. 35 cm. (Edition Steingräber, No. 1210.)   P.N. 1092
1665.   Konzert in D moll für 2 Violinen...Bearbeitung für 2 Violinen und Pianoforte von Friedrich Spiro. Leipzig, Breitkopf & Härtel [1928?]. Score and 2 parts. 31 cm. (Edition Breitkopf, No. 2377.)
P.N.: V.A.2377
1666.   Konzert No. 1 in D moll für 2 Violinen...Ausgabe für 2 Violinen & Piano bezeichnet von Joseph Joachim revidiert von Ossip Schnirlin. ...Leipzig, Simrock [c 1905]. Score and 2 parts. 31 cm. (Elite Edition, No. 652 (S).)
        Wrapper and parts autographed: Walter Höchner 1936.
P.N.: 12731.12061
1667.   Violin-Konzert...für Pianoforte u. Violine herausgegeben von Gustav Schreck, Violinstimme bezeichnet von Andreas Moser. ... Leipzig, C. F. Peters [1930?]. Score and 2 parts. 31 cm. (Edition Peters, No. 231.)   P.N.: 6783

CONCERTO IN D MINOR (S. 1043): Excerpts and arrangements

1668.   Largo from Concerto in D minor for two violins... Trans. for organ by Gordon Balch Nevin. New York, H. W. Gray [c 1916]. Pp. 3-7, 1 l.; 31 cm. (St. Cecilia Series, No. 75.) Wrapper has autograph inscription: Compliments G. B. Nevin, Cleveland.   P.N.: Largo

DUETS

Clavier

CLAVIERÜBUNG III (S. 802-805)

1669.   Four Duets, edited by Hans Bischoff. Translation by Alexander Lipsky. Scarsdale (New York), Kalmus, c 1947. 13 pp., 35 cm.
                                                                    P.N.: 152
1670.   Klavierübung III Teil, Vier Duette nach dem Erstdruck revidiert und herausgegeben von Kurt Soldan, Fingersatz von Hans Beltz. Leipzig, C. F. Peters [1938]. 2 ll.; 15, [1] pp.; illus.; facs. (music); 30 cm.
Two copies.   P.N.: 11357
1671.   Quatre duos—E moll, F dur, G dur, A moll... Edition nouvelle, rédigée par Fréd. Conr. Griepenkerl. ... Leipzig, au Bureau de Musique de C. F. Peters [1851?]. [1], 78-89 pp.; 33 cm.; wove paper. (Pièces détachées de la 4me livraison... No. 11.)   P.N.: 2696
1672.   Vier Duetten für das Piano-forte von Johann Sebastian Bach. Berlin, Trautwein [ca. 1835]. 1 l., [1], 4-9 pp.; 33 cm.; wove paper.
                                                                    P.N.: 615

CLAVIERÜBUNG III: Arrangement for violin

1673.   5 Duetten für zwey Violinen... Neue Auflage. ... Vienna, bei Tobias Haslinger [ca. 1830]. 2 parts. 34 cm., wove paper. Contents: Fughetta in C minor for clavier (S. 961) and 4 duets from the Clavier Übung III.   P.N.: T.H.293

Voice

1674.   Fourteen Duets for Soprano-Bass from the Cantatas of J. S. Bach. [Philadelphia] Association of American Choruses [ca. 1949]. 1 l., 105 pp., 26 cm. (Choral Series, No. 173.) Photo-offset lithograph process. Translation by Henry S. Drinker.
1675.   Seventeen Duets for Soprano and Alto from the Cantatas of J. S. Bach. [Philadelphia] Association of American Choruses [1949?]. 3 ll., 99 pp., 26 cm. (Choral Series, No. 179.) Photo-offset lithograph process. Translation by Henry S. Drinker.

1676. Seventeen Duets for Soprano and Alto from the Cantatas of J. S. Bach. [Philadelphia] University of Pennsylvania, n.d. 62 pp., 27 cm. (Choral Series, No. 6.)
Edited by Henry S. Drinker. Unaccompanied.

1677. Six Duets for Tenor and Bass from the Cantatas of J. S. Bach. [Philadelphia] University of Pennsylvania, n.d. 20 pp., 27 cm. (Choral series, No. 15.)
Edited by Henry S. Drinker. Unaccompanied.

FANTASIE IN C MINOR FOR CLAVIER (S. 906)

1678. Fantaisie pour le clavecin composée par J. S. Bach. No. I. Leipzig, chez C. F. Peters, Bureau de Musique [ca. 1815]. 4 pp., obl. fol., 25 × 33 cm., wove paper.
Formerly the property of Clara Wieck Schumann. Two Copies.
P.N.: 137

1679. Fantasie C-moll, Herausgegeben von Edwin Fischer. ... Berlin, Ullstein [c 1929]. 10 pp., 31 cm. (Tonmeister Ausgabe, No. 8.)
P.N.: T.A. Nr. 8

1680. Oeuvres originales, J. S. Bach, Fantaisie en Ut mineur. Nouvelle Édition revue, doigtée et annotée par Adolphe F. Wouters. ... Paris, Senart [ca. 1925]. 3 pp., 36 cm. (Musique classique, No. 643.)
At head of title: Répertoire du Conservatoire Royal de Bruxelles.
P.N.: 643

1681. Zwei Phantasien für Klavier zu zwei Händen auf Grund der Ausgabe von Hans Bischoff herausgegeben von Robert Teichmüller. Leipzig, C. F. Peters [ca. 1930]. 18 pp., 30 cm. (Edition Peters, No. 4109.)
P.N.: 10787

FANTASIE IN G MAJOR FOR ORGAN (S. 572)

1682. Fantaisie pour l'orgue ou le pianoforte composée par J. S. Bach. No. II. Leipzig, au Bureau de Musique de C. F. Peters [before 1834]. 1 l., 3-9 pp.; obl. fol.; 25 × 33 cm.; wove paper.
Formerly the property of Clara Wieck Schumann.
P.N.: 2260

FANTASIE AND FUGUE IN A MINOR FOR CLAVIER (S. 904)

1683. Fantasia con fuga, Joh. Sebastian Bach. Erfurt, Leipzig, Gotth. Wilh. Körner [1845?]. Pp. 28-36, obl. 4°, 24 × 27 cm., wove paper. (Der Orgel-Virtuos. No. 58.)
Arranged for organ.
P.N.: 21.III

1684. Fantasia con fuga pro cembalo, A minor. London, Peters Edition & Hinrichsen Edition, 195? 11 pp., 1 l., 31 cm. (Edition Peters, No. 208ᵇ.)
P.N.: 8242

176 PUBLISHED MUSIC OF J. S. BACH

FUGUES

Clavier

FUGUE IN A MINOR (S. 944)

1685. Fugue pour le piano-forte, composé par J. S. Bach. Première édition d'après un manuscrit. Vienna, chez Ant. Diabelli [1828?]. 1 l., 11 pp., obl. fol., 25 × 33 cm. (Die Kunst des Fingersatzes, No. 3.) Wove paper.
Edited by Carl Czerny. P.N.: D. et C. N°. 986

FUGUE IN A MINOR (S. 947)

1686. Oeuvres originales J. S. Bach, Fugue en La. Paris, Senart, B. Roudanez [ca. 1910]. 1 l., 3 pp., 35 cm. (Nouvelle Édition française de musique classique, No. 280.)
General editor of series: Vincent D'Indy. Revision by Blanche Selva. P.N.: S.R. & Cie. 280.

FUGUE IN C MAJOR (S. 946)

1687. Fuga. Joh. Sebastian Bach. Erfurt, Leipzig, Gotth. Wilh. Körner [1849?]. Pp. 2-3, obl. 4°, 24 × 27 cm., wove paper. (Der Orgel-Virtuos. No. 283.)
Arranged for organ. P.N.: 51

Organ

FUGUE IN B MINOR (S. 579)

1688. Fuga. Erfurt, Leipzig, Gotth. Wilh. Körner [1846?]. Pp. 49-51, obl. 4°, 24 × 27 cm., wove paper. (Der Orgel-Virtuos., No. 254.)
P.N.: VIII.6

FUGUE IN C MINOR (S. 574)

1689. Thema Legrenzianum elaboratum cum subjecto pedaliter ab Joh. Seb. Bach. Vienna, Tobias Haslinger [1832?]. 2 ll., 6 pp., 32 cm. (Saemmtliche Werke von J. S. Bach, No. 1.)
P.N.: T.H.5801

FUGUE (PASSACAGLIA) IN C MINOR (S. 582)

1690. Passacaglia für Orgel oder Pianoforte von J. S. Bach. Prague, Marco Berra [1844?]. 15 pp., 33 cm., wove paper.
Signature on title page: Rob. Ludw. Prokschy. | Organist.
P.N.: M.B.1030

1691. Passacaglia von J. S. Bach. Frankfurt a/M., bei Fr. Ph. Dunst [1833?]. 15 pp., obl. fol., 25 × 33 cm.
Below imprint is stamp: Prag bei Marco Berra. P.N.: 216

FUGUE IN D MINOR (S. 680)

1692. Fugue "Wir glauben all," The "Giant." Edited by Frederic
Archer. London, Weekes [ca. 1900]. 7, [1] pp.; obl. 8°, 25×36 cm.
(Collegiate Edition, No. 12.)   P.N.: Collegiate Edition.
                                   J. S. Bach's Fugues. (F. Archer); [and] 12
1693. Johann Sebastian Bach organ works... Edited by Charles-Marie
Widor and Albert Schweitzer... Fugue in D minor (The Giant),
edited by Edward Shippen Barnes. New York, G. Schirmer [c 1923].
9, [1] pp.; obl. fol.; 23×31 cm.   P.N.: 31150

FUGUE IN G MINOR (S. 578)

1694. Fuge ex G♭=G moll. Erfurt, Leipzig, Gotth. Wilh. Körner
[1846?]. Pp. 10-12, obl. 4°, 24×27 cm., wove paper. (Der Orgel-
Virtuos., No. 110.)   P.N.: 26
1695. Fugue (edited by Frederic Archer). London, Weekes [ca. 1900].
1 l.; 5, [1] pp. (Collegiate Edition, No. 11.)
P.N.: Collegiate Edition. J. S. Bach's Fugues. (F. Archer.); [and] 11
1696. Fugue, known as the "Little G minor Fugue"... Pedaling and
registration by Charles D. Irwin. n.p., Frank K. Root, c 1899.
Pp. 3-7, obl. fol., 22×33 cm.
     Imperfect: without title or original wrappers.
                                        P.N.: Fugue. Little G minor. 5
1697. Johann Sebastian Bach Organ works... Edited by Charles-Marie
Widor and Albert Schweitzer... Fugue in G minor (The Little).
New York, G. Schirmer [c 1912]. 1 l.; 7, [1] pp.; obl. fol.; 23×34 cm.
                                                       P.N.: 31149

Violin and Clavier

FUGUE IN G MINOR (S. 1026)

1698. Compositions pour violon et pour flûte par Jean Sebastien Bach
... Edition nouvelle, revue et corrigée critiquement par Ferd. David,
J. Hellmesberger et Fr. Hermann... [Série III] Cah. 7... No. 3,
Fugue p. [violon et piano]. ... Leipzig & Berlin, C. F. Peters, Bureau
de Musique [1867?]. Score and 1 part. 33 cm., wove paper. (Oeuvres
complètes. Série III, Cahier 7, No. 3.)   P.N.: 4563

INVENTIONS (S. 772-801)

Collections

1699. Beilage II... Die 15 zweistimmigen Inventionen und die 15 drei-
stimmigen Sinfonien im Urtext herausgegeben von Ludwig Lanshoff,
Bemerkungen zum Vortrag mit erläuternden Notenbeispielen.
Leipzig, C. F. Peters [1933]. 1 l.; vi, 17 pp.; illus. (facs.). (Edition
Peters, No. 4201.)   P.N.: 11037ᵃ

1700. Le Clavecin bien tempéré, Vol. I, 15 inventions à deux et à trois voix revus et doigtés par Oswin Keller. Leipzig, Aug. Cranz [ca. 1920]. 63 pp., 31 cm. (Edition Cranz, No. 723.)   P.N.: C.45836
1701. Complete Two & Three-Part Inventions [Zwei- und dreistimmige Inventionen] for the Pianoforte...Edited, carefully revised, phrased and fingered by G. Buonamici. London, Augener [ca. 1925]. 1 l., 61 pp., 30 cm. (Augener's Edition, No. 8012.)   P.N.: 11120
1702. 15 Zweistimmige Inventionen, 15 dreistimmige Inventionen... herausgegeben von Ignaz Friedman. Kopenhagen & Leipzig, Wilhelm Hansen, c 1921. 69 pp., 30 cm. (Wilhelm Hansen Edition, No. 2062.)   P.N.: 17388
1703. Die 15 zweistimmigen Inventionen und die 15 dreistimmigen Sinfonien im Urtext herausgegeben von Ludwig Landshoff. Leipzig, C. F. Peters [1933]. 4 ll.; 63, 11 pp.; illus. (facs.); 30 cm. (Edition Peters, No. 4201.)   P.N.: 11037
1704. Inventionen für Klavier zu zwei Händen auf Grund der Ausgabe von Hans Bischoff herausgegeben von Robert Teichmüller. Leipzig, C. F. Peters [c 1927]. 63 pp., 30 cm. (Edition Peters, No. 3870.)
                                                      P.N.: 10576
1705. Inventionen Piano (Edm. Parlow). Leipzig, Anton J. Benjamin, A.G. [c 1931]. 63 pp., 31 cm.   P.N.: A.J.B. 9614
1706. Inventionen und Sinfonien. Facsimile edition with foreword by Ralph Kirkpatrick. New York, London, C. F. Peters, c 1948. 33 unnumbered ll., obl. 8°, 19×24 cm.
   Facsimile of MS. P. 610 in the Berlin Preussischen Staatsbibliothek.
1707. Inventions à 2 et 3 voix. Edition revue et doigtée par Victor Staub. Paris, E. Gallet [1920?]. 63, [1] pp.; 32 cm. (Edition Gallet, No. 116.)   P.N.: E.G.7663
1708. Inventions à 2 et 3 voix. Paris, Durand [1932]. 2 ll.; 61, [1] pp.; 30 cm. (Édition classique A. Durand & Fils, No. 9324.)
                                                   P.N.: D. & F. 9324
1709. Inventions à 2 et 3 voix pour piano. Edition revue et doigtée par Th. Lack. Paris, Henry Lemoine, c 1915. 1 l.; 61, [1] pp.; 30 cm. (Édition nationale française Panthéon des pianistes, No. 992.)
                                               P.N.: HL.21228.P.992.
1710. Inventions à deux et à trois voix pour piano. Nouvelle édition revue et doigtée par Noel-Gallon. ... Paris, Choudens [c 1933]. 2 ll., 61 pp., 31 cm. (Édition française de musique classique de piano.)
                                                   P.N.: A.C.17434
1711. Inventions à 2 et 3 voix. Révision et annotations par B. Selva. Paris, Senart, c 1915. 33 pp., 34 cm. (Édition nationale de musique classique, No. 5024.)   P.N.: EDITION NATIONALE. M.S.
1712. Inventions and Symphonies. Edited by Karl Klindworth. Cincinnati, The John Church Company [c 1899]. 65 pp., 1 l., 31 cm. (Edition Church, No. 48.)   P.N.: 12846

1713. Inventions in Two and Three Parts for the Clavier...Edited, with a preface, and short analyses of the several pieces, by James Higgs. London, Novello [1893]. 6 pp.; 1 l.; 63, [1] pp.; 31 cm. P.N.:9543

1714. Inventsii dvukh & trekhgolosnye, Dlia Fortepiano. Moscow, Gosudarstvennoe musykal'noe isdatel'stvo, 1931. 37 pp., 36 cm. Edited by N. Zhiliaev.   P.N.: 20181; 20182

1715. Inventsii dvukh & trekhgolosnye, Dlia Fortepiano. Moscow, Gosudarstvennoe musykal'noe isdatel'stvo, 1934. 61 pp., 31 cm. Edited by N. Zhiliaev.   P.N.: M.131.g.

1716. Invenzioni a due ed a tre voci per pianoforte. Rivedute, con note illustrative e l'analisi della forma da Bruno Mugellini. ... Milan, Ricordi [ca. 1915]. 1 l., 96 pp., 30 cm. (Edition Ricordi, No. 595.) Second part has double pagination (pp. 51-96) continuous with first part.   P.N.'s: E.R.477-495; E.R.418-495

1717. Joh. Seb. Bach's Pianoforte Works. Edited by Franklin Taylor ...Two & Three-Part Inventions. ... London, Augneer [c 1913]. 2 ll., 63 pp., 31 cm. (Augener's Edition, No. 8003.)
                                                      P.N.'s: 14568, 14570

1718. Klavierwerke von Joh. Seb. Bach herausgegeben von Adolf Ruthardt. Revidierte Ausgabe. Leipzig, C. F. Peters [ca. 1930]. 63 pp., 30 cm. (Edition Peters, No. 2792.) This is Band 4 of Ruthardt's collected edition.   P.N.: 7749

1719. Pianoforte works of Joh. Seb. Bach...Two and Three-Part Inventions...Carefully revised and fingered. Boston, B. F. Wood [c 1899]. 63 pp., 30 cm. (Edition Wood, No. 190.) Based on the Czerny edition.   P.N.: B.F.W. 1009-31

1720. Progressive Studies. ... St. Louis (Mo.) Art Publication Society, c 1913. 60 unnumbered ll., 35 cm. Each of the 30 inventions published in a two-leaf form with separate caption and imprint. All edited by Frederic Lillebridge. General editors: Leopold Godowsky, Frederic Lillebridge, W. S. B. Mathews, Emil Sauer.   P.N.'s: S 26-2; S 29-2; S 31-2; S 33-2; S 35-2; S 37-2; S 39-2; S 41-2; S 45-2; S 48-2 to S 88-2 (even numbers only)

1721. Thirty Inventions, Fifteen Two-Voice, Fifteen Three-Voice Complete, Edited by Dr. Ebenezer Prout, introduction by Percy Goetschius. Boston, Oliver Ditson, c 1908. 3 ll., 61 pp., 31 cm. (Ditson Edition, No. 135.)

1722. Two- and Three-Part Inventions for Piano. Edited by Carl Czerny. ... New York, Carl Fischer [c 1903]. 63 pp., 30 cm. (Carl Fischer's Music Library, No. 304.)   P.N.: 7158-62

1723. Two- and Three-Part Inventions for the Pianoforte by J. S. Bach ...Edited and fingered by H. L. Heartz. Biographical sketch of the author by Frederic H. Ripley. Boston, White-Smith, c 1913. 63 pp., frontis., 31 cm. (Edition White-Smith, No. 1.)   P.N.: 14326-61

180 PUBLISHED MUSIC OF J. S. BACH

1724. Two and Three Part Inventions for the Pianoforte...Edited by Czerny, Griepenkerl and Roitszch. New York, G. Schirmer, 1904. 1 l., 61 pp., 30 cm. (Schirmer's Library of Musical Classics, No. 813.)
P.N.: 17199
1725. Two and Three Part Inventions for the Pianoforte...Edited by Preston Ware Orem. Philadelphia, Theodore Presser [c 1901]. 63, [1] pp.; 30 cm. (Presser Collection, No. 40.)
1726. Two and Three Part Inventions for the Pianoforte. Edited, revised and fingered by Dr. Wm. Mason. New York, G. Schirmer, c 1894. 63 pp., 30 cm. (Schirmer's Library of Musical Classics, Vol. 16.)
P.N.: 11639
1727. Two and Three-Part Inventions for the Pianoforte. Revised and fingered by Otto Fox. In two books; also complete in one volume. Boston, Evans Music Company [ca. 1910]. 63 pp., 31 cm. (Edition Evans, No. 744.)
P.N.: E.M.Co. 908-62
1728. Two and Three Part Inventions. [Edited by] Frederic Shailer Evans. Cincinnati (Ohio), The Willis Music Company, c 1908. 65 pp., 1 l., 30 cm. (Willis edition.)
P.N.: 3549
1729. Zwei- und dreistimmige Inventionen für Klavier bezeichnet und mit Erläuterungen versehen von Karl Zuschneid. Berlin, Chr. Friedrich Vieweg [1924]. 63 pp., 31 cm.
P.N.: V.1523
1730. Zwei- und dreistimmige Inventionen...Herausgegeben und bearbeitet von Eugen d'Albert. Stuttgart & Berlin, J. S. Cotta'sche Buchhandlung, 1907. 4 ll., 60 pp., 33 cm. (Edition Cotta, No. 94.)
P.N.: 125
1731. Zwei- und dreistimmige Inventionen, Inventions in 2 and 3 Parts, Piano Solo. Magdeburg, Heinrichshofen, c 1910. 67 pp., 30 cm. (Neue instruktive Ausgabe von Theodor Wiehmayer, No. 2.)
P.N.: H.V.9692
1732. Zwei- und dreistimmige Inventionen...Kritisch Ausgabe mit Fingersatz und Vortragsbezeichnungen von Dr. Hans Bischoff, In der Phrasierung ergänzt und textkritisch erweitert von Martin Frey. Leipzig, Steingräber, c 1930. 39, [1] pp.; 33 cm. (Edition Steingräber, No. 1786.)
P.N.: 149
1733. Zwei- und dreistimmige Inventionen (Sinfonien), Urtext und Bearbeitung vereinigt Jubiläums-Ausgabe (1723-1923) von Gerhard Preitz. Cologne, P. J. Tonger [1924]. 71 pp., illus., 30 cm. (Ausgabe Tonger, No. 737.)
P.N.: P.J.T. 7726

Selections

1734. Conservatory Course for Pianoforte, edited by Carl Faelten... Twenty-five Three-Part Studies. Book I [and II]. ... Boston, The Arthur P. Schmidt Co. [c 1921, c 1897]. 2 vols. 30 cm. (Schmidt's Educational Series, Nos. 184a, 184b.)

1735. Studies for the Pianoforte by J. S. Bach, 25 Two-Part Studies
including the 15 Two-Part Inventions and Selections from the Short
Preludes and the Four Duos...this edition is revised, fingered and
arranged in progressive order for use in the pianoforte classes of the
New England Conservatory by Carl Faelten. Book I [and II].
Boston, The Arthur P. Schmidt Co. [c 1921]. 2 vols. 30 cm.
(Schmidt's Educational Series, No. 183a, 183b.)
P.N.'s: A.P.S. 4399ª; A.P.S. 4399ᵇ

Selections, Arranged

1736. Fifteen Symphonies (Three-Part Inventions for the Clavier).
Arranged as Organ Trios by Caspar P. Koch. ... New York,
G. Schirmer [c 1921]. 1 l., 49 pp., obl. fol., 23 × 31 cm.
P.N.: 30254
1737. Schule des Triospiels, J. S. Bach's zweistim. Inventionen für
Orgel bearbeitet von Max Reger und Karl Straube. Berlin, Ed. Bote
& G. Bock [c 1904]. 35, [1] pp.; obl. fol.; 23 × 27 cm.
P.N.: B. & B. 17119

Two-Part Inventions (S. 772-786)

COMPLETE SETS

1738. The Academic Edition of Works by Joh: Seb: Bach. 235.
Two-Part Inventions. ... London, A. Hammond [ca. 1895]. 1 l.,
31 pp., 1 l., 30 cm. (Academic Edition, No. 235.)
      Edited, fingered and annotated by Gordon Saunders.
1739. Composizioni a due parti, G. S. Bach [riveduti da] F. Kroll.
Milan, Ricordi [ca. 1875]. 1 l., 21 pp., 34 cm. (Scelta di pezzi
classici, No. 93603.)   P.N.: 93603
1740. Fifteen Two-Part Inventions for Piano...Edited by Ferruccio
Busoni, English translation by Frederick H. Martens. New York,
G. Schirmer, c 1927. 1 l., 33 pp., 30 cm. (Schirmer's Library of
Musical Classics, No. 1512.)   P.N.: 33221
1741. 15 Two-Part Inventions for Piano...Edited by Stewart Mac-
Pherson. London, Joseph Williams [c 1916]. 1 l.; 33, [1] pp.; 31 cm.
(Berners Edition, No. 81.)   P.N.: J.W.15592
1742. Fifteen Two-Voice Inventions...Edited by Arthur Foote.
Boston, The Arthur P. Schmidt Co., c 1920. 20 pp., 30 cm. (Schmidt's
Educational Series, No. 24.)   P.N.: A.P.S.2850
1743. Fifteen Two-Voice Inventions for Piano...Edited by Ferruccio
Busoni, English translation by Lois and Guy Maier. Philadelphia,
Theodore Presser [c 1937]. 1 l., 33 pp., 31 cm. (Presser Collection,
No. 346.)   P.N.: P.C. 346-34

1744.   Fifteen Two-Voiced Inventions, Edited by Hans von Bülow. ...
St. Louis (Mo.), Kunkel [c 1897]. 31 pp., 30 cm. (Kunkel's Royal
Edition.)   P.N.: 1702-30
1745.   Inventions à deux voix. Nouvelle édition revue, doigtée et
annotée par Adolphe F. Wouters. ... London, Boosey [ca. 1897].
31 pp., 31 cm. (Répertoire du Conservatoire Royal de Bruxelles.)
Wrapper has title with imprint of both Boosey and Schott Frères.
                                                          P.N.: S.F. 5863
1746.   Inventions à 2 voix pour piano ... Avec analyses et conseils sur
l'interprétation par Georges Sporck. ... Paris, E. Ploix, c 1914. 3 ll.,
51 pp., 3 ll., 31 cm.   (Edition analytique des classiques.)
Biographical sketch of Bach by Paul Landormy
                                           P.N.'s: M. 417 S. to M. 431 S.
1747.   Invenzioni a due e a tre voci per pianoforte ... Rivedute e
diteggiate da Alessandro Longo, 111884 Fasc. I, 15 Invenzioni a due
voci. ... Milan, Ricordi [ca. 1910]. 31 pp., 32 cm.   (Biblioteca del
pianista No. 111884.)   P.N.: 111884
1748.   J. S. Bach's 15 Two-Part Inventions with Harmonic Structure at
Second Piano or Organ by Gustave L. Becker, Vol. I. ... New York,
Schroeder & Gunther [c 1925]. 1 l., 14 pp., 30 cm.   (Gotham
Edition, No. 45.)   P.N.: S. & G. inc. 1161-15
1749.   J. S. Bach's Fifteen Two-Part Inventions with Harmonic
Structure by Gustave L. Becker... Vol. II, No. 6-10. ... New York,
Gustave L. Becker [c 1922]. 15 pp., 30 cm.
1750.   J. S. Bach's Fifteen Two-Part Inventions with Harmonic
Structure by Gustave L. Becker... Vol. III, No. 11-15. New York,
Gustave L. Becker [c 1923]. 15 pp., 30 cm.
1751.   J. S. Bach's Fifteen Two Voiced Inventions Analyzed for Self-
Instruction in Polychromatic Notation by Bern Boekelman. New
York, Edward Schuberth, c 1912. 1 l.; 19, 19, [1] pp.; 34 cm.
    Secondary title reads: Harmonic Schemes for a Second Piano (or
    Harmonium), A Supplement to the Colored Edition of Bach's
    Two-Voiced Inventions by Bern Boekelman. Copyright 1912 by
    Bern Boekelman. Double register; black printing, pp. 3-19; poly-
    chrome printing, pp. 3-19.
1752.   J. S. Bach's Fünfzehn zweistimmige Inventionen in mehrfarbiger
Darstellung zur Selbstbelehrung erläutert von Bern Boekelman.
Leipzig, Jul. Heinr. Zimmermann, c 1912. 1 l.; 3-19, 3-19, [1] pp.;
33 cm.
    Secondary title reads: Harmonische Schemas für ein zweites Piano
    (oder Harmonium) als Beilage zur colorirten Ausgabe der Bach'-
    schen Zweistimmigen Inventionen verfasst von Bern Boekelman.
    Copyright 1900, 1912 by Bern Boekelman. Black printing, pp. 3-19;
    Polychrome printing, pp. 3-19.

1753. Joh. Seb. Bach Piano Works...Edited by H. Riemann...6013,
Two-Part Inventions. ... London, Augener [1895?]. 2 ll., 31 pp.,
31 cm. (Augener's Edition, No. 6013.)   P.N.: 10666
1754. Oeuvres originales J. S. Bach, 15 Inventions à 2 voix, 1ʳᵉ partie
[and 2ᵉ partie, 3ᵉ partie, 4ᵉ partie]. Paris, Senart [ca. 1910]. 4 parts.
35 cm. (Nouvelle Édition française de musique classique, Nos.
117-20.)
     General editor of series: Vincent D'Indy. Revision by Blanche
     Selva.   P.N.'s: M.S. & Cⁱᵉ. 117 to M.S. & Cⁱᵉ. 120
1755. Oeuvres pour piano seul par J. S. Bach revues par H. Henkel,
15 Inventions à 2 voix. Offenbach a/M, Johann André [ca. 1885].
27 pp., 30 cm. (Edition André, No. 18.)   P.N.: ANDRÉ 6606
1756. Pianoforte-Musik redigirt und herausgegeben von den Professoren und Lehren...J. Dachs, A Door...und A. Sturm, Joh. Seb.
Bach. (Édition revue et soigneusement doigtée par A. Sturm)...
15 inventions à 2 voix. ... Leipzig, Aug. Cranz [ca. 1895]. 18 pp.,
34 cm. (Classikerausgabe des Wiener Conservatoriums.)
                                                          P.N.: 26350
1757. 15 Inventions...Nouvelle édition soigneusement revue, corrigée
et doigtée...Oeuvres complètes, Liv. V. Offenbach a/M., chez Jean
André, [1847?]. 17 pp., 31 cm.
     At head of title: Oeuvres pour le pianoforte composés par J. S. Bach.
     Signature on first title of volume: Carl Baermann.   P.N.: 6606
1758. XV Inventions pour le clavecin composées par Mʳ. J. S. Bach.
Nouvelle édition. Leipzig, au Bureau de Musique de A. Kühnel
[1805-14]. 15 pp., obl. fol., 24×34 cm., laid paper.
     Imprint shows erasure of Hoffmeister's name and addition of
     Kühnel's.   P.N.: 51
1759. XV Inventions pour le clavecin composées par Mʳ. J. S. Bach.
Vienna, chez Hoffmeister & comp.; Leipzig, au Bureau de Musique
[1801?]. 15 pp., obl. fol., 23×33 cm., wove paper.
     Plates completely different from Kühnel's later edition with same
     plate number.   P.N.: 51
1760. 15 Kétszólamu inventió fokozatos összeállitasban, ujjrenddel
elödási jelekkel és jegyzettekel ellátta Szendy Árpád...15 zweistimmige
Inventionen progressiv geordnet, neu eingerichtet, mit Fingersatz,
Vortragszeichen und Anmerkungen versehen von Szendy Árpád. ...
Budapest, Rosznyai Károly [1906]. 33 pp., 34 cm. (Rozsnyai
Károly Kiadása, No. 186.)   P.N.: R.K. 186
1761. 30 Invenzioni a 2 e 3 parti per pianoforte di Joh. Seb. Bach edite
ed accuratemente rivedute, diteggiate e fraseggiate da Giusseppe
Buonamici. Milan, A. & G. Carisch [ca. 1915]. 39 pp., 31 cm.
     Only the 15 two-part inventions are actually included. At head of
     title: Per la classi di pianoforte del R. Istituto Musicale di Firenze

184   PUBLISHED MUSIC OF J. S. BACH

1762.   Two and Three Part Inventions for Pianoforte...With reference
to the execution and the composition analyzed and revised by
Ferruccio B. Busoni at the Moscow and Boston Conservatories of
Music, English text by Louis C. Elson. Book I, 15 Two part inventions. ... Leipzig, Breitkopf & Härtel, c 1892. 1 l., 31 pp., 33 cm.
(Instructive Edition.)   P.N.: 19772
1763.   Two-Part Inventions for Pianoforte. Analytical edition by John
Thompson. New York, Schroeder & Gunther [c 1927]. 33, [2] pp.;
30 cm. (Gotham Edition, No. 61.)   P.N.: S. & G. Inc. 1441-31
1764.   Two-Part Inventions. Edited by Henry Geehl. London, Edwin
Ashdown, c 1926. 33 pp., 31 cm.   P.N.: E.A.35652
1765.   Zweistimmige Inventionen herausgegeben von Edwin Fischer.
Berlin, Ullstein [c 1924]. 35 pp., 34 cm. (Tonmeister Ausgabe,
No. 3.)   P.N.: T.A. 3.
1766.   Zweistimmige Inventionen im Sopran- und Tenorschlüssel dargestellt für den Gebrauch der Schüler in den Klavier Ausbildungs-
klassen und der Kandidaten für der Musik-Staatsprüfung. Herausgegeben und in seinen Klavierschulen eingeführt von Franz Brixel,
Wien. ... Leipzig, Bosworth, c 1906 [c 1907]. 33 pp., 3 ll., 30 cm.
(Bosworth Edition, No. 551.)   P.N.: B. & C°. 10247
1767.   Zweistimmige Inventionen, Inventions à deux parties. ...
Berlin, Adolph Fürstner [ca. 1870]. 19 pp., 33 cm. (Bibliothek
älterer und neuerer Klaviermusik, No. 23.)
Edited by Franz Kroll.   P.N.: 27

ARRANGEMENTS FOR 4 HANDS

1768.   A Second Piano Part by Louis Victor Saar to the Fifteen Two-
Part Inventions of J. S. Bach for Two Pianos, Four Hands. New York,
G. Schirmer [c 1932]. 1 l., 39 pp., 30 cm.   P.N.: 35595
1769.   A Second Piano Part to the Fifteen Two-Part Inventions of
Johann Sebastian Bach by Ruggero Vené (with original in score).
Philadelphia, Theodore Presser [c 1944]. 41 pp., 31 cm.
                                                P.N.: S.P.B.I.-42

EXCERPTS

1770.   Two Part Invention No. 8. ... New York, Century Music
Publishing Co. [ca. 1935]. [1], 2-3, [1] pp.; 32 cm. (Century
Edition, No. 3418.)
Edited by Walter Rolfe.   P.N.: 3418-2
1771.   Invention Nr. 13 aus den 15 zweistimmigen Inventionen be-
arbeitet von F. B. Busoni.
   In: Was weisst du von Bach? Leipzig, Breitkopf & Härtel, n.d.,
p. 12. Reprinted from Joh. Seb. Bach, Zweistimmige Inventionen
Busoni-Ausgabe (Edition Breitkopf, No. 4340.)   P.N.: 30400.I
1772.   Two-Part Invention [No. 13]. Edited and fingered by Basil

Darrah, John S. Bach. Lincoln (Nebraska), The Bendix Publishing
Co. [ca. 1930]. 5 pp., 32 cm. (Conservatory Series, No. 5207.)
                                                        P.N.: C.S. 185-3

Three-Part Inventions (Sinfonias) (S. 787-801)

COMPLETE SETS

1773. The Academic Edition of Works by Joh: Seb: Bach...236,
Three-Part Inventions. ... London, A. Hammond [ca. 1895]. 1 l.,
31 pp., 30 cm. (Academic Edition, No. 236.)
    Edited, fingered, and annotated by Gordon Saunders.
1774. Akademische Neuausgabe ausgewählter Clavierwerke von Joh.
Seb. Bach. Kritisch revidirt in Bezug aus Textdarstellung, Tempo und
Vortragszeichen und mit Vorwort, Vorbemerkungen und Fingersatz
für den Studiengebrauch versehen von Heinrich Germer. Band 2.
Brunswick, Henry Litolff [ca. 1890]. 5, 47 pp.; 30 cm. (Collection
Litolff, No. 2005.)   P.N.: COLLECTION LITOLFF No. 2005
1775. Dreistimmige Inventionen herausgegeben von Edwin Fischer.
Berlin, Ullstein [c 1924]. 36 pp., 34 cm. (Tonmeister Ausgabe,
No. 4.)   P.N.: T.A.4.
1776. Fifteen Three-Part Inventions for Piano...Edited by Ferruccio
Busoni, English translation by Dr. Th. Baker. New York, G. Schirmer,
c 1926. 1 l.; 39, [1] pp.; 30 cm. (Schirmer's Library of Musical
Classics, No. 1498.)   P.N.: 32533
1777. 15 Three-Part Inventions for Piano...Edited by Stewart
MacPherson. London, Joseph Williams [c 1916]. 37 pp., 1 l., 31 cm.
(Berners Edition, No. 96.)   P.N.: J.W.15631
1778. Inventions à 3 voix. Nouvelle édition, revue et doigtée par
Adolphe F. Wouters. ... Brussels, Schott [ca. 1895]. 31, [1] pp;
34 cm. (Répertoire du Conservatoire Royal de Bruxelles.)
                                                        P.N.: S.F. 3238
1779. Inventions à 3 voix pour piano...Avec analyses et conseils sur
l'interprétation par Georges Sporck. ... Paris, E. Ploix, c 1914. 3 ll.,
54 pp., 1 l., 31 cm. (Edition analytique des classiques.)
                                                P.N.'s: M.432 S. to M.446 S.
1780. Invenzioni a due e a tre voci per pianoforte...rivedute e diteggiate
da Alessandro Longo...111885 Fasc. II, 15 Invenzioni a tre voci. ...
Milan, Ricordi [ca. 1910]. 33 pp., 32 cm. (Biblioteca del pianista,
No. 111885.)   P.N.: 111885
1781. Joh. Seb. Bach's Inventionen mit genauer Bezeichnung der
Phrasierung und neuem Fingersatz von Dr. Hugo Riemann...
Heft II, 15 dreistimmige Inventionen. Leipzig, C. F. Kahnt Nachfolger [ca. 1895]. 31 pp., 34 cm.   P.N.: 2874b
1782. Joh. Seb. Bach's Inventionen mit genauer Bezeichnung der
Phrasierung und neuem Fingersatz von Dr. Hugo Riemann...

186   PUBLISHED MUSIC OF J. S. BACH

1782. *(continued)* Heft II, 15 dreistimmige Inventionen. Leipzig,
C. F. Kahnt Nach- folger [ca. 1910]. 31 pp., 31 cm. P.N.: 2874B
1783. Joh. Seb. Bach's Inventionen mit genauer Bezeichnung der
Phrasierung und neuem Fingersatz von Dr. Hugo Riemann...6014,
15 dreistimmige Inventionen (Three-Part Inventions). London,
Augener [1895?]. 2 ll., 33 pp., 1 l., 31 cm. (Augener's Edition,
No. 6014.)   P.N.: 11088
1784. Joh. Seb. Bach's Pianoforte Works, Edited by John Farmer...
15 Three-Part Inventions. ... London, Augener [ca. 1901]. 1 l.;
iii, 2-35 pp.; 31 cm. (Augener's Edition, No. 8019.)   P.N.: 5568
1785. Oeuvres originales J. S. Bach, Inventions à 3 voix. 1re partie
[and 2e partie, 3e partie, 4e partie]. Paris, Senart [ca. 1910]. 4 parts.
35 cm. (Nouvelle Edition française de musique classique, Nos. 227-
230.)
      General editor of series: Vincent D'Indy. Revision by Blanche
Selva.   P.N.'s: M.S. & Cie. 227 to M.S. & Cie. 230
1786. Pianoforte-Musik redigirt und herausgegeben von den Professoren und Lehren...J. Dachs, A. Door...und A. Sturm, Joh. Seb.
Bach. (Edition revue et soigneusement doigtée par A. Sturm)...
15 inventions à 3 voix. ... Leipzig, Aug. Cranz [ca. 1895]. 19,
[1] pp.; 34 cm. (Classikerausgabe des Wiener Conservatoriums.)
                                                       P.N.: 38349
1787. 15 Symphonies...Nouvelle édition soigneusement revue, corrigée
et doigtée...Oeuvres complets, Liv. V. Offenbach s/M., chez Jean
André [1847?]. 19 pp., 31 cm.
      At head of title: Oeuvres pour le pianoforte composés par J. S. Bach.
Signature on first title page: Carl Baermann.   P.N.: 6607
1788. XV Simphonies pour le clavecin composées par J. S. Bach.
Leipzig, au Bureau de Musique [after 1805]. 20 pp., obl. fol.,
25 × 34 cm., wove paper.   P.N.: 56
1789. XV Simphonies pour le clavecin composées par J. S. Bach.
Propriété de l'editeur. Leipzig, au Bureau de Musique [ca. 1810?].
19 pp., obl. fol., 25 × 33 cm., wove paper.
      Plates completely reengraved and condensed.   P.N.: 56
1790. XV Simphonies pour le clavecin composées par J. S. Bach
Vienna, chez Hoffmeister & comp.; Leipzig, au Bureau de Musique
[ca. 1801]. 20 pp., obl. fol., 24 × 34 cm., wove paper. P.N.: 56
1791. 15 háromszólamu inventió fokozatos összeállitásban, ujjrenddel
elöadási jelekkel és jegyzetekkel ellátta Szendy Árpäd...15 dreistimmige Inventionen progressiv geordnet, neu eingerichtet, mit
Fingersatz, Vortragszeichen und Anmerkungen versehen von Szendy
Árpád. ... Budapest, Rosznyai Károly [1906]. 41 pp., 34 cm.
(Rozsnyai Károly Kiadása, No. 193.)   P.N.: R.K.193
1792. Three-Part Inventions, edited by Henry Geehl. London,
Edwin Ashdown, c 1926. 33 pp., 31 cm.   P.N.: E.A. 35655

EXCERPTS

1793. [Clavierbüchlein vor Wilhelm Friedemann Bach, angefangen in Cöthen den 22 Januar Aō 1720.] Positive photostat of Fantasia 11 (Sinfonia 9) from the Yale University holograph.

1794. J. S. Bach's Ten Three Voiced Inventions (Sinfonias). Analysed for self-instruction in polychromatic notation by Bern Boekelman. New York, Edward Schuberth, c 1904 [c 1913]. 1 l.; 3ª-22ª, 3-22 pp.; 1 l.; 34 cm.
Secondary title reads: Harmonic Schemes for a Second Piano (or Harmonium) as Supplement to the Colored Edition of The Three Voiced Bach-Inventions by Bern Boekelman. Copyright 1905 by Bern. Boekelman. Black printing, pp. 3ª-22ª; polychrome printing, pp. 3-22.

1795. J. S. Bach's Zehn dreistimmige Inventionen (Sinfonias) in mehrfarbiger Darstellung zur Selbstbelehrung erläutert von Bern Boekelman. Leipzig, Jul. Heinr. Zimmerman, c 1913. 1 l.; 3ª-22ª, 3-22 pp.; 1 l.; 33 cm.
Secondary title reads: Harmonische Schemas für ein zweites Piano (oder Harmonium) als Beilage zur Colorirten Ausgabe der Bach'-schen dreistimmigen Inventionen verfasst von Bern. Boekelman. Copyright 1904, 1913 by Bern. Bockelman.

1796. Three Voiced Inventions. ... New York, The American Music Teachers Protective Association Publishing Company, c 1908. 7 pp., 33 cm. (Teacher's Edition Royal.)
Contents: Nos. 1, 7, and 15.
P.N.'s: Three Voiced Invention N°. 1; Three Voiced Invention N°. 7; Three Voiced Invention N°. 15

EXCERPTS, ARRANGED

1797. Invention B dur für Geige und Laute bearbeitet von Heinz Bischoff. Augsburg, Bärenreiter [1926?]. 11, [1] pp.; 30 cm. (Bärenreiter Ausgabe, No. 79.)

ITALIENISCHES KONZERT (S. 971)

1798. Concert italien. Révision et annotations par B. Selva. Paris, Maurice Senart, c 1915. 12 pp., 34 cm. (Édition nationale de musique classique, No. 5023.) P.N.: M.S. & Cᴵᵉ.

1799. Concerto dans le style italien. Nouvelle édition revue, doigtée et annotée par Adolphe F. Wouters. ... Brussels, J. B. Katte (Antoine Ysaije & Co., sccrs.) [ca. 1890]. 15, [1] pp.; 34 cm. P.N.:J.B.K.2979.

1800. Concerto in F in the Italian Style...Edited, phrased and fingered by Geo. Farlane. [London, Joseph Williams, c 1923.] 19, [1] pp.; 31 cm. (Berners Edition, No. 715.)
Preface written and signed by Stewart MacPherson. P.N.:J.W.15948

1801. Concerto Italien pour piano. Édition revue et doigtée par
H. Dallier. ... Paris, Henry Lemoine, c 1924. 1 l., 18 pp., 2 ll., 30
cm. (Édition nationale française Panthéon des pianistes, No. 1332.)
                                              P.N.: 21,665.P.1332.HL.
1802. The Italian Concerto Composed by J. S. Bach. London,
Novello [c 1902]. 2 ll., 22 pp., 1 l., 31 cm. (Novello's School of
Pianoforte Music, No. 4.)
    General editor: Karl Klindworth.   P.N.: 11139
1803. Italienisches Konzert für Klavier zu zwei Händen auf Grund
der Ausgabe von Hans Bischoff herausgegeben von Robert Teichmüller. Leipzig, C. F. Peters [ca. 1930]. 20 pp., 30 cm. (Edition
Peters, No. 4110.)   P.N.: 10788
1804. Italienisches Konzert für Klavier zweihändig. Abdruck aus der
Gesammtausgabe von Dr. Hans Bischoff, Instruktive Neubearbeitung
von Willy Rehberg. Leipzig, Steingräber, c 1931. 15, [1] pp.; 34 cm.
(Edition Steingräber, No. 2355.)   P.N.: 2195
1805. Italienisches Konzert herausgegeben von Edwin Fischer. ...
Berlin, Ullstein [c 1927]. 24 pp., 31 cm. (Tonmeister Ausgabe,
No. 166.)   P.N.: T.A. Nr. 166
1806. Klavierübung II Teil, Concerto nach italienischen Gusto;
Overture nach französischer Art. Nach dem Erstdruck revidiert und
herausgegeben von Kurt Soldan, Fintersatz von Hans Beltz. Leipzig,
C. F. Peters [1937?]. 3 ll., 36 pp., illus., facs. (incl. music), 30 cm.
(Edition Peters, No. 4464.)   P.N.: 11355
1807. Oeuvres originales J. S. Bach, Concert italien. 1re partie [and
2e partie, 3e partie]. Paris, Maurice Senart [ca. 1910]. 3 parts.
35 cm. (Nouvelle Édition française de musique classique, Nos. 129-
131.)
    Imprint for second part reads: Maurice Senart; for third part:
M. Senart, B. Roudanez. General editor: Vincent D'Indy.
Revision by Blanche Selva.
         P.N.'s: M.S. & Cie. 129; M.S. 130; S. R. & Cie. 131.

KLAVIERBÜCHLEIN FÜR WILHELM FRIEDEMANN BACH

1808. Johann Sebastian Bach, Klavierbüchlein für Friedemann Bach
herausgegeben von Hermann Keller. Kassel, Bärenreiter, 1929. 127,
[1] pp.; obl. fol.; 24 × 33 cm.

DIE KUNST DER FUGE (S. 1080)

Scores

1809. L'Art de la fugue à quatre parties par Jean Sebastien Bach.
Paris, chez Vogt [ca. 1802]. 1 l.; [1], 2-135 pp.; 32 cm.; laid paper.
1810. L'Art de la fugue (Kunst der Fuge) par Jean Sebastien Bach.

Édition nouvelle, soigneusement revue, corrigée et doigtée, ainsi que pourvue de notifications sur l'exécution et sur mesures des temps (d'après le métronome de Maelzel) et accompagnée d'une préface par un Comité d'artistes. ... Leipzig, au Bureau de Musique de C. F. Peters [1839?]. 1 l., 79 pp., 33 cm. (Oeuvres complets, Livre III.) P.N.: 2690

1811. Joh. Seb. Bachs Kunst der Fuge mit den Notentext eingefügten Analysen und Bemerkungen von M. Ritter. ... Leipzig, Max Hesse [1910]. 81, [1] pp.; 28 cm. P.N.: M.H.V.202

1812. Die Kunst der Fuge (The Art of Fugue)...Edited and completed, with a dissertation, by Donald Francis Tovey...edition in open score for the use of students. London, Oxford University Press [c 1931]. 3 ll.; [1], i-ii, 127, [1] pp.
Professor Tovey's commentary on this edition is published separately under the title A Companion to "The Art of Fugue". ...

1813. Die Kunst der Fuge [The Art of Fugue]...Phrasierungsausgabe von Dr. Hugo Riemann. London, Augener [1914?]. 81 pp., 1 l., 31 cm. (Augener's Edition, No. 6015.) P.N.: 11434

1814. Die Kunst der Fuge durch Herrn Johann Sebastian Bach ehemahligen Capellmeister und Musikdirector zu Leipzig. [Leipzig, 1752]. 2 ll., 1-67 pp., obl. fol., 23 × 36 cm., laid paper, ¾ calf (original watered boards included in binding).
Vorbericht, on leaf 2 signed by Marpurg and dated: in der Leipziger Ostermesse 1752. Bookplate of Heinrich Bellermann on inside of original front wrapper.

1815. Die Kunst der Fuge herausgegeben von Hans Th. David. Leipzig, C. F. Peters [c 1928]. xvi, 148 pp.; 8 ll.; illus. (incl. music); facs.; 31 cm. (Edition Peters, No. 3940.)
Last 8 leaves contain Beilage zu Joh. Seb. Bach, Kunst der Fuge herausgegeben von H. Th. David. Six facsimiles from the autograph. P.N.: 10625

1816. Die Kunst der Fuge von Johann Sebastian Bach. Zürich, bey Hans Georg Nägeli [1802?]. 2 ll.; [1], 2-183 pp.; obl. fol.; 25 × 33 cm.; laid paper; ¾ calf.
General title, bound before title: Musikalische Kunstwerke im strengen Style von J. S. Bach u. andern Meistern. Zürich bey Hans Georg Nägeli. MS. notation on front flyleaf: Geschenk von A. E. Müller | in Leipzig. 1805. MS. notation in top margin of general title: Geschenk von A. E. Müller in Leipzig | 1806.

Arrangements

1817. The Art of the Fugue Transcribed for String Quartet by Roy Harris and M. D. Herter Norton. ... New York, G. Schirmer [c 1936]. xxxiv, 113 pp.; illus.; facs. (incl. music); 28 cm. P.N.: 36665

1818.   Die Kunst der Fuge...Für die Orgel übertragen und zu Studien-
zwecken mit genauer Bezeichnung des Vortrags, so wie der Manual-
u. Pedal-Applicatur versehen von G. Ad. Thomas. ... Leipzig &
Winterthur, J. Rieter-Biedermann [ca. 1865]. 6 parts. 34 cm.
Incomplete: Part 4 wanting.   P.N.'s: 440a-440f
1819.   Die Kunst der Fuge für zwei Klaviere gesetzt von Erich
Schwebsch nach der Neuordnung von Wolfgang Graeser. Wolfenbüttel & Berlin, Georg Kallmeyer, 1937. ix, 121 pp.; illus. (facs.);
33 cm.
Two copies.
1820.   Die Kunst der Fuge, Nach dem Originalsatz für die Orgel eingerichtet von Hans Schurich, Teil I Contrapunctus I-XI [and Teil II
Contrapunctus XII-XIX]. Heidelberg, Willy Müller-Süddeutscher
Musikverlag [c 1953]. 2 vols. Obl. fol., 24 × 31 cm.
                        P.N.'s: W.M. 2033 S.M.; W.M. 2034 S.M.

Excerpts

1821.   Fuga, J. S. Bach [caption-title]. Erfurt, Leipzig, Gotth. Wilh.
Körner [1850?]. Pp. 48-49, obl. 4°, 23 × 28 cm., wove paper. (Der
Orgel-Virtuos, No. 264.)
Contents: Fugue No. 1.   P.N.: XII

MAGNIFICAT (S. 243)

FULL SCORES

1822.   Magnificat à cinque voci, due violini, due oboe, tre trombi,
tamburi, basson, viola e basso continuo, del Sigl. J. S. Bach. ... Bonn,
chez N. Simrock [1811?]. 1 l., 3-53 pp., 33 cm., wove paper.
  Paper label over original imprint reads: Zu haben in Prag bey
Haas. Jesuitengasse, im Gelben Hause Nro. 186. This edition in
key of E♭ major, edited by Georg Pölchau.   P.N.: 770
1823.   Magnificat...für die Aufführung eingerichtet von Karl Straube.
Partitur. Leipzig, C. F. Peters [1909?]. 71 pp., 34 cm. (Edition
Peters, No. 29a.)
  At head of title: Max Reger zu eigen.   P.N.: 9446
1824.   Magnificat (in D dur) bearbeitet von Robert Franz. ... Breslau,
F. E. C. Leuckart (Constantin Sander) [1864?]. 2 ll., 75 pp., 34 cm.
                                            P.N.: F.E.C.L.1810
1825.   Magnificat...Nach der Ausgabe der Bach-Gesellschaft und
nach dem in der Preussischen Staatsbibliothek in Berlin befindlichen
Autograph revidiert und mit Vorwort versehen von Arnold Schering.
Leipzig, Eulenburg [1924?]. 3 ll., 88 pp., 3 ll., 19 cm. (Eulenburgs
kleine Partitur-Ausgabe, No. 964.)   P.N.: E.E.4378
1826.   Magnificat neu herausgegeben von...Herman Roth. Vienna

Wiener Philharmonischer Verlag, A.G. [1923?]. 4 ll., 98 pp., frontis. (port.), 19 cm. (Philharmonia Partituren, No. 99.) P.N.: W.Ph.V.99.

VOCAL-PIANO SCORES

1827. Magnificat. ... [Princeton, New Jersey] Association of American Choruses [1952?]. 1 l., 44 pp., 1 l., 26 cm. (Choral Series, No. 208.) Photo-offset lithograph process. Translation by Henry S. Drinker.

1828. Magnificat D dur...Klavierauszug bearbeitet von S. Jadassohn. Leipzig, Breitkopf & Härtel [ca. 1925]. 1 l., 51 pp., 27 cm. (Edition Breitkopf, No. 3360.) P.N.: J.S.B.IV.6

1829. Magnificat...im Klavierauszuge mit Text von Gustav Rösler. Leipzig, C. F. Peters [1878?]. 47 pp., 27 cm. P.N.: 6195

1830. Magnificat (in D)...Accompaniments arranged by Robert Franz. Cincinnati, John Church, c 1874. 1 l., 48 pp., 25 cm.

1831. Magnificat (in D dur) bearbeitet von Robert Franz. ... Breslau, F. E. C. Leuckart (Constantin Sander) [ca. 1860]. 59 pp., 34 cm. On front cover is stamped name: Walter Damrosch.
P.N.: F.E.C.L.1783

1832. Magnificat (in D) in Vocal Score with an Accompaniment for the Organ or Pianoforte...the adaptation to English words by the Rev. J. Troutbeck. ... London, Novello [ca. 1915]. 2 ll.; 58, [2], 8 pp.; 26 cm. (Novello's Original Octavo Edition.) Two copies.
P.N.: Bach's Magnificat. – Novello, Ewer and Co.'s Octavo Edition.

1833. Magnificat...Klavierauszug mit Text im Anschluss an die Straubésche Einrichtung neu bearbeitet von Herman Roth. Leipzig, C. F. Peters [ca. 1911]. 52 pp., 1 l., 27 cm. (Edition Peters, No. 40.) Two copies.
P.N.: 9507

1834. Magnificat...Klavierauszug mit Text im Anschluss an die Straubésche Einrichtung neu bearbeitet von Herman Roth. Leipzig, C. F. Peters [1943?]. 52 pp., 28 cm. (Edition Peters, No. 40.)
P.N.: 9507 [new plates]

1835. Magnificat...Klavierauszug mit Text im Anschluss an die Straubésche Einrichtung neu bearbeitet von Herman Roth. New York, London, Frankfurt, C. F. Peters Corporation [after 1950]. 2 ll., 52 pp., 28 cm. (Edition Peters, No. 40.) This edition contains the program notes written by Albert Riemenschneider for the 1950 performance of the *Magnificat* at the Baldwin-Wallace Bach Festival; these notes form the so-called historical preface published with this edition.
P.N.: 9507

1836. Oratorien, Messen und andere Kirchenmusik im Klavierauszuge mit Text, Bach, J. S. ... Magnificat. ... Leipzig, C. F. Peters, Bureau de Musique [ca. 1865]. 56 pp., 26 cm. Klavier-Auszug von Hugo Ulrich. Autograph signature on title page: A. Hertzberg.
P.N.: 4440

EXCERPTS

1837. All Men, Now Sing, Rejoice...English translation by Max T.
Krone, arranged and edited by M.T.K. Chicago, Ill., The Neil A.
Kjos Music Co. [c 1937]. 8 pp., 26 cm. (Northwestern University
A Cappella Choir Series, No. 507.)
German text: Freut euch und jubilirt.   P.N.: 507-6
1838. Aria – "Et exultavit" "My Soul Rejoices" from the Magnificat
...Arranged and edited by W. G. Whittaker. London, Oxford
University Press, c 1928. 6 pp., 26 cm. (Oxford Choral Songs from
the Old Masters, No. 1440.)
1839. Duet "Et misericordia" "And His mercy" from the Magnificat
...Arranged and edited by W. G. Whittaker. London, Oxford
University Press, c 1928. 7 pp., 26 cm. (Oxford Choral Songs from
the Old Masters, No. 1439.)
1840. Drei Stücke aus dem Magnificat...Für die Orgel übertragen
von Robert Schaab, No. 1 Arie [No. 6]. ... Leipzig, Rob. Forberg
[ca. 1865]. 5, [1] pp.; 31 cm.   P.N.: 461
1841. From Heav'n Above...Edited by Max T. Krone. Chicago, Ill.,
The Neil A. Kjos Music Co. [c 1937]. 9 pp., 26 cm. (Northwestern
University A Cappella Choir Series, No. 506.)   P.N.: 506-7
1842. Gloria in Excelsis Deo!...Edited by Max T. Krone. Chicago,
Ill., The Neil Al Kjos Music Co. [c 1937]. 1 l., 6 pp., 26 cm. (Northwestern University A Cappella Choir Series, No. 505.)   P.N.: 505-4

MASSES

Collections (S. 233-236)

FULL SCORES

1843. Vier kurze Messen, Vier Sanctus und Magnificat von Joh. Seb.
Bach. Partitur. Leipzig, C. F. Peters [ca. 1880]. 179 pp., 31 cm.
(Edition Peters, No. 25.)
This edition contains the so-called short masses in F major, A
major, G minor, and G major; it does not contain the four settings
of the Sanctus, nor the Magnificat called for in the title. P.N.: 4569

Single Works

MASS IN B MINOR (S. 232): Full scores

1844. Hohe Messe (H moll)...Für die Aufführung eingerichtet von
Herm. Kretzschmar. Leipzig, Breitkopf & Härtel, c 1899. 2 ll.,
271 pp., 33 cm. (Partitur-Bibliothek. Messen.)   P.N.: Part. B. 629
1845. Die hohe Messe in H moll...Nach der Ausgabe der Bach-
Gesellschaft revidiert und mit einem Vorwort versehen von Fritz
Volbach. Leipzig, Eulenburg [1920?]. xvi, 352 pp.; 2 ll.; 19 cm.
(Eulenburgs kleine Partitur-Ausgabe, No. 959.)   P.N.: E.E.3999

1846.   Die Hohe Messe in H moll...Partitur.   Hierzu Orgelstimme von
S. Jadassohn.   Leipzig, C. F. Peters [ca. 1895].   249 pp., 31 cm.
(Edition Peters, No. 24.)   P.N.: 4536
1847.   Die Hohe Messe in H-moll von Joh. Seb. Bach, nach dem
Autographum gestochen.   Partitur.   I [and II] Lieferung. ... Bonn,
bei N. Simrock; Zürich, bei H. G. Nägeli [1845? 1833?].   2 vols. in 1;
[2], 3-93 pp. (Vol. 1); [2], 3-95 pp. (Vol. 2); 33 cm.; wove paper.
Facsimile signature on title page of Vol. I: August Grüters.
                                                P.N.'s: 5414, 4377
1848.   Messe von Johann Sebastian Bach nach dem Autographum
gestochen.   Erste Lieferung. ... Zürich, bey Hans Georg Nägeli;
Bonn, bey N. Simrock [ca. 1800].   95 pp., 34 cm., laid paper (watermarked: ʃB).
       Imperfect: Part II and title for Part I wanting.   P.N.: 6
1849.   [MS. title:] Misʃa a 5 Voci.   2 Soprani Alto Tenore Basʃo
3 Trombe Tambur 2 Traverʃo 2 Oboi 2 Violini 1 Viola & Continuo
di I. S. Bach.   Facsimile-Ausgabe der Handschrift von Johann
Sebastian Bachs Hoher Messe in H-moll. ... Leipzig, Glass & Tuscher
für Insel-Verlag, 1924.   1 l., 1-95, [1] pp.; 1 l., 97-152 pp., 1 l.,
153-168 pp., 2 ll., 169-188 pp.; 40 cm.
       Copy No. 295 of 550 numbered copies.   Facsimile of Berlin Biblio-
thek MS. Bach P. 180.

MASS IN B MINOR (S. 232): Parts, vocal

1850.   Messe in H moll, Einrichtung für den Philharmonischen Chor,
Berlin (Siegfr. Ochs).   Sopran I [and Sopran II; Alt; Tenor; Bass].
Leipzig, Breitkopf & Härtel [ca. 1895].   5 parts in 1 vol. 26 cm.
(Chorbibliothek, No. 1285a/b.)
                          P.N.'s: Ch.B.1285.S.I.; Ch.B.1285.S.II;
                          Ch.B.1285.A.; Ch.B.1285.T.; Ch.B.1285.B.

MASS IN B MINOR (S. 232): Vocal-piano scores

1851.   Collection des oeuvres classiques, Die Hohe Messe (H-moll) von
Johann Sebastian Bach.   Clavier-Auszug und Stimmen nach dem
Original herausgegeben von Julius Stern, Königl. Musikdirector. ...
Berlin, Ed. Bote & G. Bock [1855?].   1 l., 247 pp., 35 cm.
       Presentation inscription to Dr. Lindner and autograph signature by
Julius Stern on title.   P.N.: B. & B. 4704.
1852.   H moll Messe, Messe en Si mineur, Mass in B minor...Clavier-
Auszug mit Text.   Brunswick, Henry Litolff [ca. 1885].   176 pp.,
28 cm. (Collection Litolff, No. 222.)
                          P.N.: COLLECTION LITOLFF No. 222
1853.   Die Hohe Messe in H moll...Klavierauszug von Gustav Rösler.
Leipzig, C. F. Peters [ca. 1885].   163 pp., 27 cm. (Edition Peters,
No. 37.)   P.N.: 8249

1854. Die hohe Messe in H moll...Vollständiger Klavier-Auszug mit
Text nach der Partitur revidiert von Josef Vockner. Vienna, Leipzig,
Universal Edition, Aktiengesellschaft [1927?]. 163 pp., 27 cm.
(Universal Edition, No. 853.)   P.N.: U.E.853
1855. Die Hohe Messe in H-moll von Joh. Seb. Bach für 2 Sopran,
Alt, Tenor u. Bass. Clavierauszug von Adolph Bernhard Marx.
Bonn, bei N. Simrock [1834?]. 126 pp., obl. fol., 26 × 33 cm., wove
paper. (Kirchen-Musik, Band 3.)
    General title reads: Kirchen-Musik...herausgegeben von...Marx.
    Clavierauszug IIIter Band. Bonn, bei N. Simrock. On inside of
    front cover is signature: Alf Angel.   P.N.: 3038
1856. Joh. Seb. Bach. Klavierauszüge...Messen. 1. Hohe Messe in
h moll. ... Leipzig, Breitkopf & Härtel [c 1927]. 1 l., 215 pp., 27 cm.
(Edition Breitkopf, No. 3105.)
    Caption title contains statement: Klavierauszug von Jul. Spengel
    (Unter Benutzung der Orgelstimme und Bezeichnungen von
    H. Kretzschmar).   P.N.: J.S.B.IV.1
1857. Johann Sebastian Bach's Werke, Für Gesang. Gesammtausgabe
für den praktischen Gebrauch. IV. Messen. Vollständiger Klavierauszug, Band 1, Nr. 1, Hohe Messe in H moll. ... Leipzig, Breitkopf
& Härtel [1899?]. 1 l., 215 pp., 28 cm. (Edition Breitkopf, No. 3105.)
    Caption title contains statement: Klavierauszug von Jul. Spengel
    (Unter Benutzung der Orgelsitmme und Bezeichnungen von
    H. Kretzschmar). Different plates from those bearing copyright
    date 1927.   P.N.: J.S.B.IV. 1.
1858. Mass in B minor...Edited by Frank Damrosch. New York,
G. Schirmer [c 1899]. vi pp., 1 l., 199 pp., 26 cm.   P.N.: 15053
1859. Mass in B minor in vocal score. ... London, Novello [1908?].
iv, 202, [1] pp.; 26 cm. (Novello's Original Octavo Edition.)
    Preface signed and dated: F. G. Edwards; October, 1907.
    Editorial note signed and dated: Arthur Sullivan; October, 1886.
    Additional editorial note dated: February, 1908.
             P.N.: J. S. Bach-Mass in B minor. – Novello,
                   Ewer and Co.'s Octavo Edition.

MASS IN B MINOR (S. 232): Piano scores with solo parts

1860. Cembalo zu J. S. Bach's Messe H moll von M. Seiffert. Leipzig
C. F. Peters [1916?]. 1 l., 76 pp., 33 cm.
    Includes vocal parts for solos, duets, etc., but not choruses.
                                                   P.N.: 10057
1861. Orchester-Bibliothek. Messen und Requiem...Bach, Hohe
Messe, H moll. (Orgel). ... Leipzig, Breitkopf & Härtel [c 1899].
1 l., 81 pp., 34 cm. (Orchesterbibliothek, No. 1095/1099.)
    Für die Aufführung eingerichtet von Herm. Kretzschmar.
                                              P.N.: Orch. B. 1095/99

MASS IN B MINOR (S. 232): Excerpts

1862. Chorus—"Cum sancto spiritu." London, Novello [ca. 1900]. 16 pp., 27 cm. (Novello's Octavo Choruses, No. 835.)
 P.N.: J. S. Bach—Mass in B minor. – Novello, Ewer and Co.'s Octavo Edition.
1863. Cruxifixus (Mass in B minor). ... London, Novello, 1923. Pp. [118]-134, 27 cm. (Novello's Octavo Choruses, No. 720.)
 P.N.: J. S. Bach—Mass in B minor. – Novello, Ewer and Co.'s Octavo Edition.

MASS IN F MAJOR (S. 233): Vocal-piano scores

1864. Joh. Seb. Bach's Messen im Klavierauszuge bearbeitet von Gustav Rösler. ... Leipzig, C. F. Peters [ca. 1890]. 47 pp., 27 cm. (Edition Peters, No. 1018a.)
 Autograph signature on title: Th. Gouvy.   P.N.: 5456
1865. Messe in F dur, Bach's Werke, Messe Nr. 2. Klavierauszug von S. Jadassohn. Leipzig, Breitkopf & Härtel [ca. 1895]. 1 l., 42 pp., 27 cm.   P.N.: J.S.B.IV.2.

MASS IN F MAJOR (S. 233): Vocal score

1866. F Major Mass. ... [Philadelphia] University of Pennsylvania [ca. 1935]. 31 pp., 26 cm. (Choral Series, No. 128.)
 Edited by Henry S. Drinker.

MASS IN A MAJOR (S. 234): Full score

1867. Missa à 4 voci, due flauti, due violini, viola ed organo di Giov. Seb. Bach, No. I. Dopo partitura autografia dell'autore. Bonn, Cologne, Presso N. Simrock [ca. 1820]. 47 pp., 33 cm., wove paper. Edited by Georg Poelchau. Signature on title: F. W. Rühl.
          P.N.: 1580

MASS IN A MAJOR (S. 234): Vocal-piano scores

1868. Joh. Seb. Bach's Messen im Klavierauszuge bearbeitet von Gustav Rösler. ... Leipzig, C. F. Peters [ca. 1890]. 45 pp., 27 cm. (Edition Peters, No. 1018b.)
 Autograph signature on title: Th. Gouvy.   P.N.: 5457
1869. Messe in A dur, Bach's Werke, Messe Nr. 3. Klavierauszug von S. Jadassohn. Leipzig, Breitkopf & Härtel [ca. 1895]. 44 pp. (pp. 43-86).   P.N.: J.S.B.IV.3.

MASS IN G MINOR (S. 235): Vocal-piano scores

1870. Joh. Seb. Bach's Messen im Klavierauszuge bearbeitet von Gustav Rösler. ... Leipzig, C. F. Peters [ca. 1890]. 48 pp., 27 cm. (Edition Peters, No. 1018c.)
 Autograph signature on title: Th. Gouvy.   P.N.: 5458

1871. Messe in G moll, Bach's Werke, Messe Nr. 4, Klavierauszug von S. Jadassohn. Leipzig, Breitkopf & Härtel [ca. 1895]. 44 pp. (pp. 87-130), 27 cm.   P.N.: J.S.B.IV.4.

MASS IN G MAJOR (S. 236): Full scores

1872. Missa quatuor vocibus cantanda comitante orchestra a Joanne Sebastiano Bach, No. II. Bonnae sumtibus N. Simrock [1828?]. 55 pp., obl. fol., 25 × 34 cm., wove paper, engraved green boards. Edited by Georg Poelchau. Stamp on title page: Walsenhaus zu Züllichau.   P.N.: 2604

MASS IN G MAJOR (S. 236): Vocal-piano scores

1873. Joh. Seb. Bach's Messen im Klavierauszuge bearbeitet von Gustav Rösler. ... Leipzig, C. F. Peters [ca. 1890]. 53 pp., 27 cm. (Edition Peters, No. 1018d.)
Autograph signature on title: Th. Gouvy.   P.N.: 5459
1874. Messe in G dur, Bach's Werke, Messe Nr. 5. Klavierauszug von S. Jadassohn. Leipzig, Breitkopf & Härtel, 1895. 46 pp. (pp. 131-76), 27 cm.   P.N.: J.S.B.IV.5.

MINUETS, SELECTED

1875. Oeuvres originales J. S. Bach, Trois Menuets. Paris, Maurice Senart [ca. 1910]. 3 pp., 35 cm. (Nouvelle Édition française de musique classique, No. 293.)
General editor of series: Vincent D'Indy. Revision by Blanche Selva.   P.N.: 293

MOTETS

Collections (S. 225-231; Anhang 159)

1876. Joh. Seb. Bach's Motetten in Partitur. Erster [and Zweites] Heft ... Leipzig, Breitkopf & Härtel [1802-1803?]. 2 vols. 34 cm., laid paper, mottled boards.
On labels and on title page of Vol. I is signature: A. W. Gottschalg.
Edited by Johann Gottfried Schicht.
1877. Joh. Seb. Bach Motetten, Klavierauszüge, Bach's Werke. Leipzig, Breitkopf & Härtel [1893?]. 3 ll., 207 pp., 27 cm.
Double pagination in Motets 2, 5, 6, and 8.
                                          P.N.: J.S.B.II.1-8
1878. Johann Sebastian Bach's six motetts. In score, with an adaptation for the pianoforte or organ, for use at rehearsals; the English version written and adapted by W. Bartholomew. ... London, Ewer & Co. [ca. 1850]. 3 ll., 143 pp., 3 ll., frontis., 39 cm., wove paper.

Frontispiece is lithograph by R. Rosenthal after the portrait by Haussmann. Penciled signature on front flyleaf: I. R. Lunn.
P.N.: Bach's Motetts.

1879. Motetten von Joh. Seb. Bach in Partitur, Neue Ausgabe. Leipzig, C. F. Peters [ca. 1906]. 133 pp., 27 cm. (Edition Peters, No. 28.)   P.N.: 8945

Single Works

MOTET NO. 1. Singet dem Herrn ein neues Lied (S. 225)

1880. Der 149te Psalm von Joh: Seb: Bach, "Singet dem Herrn ein neues Lied." Berlin, Trautwein [1828?]. 8 part-books. 18 cm. (Klassische Werke, No. 3.)
Stamp on page 1 of each part-book: Koen. Schullehrer Seminar zu Potsdam. Full series title: Klassische Werke alterer und neuerer Kirchenmusik in ausgesetzten Chorstimmen.

1881. Motet No. 1. "Sing ye to the Lord," for double chorus...Edited, with marks of expression and phrasing by Henry J. Wood, English version by G. W. Daisley. Leipzig, Breitkopf & Härtel [ca. 1904]. 1 l., 42 pp., 27 cm. (Joh. Seb. Bach Vocal Scores, Motets, No. 1.)
P.N.: 24158

1882. Sing Ye to the Lord (Singet dem Herrn), Motet for double choir. The English words adapted from psalms 149 and 150 by William Bartholomew...edited by John E. West (revised 1927). London, Novello; New York, H. W. Gray, ca. 1927. 2 ll., 92 pp., 25 cm. (Novello's Original Octavo Edition.)   P.N. 12001

1883. Sing Ye to the Lord. Edited by Charles Kennedy Scott, the words translated and adapted from the German by Beatrice E. Bulman. London, Oxford University Press, c 1929. 2 ll., 92 pp., 27 cm.

MOTET NO. 1 (S. 225): Excerpt

1884. All Breathing Life, Sing and Praise Ye the Lord, Finale from the motet "Sing Ye to the Lord." For four-part chorus of mixed voices... edited by John Finley Williamson. New York, G. Schirmer, c 1931. 12 pp., 27 cm. (G.S. 8vo Choruses, No. 7407. Westminster Choir series, No. 1.)

MOTET NO. 2. Der Geist hilft unsrer Schwachheit auf (S. 226)

1885. Motet No. 2, J. S. Bach. ...[Philadelphia] Association of American Choruses [1951?]. 43 pp., 25 cm. (Choral Series, No. 201.) Edited by Henry S. Drinker.

1886. Motet "The Spirit also Helpeth Us," for double chorus... English version by Claude Aveling. Leipzig, Breitkopf & Härtel [ca. 1905]. 1 l., 22 pp., 27 cm. (Joh. Seb. Bach Vocal Scores, Motets, No. 2.)   P.N.: 25860

1887. The Spirit also Helpeth Us (Der Geist hilft unsrer Schwachheit auf) Motet for double choir. The English words adapted from Romans VIII, 26, 27 by William Bartholomew...edited by John E. West. London, Novello; New York, H. W. Gray [1925?]. 1 l. 42 pp., 25 cm. (Novello's Original Octavo Edition.)   P.N.: 12054

MOTET NO. 3. Jesu meine Freude (S. 227)

1888. 'Jesu, Joy and Treasure.' Edited by W. G. Whittaker, English version of Franck's hymn by C. Sanford Terry. London, Oxford University Press, c 1925. 4 ll., 76 pp., 25 cm.
1889. Jesu, Priceless Treasure...Motet for Five Voices...Revised for the Leeds musical festival, 1913...translated and adapted by W. Bartholomew. London, Novello; New York, H. W. Gray [ca. 1913]. 2 ll., 57 pp., 25 cm. (Novello's Original Octavo Edition.)
       Preface signed: H.P.A. (Sir Hugh Percy Allen).   P.N.: 13803
1890. Jesus Dearest Master. ... [Philadelphia] Association of American Choruses [1951?]. 1 l., 57 pp., 26 cm. (Choral Series, No. 199.) Edited by Henry S. Drinker.
1891. Jesus, Priceless Treasure, Motet for Five Voices. Edited by Frank Damrosch. ... New York, G. Schirmer [c 1927]. 1 l., 56 pp., 26 cm. (Musical Art Society of New York, No. 8.)
       Three copies.   P.N.: 14354
1892. Motet No. 3. ... [Philadelphia] University of Pennsylvania, n.d. 44 pp., 27 cm. (Choral Series, No. 69.)
       [Edited by Henry S. Drinker.] Vocal score, unaccompanied.

MOTET NO. 4. Fürchte dich nicht, ich bin bei dir (S. 228)

1893. "Be Not Afraid," Motet...Edited by H. H. Wetzler, revised by Carl Deis. New York, G. Schirmer, c 1934. 31 pp., 27 cm. (G. Schirmer, Octavo No. 7806.)   P.N.: 36416
1894. Be Not Afraid, Motet for Double Choir...Edited by G. R. Sinclair. London, Novello; New York, H. W. Gray [1929?]. 27 pp., 25 cm. (Novello's Original Octavo Edition.)
1895. Be Not Afraid, Motet for Double Chorus...Vocal score, revised and annotated by Hermann Hans Wetzler. New York, G. Schirmer, c 1901. 2 ll., 31 pp., 27 cm. (Musical Art Society of New York, No. 45.)   P.N.: 15596
1896. "Be Not Afraid," for Eight-Part Chorus...Edited by Henry J. Wood, translation by Fanny S. Copeland. Leipzig, Breitkopf & Härtel [ca. 1909]. 26 pp., 27 cm. (Joh. Seb. Bach Vocal Scores, Motets, No. 4.)   P.N.: 26139

MOTET NO. 5. Komm, Jesu, komm (S. 229)

1897. Come, Jesu, Come (Komm, Jesu, komm), Motet for Double Choir. The English words by William Bartholomew...edited by

John E. West. London, Novello; New York, H. W. Gray [1923?].
1 l., 49 pp., 25 cm. (Novello's Original Octavo Edition.)
P.N.: 12071
1898. Motet No. 5, "Come, Jesu, Come," for Eight-Part Chorus...
Edited by Henry J. Wood. Leipzig, Breitkopf & Härtel, n.d.   1 l.,
24 pp., 1 l., 27 cm. (Breitkopf & Härtel's Anthems, Services, etc.,
No. 15.)

MOTET NO. 6.   Lobet den Herrn, alle Heiden (S. 230)

1899. Der 117te Psalm für vier Singstimmen in Musik gesetzt von
Joh. Sebastian Bach, Partiur, Nach J. S. Bach's Original-Handschrift.
Leipzig, bey Breitkopf und Härtel [ca. 1820]. 1 l., 3-13 pp., 33 cm.,
laid paper, original mottled boards.
    Below imprint is stamp: Prag bei Marco Berra.
1900. Motet No. 6. ... [Philadelphia] University of Pennsylvania, n.d.
19 pp., 27 cm. (Choral Series, No. 35.)
    [Edited by Henry S. Drinker.]
1901. Motet No. 6, "Praise the Lord All Ye Heathen"...Edited by
Henry J. Wood. Leipzig, Breitkopf & Härtel [ca. 1908]. 1 l., 15 pp.,
27 cm. (Joh. Seb. Bach Vocal Scores, Motets, No. 6.)   P.N.: 25891
1902. O Praise the Lord, All Ye Nations...Psalm 117, Motet for
Chorus and Organ...Edited by John Pointer. London, Novello;
New York, H. W. Gray, c 1930. 1 l., 28 pp., 25 cm. (Novello's
Original Octavo Edition.)   P.N.: 15562

MUSIKALISCHES OPFER (S. 1079)

Complete

1903. Compositions pour le clavecin seul par J. Seb. Bach. Edition
nouvelle, revue et corrigée critiquement, doigtée, métronomisée et
enrichie de notes sur l'exécution par C. Czerny, F. C. Griepenkerl et
F. A. Roitzsch. Leipzig & Berlin, C. F. Peters [1866?]. 51 pp.,
33 cm., wove paper. (Oeuvres de Bach, Série I, Cahier 12.)
P.N.: 4557
1904. Musical Offering...Authentic text and version for practical
performance prepared by Hans T. David for string and wind en-
sembles with keyboard instrument. ... New York, G. Schirmer
[c 1944]. 88 pp., 30 cm.
    Autograph signature on title page: Hans T. David.   P.N.: 40062
1905. Musicalisches Opfer. Sr. Königlichen Majestät in Preussen &c.
allerunterthänigst gewidmet von Johann Sebastian Bach. [Leipzig,
J. G. Schübler, 1747.] 2 ll.; 1-4 pp.; 2 ll.; [1], 2-7 pp.; obl. & upright
fol.; 24 × 38 cm.
    Unbound positive and negative photostat of Pölchau copy in Berlin
Bibliothek.

1906. Musikalisches Opfer. Seiner Königlichen Majestät von Preussen allerunterthänigst gewidmet von Johann Sebastian Bach. Neue Ausgabe mit einer Vorrede über die Entstehung dieses Werk's. Leipzig, Breitkopf & Härtel [1831?]. 1 l.; [2], 3-45 pp.; obl. fol.; 26 × 34 cm.; wove paper.
Edited by C. G. Müller, according to Kinsky.　　　P.N.: 5153
1907. Musikalisches Opfer... Version Roger Vuataz pour quatuor à cordes solo, flûte, hautbois, cor anglais, basson et clavecin. Brussels, Ars Viva, c 1937. 6, 48 pp.; 30 cm.　　　P.N.: 7405

Excerpts

1908. Compositions pour violon et pour flûte par Jean Sebastian Bach ...Edition nouvelle, revue et corrigée critiquement par Ferd. David, J. Hellmesberger et Fr. Hermann...sonate pour flûte, violon et piano. ... Leipzig & Berlin, C. F. Peters, Bureau de Musique [1867?]. Score and 2 parts. 34 cm. (Oeuvres complètes, Série III, Cahier 8, No. 3.) Wove paper.　　　P.N.: 4565
1909. [Caption title:] Fuga super thema Regium. Erfurt, Leipzig, Gotth. Wilh. Körner [1845?]. 5 pp., obl. 4°, 24 × 27 cm. (Der Orgel-Virtuos, No. 15.)
Ewer's stamp on wrapper; also stamp: Vertrag vom 13 Mai, 1846.　　　P.N.: 22.I.35
1910. G. S. Bach, Sonata a tre (da "Das Musikalische Opfer") Trascrizione per violino, violoncello e pianoforte ed interpretazione del "continuo" originale a cura di Alfredo Casella. ... Milan, Ricordi, c 1934. Score and 2 parts. 32 cm. (Edizione Ricordi, No. 1636.)
Caption of the violin part contains phrase: Revision violinistica di Alberto Poltronieri. Caption of the violoncellopart contains phrase: Revisione violoncellistica di Arturo Bonucci.　　　P.N.: E.R.1636
1911. Ricercar a 6 voci aus Musikalisches Opfer...gesetzt für Klavier zu 4 Händen von Tristram Cary. ... London, Peters Edition & Hinrichsen Edition, c 1955. 16 pp., 31 cm. (Edition Peters, No. 219a.)
　　　P.N.: Edition Peters No. 219a

NOTENBUCH FÜR ANNA MAGDALENA BACH, No. 2

Complete

1912. Johann Sebastian Bach's Notenbüchlein für Anna Magdalena Bach (1725), Siebente Auflage. Munich, Georg D. W. Callwey [after 1906]. 3 ll., 124 pp., obl. 4°, 20 × 25 cm.
Reprint of preface to first edition signed: Dr. Richard Batka; dated: Prag, im Juli 1906.

Selections

1913. Az elemi zongorajáték gyakorlati tananyaga (ujjrenddel, elöadási jelekkel, jegyzetekkel) Szerkeszti Bartók Béla...3. Bach-Bartók könnyü kis zongoradarabok. ... Budapest, Rózsavölgyi és Társa, c 1924. 16 pp., 35 cm. (Editio Paedagogia musicalis, No. 3016.)   P.N.: R. & C°. 3681
1914. Le Petit Livre de clavecin d'Anna Magdalena Bach composé de 1722 à 1725. ... Brussels, Schott Frères [ca. 1900]. 17 pp., 31 cm.
                                                                P.N.: S.F.5995
1915. Le Petit Livre de clavecin de Magdalena Bach. Edition revue et doigtée par Th. Lack. Paris, Henry Lemoine, c 1918. 15, [1] pp.; 30 cm. (Édition nationale française Panthéon des pianistes, No. 1149.)
                                                      P.N.: 21356.P.1149.HL.
1916. [Petit Livre de Magdalena. ... Paris, E. Ploix, c 1927.] 2 ll.; 39, [1] pp.; 31 cm. (Edition analytique des classiques.) Preface by Georges Sporck. Biographical note on Bach by Paul Landormy.   P.N.: G.S.547
1917. Petit Livre de Magdalena Bach. Nouvelle édition revue et doigtée par Noel-Gallon. ... Paris, Choudens [c 1933]. 1 l., 23 pp., 31 cm. (Édition française de musique classique de piano.)
                                                              P.N.: A.C.17408
1918. Le Petit Livre de Magdalena Bach. 20 pièces faciles pour piano. Edition revue et doigtée par Victor Staub. Paris, E. Gallet [ca. 1925]. 16 pp., 32 cm. (Edition Gallet, No. 170.)   P.N.: E.G.7705
1919. Le Petit Livre de Magdalena Bach (20 pièces faciles). Révision et annotations par B. Selva. Paris, Maurice Senart, c 1915. 10 pp., 34 cm. (Édition nationale de musique classique, No. 5033.)
                                                    P.N.: EDITION NATIONALE
1920. Le Petit Livre de musique d'Anna Magdalena Bach. 20 pièces faciles pour clavecin (1725). Révision par L. Garban. Paris, Durand [c 1924]. 1 l.; 24, [1] pp.; 30 cm. (Édition classique A. Durand & Fils, No. 10492.)   P.N.: D. & F. 10,492
1921. Oeuvres originales J. S. Bach, Le Petit Livre de clavecin de Magdalena Bach (20 pièces faciles). 1re partie [and 2e partie]. Paris, Maurice Senart [ca. 1910]. 2 parts. 35 cm. (Nouvelle Édition française de musique classique, Nos. 215-216.) General editor of series: Vincent D'Indy. Revision by Blanche Selva.   P.N.'s: 215; 216
1922. 20 leichte Stücke aus dem Notenbuche der Anna Magdalena Bach komponiert von Joh. Seb. Bach. Instruktive Ausgabe von Emil von Sauer. Leipzig, C. F. Peters [1930?]. 19 pp., 31 cm. (Edition Peters, No. 3829.)   P.N.: 10390

ORATORIOS

OSTER-ORATORIUM (S. 249): Vocal scores

1923. Joh. Seb. Bach, Klavierauszüge Oratorien, 1. Osteroratorium.
... Leipzig, Breitkopf & Härtel [ca. 1895]. 1 l.; 53, [1] pp.; 27 cm.
Klavierauszug von B. Todt.   P.N.: J.S.B.III.2.
1924. Oster-Oratorium..."Kommt, eilet und laufet"...21ster Jahr-
gang, Lief. III der Ausgabe der Bach-Gesellschaft. Leipzig, C. F.
Peters [1879]. 44 pp., 27 cm. (Edition Peters, No. 1672.)
Edited by Gustav Rösler.   P.N.: 6291

WEIHNACHTS-ORATORIUM (S. 248): Full scores

1925. Weihnachts-Oratorium...Nach der Ausgabe der Bach-Gesellschaft und nach dem in der Preussischen Staatsbibliothek in Berlin
befindlichen Autograph revidiert und mit Vorwort versehen von
Arnold Schering. Leipzig, Eulenburg [1922?]. vi, 296 pp.; 2 ll.;
19 cm. (Eulenburgs kleine Partitur-Ausgabe, No. 962.)
                                                P.N.: E.E.4353
1926. Weihnachts-Oratorium...Partitur. Hierzu Orgelstimme von
S. Jadassohn. Leipzig, C. F. Peters [1921?]. 204 pp., 31 cm. (Edition
Peters, No. 26.)   P.N.: 4537
1927. Weihnachts-Oratorium, Theil I und II mit ausgeführtem
Accompagnement bearbeitet von Robert Franz. Text deutsch und
englisch, Partitur mit unterlegtem Clavierauszug. Leipzig, F. E. C.
Leuckart (Constantin Sander) [ca. 1890]. 143 pp., 33 cm.
                                                P.N.: F.E.C.L.3561

WEIHNACHTS-ORATORIUM (S. 248): Vocal-piano scores

1928. The Christmas Oratorio. ... [Philadelphia] Association of
American Choruses [1950]. [1], i-viii, 4-163 pp.; 26 cm. (Choral
Series, No. 175.)
     Photo-offset lithograph process. Translation by Henry S. Drinker.
1929. The Christmas Oratorio...Translated and adapted by the
Rev. J. Troutbeck...edited by Max Spicker. ... New York, G. Schirmer [c 1909]. xxii pp., 1 l., 195 pp., 27 cm.
     Introduction by G. A. MacFarren. Two copies.   P.N.: 21600
1930. Christmas Oratorio. Vocal score. ... Leipzig, London, Brussels,
New York, Breitkopf & Härtel [1901?]. 3 ll., 160 pp., 27 cm.
     Preface by E. H. Thorne.   P.N.: V.A.1887
1931. The Christmas Oratorio...(with a separate accompaniment for
the organ or pianoforte)...The English translation and adatpation by
the Rev. J. Troutbeck. ... London, Novello [ca. 1930]. 1 l; xi, [1] pp.;
1 l.; 172 pp.; 27 cm. (Novello's Original Octavo Edition.)
     Introduction by G. A. MacFarren.   P.N.: 8410
1932. Oratorien, Messen und andere Kirchenmusik im Klavierauszug
mit Text, Bach, J. S. ... Weihnachts-Oratorium...Bearbeitung nach

der original Partitur. ... Leipzig, Berlin, C. F. Peters, Bureau de Musique [ca. 1865]. 2 ll., 160 pp., 27 cm.
Piano reduction by F. Brissler. MS. inscription on front wrapper reads: Fr. Zelle. Pred. An De— [corner torn off] | 2 Nov. 1868.
P.N.: 4428
1933. Oratorio de Noël en six parties. Réduction pour piano (ou orgue) par A. Guilmant, traduction française de Paul Collin. ... Paris, Choudens [1932?]. 162 pp., 31 cm.　　　　P.N.: A.C.13122.
1934. Weihnachts-Oratorium... Klavierauszug von Gustav Rösler. Leipzig, C. F. Peters [1878?]. 162 pp., 28 cm. (Edition Peters, No. 38.)　　　　　　　　　　　　　　　　　　P.N.: 6140
1935. Weihnachts-Oratorium... Klavierauszug von Gustav Rösler. Leipzig, C. F. Peters [ca. 1890]. 1 l., 163 pp., 28 cm. (Edition Peters, No. 38.)
Preface by Hermann Kretzschmar.　　　　　　　P.N.: 8795
1936. Weihnachts-Oratorium nach den Evangelisten Lucas, Cap. 2, V. 1-21, und Matthäus, Cap. 2, V. 1-12; Vollstaendiger Clavier-Auszug bearbeitet von Fr. Ed. Wilsing. Berlin, chez Ed. Bote & G. Bock [1848?]. 1 l., 3-148 pp.
At head of title: Collection des oeuvres classiques.
P.N.: B. & B. 3988
1937. Weihnachts-Oratorium nach den Evangelisten Lucas und Matthäus. Klavierauszug mit Text von S. Jadassohn. Leipzig, Breitkopf & Härtel [ca. 1877]. 2 ll., 160 pp., 27 cm. (Volks-Ausgabe, No. 13.)　　　　　　　　　　　　　　　　　P.N.: V.A.13.
1938. Weihnachts-Oratorium nach den Evangelisten Lucas und Matthäus... Klavierauszug mit Text von S. Jadassohn. Vienna, Leipzig, Universal-Edition, Aktiengesellschaft [ca. 1905]. 2 ll., 100 pp., 27 cm. (Universal Edition, No. 2551.)　　　P.N.: E.B.13.

WEIHNACHTS ORATORIUM (S. 248): Vocal score

1939. The Christmas Oratorio. ... [Philadelphia] University of Pennsylvania [1941]. 5 ll., 100 pp., 26 cm. (Choral Series, No. 115.) Edited by Henry S. Drinker.

WEIHNACHTS-ORATORIUM (S. 248): Excerpts

1940. Christmas Oratorio Part IV... Edited and accompaniment arranged by Ifor Jones, English version by J. M. Stein and Ifor Jones. New York, G. Schirmer [c 1942]. 1 l., 45 pp.　　　P.N.: 39754
1941. How Shall I Fitly Meet Thee, choral. ... Cleveland, Ohio, Greater Cleveland Lutheran Chorus [ca. 1935]. [3] pp., 27 cm.
1942. A Little Babe He Comes, from the Christmas Oratorio... Translation by C. S. Terry, arranged and edited by W. G. Whittaker. London, Oxford University Press, c 1929. 6 pp., 26 cm. (Oxford Choral Songs from the Old Masters, No. 1467.)

1943. Pastoral Symphony from Christmas Oratorio. Arranged as an organ solo by Henry G. Ley. London, Hinrichsen, c 1954. 7 pp., obl. 4°, 23 × 31 cm. (Edition Peters, No. 38a.)
P.N.: Edition Peters No. 38a
1944. Weihnachts-Oratorium von Joh. Seb. Bach, Aria (mit Echo) für Sopran. Arrang. von W. Rust. Berlin, Schlesinger'schen Buch- u. Musikhandlung [1858]. 5 pp., 34 cm., wove paper. (Hosianna, No. 36.)   P.N.: S. 4689 (35)
1945. Weihnachts-Oratorium von Joh. Seb. Bach, Aria (Wiegenlied) für Alt. 1ste Beilage der Berliner Musikzeitung "Echo" 1858. Arrang. von W. Rust. Berlin, Schlesinger'sche Buch- und Musikhandlung [1858]. 5 pp., 34 cm., wove paper. (Sion, Vol. 3, No. 56.)
P.N.: S. 4689 (17)
1946. With All Thy Hosts. From Christmas Oratorio. ... Cleveland, Ohio, Greater Cleveland Lutheran Chorus [ca. 1935]. [3] pp., 27 cm.   P.N.: 21600

ORGAN WORKS

Collections

1947. Complete Organ Works, a critico-practical edition in eight volumes provided with a preface containing general observations on the manner of performing the preludes and fugues and suggestions for the interpretation of the compositions contained in each volume by Charles-Marie Widor...and Dr. Albert Schweitzer. ... New York, G. Schirmer, c 1912-c 1954. 6 vols. Obl. fol., 25 × 33 cm.
Six vols. only of the projected eight. Widor's name replaced by that of Édouard Nies-Berger in Vol. 6.
P.N.'s: 22699, 22710, 22704, 22712, 22706, 43190
1948. Johann Sebastian Bach's Compositionen für die Orgel. Kritisch-korrecte Ausgabe von Friedrich Conrad Griepenkerl und Ferdinand Roitzsch. Leipzig, im Bureau de Musique von C. F. Peters [1844-47]. 7 vols. Obl. fol., 25 × 33 cm.; 26 × 33 cm., wove paper.
Imperfect: Vol. 3 wanting.
P.N.'s: 2910, 2968, 2982, 3061, 3062, 2893
1949. Johann Sebastian Bach's Compositionen für die Orgel. Kritisch-korrecte Ausgabe von Friedrich Conrad Griepenkerl und Ferdinand Roitzsch, Eingeführt im Conservatorium der Musik zu Leipzig. Leipzig & Berlin, C. F. Peters, Bureau de Musique [1870?]. 4 vols. Obl. fol., 25 × 33 cm., wove paper. (Edition Peters Nos. 240-47.)
Vols. 1 and 3 have the signature of Wm. B. Colson.
P.N.'s: 2893, 2910, 2938, 2968
1950. Johann Sebastian Bach's Compositionen für die Orgel. Kritisch-korrecte Ausgabe von Friedrich Conrad Griepenkerl und Ferdinand Roitzsch. Leipzig, C. F. Peters, Bureau de Musique [1881?]. 9 vols. Obl. fol., 26 × 33 cm., wove paper.

Prefaces from first edition reprinted with same dates.

P.N.'s: 8656-8663, 6421

1951. Johann Sebastian Bach's Compositionen für die Orgel. Kritisch-korrecte Ausgabe von Friedrich Conrad Griepenkerl und Ferdinand Roitzsch...Neue Ausgabe von Max Seiffert. Leipzig, C. F. Peters [1904?]. 76 pp., obl. fol., 27 × 34 cm., wove paper. Vol. 9 only, of the 1881 edition.

P.N.: 6421

1952. Johann Sebastian Bach's Compositionen für die Orgel. Kritisch-korrecte Ausgabe von Friedrich Conrad Griepenkerl und Ferdinand Roitzsch. Leipzig, C. F. Peters; New York, London, C. F. Peters [1952]. 9 vols. and preface. Obl. fol., 23 × 31 cm. (Edition Peters, Nos. 240-47, 2067.)

Separately published (c 1950) are translations of the original prefaces, with a special preface written by Albert Riemenschneider.

P.N.'s: 8656-8663, 6421; Peters Edition 240/247, 2067

1953. Johann Sebastian Bach's Werke für Orgel. Gesammtausgabe für den praktischen Gebrauch. ... Leipzig, Breitkopf & Härtel [1899-1902]. 9 vols. 32 cm.

Prefaces signed by Ernst Naumann, in Vols. 1 and 7.

P.N.'s: J.S.B.Org.1 – J.S.B.Org.9

1954. Oeuvres complètes pour orgue de J.-S. Bach annotées et doigtées par Marcel Dupré...Volume I [to XII]. Paris, S. Bornemann, c 1938-c 1941. 12 vols. in 4. Obl. fol., 26 × 34 cm.

P.N.'s: S.B.5274-5, S.B. 5277-9, S.B.5281, S.B.5283-4, S.B.5288-91.

1955. Oeuvres complètes pour orgue. Edition critique et pratique en huit volumes précédée d'une Préface contenant les observations générales sur l'interprétation et l'analyse des compositions contenues dans chaque volume par Charles-Marie Widor ... et Dr. Albert Schweitzer. ... New York & London, G. Schirmer, c 1914-1924. 4 vols. in 2. Obl. fol., 25 × 34 cm.

Imperfect: Vol. 5 wanting. Five vols. only, of the projected eight, published.

P.N.'s: 22699, 22717, 22704, 31908 & 22705

1956. Oeuvres complètes pour orgue. Révision par Gabriel Fauré... 1er volume [to 3me]. Paris, Durand [c 1916-20]. 14 parts in 3 vols. Obl. fol., 24 × 32 cm. (Edition classique A. Durand & Fils.)

P.N.'s: D. & F. 9440 – D. & F. 9450; D. & F. 9824 – D. & F. 9826

1957. Organ Works, W. T. Best edition newly revised by Dr. A. Eaglefield Hull, Volume I [to X]. London, Augener [c 1914]. 10 vols. Obl. fol., 25 × 34 cm.

P.N.'s: 6491, 7258, 8176, 8274, 8320, 8392, 8428, 8577-8, 9041-2, 9145, 9157, 9192, 9406, 9853, 9973, 10277, 10357, 10267, 10521, 11403, 11852, 12800

1958.   The Organ Works of John Sebastian Bach, edited by J. F. Bridge...
& James Higgs ... Books X.—Toccata, preludes, and fugues. London,
Novello [1891]. 2 ll.; [1], 196-243, [1] pp.; 1 l.; obl. fol.; 26 × 36 cm.
Penciled signature on title page: Herbert Sesson | Kansas City Mo.
1901.   P.N.: 9158
1959.   The Organ Works of John Sebastian Bach, in three volumes.
London, Novello [1881-95]. 12 books in 3 vols. Obl. fol., 26 × 36 cm.
                          P.N.'s: 6201, 6366, 6654, 6872, 7008, 7212,
                                 7472, 7635, 7847, 9158, 9664, 9935

Selections

1960.   Bach-Album, Sammlung berühmter Orgelkompositionen von
Johann Sebastian Bach herausgegeben von Ernst H. Wolfram.
Leipzig, C. F. Peters [ca. 1885]. 4 vols. in 1. Obl. fol., 23 × 31 cm.
(Edition Peters, Nos. 2178a-2178d.)   P.N.'s: 6786-6789
1961.   Compositions pour orgue, Quatre Concertos manuale, trois
préludes fantaisie et deux fugues. 8eme livre. Paris, S. Richault
[ca. 1850]. 8 [?] vols. 34 cm., wove paper.
     Library has Vols. 8, 4, and 3 respectively, bound in one volume.
Title of Vol. 4: ... 14 pièces, préludes, fugues, cansonnette, fantaisies,
toccata et trio; Title of Vol. 3: ... 10 pièces, préludes, fantaisie,
fugues et toccata.   P.N.'s: 9431 R., 8780 R., 9704 R.
1962.   Joh. Seb. Bach Orgelwerke herausgegeben von Karl Straube.
Band II. Leipzig, C. F. Peters [c 1913]. 126 pp., obl. fol., 27 × 34 cm.
(Edition Peters, No. 3331.)   P.N.: 9717
1963.   Joh. Seb. Bach Orgelwerke herausgegeben von Paul Homeyer
[und] William Eckhardt. ... Leipzig, Steingräber, c 1911 [c 1921].
5 vols. in 2. Obl. fol., 23 × 31 cm. (Edition Steingräber, Nos. 64-66,
2172-73.)
     Prefaces to Vols. 4 and 5 are dated 1917; first page of text of Vols. 4
and 5 bears copyright date 1921.   P.N.'s: 590-592, 2032, 2033
1964.   Kompositionen für Orgel von Johann Sebastian Bach, I. Band:
...kritisch revidiert, mit Fingersatz und Vortragsbezeichnungen
herausgegeben von Johannes Schreyer. Leipzig, Friedrich Hofmeister
[1889]. 1 l.; iv, 59 pp.; obl. fol.; 26 × 34 cm.   P.N.: 1
1965.   Organ Works of John Sebastian Bach...Book II...8 miscellane-
ous compositions edited by Alfred J. Silver. New York, J. Fischer
[c 1915]. 1 l., 36 pp., 1 l., obl. fol., 25 × 33 cm. (Fischer Edition,
No. 3951.)   P.N.: J.F. & B. 3951-34
1966.   Orgel-Album, Die berühmtesten Compositionen für die Orgel
von Johann Sebastian Bach ausgewählt, revidiert, mit Fingersatz und
Vortragszeichen versehen von Josef Vockner. Vienna, Universal-
Edition Actiengesellschaft [ca. 1905]. 157, [1] pp.; obl. fol.;
24 × 31 cm.   P.N.: U.E.700

1967. Orgel-Album hervorragende Tonsätze von J. S. Bach. Ausgewählt und mit Bezeichnung des Vortrages und der Pedalapplicatur
versehen von Dr. W. Volckmar. Brunswick, Henry Litolff [ca. 1865].
127 pp., 31 cm. (Collection Litolff, No. 49.)
　　　　　　　　　　　　　　　　　P.N.: COLLECTION LITOLFF No. 49
1968. Orgelwerke von Joh. Seb. Bach progressiv geordnet und mit
Fingersatz versehen von S. de Lange. Eingeführt am Konservatorium
für Musik in Stuttgart. ... Leipzig, C. F. Peters, 1894. 14 parts in
1 vol. Obl. fol., 23 × 31 cm. (Edition Peters, Nos. 3747a-470.)
Parts 5, 7, and 9 published by J. Rieter-Biedermann.
　　　　　　　　　　　　P.N.'s: 1913-1922; 2272-73; 2483-84

PASSIONS

JOHANNESPASSION (S. 245): Full scores

1969. Grosse Passionsmusik nach dem Evangelium Johannis von
Johann Sebastian Bach. Partitur, Ihrer Königlichen Hoheit, der
Kronprinzessin von Preussen in tiefster Ehrfurcht zugeeignet vom
Verleger. ... Berlin, T. Trautwein, 1831. 2 ll.; [1], 2-113 pp.;
34 cm.; wove paper.　　　　　　　　　　　　　　P.N.: 370
1970. Joh. Seb. Bach's Passionsmusik nach dem Evangelisten Johannes.
Partitur, Hierzu Orgel- und Cembalostimme von Max Seiffert.
Leipzig, C. F. Peters [1922?]. 147 pp., 31 cm. (Edition Peters,
No. 27.)　　　　　　　　　　　　　　　　　　P.N.: 4549
1971. Johann Sebastian Bachs Gesangwerke, Passionsmusik nach dem
Evangelisten Johannes bearbeitet von Heinrich Reimann. ... Leipzig,
Brussels, London, etc., Breitkopf & Härtel [1903]. viii, 244 pp.;
33 cm.　　　　　　　　　　　　　　　　　P.N.: Part.B.1806
1972. Johannespassion, The Passion of Our Lord (St. John), La Passion
de St. Jean. The English translation is by the Rev. J. Troutbeck,
published by Novello & Co., London, by whose kind permission that
translation is used in this edition. Vienna, Wiener Philharmonischer
Verlag, A.G. [1923?]. 4 ll., 324 pp., frontis. (port.), 19 cm. (Philharmonia Partituren, No. 101.)
Edited by Herman Roth.　　　　　　　　　　P.N.: W.Ph.V.101
1973. Passion nach dem Evangelisten Johannes von Johann Sebastian
Bach. Nach der Ausgabe der Bach-Gesellschaft und nach dem in der
Preussischen Staatsbibliothek in Berlin befindlichen Autograph und
Stimmenmaterial revidiert und mit einer Einführung versehen von
Arnold Schering. Leipzig, Eulenburg [1925?]. x, 190 pp.; 2 ll.;
19 cm. (Eulenburgs kleine Partitur-Ausgabe, No. 965.)
　　　　　　　　　　　　　　　　　　　　P.N.: E.E.4453.
1974. Passions-Musik nach dem Evangelium Iohannis von Joh. Seb.
Bach. Mit der Partitur u. dem Klavierauszuge, welche in demselben
Verlage erschienen sind, übereinstimmend. Berlin, bei T. Trautwein

208 PUBLISHED MUSIC OF J. S. BACH

1974. *(continued)* [1831?]. 4 part-books (24 pp. each). Obl. 8°, 18×27 cm., wove paper. (Klassischewerke älterer und neuerer Kirchenmisuk, No. 13.) Vocal parts only. Stamp on front wrapper, and page 1 of each part: Koen. Schullehrer Seminar zu Potsdam. P.N.: 372

JOHANNESPASSION (S. 245): Vocal-piano scores

1975. Grosse Passions Musik nach dem Evangelium Johannis...Vollständiger Klavierauszug von L. Hellwig. Berlin, bei T. Trautwein [1830?]. 1 l., [1], 2-101 pp.; obl. fol.; 25×33 cm.; wove paper. P.N.: 365
1976. Joh. Seb. Bach's Passionsmusik nach dem Evangelisten Johannes. Klavierauszug von Gustav Rösler. Leipzig, C. F. Peters [ca. 1900]. 1 l.; iii, 3-135 pp.; 28 cm. (Edition Peters, No. 39.) Preface by Herman Kretzschmar. P.N.: 8909
1977. Johannes-Passion, Oratorium von Joh. Seb. Bach. Klavierauszug mit Text nach der Partitur bearbeitet von Viktor Keldorfer. Vienna, Leipzig, Universal-Edition [1910]. 150 pp., 28 cm. (Universal-Edition, No. 2641.) P.N.: U.E.2641
1978. Opern und Oratorien im Klavier-Auszug mit Text bearbeitet von Brissler, Horn, Stern, Ulrich. Leipzig, Berlin, C. F. Peters, Bureau de Musique [ca. 1865]. 1 l., 132 pp., 26 cm. P.N.: 4442
1979. Oratorien, Messen und andere Kirchenmusik im Klavierauszug mit Text, Bach, J. S. – Johannes-Passion...Bearbeitung nach der original Partitur. Leipzig, Berlin, C. F. Peters, Bureau de Musique [ca. 1865]. 2 ll., 132 pp., 26 cm. P.N.: 4442
1980. The Passion of Our Lord (according to St. John) Set to Music by Johann Sebastian Bach. The English translation and adaptation by the Rev. J. Troutbeck. ... London, Novello [1927?]. vi pp.; 3 ll.; 145, [1] pp.; 1 l.; 8 pp.
1981. The Passion of Our Lord According to Saint John Set to Music by John Sebastian Bach. The verse numbers translated by Dr. T. A. Lacey, edited by Ivor Atkins. ... London, Novello, c 1929. 3 ll., 149 pp., 28 cm. (Novello's Original Octavo Edition.) P.N.: 15454
1982. La Passion selon Saint-Jean, Oratorio en deux parties. Réduction pour piano (ou orgue) par A. Guilmant, traduction française de Maurice Bouchor. ... Paris, Choudens [1932?]. 1 l.; 4, 3-212 pp. (Edition Choudens.) P.N.: I.G.67
1983. Passionmusik nach dem Evangelisten Johannes. Klavierauszug nach der Ausgabe der Bachgesellschaft, Arrangement von S. Jadassohn. Leipzig, Breitkopf & Härtel [1928?]. 129 pp., 28 cm. (Edition Breitkopf, No. 480.) P.N.: V.A.480

JOHANNESPASSION (S. 245): Vocal score

1984. The St. John Passion. ... [Philadelphia] University of Pennsyl-

vania [1943?]. x, 86 pp.; 26 cm. (Choral Series, No. 150.)
Edited by Henry S. Drinker.

JOHANNESPASSION (S. 245): Excerpts

1985. Jesus, Thou Who Knewest Death, From Bach's Passion According to St. John. Cleveland, O., Greater Cleveland Lutheran Chorus [ca. 1935]. Single sheet, 28 cm.

LUKASPASSION (S. 246): Vocal-piano score

1986. Passionsmusik nach dem Evangelisten Lukas. Vollständiger Klavierauszug mit Text, Englische Übersetzung von Mrs. John P. Morgan. Leipzig, Breitkopf & Härtel [ca. 1886]. 3 ll., 123, [1] pp.; 27 cm. (Edition Breitkopf, No. 732.)   P.N.: V.A. 732.

LUKASPASSION (S. 246): Excerpts

1987. A Selection from the Passion of Our Lord According to St. Luke, attributed to J. S. Bach. Arranged by A. Hastings Kelk and J. Michael Diack. Glasgow, Paterson, c 1926. 2 ll., 56 pp., 27 cm.
P.N.: St. Luke

MATTHÄUSPASSION (S. 244): Full scores

1988. Grosse Passionsmusik nach dem Evangelium Matthaei von Johann Sebastian Bach. Partitur, Seiner Königlichen Hoheit dem Kronprinzen von Preussen in tiefster Ehrfurcht vom Verleger zugeeignet. ... Berlin, In der Schlesinger'schen Buch- und Musikhandlung, 1830. 3 ll.; [i], ii-viii, 5-324 pp.; 34 cm.; wove paper. Signature on front flyleaf: Anna Benda. Pages 10, 40, 60, 70 misnumbered respectively: 01, 04, 06, 07.

1989. Joh. Seb. Bach's Passionsmusik nach dem Evangelisten Matthäus mit ausgeführtem Accompagnement bearbeitet von Robert Franz. Partitur. Leipzig, Breitkopf & Härtel [1867?]. 3 ll., 285 pp., 34 cm. Preface dated: Januar 1867.   P.N.: 10978

1990. Das Leiden unseres Herrn Jesu Christi nach dem Evangelisten Matthaeus. Urtext der Autographen Partitur und der Stimmen durchgesehen und mit einem Vorbericht für die Aufführung herausgegeben von Max Schneider. ... Leipzig, Breitkopf & Härtel [1937?]. ⟨ll., 289 pp., 33 cm. (Partitur-Bibliothek, No. 2537.)
P.N.: B.W.IV.R.

1991. Matthäus-Passion, Oratorium von Joh. Seb. Bach. Partitur. Leipzig, C. F. Peters [ca. 1875]. 2, 268 pp.; 31 cm. (Edition Peters, No. 23.)
Bookplate on front pastedown: Ex libris Erich Borgers. Edited by S. Jadassohn.   P.N.: 4535

1992. [MS. title:] Passio Domini nostri I.C. secoundum Evangelistam Matthaeum Poesia per Dominum Henrici alias Picander dictus. Musica di G. S. Bach. Faksimile-Ausgabe der Handschrift von

210   PUBLISHED MUSIC OF J. S. BACH

1992. *(continued)* Johann Sebastian Bach Matthäuss-Passion. ...Leipzig, für den Insel-Verlag, 1922. 82 unnumbered ll., 38 cm.
 Copy No. 493 of 500 numbered copies. Facsimile of Berlin Bibliothek MS. Bach P 25.

1993. Passionsmusik nach dem Evangelisten Matthäus...Herausgegeben von Georg Schumann. Ausgabe in elegantem Einband mit einer Heliogravüre Bachs nach dem Originalgemälde von Haussmann, Einbandzeichnung von Dr. Max Lange. Leipzig, Eulenburg [ca. 1895]. 1 l., 424 pp., 19 cm. (Eulenburgs kleine Partitur-Ausgabe, No. 3.)
 Imperfect: Frontispiece wanting.   P.N.: E.E.2645

1994. Passionsmusik nach dem Evangelisten Matthäus herausgegeben von Siegfried Ochs. Leipzig, C. F. Peters [1929?]. 1 l.; 223, 10 pp.; 33 cm. (Edition Peters, No. 4000.)   P.N.: 10624

1995. Passionsmusik nach dem Evangelisten Matthaeus...Partitur. Leipzig, Berlin, C. F. Peters, Bureau de Musique [ca. 1865]. 1 l., 268 pp., 27 cm. (Edition Peters, No. 23.)
 Front pastedown and front flyleaf contain detailed lists of performances from 11 March, 1829, to 24 March, 1923, together with names of conductors, soloists, etc. Edited by S. Jadassohn.
          P.N.: 4535

MATTHÄUSPASSION (S. 244): Choral parts

1996. [Grosse Passionsmusik nach dem Evangelium Matthaei. Schlesinger? 1831?] 8 part-books, 27 cm., wove paper.
 Imperfect: wrappers, with title, wanting. Unopened. P.N.: 1687

MATTHÄUSPASSION (S. 244): Vocal-piano scores

1997. Collection des oeuvres classiques, Joh. Seb. Bach's Passions-Musik nach dem Evangelisten Matthäus. Vollständiger Klavier-Auszug mit Worten bearbeitet von F. Ed. Wilsing. ... Berlin, Ed. Bote & G. Bock [ca. 1860]. 189 pp., 35 cm.   P.N.: B. & B. 3698

1998. Grosse Passions-Musik (according to the Gospel of St. Matthew) ...The English translation and adaptation by Miss H. F. H. Johnston, the whole edited & revised by William Sterndale Bennett. ... London, Lamborn, Cock, Hutchings & Co. (late Leader & Cock) [1862?]. 3 ll., 159 pp., 37 cm.
 Edition based on that of A. B. Marx.   P.N.: L. & C.2943

1999. Grosse Passionsmusik nach dem Evangelium Matthaei von Johann Sebastian Bach. Vollständiger Klavierauszug von Adolph Bernhard Marx. Seiner königl. Hoheit dem Kronprinzen von Preussen in tiefster Ehrfurcht gewidmet vom Verleger. ... Berlin, in der Schlesinger'schen Buch- und Musikhandlung, 1830. 1 l., 190 pp., obl. fol., 26 × 33 cm., wove paper.
 On inside of front cover, the signature: I: Klengel. 1848. P.N.: 1571

2000. Das Leiden unseres Herrn Jesu Christi nach dem Evangelisten
Matthaeus. Klavierauszug nach dem Urtext der Autographen
Partitur und der Stimmen von Max Schneider. Leipzig, Breitkopf &
Härtel [1935]. 5 ll., 168 pp., illus. (facs.), 29 cm. (Veröffentlichungen
der Neuen Bachgesellschaft, Vol. 35, No. 3.)   P.N.: 30717
2001. Matthäus-Passion...Klavierauszug mit Gesang. Vienna, Universal-Edition, A.G. [1934?]. 167 pp., 27 cm. (Universal-Edition,
No. 840.)
    Edited by Josef Vockner.   P.N.: U.E.840
2002. Matthäus-Passion, Oratorium von Joh. Seb. Bach. Klavierauszug. Neuausgabe von Schultze-Biesantz. Brunswick, Henry
Litolff [ca. 1915]. 212 pp., 28 cm. (Collection Litolff, No. 2402.)
                               P.N.: COLLECTION LITOLFF No. 2402
2003. Matthäus-Passion, Oratorium von Joh. Seb. Bach. Klavierauszug von Julius Stern. Leipzig, C. F. Peters [ca. 1905]. 166 pp.,
28 cm. (Edition Peters, No. 36.)   P.N.: 7644
2004. The Passion According to St. Matthew...Edited and the English
words revised by Charles V. Sanford. ... London, Stainer & Bell
[c 1910]. 2 ll., 192 pp., 27 cm.
    Based on the Stern piano arrangement.   P.N.: St. & B. Ltd.466.
2005. The Passion According to Saint Matthew...English version by
Claude Aveling, vocal score by S. Jadassohn. Leipzig, Breitkopf &
Härtel [c 1906]. 2 ll., 192 pp., 28 cm.   P.N.: 25286.
2006. La Passion de Jésus-Christ selon l'Évangile de saint Matthieu.
Version française par G. Antheunis, adaptation du texte biblique et
réduction au piano par F. A. Gevaert, partition vocale avec accompagnement de piano. ... Paris, Brussels, Henry Lemoine, c 1897.
1 l.; viii pp.; 1 l.; [ix]-xii, 237, 19 pp.; 30 cm.   P.N.: 18.619.HL.
2007. La Passion selon Saint-Mathieu, Oratorio en deux parties.
Réduction pour piano (ou orgue) par Raoul Moreau, version française
de Arthur Bernède. ... Paris, Choudens [c 1929]. 2 ll.; vi, 206 pp.;
31 cm. (Edition Choudens.)   P.N.: A.C.17138
2008. La Passion, traduction française de Mr. Maurice Bourges,
musique de J. S. Bach. Partition piano et chant. Paris, Mce.
Schlesinger [1844?]. 4 ll., 196 pp., 27 cm., wove paper.
    Based on piano edition of A. B. Marx.   P.N.: M.S.3973
2009. Passion music (according to the Gospel of St. Matthew). Words
English and German. The English translation and adaptation by
John S. Dwight, Full vocal score, with pianoforte accompaniment
mainly by Julius Stern. Boston, Oliver Ditson, c. 1869, 1 l., 221 pp.,
228 cm.
    Penciled note at top of title reads: Mr. Lang. | April 29th 1874.
2010. The Passion of our Lord According to S. Matthew ... Edited
by Edward Elgar and Ivor Atkins. London, Novello, c. 1911. vi pp.,
1 l., 197 pp., 28 cm. (Novello's Original Octavo Edition.)   P.N.: 13443

2011. The Passion of Our Lord According to S. Matthew...Edited by Edward Elgar and Ivor Atkins, Revised 1938 by Ivor Atkins. London, Novello, 1938. vi pp., 1 l., 197 pp., 29 cm. (Novello's Original Octavo Edition.)   P.N.: 13443

2012. The Passion of Our Lord According to S. Matthew. English translation and adaptation by the Rev. Dr. Troutbeck...vocal score edited by H. W. Nicholl. New York, G. Schirmer [c 1905]. xii, 219 pp., 27 cm.
Two copies.   P.N.: 17136

2013. The Passion of Our Lord (According to S. Matthew)...The English translation and adaptation by Miss H. F. H. Johnston. ... London, Novello, Ewer [1871]. xv, viii, 187, [1] pp.; 27 cm. Edited by W. Sterndale Bennett. Introduction by George A. Mac-Farren.   P.N.: Bach's Passion Music – Novello, Ewer and Co's Octavo Edition.

2014. The Passion of Our Lord According to S. Matthew...The English translation by the Rev. Dr. Troutbeck. ... London, Novello [1894?]. xi, [1], 188 pp.; 26 cm. (Novello's Original Octavo Edition.)
                                                   P.N.: 8098

2015. The Passion of Our Lord (According to S. Matthew)...The English translation by John Oxenford, the music edited by J. Pittman. London, New York, Boosey & Co. [ca. 1875]. 1 l.; v, [i], 152 pp.; 29 cm.

2016. The Passion of Our Lord According to St. Matthew...The piano arrangements by Julius Stern and Robert Franz, the text translated and adapted by John S. Dwight. Boston, Oliver Ditson, c 1912. xi, [i], 262 pp.; 28 cm.   P.N.: 5-39-66705-262

2017. The Passion of Our Lord According to St. Matthew...The piano arrangements by Julius Stern and Robert Franz, the text translated and adapted by John S. Dwight, revised and edited by Louis Koemmenich. Boston, Oliver Ditson, c 1916. xi, [i], 262 pp.; 28 cm.
                                                   P.N.: 5-39-66705-262

2018. The Passion of Our Lord According to St. Matthew...The piano arrangements by Julius Stern and Robert Franz, the text translated and adapted by John S. Dwight, revised and edited by Louis Koemmenich. Bryn Mawr, Pennsylvania, Oliver Ditson, Theodore Presser, c 1916. xi, [i], 262 pp.   P.N.: 5-29-66705-262

2019. Passionsmusik nach dem Evangelisten Matthäus. Vollständiger Klavierauszug von S. Jadassohn. Leipzig, Breitkopf & Härtel [ca. 1910]. 2 ll., 317 pp., 28 cm. (Edition Breitkopf, No. 11.)
                                                   P.N.: E.B.11

2020. A Short Passion (from St. Matthew's Gospel)...Arranged and edited by W. Gillies Whittaker, English text by C. Sanford Terry, Welsh text by E. T. Davies and Gwilym Williams. London, Oxford University Press [c 1931]. xxiii, 135 pp.; 25 cm.

MATTHÄUSPASSION (S. 244): Piano scores

2021. Grosse Passionsmusik nach dem Evangelisten Matthäus...Vollständiger Klavierauszug zu vier Händen nach der Partitur-Ausgabe der Bach-Gesellschaft und mit Beifügung der Textesworte bearbeitet von August Horn. Leipzig, Bartholf Senff; London, J. J. Ewer [ca. 1855]. 191 pp., 34 cm.					P.N.: 438
2022. Matthäus-Passion, Oratorium von Joh. Seb. Bach. Klavierauszug von S. Jadassohn. Leipzig, C. F. Peters [ca. 1905]. 59 pp., 32 cm. (Edition Peters, No. 385.)				P.N.: 6740
2023. Passionsmusik nach dem Evangelisten Matthäus. Arrangement für Pianoforte allein mit Beifügung der Textesworte von Selmar Bagge. Leipzig, Breitkopf & Härtel [before December, 1878]. 3 ll., 136 pp., 28 cm. (Volksausgabe, No. 12.)			P.N.: V.A.12

MATTHÄUSPASSION (S. 244): Vocal score

2024. The St. Matthew Passion. ... [Philadelphia] University of Pennsylvania [1942]. xvi, 121 pp.; 26 cm. (Choral Series, No. 147.) Edited by Henry S. Drinker.

MATTHÄUSPASSION (S. 244): Excerpts

2025. Arie mit obligater Violine "Erbarme dich mein Gott" aus der Passionsmusik nach dem Evangelium Matthäi Cap. 26, 27 von Johann Sebastian Bach, Mit Pianoforte Begleitung eingerichtet von Ludwig Hellwig. Berlin, T. Trautwein [1829?]. [1], 2-7 pp.; obl. fol.; 25 × 33 cm.; wove paper.					P.N.: 309
2026. The Chorals from "St. Matthew Passion Music". ... Boston, Oliver Ditson, c 1849. 8 pp., 26 cm. (Choral Music, No. 923.)
									P.N.: 76916-8
2027. The Chorals from "St. Matthew Passion Music". ... Boston, Oliver Ditson, c 1849. 11, [1] pp.; 28 cm.
	This edition includes two chorale melodies in addition to the 12 chorales in the other Ditson edition with same title and imprint.
2028. Duett für zwei weibliche Stimmen "So ist mein Jesu nun gefangen" mit Doppel-Chor aus der Passionsmusik (nach dem Evangelium Matthäi Cap. 26 u. 27.) von Johann Sebastian Bach. Mit Pianoforte-Begleitung eingerichtet von Ludwig Hellwig. Berlin, T. Trautwein [1829?]. [1], 2-13 pp.; obl. fol.; 25 × 34 cm.; wove paper.					P.N.: 310
2029. Here Yet Awhile (St. Matthew Passion) Double Choir. ... New York, M. Witmark [ca. 1915]. 11, [1] pp.; 27 cm. (Witmark Choral Library, No. 2531.)		P.N.: M.W. & Sons 19205-10
2030. No. 78: Chorus—"Here Yet Awhile". ... London, Novello [ca. 1910]. Pp. 181-87, [188]; 27 cm. (Novello's Octavo Choruses, No. 337.)					P.N.: 8098

2031.   O Man, Bewail Thy Grievous Sin (Choral) from "The Passion
According to St. Matthew" for Chorus of Mixed Voices...Edited by
H. Clough-Leighter. Boston, E. C. Schirmer, 1929. 22 pp., 1 l.,
28 cm. (Choral Music, No. 1120.)   P.N.: E.C.S. N°. 429
2032.   O Man, Bewail Thy Grievous Sin. For four part chorus of
mixed voices with piano or organ accompaniment ... No. 35 in the
"St. Matthew Passion." Edited by H. W. Nicholl. New York,
G. Schirmer, c 1905, c 1932. 16 pp., 27 cm. (G. Schirmer's Choral
Church Music, No. 8463.)   P.N.: 38785

PASTORALE IN F MAJOR (ORGAN) (S. 590)

2033.   Pastorale in F major...edited by Walter E. Buszin. St. Louis,
Mo., Concordia [c 1949]. 12 pp., 32 cm. (Anthology of Sacred
Music.)
2034.   Pastorella di Seb: Bach. Berlin, Schlesinger'schen Buch- und
Musikhandlung [1825?]. Pp. 2-3, obl. 4°, 25 × 33 cm., wove paper.
Published as supplement to the Berliner Musikalische Zeitung for
1825, under editorship of Adolph Bernhard Marx. Signature on
recto of first leaf: W. Rust.   P.N.: 1337

PRELUDES

Clavier

6 LITTLE PRELUDES (S. 933-938)

2035.   Litolff's Akademische Ausgabe der Pianoforte-Classiker. Kritisch revidirt und für das Studium bezeichnet von Heinrich Germer...
6 Petits Préludes pour les commençants. ... Brunswick, Henry Litolff
[ca. 1897]. 8 pp., 35 cm. (Litolff's Akademische Ausgabe, No. 9002.)
          P.N.: Litolff's Akademische Ausgabe, No. 2
2036.   Pianoforte-Musik redigirt und herausgegeben von den Professoren und Lehren...J. Dachs, A. Door...und A. Sturm, Joh. Seb.
Bach (Edition revue et soigneusement doigtée par A. Sturm)...6
Petits Préludes pour les commençants. ... Leipzig, Aug. Cranz
[ca. 1895]. 7, [1] pp.; 34 cm. (Classikerausgabe des Wiener Conservatoriums.)   P.N.: C.26287
2037.   6 Petits Préludes à l'usage des commençans...Nouvelle edition
soigneusement revue, corrigée et doigtée...Oeuvres complets, Liv. V.
Offenbach s/M., chez Jean André [1847?]. 7 pp., 31 cm.
     Signature on first title page: Carl Baermann.   P.N.: 6608
2038.   Six Preludes á l'usage des commençants pour le clavecin composées par J. S. Bach. Leipzig, chez Hoffmeister et Kühnel [1802?].
7 pp., obl. fol., 24 × 34 cm., wove paper.   P.N.: 89
2039.   Six Preludes á l'usage des commençants pour le clavecin com-

posées par J. S. Bach. Leipzig, chez Ambroise Kühnel [after 1805].
7 pp., obl. fol., 25 × 33 cm., laid paper. P.N.: 89
2040. Six Preludes á l'usage des commençants pour le clavecin composées par J. S. Bach. Leipzig, chez C. F. Peters, Bureau de Musique
[ca. 1815?]. 7 pp., obl. fol., 25 × 33 cm., wove paper.
First line of imprint erased and Peters' name substituted for
Kühnel's. P.N.: 89

12 LITTLE PRELUDES (S. 924-32, 939-43, 999)

2041. 12 Petits Préludes ou exercices à l'usage des commençans...
nouvelle édition soigneusement revue, corrigée et doigtée...Oeuvres
complets, Liv. V. Offenbach s/M., chez Jean André [1847?]. 11 pp.,
31 cm.
Signature on title page: Carl Bacrmann. P.N.: 6609
2042. Joh. Seb. Bach, Oeuvres pour piano. Revues et soigneusement
doigtées par A. Sturm... 12 kleine Präludien für Anfänger. ... Leipzig,
Aug. Cranz [ca. 1910]. 14 pp., 31 cm. (Edition Cranz, No. 194.)
P.N.: 40437
2043. Litolff's Akademische Ausgabe der Pianoforte-Classiker. Kritisch revidirt und für das Studium bezeichnet von Heinrich Germer...
12 Petits Préludes ou exercices pour les commençants. ... Brunswick,
Henry Litolff [ca. 1897]. 15, [1] pp.; 35 cm. (Litolff's Akademische
Ausgabe, No. 9001.) P.N.: Litolff's Akademische Ausgabe, No. 1
2044. Pianoforte-Musik redigirt und herausgegeben von den Professoren und Lehren...J. Dachs, A. Door...und A. Sturm, Joh. Seb.
Bach (edition revue et soigneusement doigtée par A. Sturm), 12 Petits
Préludes ou exercices pour les commençants. ... Leipzig, Aug. Cranz
[ca. 1895]. 13, [1] pp.; 34 cm. (Classikerausgabe des Wiener
Conservatoriums.) P.N.: 26286
2045. Zwölf kleine Präludien für das Pianoforte von J. S. Bach.
Zunächst für den Gebrauch in den Elementarklassen an "Taussig's
Schule des höheren Klavierspiels" herausgegeben...von Otto
Lessmann. ... Berlin, Schlesinger'schen Buch- u. Musikhandlung
(Rob. Lienau) [ca. 1865]. 21 pp., 34 cm. P.N.: S. 6335

15 LITTLE PRELUDES (S. 924-30, 934-38, 940-42)

2046. Quinze Préludes de J. S. Bach revus, mis en ordre et doigtés par
Alexandre Longo. ... Milan, G. Ricordi [ca. 1915]. 1 l., 21 pp.,
32 cm. (Édition populaire Ricordi Oeuvres classiques pour piano,
No. 115856.)
Preface signed by Gabriel Fauré. P.N.: 115856

18 LITTLE PRELUDES (S. 924-943, 999)

2047. Akademische Neuausgabe ausgewählter Clavierwerke von Joh.
Seb. Bach. Kritisch revidirt in Bezug auf Textdarstellung, Tempo und
Vortragszeichen und mit Vorwort, Vorbemerkungen und Fingersatz

216   PUBLISHED MUSIC OF J. S. BACH

2047. *(continued)* für den Studiengebrauch versehen von Heinrich
Germer, Band 1. Brunswick, Henry Litolff [ca. 1890]. 6, 47 pp.; 30 cm.
(Collection Litolff, No. 2004.)   P.N.: COLLECTION LITOLFF No. 2004
2048.   18 Petits Préludes pour piano... Avec analyses et conseils sur
l'interprétation par Georges Sporck. ... Paris, E. Ploix, c 1914. 1 l.,
46 pp., 31 cm. (Edition analytique des classiques.)
Biographical note on Bach by Paul Landormy.
                                        P.N.'s: M.390.S. to M.407.S.
2049.   18 Little Preludes (18 Petits Préludes) for Piano... Edited by
Stewart MacPherson. London, Joseph Williams [c 1916]. 29,
[1] pp.; 31 cm. (Berners Edition.)   P.N.: J.W.15572
2050.   Eighteen Little Preludes for the Piano. Edited by Karl Klindworth. Cincinnati, John Church [c 1900].   19, [1] pp.; 31 cm.
(Edition Church, No. 67.)   P.N.: 13494
2051.   Joh. Seb. Bach's Pianoforte Works, edited by Franklin Taylor...
18 Short Preludes. ... London, Augener [c 1913].   1 l., 27 pp., 1 l.,
31 cm. (Augener's Edition, No. 8020.)   P.N.'s: 14528, 14529
2052.   Kleine Präludien oder Übungen für Anfänger revidiert von
Ernst von Dohnányi. Petits Préludes pour les commençants, Short
Preludes for the Beginners. Budapest, Rózsavölgyi [c 1922]. 30 pp.,
32 cm.   P.N.: R. és Tˢᵃ 4349
2053.   Oeuvres originales J. S. Bach, 6 Petits Préludes. Paris, Maurice
Senart [ca. 1910]. 2 parts. 35 cm. (Nouvelle Édition française de
musique classique, Nos. 115-116.)   P.N.'s: 116; 115.
2054.   Petits Préludes, révision et annotations par Blanche Selva.
Paris, Maurice Senart, c 1915. 16 pp., 34 cm. (Édition nationale de
musique classique, No. 5043.)   P.N.: EDITION NATIONALE. M.S.
2055.   15 válogatott kis praeludium fokozatos összeállitásban, ujjrenddel,
elödási jelekkel és jegyzetekkel ellátta Szendy Árpád... 15 ausgewählte kleine Praeludien progressiv geordnet, neu eingerichtet,
mit Fingersatz, Vortragzeichen und Anmerkungen versehen von
Szendy Árpád. ... Budapest, Rozsnyai Károly [1906]. 25, [1] pp.;
34 cm. (Rozsnyai Károly Kiadása, No. 180.)   P.N.: R.K.180
2056.   12 kleine Präludien und 6 kleine Präludien herausgegeben von
Edwin Fischer. ... Berlin, Ullstein [c 1924]. 24 pp., 34 cm. (Tonmeister Ausgabe, No. 1.)   P.N.: T.A.1

Organ

2057.   Johann Sebastian Bach's Compositionen für die Orgel. Kritisch-
korrecte Ausgabe von F. K. Griepenkerl und F. A. Roitzsch... Band
VIII... No. 11. Praeludium G dur... Leipzig & Berlin, C. F. Peters,
Bureau de Musique [ca. 1848]. 1 l., pp. 82-84, obl. fol., 26 × 33 cm.
Issued as a separate with its own title, but with original pagination
and from the original plates.   P.N.: 3335

PRELUDES AND FUGUES

Clavier

2058. [Fughettes. J.-S. Bach. Paris, E. Ploix, c 1914.] 2 ll., 36 pp., 1 l., 31 cm. (Édition analytique des classiques.) Copyright held by Georges Sporck. Biographical note on Bach by Paul Landormy.   P.N.'s: M.408.S. to M.416.S.

2059. Joh. Seb. Bach's Pianoforte Works. Edited by Franklin Taylor ...Short Preludes and Fugues. ... London, Augener [c 1913, 1915]. 1 l., 47 pp., 1 l., 31 cm. (Augener's Edition, No. 8020a.)
P.N.'s: 14528, 14529, 14858

2060. Klavierwerke von Joh. Seb. Bach herausgegeben von Adolf Ruthardt, Revidierte Ausgabe. Leipzig, C. F. Peters [ca. 1930]. 1 l., 47 pp., 30 cm. (Edition Peters, No. 2791.) Title on wrapper: ... Kleine Präludien, Fughetten. This is Band 3 of Ruthardt's collected edition of 10 volumes.   P.N.: 7748

2061. Kleine Präludien und Fugen, Short Preludes and Fugues, Piano Solo. Magdeburg, Heinrichshofen, c 1910. 57 pp., 30 cm. (Neue instruktive Ausgabe von Theodor Wiehmayer, No. 1.) Preface in German and in English translated by John Bernhoff and Roy B. Campbell.   P.N.: H.V.9691

2062. Kleine Präludien usw. für Klavier zu zwei Händen auf Grund der Ausgabe von Hans Bischoff herausgegeben von Robert Teichmüller. Leipzig, C. F. Peters [c 1929]. 52 pp., 30 cm. (Edition Peters, No. 3871.)   P.N.: 10643

2063. Little Preludes and Fugues, Kleine Präludien und Fugen... arranged in progressive order. Philadelphia, Theodore Presser [c 1903]. 46 pp., 1 l., 30 cm. (Presser Collection, No. 128.) Edited by Preston Ware Orem.

2064. Petits Préludes & Fugues pour piano. Nouvelle édition revue et doigtée par Th. Lack. Paris, Henry Lemoine, c 1915. 1 l., 47 pp., 1 l., 30 cm. (Édition nationale française Panthéon des pianistes, No. 993.)   P.N.: HL. 21229.P.993.

2065. Petits Préludes & fuguettes. Nouvelle édition revue et doigtée par Noel-Gallon. ... Paris, Choudens [c 1933]. 1 l., 49 pp., 31 cm. (Édition française de musique classique de piano.)   P.N.: A.C.17410

2066. Petits Préludes et petites fugues. Paris, A. Durand [1931]. 1 l.; 47, [1] pp.; 30 cm. (Édition classique A. Durand & Fils, No. 9320.)   P.N.: D. & F. 9320

2067. Petits Préludes et petites fugues à 2 et 3 voix. Édition revue et doigtée par Victor Staub. Paris, E. Gallet [ca. 1920]. Pp. 3-49, [1]; 32 cm. (Edition Gallet, No. 83.)   P.N.: E.G.7634

2068. Pianoforte-Musik redigirt und herausgegeben von den Professoren und Lehren...J. Dachs, A. Door...und A. Sturm...(redigirt

2068. *(continued)* und herausgegeben von ... A. Sturm)...6 Petites Fugues et fuguettes. ... Leipzig, Aug. Cran [ca. 1895]. 17, [1] pp.; 34 cm. (Classikerausgabe des Wiener Conservatoriums.)
P.N.: C.26288

2069. Pianoforte Works of Joh. Seb. Bach...21 Short Preludes and 6 Fugues...carefully revised and fingered. Boston, B. F. Wood [c 1903]. 50 pp., 1 l., 30 cm. (Edition Wood, No. 238.) Edited by Robt. Braun Eilenberg.   P.N.: B.F.W. 1592-49

2070. Praeluiumok és kis fugák fokozatos összeállitasban, ujjrenddel, elöadási jelekkel és jegyzetekkel ellátta Szendy Árpád, Präludien und Fughetten progressiv geordnet, neu eingerichtet, mit Fingersatz, Vortragszeichen und Anmerkungen versehen von Szendy Árpád. ... Budapest, Rozsnyai Károly [1907]. 32 pp., 34 cm. (Rozsnyai Károly Kiadása, No. 198.)   P.N.: R.K.198.

2071. Preludio con fuga—A moll...Édition nouvelle, rédigée par Fréd. Conr. Griepenkerl. ... Leipzig, au Bureau de Musique de C. F. Peters [1851?]. [1], 16-22 pp.; 33 cm.; wove paper. (Pièces détachées de la 4me livraison...No. 2.)   P.N.: 2696

2072. Short Preludes and Fugues for the Pianoforte. Edited and fingered by Dr. Wm. Mason. New York, G. Schirmer, c 1895. 2 ll., 35 pp., 30 cm. (Schirmer's Library of Musical Classics, Vol. 15.)
P.N.: 12124

2073. Short Preludes and Other Pieces for the Clavier by John Sebastian Bach. Edited, with a short preface, by James Higgs. This book also includes an appendix containing twenty short and easy pieces from the Clavier Book of Anna Magdalena Bach. London, New York, Novello, Ewer [1893]. 2 ll., 49 pp., 31 cm. P.N.: 9549

2074. Six Préludes et six petites fugues de J. S. Bach revus, mis en ordre et doigtés par Alexandre Longo. ... Paris, Soc. an. des éditions Ricordi [ca. 1915]. 26 pp., 32 cm. (Édition populaire Ricordi Oeuvres classique pour piano, No. 115857.)   P.N.: 115857

PRELUDES (FANTASIES OR TOCCATAS) AND FUGUES

Organ, Collections

2075. J. S. Bach Oeuvres pour orgue, Préludes et fugues, Livre I [II, III], Notices et commentaires par Louis Vierne. ... Paris, Maurice Senart, c 1924. 3 vols. in 1. 34 cm. (Édition nationale, Nos. 5201-5203.)   P.N.'s: E.M.S. 5201 – E.M.S. 5203

2076. Johann Sebastian Bach's noch wenig bekannte Orgelcompositionen (auch am Pianoforte von einem oder zwei Spielern ausführbar) gesammelt und herausgegeben von Adolph Bernhard Marx. Leipzig, Breitkopf & Härtel [1833?]. 3 parts in 1. Obl. 4°, 25 × 33 cm., wove paper.   P.N.'s: 5469, 5470, 5471

2077. Sebastin Johan Bach's Grand Studies for the Organ Consisting
of Preludes, Fugues, Toccatas, and Fantasias. Never before published
in this country. These studies may be played on the piano forte by
one or two performers; A separate part for the double bass or violoncello arranged from the pedale by Signor Dragonetti is added to this
edition. London, Coventry & Hollier and Cramer, Addison & Beale
[1836-37?]. 9 [?] parts. Obl. fol., 27 × 36 cm., wove paper & laid
paper.
   Library has Books 1, 2, and 4. Book 4 has book review from
The Atlas, October 8, 1837, included in the original sewing.
                              P.N.: BACH's Fugues &c. N°. 1 [and 2 & 4]
2078. John Sebastian Bach's Grand Studies for the Organ Consisting
of Preludes, Fugues, Toccatas, and Fantasias. Never before published
in this country. These studies may be played on the piano forte by
one or two performers; a separate part for the double bass or violoncello arranged from the pedale by Signor Dragonetti is added to this
edition. London, Coventry & Hollier and Cramer, Addison & Beale
[1845?]. 9 parts in 1 vol. Obl. fol., 25 × 35 cm., wove paper.
   Imperfect: 'Cello part wanting throughout. Signature on title
page of Book 1: Walter E. Bridson Royal College of Music.
                              P.N.'s: BACH's Fugues, &c. N°. 1 [and 2 to 9]
2079. Leichte Präludien und Fugen für Orgel...progressiv geordnet
und mit Finger- und Pedalsatz versehen von A. Hänlein. Leipzig,
C. F. Peters [ca. 1928]. 39 pp., obl. fol., 23 × 31 cm. (Edition Peters,
No. 2880.)   P.N.: 8336
2080. Sechs Präludien und Fugen für Orgel oder Pianoforte mit
Pedal...Neue correcte Ausgabe. Vienna, Tobias Haslinger [1838?].
65 pp., 35 cm., wove paper.   P.N.: T.H.4085
2081. Sechs Praeludien und sechs Fugen für Orgel oder Pianoforte
mit Pedal. ... Vienna, J. Riedls Kunsthandlung [before 1815].
63 pp., obl. fol., 25 × 32 cm., wove paper.   P.N.: 724
2082. 12 Preludes & Fugues for the Organ...Edited by Scotson Clark.
London, Augener [ca. 1880]. 79 pp., 30 cm. (Augener & Co.'s
Edition, No. 8740.)   P.N.'s: 27-38

Organ, Arrangement

2083. 6 Präludien und Fugen für Orgel...für Pianoforte zu zwei
Händen gesetzt von Franz Liszt, Heft 1 [and Heft 2] Leipzig,
C. F. Peters [ca. 1890]. 2 vols. in 1. 30 cm. (Edition Peters, Nos.
222-223).   P.N.'s: 7163, 7164

Organ, Selections

8 LITTLE PRELUDES AND FUGUES (S. 553-560)

2084. Acht kleine Präludien und Fugen für die Orgel. Neue Ausgabe von Karl Straube. Leipzig, C. F. Peters [c 1934]. 1 l., 24 pp., obl. fol., 27 × 34 cm. (Edition Peters, No. 4442.)   P.N.: 11238

2085. Eight Little Preludes and Fugues for the Organ. Edited by Caspar Koch, Hammond organ registration by Porter Heaps. Pittsburgh, Pa., Volkwein [c 1949]. xi, 2-33 pp.; 31 cm.
Signature on front wrapper: Caspar Koch.   P.N.: Eight Little

2086. Eight Little Preludes and Fugues for the Organ. Edited by James H. Rogers. Boston, Oliver Ditson [c 1922]. 2 ll.; 41, [3] pp.; 31 cm. (Ditson Edition, No. 350.)   P.N.: 73886-41

2087. Eight Short Preludes and Fugues...The fingering, pedaling, registration and metronome indications by Henry M. Dunham. ... Boston, Leipzig, New York, Arthur P. Schmidt, c 1888. 31, [1] pp.; 34 cm.   P.N.: A.P.S. & C°. 1640

Organ, Single Works

PRELUDE AND FUGUE IN A MAJOR (S. 536)

2088. J. S. Bach's Organ Works. Edited and fingered by Frederic Archer. London, Weekes & co. [ca. 1900]. 9, [1] pp.; obl. 8°; 25 × 35 cm. (Collegiate Edition, No. 10.)
P.N.: Collegiate Edition.
J. S. Bach's Fugues. (F. Archer.)

2089. [Caption title:] Praeludium und fuga. Erfurt, Leipzig, Gotth. Wilh. Körner [1850?]. 6 pp., obl. 4°, 24 × 28 cm., wove paper. (Der Orgel-Virtuos, No. 242.)   P.N.: 79

PRELUDE AND FUGUE IN A MINOR (S. 543)

2090. Johann Sebastian Bach Organ Works...Edited by Charles-Marie Widor and Albert Schweitzer...Prelude and Fugue in A Minor. New York, G. Schirmer [c 1912]. 1 l.; 15, [1] pp.; obl. fol.; 23 × 31 cm.   P.N.: 31148

PRELUDE AND FUGUE IN A MINOR (S. 551)

2091. Prelude et fugue pour l'orgue ou le piano-forte composé par J. S. Bach, No. I. Leipzig, au Bureau de Musique de C. F. Peters [1834?]. 1 l., 3-7 pp., obl. fol., 25 × 33 cm., wove paper.   P.N.: 2261

PRELUDE AND FUGUE IN B MINOR (S. 544)

2092. Johann Sebastian Bach Präludium und Fuge H-moll für Orgel herausgegeben in Faksimile-Reproduktion nach der Original-Handschrift des Musikhistorischen Museums in Köln von Georg Kinsky. Vienna, New York, Universal-Edition, A.G., c 1923. v pp., 1 l., 9 pp., 33 cm. (Musikalische Seltenheiten Wiener Liebhaberdruck, Band 6.)

PRELUDE AND FUGUE IN C MAJOR (S. 545)

2093.   J. S. Bach's Organ Works, edited by W. T. Best.   First series,
The Great Preludes and Fugues. No. 9821. ... London, Augener
[ca. 1915]. 1 l., 8 pp., 1 l., obl. fol., 24 × 33 cm.   P.N.: 6491

PRELUDE AND FUGUE IN C MAJOR (S. 553)

2094.   J. S. Bach's Organ Works. Edited and fingered by Frederic
Archer. London, Weekes [ca. 1900]. 1 l.; 5, [1] pp.; obl. 8°;
25 × 35 cm. (Collegiate Edition No. 3.)
                                             P.N.: Collegiate Edition.
                                          J. S. Bach's Fugues. (F. Archer)

PRELUDE (FANTASIE) AND FUGUE IN C MINOR (S. 562)

2095.   [Caption title:] Fantasia. Erfurt, Leipzig, Gotth. Wilh. Körner
[1845?]. Pp. 10-12, obl. 4°, 23 × 27 cm., wove paper. (Der Orgel-
Virtuos, No. 5.)   P.N.: 21.I

PRELUDE (FANTASIE) AND FUGUE IN C MINOR (S. 537)

2096.   [Caption title:] Fantasia e Fuga in C moll. Erfurt, Leipzig,
Gotth. Wilh. Körner [1845?]. Pp. 29-34, obl. 4°, 23 × 27 cm., wove
paper. (Der Orgel-Virtuos, No. 125.)   P.N.: VII.4.33

PRELUDE AND FUGUE IN D MAJOR (S. 532)

2097.   Johann Sebastian Bach Organ works... Edited by Charles-Marie
Widor and Albert Schweitzer... Prelude and Fugue in D Major. ...
New York, G. Schirmer [c 1912]. 2 ll., 16 pp., 2 ll., obl. fol.,
23 × 31 cm.   P.N.: 31135

PRELUDE (TOCCATA) AND FUGUE IN D MINOR (DORIAN) (S. 538)

2098.   Toccata et fugue pour l'orgue ou le piano-forte composée par
J. S. Bach, No. III. Leipzig, au Bureau de Musique de C. F. Peters
[before 1834]. 1 l., 3-15 pp., obl. fol., 25 × 33 cm., wove paper.
Formerly the property of Clara Wieck Schumann.   P.N.: 2264

PRELUDE AND FUGUE IN D MINOR (S. 554)

2099.   J. S. Bach's Organ Works. Edited and fingered by Frederic
Archer. London, Weekes [ca. 1900]. 1 l.; 5, [1] pp.; obl. 8°;
25 × 35 cm. (Collegiate Edition, No. 6.)
                                             P.N.: Collegiate Edition.
                                J. S. Bach's Fugues. (F. Archer.) [and] 6

PRELUDE AND FUGUE IN E MINOR (S. 533)

2100.   J. S. Bach's Organ Works. Edited and fingered by Frederic
Archer. London, Weekes [ca. 1900]. 1 l.; 5, [1] pp.; obl. 8°;
25 × 36 cm. (Collegiate Edition, No. 9.)   P.N.: Collegiate Edition.
                                          J. S. Bach's Fugues. (F. Archer.)

2101. Johann Sebastian Bach Organ Works...Edited by Charles-
Marie Widor and Albert Schweitzer...Prelude and Fugue in E
Minor (The Cathedral). New York, G. Schirmer [c 1912]. iii,
2-5, [1] pp.; obl. fol.; 23 × 31 cm.   P.N.: 31146

PRELUDE AND FUGUE IN E MINOR (S. 555)

2102. J. S. Bach's Organ Works. Edited and fingered by Frederic
Archer. London, Weekes [ca. 1900]. 1 l., 5, [1] pp.; obl. 8°;
25 × 35 cm. (Collegiate Edition, No. 5.)   P.N.: Collegiate Edition.
                                        J. S. Bach's Fugues. (F. Archer.)

PRELUDE AND FUGUE IN E FLAT MAJOR (S. 552)

2103. Johann Sebastian Bach Organ Works...Edited by Charles-
Marie Widor and Albert Schweitzer...Prelude and Fugue in E♭
Major (St. Anne's). New York, G. Schirmer [c 1912]. v, 3-21 pp.;
1 l.; obl. fol.; 23 × 31 cm.   P.N.: 31145

PRELUDE (TOCCATA) AND FUGUE IN F MAJOR (S. 540)

2104. Toccata et fugue pour l'orgue ou le piano-forte composée par
J. S. Bach, No. II. Leipzig, au Bureau de Musique de C. F. Peters
[before 1834]. 1 l., 3-15 pp., obl. fol., 25 × 33 cm., wove paper.
Formerly the property of Clara Wieck Schumann.   P.N.: 2263

PRELUDE AND FUGUE IN F MINOR (S. 534)

2105. [Caption title:] Praeludium und Fuga. Erfurt, G. Wilh. Körner
[1852?]. Pp. 18-24, obl. 4°, 24 × 28 cm., wove paper. (Sämmtliche
Orgel-Compositionen, Heft 2.)
Joint editors: Gotthilf Wilhelm Körner and Friedrich Kühmstedt.
                                        P.N.: 26.II

PRELUDE AND FUGUE IN G MAJOR (S. 541)

2106. Prelude et fugue pour l'orgue ou le piano-forte composé par
J. S. Bach, No. II. Leipzig, au Bureau de Musique de C. F. Peters
[1834?]. 1 l., 3-9 pp., obl. fol., 25 × 33 cm., wove paper.
Formerly the property of Clara Wieck Schumann.   P.N.: 2262

PRELUDE AND FUGUE IN G MINOR (S. 535)

2107. Prelude et fugue pour l'orgue ou le piano-forte composé par
J. S. Bach, No. III. Leipzig, au Bureau de Musique de C. F. Peters
[1834?]. 1 l., 3-9 pp., obl. fol., 25 × 33 cm., wove paper.
Formerly the property of Clara Wieck Schumann.   P.N.: 2265

PRELUDE (FANTASIE) AND FUGUE IN G MINOR (S. 542)

2108. Johann Sebastian Bach Organ Works...Edited by Charles-
Marie Widor and Albert Schweitzer...Prelude and Fugue in G
Minor (The Great). New York, G. Schirmer [c 1912]. vii, 2-15 pp.;
obl. fol.; 23 × 31 cm.   P.N.: 31147

SANCTUS (S. 237-241)

2109. Joh. Seb. Bach. Klavierauszüge…Messen…7. Sanctus in C dur,
8. Sanctus in D dur, 9. Sanctus in d moll, 10. Sanctus in G dur,
11. Sanctus in D dur. … Leipzig, Breitkopf & Härtel [ca. 1895].
32 pp., 27 cm.
Editing attributed to S. Jadassohn.
                                        P.N.'s: J.S.B.IV.7 to J.S.B.IV.11.

SONATAS

Flute, Unaccompanied (S. 1013)

2110. Sonate A moll, La mineur—A minor; Flöte solo (Flöte und
Klavier). (Schwedler-Schreck) [London, C. F. Peters, c1939].
Score and 1 part. 31 cm. (Edition Peters, No. 3332.)
Clavier accompaniment by Gustav Schreck.   P.N.: 10054
2111. Sonate A moll für Flöte solo…herausgegeben von Maximilian
Schwedler, Klavierbegleitung von Gustav Schreck. Leipzig, C. F.
Peters [1931?]. Score and 1 part. 30 cm. (Edition Peters, No. 3332.)
                                                    P.N.: 10054

Flute and Clavier (S. 1030-1035)

2112. Compositions pour violon et pour flûte par Jean Sebastien Bach
…Edition nouvelle, revue et corrigée critiquement par Ferd. David,
J. Hellmesberger et Fr. Hermann…Cah. 6…Six Sonatas pour flûte
ou violon et piano. … Leipzig & Berlin, C. F. Peters, Bureau de
Musique [1866?]. Score and 1 part. 33 cm., wove paper. (Oeuvres
complètes, Série III, Cahier 6.)   P.N.: 4553
2113. Sechs Sonaten für Klavier und Flöte…herausgegeben von
Wilhelm Barge, Hermann Spiro und B. Todt. Leipzig, Breitkopf &
Härtel [ca. 1930]. Score and 1 part (in 2 vols. each). 31 cm. (Edition
Breitkopf, No. 2427-28.)   P.N.'s: E.B.2427; E.B.2428
2114. Sechs Sonaten für Klavier und Flöte oder Violine…heraus-
gegeben von Ferd. David und Fr. Hermann. Leipzig, C. F. Peters
[1935?]. Score and 1 part (in 2 vols. each). 31 cm. (Edition Peters
Nos. 234-235.)   P.N.'s: 7790; 7791
2115. Sechs Sonaten für Pianoforte und Flöte…No. 1-3 [and No. 4-6]
herausgegeben von Gustav Schreck und Max Schwedler, Violinstimme bezeichnet von Andreas Moser. Leipzig, C. F. Peters [1909?].
Score and 1 part (flute and violin bound together). 30 cm. (Edition
Peters, No. 234a, 235a.)   P.N.'s: 9411; 9482
2116. Sonatas for Flute and Piano. Study version edited by Georges
Barrère, Volume I [and Volume II]. … Boston, Mass., The Boston
Music Co., c1944. Score and 1 part (in 2 vols. each). 31 cm.
                        P.N.'s: B.M.Co. 10258; B.M.Co. 10259

2117.   Sonaten Nr. 1-3 [and 4-6] für Flöte oder Violine und obligates Cembalo (Klavier). Nach den Autographen und Zeitgenössischen Handschriften revidiert und herausgegeben von Kurt Soldan. Leipzig, C. F. Peters [1936?]. Score and 2 parts (in 2 vols. each, except for viola da gamba). 31 cm. (Edition Peters, Nos. 4461a, 4461b.)
   Title of Vol. II varies, after *Violine*, as follows: und Basso Continuo nach zeitgenössischen Handschriften revidiert und herausgegeben von Kurt Soldan, Continuo-Aussetzung von Waldemar Woehl.
   Viola da gamba part included for Vol. II.   P.N.'s: 11315; 11408

Flute, Clavier, and Violin (S. 1038)

2118.   Compositions pour violon et pour flûte par Jean Sebastien Bach ...Édition nouvelle, revue et corrigée critiquement par Ferd. David, J. Hellmesberger & Fr. Hermann...Cah. 8...No. 2, Sonate pour flûte, violon et piano. ... Leipzig & Berlin, C. F. Peters, Bureau de Musique [1867?]. Score and 2 parts. 34 cm., wove paper. (Oeuvres complètes, Série III, Cahier 8, No. 2.)
   Edited by Fr. Hermann.   P.N.: 4566

Organ, Collections (S. 525-530)

2119.   Practische Orgelschule enthaltend sechs Sonaten für zwey Manuale und durchaus obligates Pedal von Joh. Sebast. Bach. Zurich, Hans Georg Nageli und Comp. [1827?]. 1 l., 94 pp., obl. fol., 26 × 35 cm., wove paper.
   Pastedown over imprint reads: Francfort s/M chez Charles Auguste André.   P.N.: N. u. C. 2.

Organ, Single Works

SONATA NO. 1 (S. 525)

2120.   Johann Sebastian Bach's Compositionen für die Orgel, Kritisch-korrecte Ausgabe von Fried. Konr. Griepenkerl und Ferd. Roitzsch, Daraus sind nachstehende Stücke einzeln zu haben: Aus dem 1sten Bande: [6 sonatas listed]. Leipzig, im Bureau de Musique von C. F. Peters [ca. 1845]. 10 pp., obl. fol., 27 × 34 cm., wove paper.
   This is a separate edition, printed from same plates as Vol. I of the collected edition by Griepenkerl and Roitzsch.   P.N.: 2893

2121.   No. I. A Trio, composed originally for the organ by John Sebastian Bach, and now adapted for three hands upon the piano forte. [London] To be had only of Mr. C. F. Horn, Queen Square No. 25 and Mr. S. Wesley, Arlington Street Camden Town No. 27 [1809?]. 1 l., 13 pp., 33 cm., laid paper.
   Numeral at the beginning is supplied in ink. Signature on title page: A. J. Balfour; Autographs of S. Wesley and C. F. Horn.

SONATA NO. 2 (S. 526)

2122. No. II. A Trio, composed originally for the organ by John
Sebastian Bach, and now adapted for three hands upon the piano forte.
[London] To be had only of Mr. C. F. Horn, Queen Square No. 25
and Mr. S. Wesley, Arlington Street Camden Town No. 27 [1809?].
[1], 14-27 pp.; 33 cm.; laid paper.
> Numeral at beginning is supplied in ink. Pagination continuous
> with that of Sonata No. I. On title page: autograph signatures of
> S. Wesley and C. F. Horn.

SONATA NO. 3 (S. 527)

2123. No. III. A Trio, composed originally for the organ by John
Sebastian Bach, and now adapted for three hands upon the piano
forte. [London] To be had of Mr. C. F. Horn, Queen Square No. 25;
at Mr. Birchall's, New Bond Street; & at Mr. Ball's Piano Forte
Manufactory, Duke St. Grosvenor Square [1809?]. [1], 28-47 pp.;
33 cm.; laid paper.
> Numeral at beginning is supplied in ink. Pagination continuous
> with that of Sonata No. II. On title page: autograph signatures of
> S. Wesley and C. F. Horn.

SONATA NO. 4 (S. 528)

2124. No. IV. A Trio, composed originally for the organ by John
Sebastian Bach, and now adapted for three hands upon the piano
forte. [London] To be had of Mr. C. F. Horn, Queen Square No. 25;
at Mr. Birchall's, New Bond Street; & at Mr. Ball's Piano Forte
Manufactory, Duke St. Grosvenor Square [1809?]. [1], 48-63 pp.;
33 cm.; wove paper.
> Numeral at beginning is supplied in ink. Pagination continuous
> with that of Sonata No. III. On title page: autograph signatures of
> S. Wesley and C. F. Horn.

SONATA NO. 5 (S. 529)

2125. No. V. A Trio, composed originally for the organ by John
Sebastian Bach, and now adapted for three hands upon the Piano
Forte. [London] To be had of Mr. C. F. Horn, Queen Square No. 25;
at Mr. Birchall's, New Bond Street; & at Mr. Ball's Piano Forte
Manufactory, Duke St. Grosvenor Square [1809?]. [1], 64-81 pp.;
33 cm.; wove paper.
> Numeral at beginning is supplied in ink. Pagination continuous
> with that of Sonata No. 4. On title page: signature and date:
> Miſs Crane | 30th of Novr. | 1810 |; also, autograph signatures of
> S. Wesley and C. F. Horn.

SONATA NO. 6 (S. 530)

2126. No. VI. A Trio, composed originally for the organ by John

226 PUBLISHED MUSIC OF J. S. BACH

2126. *(continued)* Sebastian Bach, and now adapted for three hands upon the piano forte. [London] To be had of Mr. C. F. Horn, Queen Square No. 25; at Mr. Birchall's, New Bond Street; & at Mr. Ball's Piano Forte Manufactory, Duke St. Grosvenor Square [1809?]. [1], 82-99 pp.; 33 cm.; wove paper. Numeral at beginning is supplied in ink. Pagination continuous with that of Sonata No. 5. On title page: signature and date: Miſs Crane | Octʳ. 29ᵗʰ 1810 |; also, autograph signatures of S. Wesley and C. F. Horn.

Viola da Gamba and Clavier (S. 1027-1029)

2127. Drei Sonaten für Klavier und Viola da Gamba…Für Viola und Klavier herausgegeben von Ernst Naumann. … Leipzig, Breitkopf & Härtel [ca. 1925]. Score and 1 part. 30 cm. (Edition Breitkopf, No. 3359.) P.N.'s: E.B.2426 (E.B.3359); E.B.3359
2128. Drei Sonaten für Klavier und Viola da Gamba…Für Violoncello und Klavier herausgegeben von Julius Klengel. … Leipzig, Breitkopf & Härtel [ca. 1925]. Score and 1 part. 31 cm. (Edition Breitkopf, No. 2426.) P.N.'s: E.B.2426 (E.B.3359); E.B.2426
2129. Drei Sonaten für Viola da Gamba und Cembalo (Klavier) nach den Quellen herausgegeben von Rolf van Leyden. Leipzig, C. F. Peters [1935?]. Score and 1 part. 31 cm. (Edition Peters, No. 4286.) P.N.: 11042
2130. Trois Sonates pour piano et viola da gamba ou violoncelle composées par J. Seb. Bach. Edition nouvelle, revue, doigtée et enrichie de notes sur l'exécution par Fr. Grützmacher. Leipzig & Berlin, C.F. Peters, Bureau de Musique [ca. 1865]. Score and 1 part. 34 cm., wove paper. (Oeuvres de Bach, Série IV, Cahier 2.) P.N.'s: 4530, 4531, 4532

Violin, Unaccompanied (S. 1001-1006), *Collections*

2131. Les Chef-d'oeuvres de l'art du violon pour étude et interprétation par Jenö Hubay…Bach, Sonates…(Violon seul). … Vienna, Édition Universelle [1922?]. 2 vols. 30 cm. (Universal-Edition, Nos. 6976-6977.) P.N.'s: H.824; H.825
2132. Sechs Sonaten für die Violine allein…Neu herausgegeben von Oscar Biehr, Heft I [and Heft II]. Leipzig, Steingräber [1906]. 2 vols. 34 cm. (Edition Steingräber, Nos. 1414-15.) P.N.'s: 1292; 1293
2133. Sechs Sonaten für die Violine…mit hinzufügter Begleitung des Pianoforte von Robert Schumann…Pianoforte (Partitur). Leipzig, Breitkopf & Härtel [ca. 1877]. 1 l., 101 pp., 32 cm. (Volksausgabe, No. 9.) P.N.: V.A.9

2134. Sechs Sonaten für die Violine allein von Joh. Seb. Bach. Studio ossia tre sonate per il violino solo senza basso, Zum Gebrauch bei dem Conservatorium der Musik zu Leipzig, mit Fingersatz, Bogenstrichen und sonstigen Bezeichnungen versehen von Ferd. David...Heft I... Neue Ausgabe. Leipzig, bei Fr. Kistner [1843?]. 19 pp., 34 cm., wove paper. P.N.: 1385

2135. Sechs Sonaten für die Violine allein von Joh. Seb. Bach. Studio ossia tre sonate per il violine solo senza basso, Zum Gebrauch bei dem Conservatorium der Musik zu Leipzig, mit Fingersatz, Bogenstrichen und sonstigen Bezeichnungen versehen von Ferd. David... Heft II...Neue Ausgabe. Leipzig, bei Fr. Kistner [1843?]. 25 pp., 34 cm., wove paper. P.N.: 1386

2136. Sechs Sonaten für die Violine allein von Joh. Seb. Bach. Studio ossia tre Sonate per il violino solo senza basso, Zum Gebrauch bei dem Conservatorium der Musik zu Leipzig, mit Fingersatz, Bogenstrichen und sonstigen Bezeichnungen versehen von Ferd. David...Heft III... Neue Ausgabe. Leipzig, bei Fr. Kistner [1843?]. 23 pp., 34 cm., wove paper. P.N.: 1387

2137. 6 Sonaten für Violine solo von Joh. Seb. Bach. Neuausgabe von A. Schulz. Brunswick, Henry Litolff [ca. 1915]. 64 pp., 31 cm. (Collection Litolff, No. 2396.) P.N.: COLLECTION LITOLFF No. 2396

2138. Sechs Sonaten (Sonaten und Partiten) für Violine von Joh. Seb. Bach, Neu-Ausgabe von Bram Eldering. Mainz, B. Schott [ca. 1922]. 1 l.; 49, [1] pp.; 31 cm. (Edition Schott, No. 126.) P.N.: 30999

2139. Sechs Sonaten und sechs Suiten für Violine und Violoncello solo herausgegeben und eingeleitet von Ernst Kurth. Munich, Drei Masken Verlag, 1921. xxi pp.; 1 l.; 157, [1] pp.; 1 l.; 19 cm.

2140. Sei solo à violino senza Baſſo accompagnato. Libro primo, Da Joh. Seb. Bach. ao. 1720. [Kassel & Basel, Bärenreiter, 1950.] 24 ll., 33 cm. No general title page; colophon gives imprint and the statement: Dieses Faksimile würde aus Anregung von Dr. Bernhard Sprengel, Hannover, herausgegeben. Nachwort signed: Wilhelm Martin Luther; dated: Göttingen, im Juli, 1950. Facsimile of Berlin Bibliothek MS. P 967.

2141. Six Sonatas for violin solo...Edited by Eduard Herrmann. New York, G. Schirmer, c 1900. 1 l., 61 pp., 30 cm. (Schirmer's Library of Musical Classics, Vol. 221.) Copyright renewal dated c 1929. P.N.: 15211

2142. Six Sonatas for Violin Solo. Edited by Leopold Auer. New York, Carl Fischer [c 1917]. 45, [1] pp., 30 cm. (Carl Fischer's Music Library, No. 788.) P.N.: 19544-43

2143. Six Sonates ou suites pour violon seul par J. Seb. Bach. Edition nouvelle, revue et doigtée par J. Hellmesberger. ... Leipzig, C. F. Peters [ca. 1890]. 39 pp., 34 cm. (Oeuvres de Bach, Série III, Cah. 4.) P.N.: 4551

2144.   Six Sonates pour le violon de J. S. Bach revues, corrigées et doigtées par J. Garcin. ... Paris, Magazin de musique du Conservatoire Anc^{ne}. M^{on}. O'Kelly; Ulysse T. du Wast, Succ^r. de E. Lacombe ...[ca. 1895]. 52 pp., 33 cm.   P.N.: U.T.W.291

2145.   6 Sonates pour le violon par J. S. Bach. Revues, corrigées et doigtées par H. Leonard...Cette édition est revue pour être exécutée avec l'accompag^t. de piano de Schumann. Paris, Costallat [ca. 1899]. 1 l., 47 pp., 35 cm.   P.N.: 15133.R.

2146.   Sonatas and partitas for solo violin. Edited by Jan Hambourg. [London] Oxford University Press [c 1934]. 2 ll., 75 pp., 31 cm.

2147.   Sonaten und Partiten für Violine (Adolf Busch). Revision 1931. ... Leipzig, N. Simrock [c 1931]. 67, [1] pp.; 32 cm. (Elite Edition, No. 720(S).)   P.N.: 15257

2148.   Sonaten und Partiten für Violine allein herausgegeben von Joseph Joachim und Andreas Moser. 1. Heft [and 2. Heft]. Berlin, Ed. Bote & G. Bock [c 1908]. 2 vols. 35 cm.
        English translation of Preface by M. Radford; French translation by Henri Marteau.   P.N.'s: B. & B. 16195; B. & B. 16196

2149.   Sonaten und Partiten für Violine allein (mit unterlegter Originalstimme) bearbeitet von Henri Marteau. Leipzig, Steingräber, c 1922. 87, [1] pp.; 34 cm. (Edition Steingräber, No. 2262.)   P.N.: 2097

2150.   Sonaten und Partiten für Violine solo. Neue Ausgabe von Carl Flesch. Leipzig, C. F. Peters [c 1930-31]. 2 ll., 105 pp., 33 cm. (Edition Peters, No. 4308.)
                        P.N.'s: 10820^a-10820^c, 10837^a-10837^c

2151.   Sonates pour violon seul révision d'après la notation de J. S. Bach par Paul LeMaître. ... Paris, A. Durand [1934?]. 1 l., 54 pp., 30 cm. (Édition classique A. Durand & Fils, No. 9331.)
                        P.N.: D. & F. 9331

2152.   Studio osia tre sonate per il violino solo del Sigr. Seb. Bach... Nuova editione. Bonn, N. Simrock [1828?]. [2], 3-4 pp.; 35 cm.; wove paper.
        Contents: three sonatas and three suites.   P.N.: 169

2153.   Violinsonaten, Sonates pour violon, Violin Sonatas, Violino solo ...Revidiert von Arnold Rosé. ... Vienna, Universal-Edition, A.G. [1935?]. 53 pp., 30 cm. (Universal-Edition, No. 295.) P.N.: U.E.295

Violin, Unaccompanied, Single Works

SONATA NO. I IN G MINOR (S. 1001)

2154.   Sechs Sonaten für die Violine von Johann Sebastian Bach mit hinzugefügter Begleitung des Pianoforte von Robert Schumann, Sonata I, Adagio, Fuga, Siciliano und Presto. ... Leipzig, bei Breitkopf & Härtel [ca. 1853]. 15 pp., 33 cm., wove paper.
                        P.N.: 8736

SONATA NO. 2 IN B MINOR (S. 1002)

2155.   Sechs Sonaten für die Violine von Johann Sebastian Bach mit
hinzugefügter Begleitung des Pianoforte von Robert Schumann...
Sonata II, Allemanda (mit Double), Corrente (mit Double), Sarabande (mit Double), Tempo di Bourée (mit Double). ... Leipzig, bei
Breitkopf & Härtel [ca. 1853]. 17 pp., 33 cm., wove paper.
                                                                P.N.: 8737

SONATA NO. 3 IN A MINOR (S. 1003)

2156.   Sechs Sonaten für die Violine von Johann Sebastian Bach mit
hinzugefügter Begleitung des Pianoforte von Robert Schumann...
Sonata III. Grave, Fuga, Andante, Allegro. ... Leipzig, bei Breitkopf
& Härtel [ca. 1853]. 15 pp., 33 cm., wove paper.   P.N.: 8738

SONATA NO. 4 IN D MINOR (S. 1004)

2157.   Sechs Sonaten für die Violine von Johann Sebastian Bach mit
hinzugefügter Begleitung des Pianoforte von Robert Schumann...
Sonata IV, Allemanda, Corrente, Sarabanda, Giga, Ciaconna. ...
Leipzig, bei Breitkopf & Härtel [ca. 1853]. 23 pp., 33 cm., wove
paper.   P.N.: 8739

SONATA NO. 5 IN C MAJOR (S. 1005)

2158.   Sechs Sonaten für die Violine von Johann Sebastian Bacith m
hinzugefügter Begleitung des Pianoforte von Robert Schumann...
Sonata V, Adagio, Fuga, Largo, Allegro. ... Leipzig, bei Breitkopf &
Härtel [ca. 1853]. 19 pp., 33 cm., wove paper.   P.N.: 8740

SONATA NO. 6 IN E MAJOR (S. 1006)

2159.   Sechs Sonaten für die Violine von Johann Sebastian Bach mit
hinzugefügter Begleitung des Pianoforte von Robert Schumann...
Sonata VI, Preludio, Loure, Gavotte und Rondo, Menuetto 1 u. 2.,
Bourre, Giga. ... Leipzig, bei Breitkopf & Härtel [ca. 1853]. 17 pp.,
33 cm., wove paper.   P.N.: 8741
2160.   Prelude to 6th Violin Sonata in E Major for Piano Solo.
Arranged by Paul Van Katwijk. London, J. & W. Chester [c 1938].
1 l.; 9, [1] pp.; 34 cm.   P.N.: J.W.C.2245

Violin and Clavier, Collections (S. 1014-1019)

2161.   Clavier Sonaten mit obligater Violine von Johann Sebastian
Bach. Zurich, bey Hans Georg Nägeli [ca. 1805]. Score and 1 part.
Obl. fol., 24 × 33 cm., laid paper.
2162.   Sechs Sonaten für Klavier und Violine Bearbeitung von Ernst
Naumann. ... Leipzig, Breitkopf & Härtel [1903?]. Score and 1 part
(in 2 vols. each). 31 cm. (Edition Breitkopf, Nos. 483a, 483b.)
                                      P.N.'s: N.B.III.2; N.B.IV.1

2163. Sechs Sonaten für Klavier und Violine herausgegeben von
Ferd. David. Leipzig, C. F. Peters [ca. 1925]. Score and 1 part
(in 2 vols. each). 31 cm. (Edition Peters, Nos. 232-33.)
P.N.'s: 7281, 7282
2164. Sechs Sonaten für Pianoforte und Violine...No. 1-3 [and
No. 4-6] herausgegeben von Gustav Schreck, Violinstimme bezeichnet
von Andreas Moser. Leipzig, C. F. Peters [ca. 1910]. Score and
1 part (in 2 vols. each). 30 cm. (Edition Peters, Nos. 232a, 233a.)
P.N.'s: 9013; 9256
2165. Sechs Sonaten für Violine und Klavier...Revidiert und bezeichnet von Carl Nowotny. Vienna, Universal-Edition (Aktiengesellschaft) [1927?]. Score and 1 part (in 2 vols. each). 31 cm.
Imperfect: Vol. I wanting.   P.N.: U.E.2842; U.E.2842ª
2166. Sechs Sonaten für Violine und Piano...herausgegeben und mit
Phrasierungen, Fingersätzen und Stricharten versehen von Leo
Portnoff. ... Leipzig, Aug. Cranz [ca. 1930]. Score and 1 part
(in 2 vols. each). 32 cm. (Edition Cranz, Nos. 456-57.)
P.N.'s: C.43382; C. 43383
2167. Six Grandes Sonates pour le pianoforte et violon obligé composées par Jean Sebastien Bach. Edition nouvelle, soigneusement
revue, corrigée, métronomisée et doigtée; enrichie de notes sur
l'exécution et accompagnée d'une préface. ... Leipzig, au Bureau de
Musique de C. F. Peters [1841?]. Score and 1 part. 33 cm., wove
paper. (Oeuvres complets, Livre 10.)   P.N.: 2766
2168. Six Grandes Sonates pour piano et violon...Soigneusement
revues et doigtées par J. N. Rauch, Vol. I [and Vol. II]. Brunswick,
Henry Litolff [ca. 1930]. Score and 1 part (in 2 vols. each). 31 cm.
P.N.'s: COLLECTION LITOLFF No. 881
COLLECTION LITOLFF No. 882

Violin and Clavier, Single Works

SONATA NO. 1 IN B MINOR (S. 1014)

2169. Sonata No. 1 in B Minor for Violin and Piano...Violin part
edited by Hugo Kortschak, piano part edited by Edwin Hughes.
New York, G. Schirmer, c 1926. Score and 1 part. 31 cm. (Schirmer's
Library of Musical Classics, Vol. No. 1503.)   P.N.: 32567

SONATA NO. 2 IN A MAJOR (S. 1015)

2170. Sonata No. 2 in A for Violin and Piano...Violin part edited by
Hugo Kortschak, piano part edited by Edwin Hughes. New York,
G. Schirmer, c 1926. Score and 1 part. 31 cm. (Schirmer's Library
of Musical Classics, Vol. No. 1507.)   P.N.: 32886

SONATA NO. 3 IN E MAJOR (S. 1016)

2171. Sonata No. 3 in E for Violin and Piano...Violin part edited by Hugo Kortschak, piano part edited by Edwin Hughes. New York, G. Schirmer, c 1927. Score and 1 part. 31 cm. (Schirmer's Library of Musical Classics, Vol. No. 1487.)   P.N.: 33022

SONATA NO. 4 IN C MINOR (S. 1017)

2172.   Sonata No. 4 in C Minor for Violin and Piano...Violin part edited by Hugo Kortschak, piano part edited by Edwin Hughes. New York, G. Schirmer, c 1928. Score and 1 part. 31 cm. (Schirmer's Library of Musical Classics, Vol. No. 1516.)   P.N.: 34428

SONATA NO. 5 IN F MINOR (S. 1018)

2173.   Sonata No. 5 in F Minor for Violin and Piano...Violin par. edited by Hugo Kortschak, piano part edited by Edwin Hughest New York, G. Schirmer, c 1928. Score and 1 part. 31 cm. (Schirmer's Library of Musical Classics, Vol. No. 1525.)   P.N.: 33943

2174.   Largo aus der 5ten Sonate für Pianoforte und Violine von Johann Sebastian Bach für 2 Violinen, Viola und Violoncell eingerichtet von Louis Roessel. ... Leipzig, im Bureau de Musique von C. F. Peters [1855?]. 4 parts. 34 cm.   P.N.: 3866

SONATA NO. 6 IN G MAJOR (S. 1019)

2175.   Sonata No. 6 in G for Violin and Piano...Violin part edited by Hugo Kortschak, piano part edited by Edwin Hughes. New York, G. Schirmer, c 1929. Score and 1 part. 31 cm. (Schirmer's Library of Musical Classics, Vol. No. 1533.)   P.N.: 34428

SONATA IN G MINOR FOR VIOLIN (OR FLUTE) AND CLAVIER (S. 1020)

2176.   Adagio, E dur. ... Leipzig, Breitkopf & Härtel [ca. 1866]. Score & 1 part. 34 cm., wove paper. (Lyrische Stücke, No. 3.) Transposed arrangement of the second movement for violoncello and piano.   P.N.: 11059

SONATA IN F MAJOR FOR VIOLIN AND CLAVIER (S. 1022)

2177.   Sonate F dur für Violine und Cembalo herausgegeben von Ludwig Landshoff, Erstausgabe 1936. Leipzig, C. F. Peters [c 1936]. Score and 2 parts. 31 cm. (Edition Peters, No. 4460.) Two violin parts included, one "discordate" and one "senza la scordatura."   P.N.: 11317

SONATA IN E MINOR FOR VIOLIN AND CLAVIER (S. 1023)

2178.   Compositions pour violon et pour flûte par Jean Sebastien Bach ...Édition nouvelle, revue et corrigée critiquement par Ferd. David, J. Hellmesberger et Fr. Hermann...Cah. 7...No. 2, Sonate p. [violon et piano]. ... Leipzig & Berlin, C. F. Peters, Bureau de Musique [1867?]. Score and 1 part. 33 cm. (Oeuvres complètes, Série III, Cahier 7, No. 2.)   P.N.: 4562

Two Violins and Clavier, Trio Sonatas, Collections (S. 1037-1039)

2179. Sonaten (Trios) für Klavier und 2 Violinen oder Klavier, Flöte
und Violine herausgegeben von Friedrich Hermann. Leipzig,
C. F. Peters [1932?]. Score and 2 parts. 31 cm. (Edition Peters,
No. 237.)   P.N.: 8160
2180. Trio-Sonaten. Neue Urtext-Ausgabe von Ludwig Landshoff.
Leipzig, C. F. Peters, [c 1936, c 1937]. Score and 6 parts (in 2 vols.
each). 31 cm. (Edition Peters, No. 4203a, 4203b.)
Second Violin part: Vol. I only; Flute part: Vol. II only.
                                               P.N.'s: 11321; 11345
2181. Zwei Sonaten...mit Pianoforte bearbeitet von Ferdinand David.
Leipzig, Breitkopf & Härtel [1924?]. Score and 2 parts. 31 cm.
(Edition Breitkopf, No. 3671.)   P.N.: E.B.3671

Two Violins and Clavier, Trio Sonatas, Single Works

SONATA IN C MAJOR FOR 2 VIOLINS AND CLAVIER (S. 1037)

2182. Compositions pour violon et pour flûte par Jean Sebastien Bach
...Edition nouvelle, revue et corrigée critiquement par Ferd. David,
J. Hellmesberger & Fr. Hermann...Cah. 8...No. 1. Sonate pour
2 violons et piano. ... Leipzig & Berlin, C. F. Peters, Bureau de
Musique [1867?]. Score and 2 parts. 34 cm., wove paper. (Oeuvres
complètes, Série III, Cahier 8, No. 1.)
This sonata edited by Friedrich Hermann.   P.N.: 4564

SONGS, SACRED

Collections (S. 439-518)

2183. Four Chorales from the Schemelli Gesang-Buch. ... Arranged for
voice and piano and edited by W. Gillies Whittaker, English texts by
Albert C. Latham. London, Oxford University Press, c 1930. 8 pp.,
26 cm. (The Oxford Choral Songs from the Old Masters, No. 1506.)
2184. Geistliche Lieder (aus dem Schemellischen Gesangbuch) für
eine Singstimme und Basso Continuo...Für den praktischen Gebrauch
herausgegeben von Herman Roth. Leipzig, C. F. Peters [ca. 1915].
44 pp., 27 cm. (Edition Peters, No. 3392a.)   P.N.: 9747
2185. Geistliche Lieder aus Schemelli's Gesangbuch und dem Notenbuch der Anna Magdalena Bach ausgewählt und für eine Singstimme mit Orgelbegleitung bearbeitet von Ludwig Landshoff.
Leipzig, Breitkopf & Härtel [1905]. iv, 36 pp.; obl. fol.; 24 × 31 cm.
                                               P.N. V.A.2128
2186. Geistliche Lieder und Arien aus Schemelli's Gesangbuch und
dem Notenbuch der Anna Magdalena Bach. Für eine Singstimme

mit Pianoforte (Orgel oder Harmonium). Leipzig, Breitkopf &
Härtel [ca. 1900]. 1 l.; 86, [4] pp.; 27 cm. (Edition Breitkopf,
No. 2817.)
Accompaniment edited by Ernst Naumann.
P.N.'s: E.B.2817; E.B.4738; J.S.B.VI.
2187. J. S. Bach's Original Hymn-Tunes for Congregational Use.
Edited, with notes, by Charles Sanford Terry. London, Humphrey
Milford, Oxford University Press, 1922. 64 pp., 1 l., 23 cm.
2188. 32 Hengellistä laulua yhdelle äänelle ja uruille tai pianolle
valitut kirkkovuoden juhlapäiviä silmällä pitäen, 32 Andliga sånger
för en röst och orgel eller piano valda   med hänsyn till kyrkoårets
högtidsdagar, Toimittanut John Sundberg, Tekstit suomeksi sovittanut
Ilta Koskimies, Texterna försvenskade av Nino Runeberg. ...
Porvoo-Borgå, Werner Söderström Osakeyhtiö [1925?]. 41 pp.,
30 cm.
2189. Die Lieder für eine Singstimme und Basso Continuo aus dem
Notenbuch der Anna Magdalena Bach. Für den praktischen Gebrauch
herausgegeben von Herman Roth. Leipzig, C. F. Peters [1920].
18 pp., 27 cm. (Edition Peters, No. 3392ᵇ.)   P.N.: 10228
2190. 69 Choräle mit beziffertem Bass...herausgegeben von C. F.
Becker. Zweite nach dem Originaldrucke vom Jahre 1736 durchgesehene Ausgabe. Leipzig, Breitkopf & Härtel [1882?]. 1 l., 33 pp.,
obl. 8°, 19×28 cm.   P.N.: E.B.730.
2191. 69 Geistliche Lieder und Arien mit beziffertem Bass aus G. Chr.
Schemellis Musikalischem Gesangbuch Leipzig 1736. Leipzig, C. F.
Peters, c 1949. 39, [1] pp.; 28 cm. (Edition Peters, No. 4573.)
P.N.: 11575
2192. Seb. Bachs Gesänge zu G. Chr. Schemellis "Musicalischem
Gesangbuch" Leipzig 1736. Mit ausgearbeitetem Generalbass
herausgegeben von Max Seiffert, Dritte durchgesehene Ausgabe.
Kassel, Bärenreiter [1924?]. vii, 72 pp.; 27 cm. (Bärenreiter Ausgabe
888.)
2193. Ten Schemelli Chorales...Edited by Walter E. Buszin. St.
Louis, Mo., Concordia, c 1945. 12 pp., 27 cm. (Anthologia Lutherana, No. B 3.)   P.N.: Ten Schemelli Chorales, 10
2194. Twenty Sacred Songs...Selected from the Schemelli collection
and arranged for voice and pianoforte accompaniment by Robert
Franz, the English version by the Rev. Dr. Troutbeck. London,
Novello; New York, H. W. Gray [1889?]. 1 l., 37 pp., 28 cm.
P.N.: 7788
2195. Zwanzig geistliche Lieder der Schemellischen Sammlung ent-
nommen, und für eine Singstimme mit Pianoforte ausgearbeitet von
Robert Franz. Leipzig, F. E. C. Leuckart (Constantin Sander)
[ca. 1890]. 1 l., 35 pp.. 28 cm.   P.N.: F.E.C.L.4024

2196. Zwanzig geistliche Lieder der Schemellischen Sammlung ent-
nommen und für eine Singstimme mit Pianoforte ausgearbeitet von
Robert Franz...C. Ausgabe für tiefere Stimme. ... Leipzig, F. E. C.
Leuckart, c 1907. 1 l., 31 pp., 28 cm.   P.N.: F.E.C.L. 6045

Arrangements

2197. Dearest Lord Jesus (Liebster Herr Jesu)...Arranged by Louis
Victor Saar (Three-Part Song for Women's Voices). Boston, Oliver
Ditson, c 1928. 4 pp., 27 cm. (Johann Sebastian Bach Choral
Compositions, Octavo No. 14,200.)   P.N.: 76239 – 4
2198. Four Sacred Songs, Komm, süsser Tod; Vergiss mein nicht;
O liebe Seele, zieh' die Sinnen; Mein Jesu, was für Seelenweh...
edited and arranged by Bernard Jackson for organ. [London]
Oxford University Press [c 1928]. 10 pp., 1 l., 32 cm.
2199. Komm, süsser Tod, Come, Thou Sweet Death. Chorus for
men's voices—A Capella...arranged by Edward T. Canby. New
York, Harold Flammer, c 1939. 5 pp., 26 cm. (Princeton University
Series of Choral Music, No. 7.)   P.N.: 1679

SONGS, SECULAR

Collection

2200. Sechs deutsche Lieder von Joh. Seb. Bach. Mit Klavier-
Begleitung versehen von Vincenz Lachner, Herausgegeben von
C. H. Bitter. Berlin, Posen, Ed. Bote & G. Bock [1865?]. 1 l.,
3-15 pp., 34 cm., wove paper.
A collection of 6 songs from the Second Book of Anna Magdalena
Bach, with added accompaniment by Lachner and edited by
Bitter.   P.N.: 7051

Arrangement

2201. Arioso ("My Heart Is Fixed"). Arranged by Carl Engel...
Organ (Transcribed by Edward Shippen Barnes). Boston, Mass.,
The Boston Music company [c 1920]. 5, [1] pp., 31 cm.
Organ arrangement of the song "Bist du bei mir," No. 25 in the
Second Book of Anna Magdalena Bach.   P.N.: B.M.Co. 6615

SUITES

Clavier

ENGLISH SUITES (S. 806-811), Collections

2202. Angliiskie suity, Dlia fortepiano, Tom I...(H. Pachulski).
Moscow, Gosudarstvennoe musykal'noe isdatel'stvo, 1931. 50 pp.,
32 cm.   P.N.: 38930

2203. Bach's English Suites. Revised and fingered by Karl Klindworth.
... Cincinnati, New York, etc., John Church [c 1897]. 2 vols. in 1.
32 cm. (Edition Church, No. 15.)
                              P.N.'s: 11349-24; 12038-23; 12039-18;
                                      12040-17; 12041-24; 12042-28
2204. Compositions pour le piano-forte sans et avec accompagnement
par Jean Sebastien Bach, edition nouvelle, soigneusement revue,
corrigée, métronomisée et doigtée; enrichie de notes sur l'exécution et
accompagnée d'une préface par Fréd. Conr. Griepenkerl. ... Leipzig,
au Bureau de Musique de C. F. Peters [1842?]. 1 l.; [1], 4-83 pp.;
33 cm.; wove paper.   P.N.: 2783
2205. English Suites for the Pianoforte in Two Volumes. After the
edition of Karl Czerny. New York, G. Schirmer, c 1896. 2 vols. in 1.
30 cm. (Schirmer's Library of Musical Classics, Vol. 17-18.)
                              P.N.'s: 12610, 12611
2206. English Suites for the Pianoforte...Revised by Hans Semper.
Boston, London, B. F. Wood [ca. 1925]. 2 vols. 31 cm. (Edition
Wood, No. 945-46.)   P.N.'s: B.F.W.6236-54; 6237-61
2207. Joh. Seb. Bach, Oeuvres pour piano...6 suites anglaises – 6
grössere, genannt englische, Suiten. (Jos. Meyer). Leipzig, Aug.
Cranz [ca. 1920]. 103 pp., 31 cm. (Edition Cranz, No. 631.)
                              P.N.: C.44940
2208. Joh. Seb. Bach's Pianoforte Works. Edited by Franklin Taylor
...English Suites. ... London, Augener [c 1915]. 1 l., 53 pp., 31 cm.
(Augener's Edition, No. 8017a.)
Contents: Suites 1-3.   P.N.: 14890
2209. Joh. Seb. Bach's Pianoforte Works. Edited by Franklin Taylor
...English Suites. ... London, Augener [c 1917]. 61 pp., 1 l., 31 cm.
(Augener's Edition, No. 8017b.)
Contents: Suites 4-6.   P.N.: 15067
2210. Klavierwerke von Joh. Seb. Bach herausgegeben von Adolf
Ruthardt, Revidierte Ausgabe. Leipzig, C. F. Peters [ca. 1930].
55 pp., 30 cm. (Edition Peters, No. 2794.)
Contents: Suites 1-3. This is Band 6 of Ruthardt's collected edition.
                              P.N.: 7751
2211. Klavierwerke von Joh. Seb. Bach herausgegeben von Adolf
Ruthardt, Revidierte Ausgabe. Leipzig, C. F. Peters [ca. 1930].
61 pp., 30 cm. (Edition Peters, No. 2795.)
Contents: Suites 4-6. This is Band 7 of Ruthardt's collected edition.
                              P.N.: 7752
2212. Suiten für Klavier...Zweiter Band, Sechs grössere Suiten (genannt "englische"). ... Leipzig, Breitkopf & Härtel [1896]. 85 pp.,
33 cm. (Urtext klassischer Musikwerke.)
Edited by Ernst Naumann.   P.N.'s: A.A.81 to A.A.86.

2213. Suites anglaises pour piano. Edition revue et doigtée par H. Dallier. ... Paris, Henry Lemoine, c 1922. 1 l.; 107, [1] pp.; 30 cm. (Édition nationale française Panthéon des pianistes, No. 1220.)
P.N.: HL21,462.P.1220

2214. Suites anglaises, Volume I., Nos. 1-3 [and Volume II, Nos. 4-6], révision par Maurice Emmanuel. ... Paris, A. Durand [c 1916]. 2 vols. in 1. 30 cm. (Édition classique A. Durand & Fils, Nos. 9365-9366.)
P.N.'s: D. & F. 9365; D. & F. 9366

2215. Suites anglaises pour piano, Volume II (H. Pachulski.). Moscow, P. Jurgenson [ca. 1930]. 59 pp., 31 cm. (Isdanie Jurgenson, No. 982.)
Contents: Suites 4-6.
P.N.: 38931

2216. Suites inglesi per pianoforte rivedute da Alessandro Longo, No. 1 a 3. Testo italiano, Texte français, English text. Milan, G. Ricordi, c 1918. 1 l., 53 pp., 32 cm. (Edizione Ricordi, No. 6.)
P.N.: E.R.6.

2217. Suites inglesi per pianoforte rivedute da Alessandro Longo, No. 4 a 6. Testo italiano, Texte français, English text. Milan, G. Ricordi, c 1918. 2 ll., 59 pp., 32 cm. (Edizione Ricordi, No. 7.)
P.N.: E.R.7

2218. Suites inglesi per pianoforte rivedute, con note illustrative e l'analisi della forma da Bruno Mugellini. ... Milan, G. Ricordi [1901]. 5 ll., 100 pp., 30 cm. (Edizioni Ricordi, No. 444.)
Contents: Suites 2, 3, 4 & 5.
P.N.: E.R.444.

ENGLISH SUITE NO. 1 (S. 806)

2219. Englishe Suite, Nr. 1, A-dur. Herausgegeben von Edwin Fischer. ... Berlin, Ullstein [c 1926]. 24 pp., 31 cm. (Tonmeister Ausgabe, No. 287.)
P.N.: T.A.Nr.287

2220. Oeuvres originales J. S. Bach, Suites anglaises, Suite 1re. Nouvelle Édition revue, doigtée et annotée par Adolphe F. Wouters. ... Paris, Maurice Senart [c 1925]. 13 pp., 35 cm. (Musique classique, Nos. 605-7.)
P.N.'s: M.S. & Cie. 605; M.S. & Cie. 606; M.S. & Cie. 607.

ENGLISH SUITE NO. 2 (S. 807)

2221. Englische Suite, Nr. 2, A-moll. Herausgegeben von Edwin Fischer. ... Berlin, Ullstein [c 1926]. 24 pp., 31 cm. (Tonmeister Ausgabe, No. 288.)
P.N.: T.A.Nr.288

2222. Oeuvres originales J. S. Bach, Suites anglaises, Suite 2e. Nouvelle Édition revue, doigtée et annotée par Adolphe F. Wouters. ... Paris, Maurice Senart [ca. 1925]. 15 pp., 36 cm. (Musique classique, Nos. 608-10.)
P.N.'s: M.S. & Cie. 608; M.S. & Cie. 609; M.S. & Cie. 610.

ENGLISH SUITE NO. 3 (S. 808)

2223. Englische Suite, G moll, Sol mineur. ... Berlin, Adolph Fürstner [ca. 1909]. 13 pp., 33 cm. (Bibliothek älterer und neuerer Klavier-Musik, No. 47.)

Edited by Franz Kroll. P.N.: 50

2224. Englische Suite No. 3 | G moll... auf Grund der Ausgabe von Hans Bischoff herausgegeben von Robert Teichmüller. Leipzig, C. F. Peters [ca. 1930]. 19 pp., 30 cm. (Edition Peters, No. 4112.) P.N.: 10790

2225. Englische Suite, Nr. 3, G-moll. Herausgegeben von Edwin Fischer. ... Berlin, Ullstein [c 1926]. 20 pp., 31 cm. (Tonmeister Ausgabe, No. 289.) P.N.: T.A.Nr.289

2226. Grandes Suites dites Suites Angloises pour le clavecin composées par J. Seb. Bach, No. I. Leipzig, chez Hoffmeister & Kühnel (Bureau de Musique) [ca. 1805?]. 15 pp., obl. fol., 24 × 34 cm., laid paper. English suite No. 3 in G minor. P.N.: 412

2227. Grandes Suites dites Suites Angloises pour le clavecin composées par J. Seb. Bach, No. I. Leipzig, chez Ambroise Kühnel (Bureau de Musique) [after 1805]. 15 pp., obl. fol., 24 × 34 cm., laid paper. English suite No. 3 in G minor. P.N.: 412

2228. Oeuvres originales J. S. Bach, Suites anglaises, Suite 3ᵉ. Nouvelle Édition revue, doigtée et annotée par Adolphe F. Wouters. ... Paris, Maurice Senart [ca. 1925]. 1 l., 15 pp., 35 cm. (Musique classique, Nos. 611-13.) P.N.'s: M.S. & Cⁱᵉ. 611; M.S. & Cⁱᵉ. 612; M.S. & Cⁱᵉ. 613.

2229. Suite inglese in sol minore... [riveduti da] F. Kroll. Milan, G. Ricordi [ca. 1875]. 1 l., 13 pp., 34 cm. (Scelta di pezzi classici, No. 93627.) P.N.: 93627

ENGLISH SUITE NO. 3 (S. 808): Excerpts

2230. Gavotte [in] G minor...Edited and fingered by Frederic Lillebridge. St. Louis, Mo., Art Publication Society, c 1913. Pp. [1], 2-3, 3-4, [5-6]; frontis. (port.); 35 cm. (Selected Edition, Progressive Series, No. 2.) P.N.: Ano. 21-2

ENGLISH SUITES NO. 4 (S. 809)

2231. The Academic Edition of Works by Joh: Seb: Bach...261, Suite anglaise in F. ... London, A. Hammond [ca. 1895]. 19, [1] pp.; 30 cm. (Academic Edition, No. 261.)

2232. Englische Suite, Nr. 4, F-dur. Herausgegeben von Edwin Fischer. ... Berlin, Ullstein [c 1926]. 20 pp., 31 cm. (Tonmeister Ausgabe, No. 290.) P.N.: T.A.Nr.290

2233. Klassische Klavierwerke aus Hans von Bülow's Concert-programmen...Bach, Joh. Seb., Suite, F dur (No. 4 der englischen Suiten)...Revidiert und mit genauen Fingersatz- und Vortragsbezeichnungen herausgegeben von Hans von Bülow. ... Vienna, Leipzig, Universal-Edition A.G. [1927?]. 16 pp., 31 cm. (Universal-Edition, No. 1323ᵃ.) P.N.: U.E.1323ᵃ. V.A.2608

2234. Oeuvres originales J. S. Bach, Suites anglaises, Suite 4ᵉ.
Nouvelle Édition revue, doigtée et annotée par Adolphe F. Wouters.
... Paris, Maurice Senart [ca. 1925]. 13 pp., 35 cm. (Musique
classique, Nos. 614-16.)   P.N.: M.S. & Cᴵᵉ. 614;
                                    M.S. & Cᴵᵉ. 615; M.S. & Cᴵᵉ. 616.
2235. Suite, F-dur (Fa-majeur).... Berlin, Adolph Fürstner [ca. 1870].
13 pp., 33 cm. (Bibliothek älterer und neuerer Klavier-Musik,
No. 30.)
Edited by Franz Kroll.   P.N.: 33
2236. Suite in fa maggiore...[riveduti da] F. Kroll. ... Milan,
G. Ricordi [ca. 1875]. 1 l.; 13, [1] pp.; 34 cm. (Scelta di pezzi
classici, No. 93610.)   P.N.: 93610

ENGLISH SUITE NO. 5 (S. 810)

2237. Englische Suite, Nr. 5, E-moll. Herausgegeben von Edwin
Fischer. ... Berlin, Ullstein [c 1926]. 24 pp., 31 cm. (Tonmeister
Ausgabe, No. 291.)   P.N.: T.A.Nr.291
2238. Oeuvres originales J. S. Bach, Suites anglaises, Suite 5ᵉ.
Nouvelle Édition revue, doigtée et annotée par Adolphe F. Wouters.
... Paris, Maurice Senart [ca. 1925]. 15 pp., 35 cm. (Musique
classique, Nos. 617-619.)   P.N.'s: M.S. & Cᴵᵉ. 617;
                                    M.S. & Cᴵᵉ. 618; M.S. & Cᴵᵉ. 619

ENGLISH SUITE NO. 6 (S. 811)

2239. Englische Suite, Nr. 6, D-moll. Herausgegeben von Edwin
Fischer. ... Berlin, Ullstein [c 1926]. 28 pp., 31 cm. (Tonmeister
Ausgabe, No. 292.)   P.N.: T.A.Nr.292
2240. Grandes Suites dites Suites Angloises pour le clavecin composées
par J. Seb. Bach, No. II. Leipzig, chez A. Kühnel (Bureau de
Musique) [ca. 1810?]. 15 pp., obl. fol., 24×34 cm., laid paper.
English suite No. 6 in D minor.   P.N.: 1009
2241. Oeuvres originales, J. S. Bach, Suites anglaises, Suite 6ᵉ.
Nouvelle Édition revue, doigtée et annotée par Adolphe F. Wouters.
... Paris, Maurice Senart [ca. 1925]. 19 pp., 36 cm. (Musique
classique, Nos. 620-22.)   P.N.'s: M.S. & Cᴵᵉ. 620;
                                    M.S. & Cᴵᵉ. 621; M.S. & Cᴵᵉ. 622

FRENCH SUITES (S. 812-817), Collections

2242. Frantsuzskie suity, Shest malen'kikh suit, Dlia Fortepiano.
Moscow, Gosudarstvennoe musykal'noe isdatel'stvo, 1933. 55 pp.,
32 cm.
Edited by N. Zhiliaev.   P.N.: 37778
2243. Französische Suiten, French Suites, piano solo. Magdeburg,
Heinrichshofen, c 1913. 59 pp., 30 cm. (Neue instruktive Ausgabe
von Theodor Wiehmayer, No. 19.)   P.N.: H.V.11337

2244. Französische Suiten für Klavier...auf Grund der Ausgabe von Hans Bischoff herausgegeben von Robert Teichmüller. Leipzig, C. F. Peters [ca. 1930]. 63 pp., 30 cm. (Edition Peters, No. 3872.) P.N.: 10644

2245. French Suites for the pianoforte after the edition of Czerny. Boston, B. F. Wood [ca. 1900]. 2 ll., 55 pp., 30 cm. (Edition Wood, No. 987.) Revised by H. Semper. P.N.: B.F.W.6305-56

2246. French Suites for the Pianoforte, after the edition of Karl Czerny. New York, G. Schirmer, 1896. 3 ll.; pp. 3-55, [1]; 30 cm. (Schirmer's Library of Musical Classics, Vol. 19.) P.N.: 12612

2247. Joh. Seb. Bach, Oeuvres pour piano...6 suites françaises—6 französische Suiten (Oswin Keller). ... Leipzig, Aug. Cranz [c 1933]. 47 pp., 31 cm. (Edition Cranz, No. 518). P.N.: C. 44460

2248. Joh. Seb. Bach, Suiten für Klavier. Erster Band, Sechs kleinere Suiten (genannt "französische"). ... Leipzig, Breitkopf & Härtel [1896]. 2 ll., 65 pp., 33 cm. (Urtext klassischer Musikwerke.) Edited by Ernst Naumann. P.N.'s: A.A.73 to A.A.80

2249. Joh. Seb. Bach's Pianoforte Works. Edited by Franklin Taylor ...French Suites. London, Augener [c 1941]. 1 l.; 61, [1] pp. (Augener's Edition, No. 8021.) P.N.: 14647

2250. Klavierwerke von Joh. Seb. Bach herausgegeben von Adolf Ruthardt. Neu revidierte Ausgabe. Leipzig, C. F. Peters [ca. 1930]. 1 l., 55 pp., 30 cm. (Edition Peters, No. 2793.) This is Band 5 of Ruthardt's collected edition. P.N.: 7750

2251. Pianoforte-Musik redigirt und herausgegeben von den Professoren und Lehren...J. Dachs, A. Door...und A. Sturm. Joh. Seb. Bach (édition revue et soigneusement doigtée par A. Sturm)...6 Suites françaises. ... Leipzig, Aug. Cranz [ca. 1895]. 35, [1] pp.; 34 cm. (Classikerausgabe des Wiener Conservatoriums.) P.N.: 38345

2252. Suiten, Urtext-Ausgabe. Band I, 6 kleinere (französische) Suiten. ... Leipzig, Breitkopf & Härtel [1866-69]. 43 pp., 33 cm. (Breitkopf & Härtel's Klavier-Bibliothek.) P.N.: 11344

2253. Suites françaises pour piano. Édition revue et doigtée par H. Dallier. ... Paris, Henry Lemoine, c 1923. 3 ll.; 53, [1] pp.; 30 cm. (Édition nationale française Panthéon des pianistes, No. 1245.) P.N.: 21534.P.1245.HL.

2254. Suites françaises. Révision par M. Emmanuel. Paris, A. Durand [1927?]. 1 l.; x, 53 pp.; 1 l.; 30 cm. (Édition classique A. Durand & Fils, No. 9364.) P.N.: D. & F. 9364

2255. Suites francesi per pianoforte ordinate e diteggiate, con note illustrative e la maniera d'esecuzione di tutti gli abbellimenti da Bruno Mugellini. ... Milan, G. Ricordi [ca. 1915]. 4 ll., 84 pp. (Edizione Ricordi, No. 446.) P.N.: E.R.446

240   PUBLISHED MUSIC OF J. S. BACH

2256. Suites francesi per pianoforte rivedute da Alessandro Longo. Testo italiano, texte français, English text. Milan, G. Ricordi, c 1918. 2 ll., 59 pp., 32 cm. (Edizione Ricordi, No. 8.)   P.N.: E.R.8

FRENCH SUITE NO. 1 (S. 812)

2257. The Academic Edition of Works by Joh: Seb: Bach...Suite française in F [i.e., D minor]. ... London, A. Hammond [ca. 1895]. 1 l.; 7, [3] pp.; 30 cm. (Academic Edition, No. 262.) Annotated and fingered by Gordon Saunders.

2258. Französische Suite Nr. 1, D-moll herausgegeben von Edwin Fischer. Berlin, Ullstein [c 1926]. 12 pp., 34 cm. (Tonmeister Ausgabe, No. 281.)   P.N.: T.A. 281

2259. VI Suites pour le clavecin composées par J. S. Bach, Oeuvre I, No. 1. Leipzig, au Bureau de Musique de A. Kühnel [after 1805]. 7 pp., obl. fol., 24 × 34 cm., wove paper. French Suite No. 1 in D minor.   P.N.: 138

FRENCH SUITE NO. 2 (S. 813)

2260. Französische Suite Nr. 2, C-moll herausgegeben von Edwin Fischer. Berlin, Ullstein [c 1926]. 12 pp., 34 cm. (Tonmeister Ausgabe, No. 282.)   P.N.: T.A.282

2261. VI Suites pour le clavecin composées par J. S. Bach, Oeuvre I, No. II. Leipzig, Bureau de Musique (Hoffmeister et Kühnel) [1803?]. 7 pp., obl. fol., 24 × 34 cm., wove paper. French Suite No. 2 in C minor.   P.N.: 161

FRENCH SUITE NO. 3 (S. 814)

2262. Französische Suite Nr. 3, H-moll herausgegeben von Edwin Fischer. Berlin, Ullstein [c 1927]. 12 pp., 34 cm. (Tonmeister Ausgabe, No. 283.)   P.N.: T.A.Nr. 283

2263. VI Suites pour le clavecin composées par J. S. Bach, Oeuvre I, No. III. Leipzig, au Bureau de Musique (Hoffmeister et Kühnel) [1803?]. 7 pp., obl. fol., 24 × 34 cm., wove paper. French Suite No. 3 in B minor.   P.N.: 186

FRENCH SUITE NO. 4 (S. 815)

2264. Französische Suite Nr. 4, Es-dur herausgegeben von Edwin Fischer. Berlin, Ullstein [c 1926]. 12 pp., 34 cm. (Tonmeister Ausgabe, No. 284.)   P.N.: T.A. 284

2265. VI Suites pour le clavecin composées par J. S. Bach, Oeuvre I, No. IV. Leipzig, au Bureau de Musique de A. Kühnel [after 1805]. 7 pp., obl. fol., 24 × 34 cm., wove paper. French suite No. 4 in E♭ Major.   P.N.: 227

FRENCH SUITE NO. 5 (S. 816)

2266. Französische Suite Nr. 5, G-dur herausgegeben von Edwin

Fischer. Berlin, Ullstein [c 1926]. 16 pp., 34 cm. (Tonmeister
Ausgabe, No. 285.)   P.N.: T.A.285
2267. French Suite No. 5...Edited by Emil Sauer. St. Louis, Mo.,
Art Publication Society, c 1913. 2 parts. 35 cm. (Selected Edition,
Progressive Series.)   P.N.'s: Pt. I: Ano. 92-2; 92,6;
                                                Pt. II: Ano. 93-2; 93.6
2268. Oeuvres originales J. S. Bach, 5ᵉ suite française en Sol. Paris,
M. Senart; B. Roudanez [ca. 1910]. 9 pp., 35 cm. (Nouvelle
Édition française de musique classique, Nos. 351-352.)
General editor of series: Vincent D'Indy.
                                P.N.'s: S.R. et Cⁱᵉ. 351 to S.R. et Cⁱᵉ. 352
2269. VI Suites pour le clavecin composées par J. S. Bach, Oeuvre I,
No. V. Leipzig, au Bureau de Musique de A. Kühnel [after 1805].
7 pp., obl. fol., 24 × 34 cm., wove paper.
French Suite No. 5 in G Major.   P.N.: 246

FRENCH SUITE NO. 5 (S. 816): Excerpts

2270. Sarabande from the Fifth French Suite...transcribed for organ
by James H. Rogers. New York, G. Schirmer [c 1913]. 5 pp.,
34 cm. (Organist's Repertoire, 3rd series, No. 59.)   P.N.: 24310

FRENCH SUITE NO. 6 (S. 817)

2271. Französische Suite Nr. 6, E-dur herausgegeben von Edwin
Fischer. Berlin, Ullstein [c 1926]. 12 pp., 34 cm. (Tonmeister
Ausgabe, No. 286.)   P.N.: T.A.Nr.286
2272. Oeuvres originales J. S. Bach, 6ᵉ suite française. Paris, M.
Senart; B. Roudanez [ca. 1910]. 9 pp., 35 cm. (Nouvelle Édition
française de musique classique, Nos. 277-78.)
General editor of series: Vincent D'Indy.
                                P.N.'s: S.R. & Cⁱᵉ 277; S.R. & Cⁱᵉ. 278
2273. VI suites pour le clavecin composées par J. S. Bach, Oeuvre I,
No. VI. Leipzig, au Bureau de Musique de A. Kühnel [after 1805].
7 pp., obl. fol., 24 × 34 cm., wove paper.   P.N.: 247

PARTITAS (S. 825-830), Collections

2274. Clavir Übung bestehend in Praeludien, Allemanden, Couranten,
Sarabanden, Giguen, Menuetten, und andern Galanterien; denen
Liebhabern zur Gemüths Ergoetzung verfertiget von Iohann Sebastian
Bach...Opus I. [Leipzig] in Verlegung des Autoris, 1731. 1 l.,
73 pp., obl. fol., 21 × 28 cm., laid paper, ¾ velum.
    Stamp of Bibliothek von Ludwig Haunx, Konstanz on front flyleaf
and back pastedown, together with his shelfmark on front flyleaf.
2275. Compositions pour le piano-forte sans et avec accompagnement
par Jean Sebastien Bach. Edition nouvelle, soigneusement revue,
corrigée et doigtée, ainsi que pourvue de notifications sur l'exécution
et sur les mesures des temps (d'après le métronome de Maelzel) et

242   PUBLISHED MUSIC OF J. S. BACH

accompagnée d'une préface par Charles Czerny. Leipzig, au Bureau
de Musique de C. F. Peters [1840?]. [3], 4-91 pp.; 33 cm.; wove
paper. (Oeuvres complets, Liv. 5.)   P.N.: 2746
2276. Joh. Seb. Bach, Piano works...Partitas (Czerny) 2 books. ...
London, Augener [ca. 1910]. 2 vols. 31 cm. (Augener's Edition,
Nos. 7981a, 7981b.)   P.N.'s: 14959; 15005
2277. Klavierübung I Teil, Partiten. Nach dem Erstdruck revidiert
und herausgegeben von Kurt Soldan, Fingersatz von C. A. Martienssen. Leipzig, C. F. Peters [1937?]. 2 vols. in 1. 30 cm. (Edition
Peters, No. 4463a.)   P.N.'s: 11334, 11346
2278. Klavierwerke von Joh. Seb. Bach herausgegeben von Adolf
Ruthardt. Revidierte Ausgabe. Leipzig, C. F. Peters [ca. 1930].
56 pp., 30 cm. (Edition Peters, No. 2796.)
   This is Band 8 of Ruthardt's collected edition. Contents: Partitas
   1-3.   P.N.: 7778
2279. Klavierwerke von Joh. Seb. Bach herausgegeben von Adolf
Ruthardt. Neu revidierte Ausgabe. Leipzig, C. F. Peters [ca. 1930].
63 pp., 30 cm. (Edition Peters, No. 2796.)
   This is Band 9 of Ruthardt's collected edition. Contents: Partitas
   4-6.   P.N.: 7779
2280. Partitas for the Pianoforte, in two volumes. ... Boston, London,
B. F. Wood [ca. 1925]. 2 vols. in 1. 31 cm. (Edition Wood, No.
980.)   P.N.'s: B.F.W.6335-49; B.F.W. 6336-63
2281. Partitas for the Pianoforte, in two volumes...Edited and fingered
by Czerny, Griepenkerl and Roitzsch. New York, G. Schirmer,
1908. 2 vols. in 1. 30 cm. (Schirmer's Library of Musical Classics,
Vols. 20-21.)   P.N.'s: 20491-20492
2282. Partitas pour piano. Édition revue et doigtée par H. Dallier. ...
Paris, Henry Lemoine, c 1923. 2 vols. in 1. 30 cm. (Édition nationale
française Panthéon des pianistes, Nos. 1229-30.)
           P.N.'s: 21,518.P.1229.HL.; 21,519.P.1230.HL.
2283. Partitas, 1er cahier Nos. 1-3 [and 2me cahier Nos. 4-6]. Révision
par Maurice Emmanuel. ... Paris, A. Durand [c 1917, c 1916].
2 vols. in 1. 30 cm. (Édition classique A. Durand & Fils, Nos.
9416-17.)   P.N.'s: D. & F. 9416; D. & F. 9417
2284. Partite per pianoforte rivedute, con note critiche, la maniera di
esecuzione degli abbellimenti e l'analisi della forma da Bruno
Mugellini. ... Milan, G. Ricordi [ca. 1910]. 1 l., 55 pp., 30 cm.
(Edizioni Ricordi, No. 466.)
   Contents: Partitas 1-3.   P.N.: E.R.466-549
2285. Partite rivedute, con note critiche, la maniera di esecuzione degli
abbellimenti e l'analisi della forma da Bruno Mugellini. ... [Milan,
G. Ricordi, ca. 1910.] 66 pp., 30 cm. (Edizioni Ricordi, No. 468.)
   Contents: Overture in the French style; Partita 6.
                                          P.N.: E.R.468-594

2286. Partiten für Klavier...auf Grund der Ausgabe von Hans Bischoff herausgegeben von Robert Teichmüller. Leipzig, C. F. Peters [ca. 1930]. 33 pp., 30 cm. (Edition Peters, No. 4113.)   P.N.: 10791

2287. Partity, Ch. I, No. 1-3, Dlia fortepiano. Pod. red. A. B. Goldenveisera [Goldenweiser]. [Moscow] Gosudarstvennoe musykal'noe isdatel'stvo [1932]. 61 pp., 31 cm.   P.N.: M.12137.g.

2288. Die sechs Partiten für Klavier...herausgegeben von August Schmid-Lindner, Vorwort und Erläuterungen. Vienna, Universal-Edition A.G., c 1932. 2 vols. in 1. 30 cm. (Jubiläums-Ausgabe.)
P.N.: U.E.1059^a, U.E. 1059^b

2289. 6 Partitas. Révision et annotations par Blanche Selva. Paris, Maurice Senart, c 1920. 80 pp., 34 cm. (Edition nationale de musique classique, No. 5022.)
P.N.'s: 29-5022; 30-5022; 132-5022; 133-5022; 394-5022; 282-5022; 283-5022; 284-5022; 346-5022; 347-5022; 348-5022; 222-5022; 223-5022; 224-5022; 395-5022.

PARTITA NO. I IN B FLAT MAJOR (S. 825)

2290. The Academic Edition of Works by Joh: Seb: Bach...264, Partita in B flat. ... London, A. Hammond [ca. 1895]. 15, [1] pp.; 30 cm.
Fingered and annotated by Gordon Saunders.

2291. Exercices pour le clavecin par J. S. Bach, Oeuvre I, Partie 1. Vienna, chez Hoffmeister & comp., Leipzig, au Bureau de Musique [1801?]. 11 pp., obl. fol., 24 × 34 pp., wove paper.
Partita No. 1 in B♭ Major.

2292. Oeuvres originales J. S. Bach, Partita I, en Si♭, 1re partie [and 2e partie]. Paris, Maurice Senart [ca. 1910]. 2 parts. 35 cm. (Nouvelle Édition française de musique classique, Nos. 29-30.)
General editor of series: Vincent D'Indy. Revision by Blanche Selva.   P.N.'s: M.S. & Cie. 29; M.S. 30-5022

2293. Partita in B Flat. Transcribed for pianoforte by Harold Bauer. New York, G. Schirmer [c 1921]. 19 pp., 30 cm.   P.N.: 29635

2294. Partita, Praeludium. ... Berlin, Adolph Fürstner [ca. 1870]. 13 pp., 33 cm. (Bibliothek älterer und neuerer Clavier-Musik, No. 6.) Edited by Franz Kroll.   P.N.: 6

2295. Partita Si♭ maggiore...[riveduti da] F. Kroll. Milan, G. Ricordi [ca. 1875]. 1 l., 13 pp., 34 cm. (Scelta di pezzi classici, No. 93586.)   P.N.: 93586

PARTITA NO. 2 IN C MINOR (S. 826)

2296. Exercices pour le clavecin par J. S. Bach, Oeuvre I, Partie 2. Vienna, chez Hoffmeister & comp.; Leipzig, au Bureau de Musique [1801?]. 16 pp., obl. fol., 24 × 34 cm., wove paper.
Partita No. 2 in C Minor.   P.N.: 67

2297. Oeuvres originales J. S. Bach, Partita II en Ut. 1ʳᵉ partie [and
2ᵉ partie]. Paris, Maurice Senart [ca. 1910]. 2 parts. 35 cm.
(Nouvelle édition française de musique classique, Nos. 132-133.)
General editor of series: Vincent D'Indy. Revision by Blanche
Selva.   P.N.'s: M.S. & Cie. 132; M.S. & Cie. 133.
2298. Partita in do minore...[riveduti da] F. Kroll. Milan, G. Ricordi
[ca. 1875]. 1 l., 15 pp., 34 cm. (Scelta di pezzi classici, No. 93618.)
                                                    P.N.: 93618
2299. Partita, Sinfonia.... Berlin, Adolph Fürstner [ca. 1870]. 14 pp.,
33 cm. (Bibliothek älterer und neuerer Klavier-Musik, No. 38.)
Edited by Franz Kroll.   P.N.: 41

PARTITA NO. 3 IN A MINOR (S. 827)

2300. Exercices pour le clavecin par J. S. Bach, Oeuvre I, Partie 3.
Vienna, chez Hoffmeister & comp.; Leipzig, au Bureau de Musique
[1802?]. 12 pp., obl. fol., 26 × 35 cm., wove paper.
Partita No. 3 in A Minor.   P.N.: 68
2301. Exercices pour le clavecin par J. S. Bach, Oeuvre I, Partie 3.
Leipzig, au Bureau de Musique de A. Kühnel [after 1805]. 12 pp.,
obl. fol., 24 × 34 cm., wove paper.
Partita No. 3 in A minor.   P.N.: 68
2302. Oeuvres originales J. S. Bach, Partita III. 1ʳᵉ partie [and 2ᵉ
partie]. Paris, Maurice Senart [ca. 1910]. 2 parts. 35 cm. (Nouvelle
Édition française de musique classique, Nos. 394-95.)
General editor of series: Vincent D'Indy. Revision by Blanche
Selva.   P.N.'s: M.S. & Cie. 394; M.S. & Cie. 395.

PARTITA NO. 4 IN D MAJOR (S. 828)

2303. Exercices pour le clavecin par J. S. Bach, Oeuvre I, Partie 4.
Vienna, chez Hoffmeister & comp.; Leipzig, au Bureau de Musique
[1802?]. 19 pp., obl. fol., 26 × 36 cm., wove paper.
Partita No. 4 in D Major.   P.N.: 71
2304. Exercices pour le clavecin par J. S. Bach, Oeuvre I [Part. 4].
Leipzig, au Bureau de Musique de A. Kühnel [after 1805]. 19 pp.,
obl. fol., 24 × 34 cm., wove paper.
Partita No. 4 in D Major.   P.N.: 71
2305. Oeuvres originales J. S. Bach, Partita IV, en Ré. 1ʳᵉ partie [and
2ᵉ partie, 3ᵉ partie]. Paris, M. Senart; B. Roudanez [ca. 1910].
3 parts. 35 cm. (Nouvelle Édition française de musique classique,
Nos. 282-84.)
General editor of series: Vincent D'Indy. Revision by Blanche
Selva.   P.N.'s: S.R. & Cⁱᵉ. 282 to S.R. & Cⁱᵉ. 284.

PARTITA NO. 5 IN G MAJOR (S. 829)

2306. Exercices pour le clavecin par J. S. Bach, Oeuvre I, Partie 5.

Vienna, chez Hoffmeister & comp.; Leipzig, au Bureau de Musique
[1802?]. 15 pp., obl. fol., 26 × 36 cm., wove paper.
Partita No. 5 in G Major.   P.N.: 72
2307. Exercices pour le clavecin par J. S. Bach, Oeuvre I, Partie 5.
Leipzig, au Bureau de Musique de A. Kühnel [after 1805]. 15 pp.,
obl. fol., 24 × 34 cm., wove paper.
Partita No. 5 in G Major.   P.N.: 72
2308. Oeuvres originales J. S. Bach, Partita V, en Sol. 1ᵣₑ partie
[and 2ᵉ partie, 3ᵉ partie]. Paris, M. Senart; B. Roudanez [ca. 1910].
3 parts. 35 cm. (Nouvelle Édition française de musique classique,
Nos. 346-48.)
General editor of series: Vincent D'Indy. Revision by Blanche
Selva.   P.N.'s: S.R. & Cⁱᵉ. 346; M.S. & Cⁱᵉ. 347;
                                          M.S. & Cⁱᵉ. 348.

PARTITA NO. 6 IN E MINOR (S. 830)

2309. Exercices pour le clavecin par J. S. Bach, Oeuvre I, Partie 6.
Vienna, chez Hoffmeister & comp.; Leipzig, au Bureau de Musique
[1802?]. 23 pp., obl. fol., 26 × 36 cm., wove paper.
Partita No. 6 in E Minor.   P.N.: 73
2310. Exercices pour le clavecin par J. S. Bach, Oeuvre I [Part. 6].
Leipzig, au Bureau de Musique de A. Kühnel [after 1805]. 23 pp.,
obl. fol., 24 × 34 cm., wove paper.
Partita No. 6 in E Minor.   P.N.: 73
2311. Oeuvres originales J. S. Bach, Partita VI, en Mi. 1ᵣₑ partie
[and 2ᵉ partie, 3ᵉ partie]. Paris, M. Senart; B. Roudanez [ca. 1910].
3 parts. 35 cm. (Nouvelle Édition française de musique classique,
Nos. 222-24.)
General editor of series: Vincent D'Indy. Revision by Blanche
Selva.   P.N.'s: S.R. & Cⁱᵉ. 222 to S.R. & Cⁱᵉ. 224.

PARTITA IN B MINOR (AUS: KLAVIERÜBUNG TEIL II; Ouverture nach
französischer Art) (S. 831)

2312. Ouverture nach Französischer Art für Klavier (Cembalo)
(Ursprüngliche Fassung in C-moll)...Zum ersten Mal herausgegeben von Hans David. Mainz, Leipzig, B. Schott [c 1935]. 19,
[5] pp.; 31 cm. (Edition Schott, No. 2380.)   P.N.: B.S.S.34267
2313. Echo aus: Partita/Französische Ouverture...(Kurt Soldan).
[London] Peters, c 1937. [3] pp., 31 cm. (Edition Peters, No. 4464c.)

SUITE IN F MAJOR (S. 820)   P.N.: 11355

2314. Oeuvres originales, J. S. Bach, Suite en Fa majeur. Nouvelle
édition revue, doigtée et annotée par Adolphe F. Wouters... Paris,
Maurice Senart [ca. 1925]. 1 l.; 7, [1] pp.; 35 cm. (Musique
classique, Nos. 650-51.)   P.N.'s: M.S. & Cⁱᵉ. 650; M.S. & Cⁱᵉ 651

SUITE IN F MINOR (Fragment) (S. 823)

2315. Oeuvres originales J. S. Bach, fragment d'une suite. Paris, M. Senart; B. Roudanez [ca. 1910]. 4 pp., 35 cm. (Nouvelle Édition française de musique classique, No. 281.) General editor of series: Vincent D'Indy. Revision by Blanche Selva. P.N.: S.R. & Cⁱᵉ. 281

SUITE IN A MAJOR (Fragment) (S. 824)

2316. Oeuvres originales J. S. Bach, 3 morceaux en forme de suite. Paris, Maurice Senart [ca. 1910]. 5 pp., 35 cm. (Nouvelle édition française de musique classique, No. 279.) General editor of series: Vincent D'Indy. Revision by Blanche Selva. P.N.: 279

Orchestra

SUITE (OVERTURE) NO. 1 IN C MAJOR (S. 1066)

2317. Ouverture ou suite en Ut majeur pour 2 violons, viola, 2 hautbois, basson, violoncelle et basse composée par Jean Sebastien Bach publiée pour la première fois par S. W. Dehn, No. 1. Leipzig, au Bureau de Musique de C. F. Peters [1853?]. Score and 7 parts. 33 cm., wove paper. P.N.'s: Score: 3541; Parts: 3542
2318. Ouverture (Suite) Nr. 1. Partitur herausgegeben von Kurt Soldan. Leipzig, C. F. Peters [1934?]. 2 ll., 31 pp., 33 cm. (Edition Peters, No. 4416.) P.N.: 11062
2319. Suite Nr. 1 C dur für 2 Oboen, Fagott, 2 Violinen, Viola und Continuo...herausgegeben und mit Vorwort versehen von Wilhelm Altmann. Leipzig, Eulenburg [1926?]. 3 ll., 28 pp., 3 ll., 19 cm. (Eulenburgs kleine Partitur-Ausgabe, No. 856.) P.N.: E.E.4645

SUITE (OVERTURE) NO. 2 IN B MINOR (S. 1067)

2320. Grössere Orchesterwerke...Bach, J. S. ... Ouvertüre (Suite) h moll für den praktischen Gebrauch bearbeitet von Max Reger (6 Stimmen). ... Leipzig, Breitkopf & Härtel [c 1915]. 1 l., 16 pp., 34 cm. (Edition Breitkopf, No. 2351.) P.N.: Part. B. 2351
2321. Ouverture ou suite en Si mineur pour 2 violins, viola, violoncelle, flûte et basse composée par Jean Sebastien Bach. Publiée pour la première fois d'après le manuscrit original par S. W. Dehn, No. 2. Leipzig, au Bureau de Musique de C. F. Peters [1853?]. Score and 5 parts. 33 cm., wove paper. P.N.'s: Score: 3544; Parts: 3545
2322. Ouverture (Suite) Nr. 2, Partitur herausgegeben von Kurt Soldan. Leipzig, C. F. Peters [1934?]. 2 ll., 23 pp. (Edition Peters, No. 4417.) P.N.: 11063
2323. Suite in B minor No. 2, for flute and string orchestra. New York,

E. F. Kalmus, c 1933. 1 l., 28 pp., 1 l., 19 cm. (Kalmus Miniature Orchestra Scores, No. 72.)

2324. Suite No. 2 H moll für Flöte, 2 Violinen, Viola und Continuo... Herausgegeben und mit einem Vorwort versehen von Wilhelm Altmann. Leipzig, Eulenburg [1913?]. 2 ll., 28 pp., 2 ll., 19 cm. (Eulenburgs kleine Partitur-Ausgabe, No. 821.)   P.N.: E.E.3838

SUITE NO. 3 IN D MAJOR (S. 1068)

2325. Joh. Seb. Bachs Werke, Suite (Ouvertüre) in D dur für Orchester zum praktischen Gebrauch bearbeitet von Max Reger. Partitur. Leipzig, Breitkopf & Härtel [c 1915]. 1 l., 29 pp., 34 cm. (Edition Breitkopf, No. 2350.)   P.N.: Part. B. 2350

2326. Ouverture ou suite en Ré majeur pour 2 violons, viola, basse, timballes, 2 hautbois et 3 trompettes composée par Jean Sebastien Bach publiée pour la première fois par S. W. Dehn, No. 3. Leipzig, au Bureau de Musique de C. F. Peters [1854?]. Score and 10 parts. 33 cm., wove paper.   P.N.'s: Score: 3556; Parts: 3557

2327. Ouverture (Suite) Nr. 3. Partitur herausgegeben von Kurt Soldan. Leipzig, C. F. Peters [1934?]. 2 ll., 27 pp., 33 cm. (Edition Peters, No. 4418.)   P.N.: 11200

2328. Suite in D-dur (Ouverture, Air, Gavotte, Bourrée und Gigue) für Orchester componirt von Joh. Seb. Bach. Neue Ausgabe, Für die Aufführungen im Gewandhause zu Leipzig genau bezeichnet u. herausgegeben von Ferdinand David. Die Clarinetten und die drei Trompeten aus den für die jetzigen Instrumente nich ausführbaren Bach'schen Trompeten, für die Aufführungen im Gewandhause zu Leipzig arrangirt von Felix Mendelssohn Bartholdy. ... Leipzig, Bartholf Senff [ca. 1855?]. 27 pp., 34 cm., wove paper.   P.N.: 473

2329. Suite Nr. 3 D dur für 2 Oboen, 3 Trompeten, Pauken, 2 Violinen, Viola und Continuo...Herausgegeben und mit Vorwort versehen von Wilhelm Altmann. Leipzig, Eulenburg [1913?]. 3 ll., 38 pp., 2 ll., 19 cm. (Eulenburgs kleine Partitur-Ausgabe, No. 818.)
P.N.: E.E.3835

SUITE NO. 3 (S. 1068): Arrangements

2330. Suite (in D-dur) von Joh. Seb. Bach für Pianoforte u. Violine übertragen und zum Gebrauch beim Conservatorium der Musik zu Leipzig mit Vortragszeichen versehen von Ferdinand David. Leipzig, Bartholf Senff; London, J. J. Ewer [ca. 1855]. Score and 1 part. 33 cm., wove paper.   P.N.: 475

SUITE NO. 4 IN D MAJOR (S. 1069)

2331. Ouverture (Suite) Nr. 4. Partitur herausgegeben von Kurt Soldan. Leipzig, C. F. Peters [1934?]. 2 ll., 28 pp., 33 cm. (Edition Peters, No. 4419.)   P.N.: 11201

2332. Suite No. 4 D dur für 3 Oboen, Fagott, 3 Trompeten, Pauken, 2 Violinen, Viola und Continuo...Herausgegeben und mit Vorwort versehen von Wilhelm Altmann. Leipzig, Eulenburg [1927]. 2 ll., 38 pp., 2 ll., 19 cm. (Eulenburgs kleine Partitur-Ausgabe, No. 861.)
P.N.: E.E.4469

Violin and Clavier (S. 1025)

2333. Compositions pour violon et pour flûte par Jean Sebastien Bach ...Edition nouvelle, revue et corrigée critiquement par Ferd. David, J. Hellmesberger et Fr. Hermann...Cah. 7...No. 1, Suite p. violon et piano. ... Leipzig & Berlin, C. F. Peters, Bureau de Musique [1866?]. Score and 1 part. 33 cm., wove paper. (Oeuvres complètes, Série III, Cahier 7, No. 1.)   P.N.: 4555

Violoncello

COLLECTIONS (S. 1007-1012)

2334. Ioh. Seb. Bachs Compositionen für Violoncello solo. Mit Begleitung des Pianoforte herausgegeben von Dr. W. Stade...No. 1 Sechs Sarabanden. ... Leipzig, Gustav Heinze [ca. 1860]. Score and 1 part. 34 cm., wove paper.
This collection consists of the fourth movements (Sarabands) from each of the six suites for solo 'cello, with added piano accompaniment by Friedrich Wilhelm Stade.   P.N.: G. 85 H.
2335. Sechs Sonaten für das Violoncell...Zum Vortrag bezeichnet von J. J. F. Dotzauer. Neue Ausgabe. Leipzig, Breitkopf & Härtel [ca. 1865]. 1 l.; 3-29, [1] pp.; 34 cm.; wove paper.   P.N.: 10901
2336. Sechs Sonaten für Violoncell allein...Nach der original Ausgabe. n.p. [ca. 1825]. 1 l.; [1], 2-36 pp.; 26 cm.; laid paper.
2337. Sechs Sonaten (Suiten) für Violoncell allein...neu herausgegeben von Wilhelm Jeral. Vienna, Universal-Edition A.G. [1927?]. 51 pp., 30 cm.   P.N.: 1541
2338. Sechs Suiten für Violoncelle allein. ... herausgegeben mit dem Faksimile der Handschrift von Paul Grümmer und E. H. Müller von Asow. ... Vienna, Leipzig, Ludwig Doblinger (Bernhard Herzmansky) [1944]. 2 vols. 38 cm.
Copy 209 of 1000 numbered copies.   P.N.: D. 8021
2339. Sechs Suiten (Sonaten) für Violoncello solo...herausgegeben von Fr. Grützmacher, Original-Ausgabe. Leipzig, C. F. Peters [ca. 1925]. 39 pp., 34 cm. (Edition Peters, No. 238a.)   P.N.: 4962
2340. Sechs Suiten (Sonaten) für Violoncello solo...Neue Ausgabe von Hugo Becker. Leipzig, C. F. Peters [ca. 1890]. 45 pp., 34 cm.
P.N.: 9148

2341. 6 Solo Sonatas (Suites) for Violoncello, edited by Percy Such. ...
London, Augener [c. 1919]. 1 l., 55 pp., 1 l., 31 cm. (Augener's
Edition, No. 7663.)   P.N.: 15226
2342. Six Sonates ou études pour le violoncelle solo composées par
J. Sebastien Bach. Oeuvre posthume. Leipzig, chez H. A. Probst
[1828?]. [1], 2-45 pp.; 34 cm.; wove paper.   P.N.: 165
2343. Six Sonates ou suites pour violoncelle seul par J. Seb. Bach.
Edition nouvelle, revue et arrangée pour être exécutée aux concerts
par Fr. Grützmacher. Leipzig & Berlin, C. F. Peters, Bureau de
Musique [ca. 1865]. 1 l., 3-35 pp.; 34 cm. (Oeuvres de Bach, Série
IV, Cahier 1.)   P.N.: 4546
2344. Six Suites for Violoncello Solo. Revised and edited by Frits
Gaillard. New York, G. Schirmer, c 1939. 1 l., 53 pp., 31 cm.
(Schirmer's Library of Musical Classics, Vol. 1565.)   P.N.: 37034
2345. Six Suites pour violoncelle seul...Analyse du phrasé, doigtés et
coups d'archet par Diran Alexanian. Paris, Francis Salabert [c 1929].
xxxxvii, [1], 84 pp.; 34 cm.; facs.
Introduction contains facsimile of Anna Magdalena's copy.
                                                      P.N.: SECA 16
2346. Six Suites pour violoncelle seul. Révision par Fernand Pollain.
Paris, A. Durand [c 1918]. 1 l., 51, [1] pp.; 30 cm. (Édition classique,
No. 9546.)   P.N.: D. & F. 9546

ARRANGEMENTS

2347. Sechs Suiten (Sonaten für Violoncell solo) für Violine solo
übertragen von Joseph Ebner. Leipzig, Zürich, Hug [1913]. 1 l.;
47, [1] pp.; 30 cm.   P.N.: G.H. 5151
2348. 6 Suites (sonatas) for Violoncello Solo. Transcribed, fingered &
revised for violin solo by Tivadar Nachèz. ... London, Augener
[c 1924]. 1 l., 40 pp., 1 l., 32 cm. (Augener's Edition, No. 7921.)
                                                      P.N.: 16216

SUITE NO. 1 IN G MAJOR (S. 1007)

2349. Ioh. Seb. Bachs Compositionen für Violoncello solo. Mit Begleitung des Pianoforte herausgegeben von Dr. W. Stade...No. 2,
Sonate No. I G dur. ... Leipzig, Gustav Heinze [ca. 1860]. Score and
2 parts. 34 cm., wove paper.
Alternate arrangement for viola included.   P.N.: G. 86 H.
2350. Sechs Sonaten (Suiten) für Violoncell allein. Genau bezeichnet
für Unterricht und praktischen Gebrauch von Julius Klengel, Nr. 1.
G dur. ... Leipzig, Breitkopf & Härtel [1928?]. 8 pp., 30 cm.
(Edition Breitkopf, No. 3971.)   P.N.: E.B.3971

SUITE NO. 2 IN D MINOR (S. 1008)

2351. Ioh. Seb. Bachs Compositionen für Violoncello solo. Mit
Begleitung des Pianoforte herausgegeben von Dr. W. Stade...No. 3,

2351. *(continued)* Sonate No. II. ... Leipzig, Gustav Heinze [ca. 1860]. Score and 2 parts. 34 cm., wove paper.
Alternate arrangement for viola included.   P.N.: G. 93 H.

2352. Sarabande from the Second Suite for Violoncello...Arranged for organ by E. Stanley Roper. London, Oxford University Press [c 1929]. 1 l., 4 pp., 1 l., 32 cm.

2353. Sechs Sonaten (Suiten) für Violoncell allein. Genau bezeichnet für Unterricht und praktischen Gebrauch von Julius Klengel... Nr. 2. D moll. ... Leipzig, Breitkopf & Härtel [1930?]. 1 l., 7 pp., 30 cm. (Edition Breitkopf, No. 3972.)   P.N.: E.B. 3972

SUITE NO. 3 IN C MAJOR (S. 1009)

2354. Ioh. Seb. Bachs Compositionen für Violoncello solo. Mit Begleitung des Pianoforte herausgegeben von Dr. W. Stade...No. 4, Sonate No. III. ... Leipzig, Gustav Heinze [ca. 1860]. Score and 2 parts. 34 cm., wove paper.
Alternate arrangement for viola included.   P.N.: G. 94 H.

2355. Sechs Sonaten (Suiten) für Violoncell allein. Genau bezeichnet für Unterricht und praktischen Gebrauch von Julius Klengel...Nr. 3, C dur. ... Leipzig, Breitkopf & Härtel [1930?]. 1 l., 7 pp., 30 cm. (Edition Breitkopf, No. 3973.)   P.N.: V.A.3973

2356. Suite III (Original C-dur)...aus J. S. Bach Sechs Suiten für Violine solo nach den Suiten für Violoncell bearbeitet von Ferdinand David. [Berlin, Max Hesses Verlag, 1905.] 8 pp., 28 cm.
Published as music supplement for Vol. V, No. 2 (Oct., 1905) of *Die Musik.*

SUITE NO. 4 IN E FLAT MAJOR (S. 1010)

2357. Ioh. Seb. Bachs Compositionen für Violoncello solo. Mit Begleitung des Pianoforte herausgegeben von Dr. W. Stade...No. 5, Sonate No. IV Es dur. ... Leipzig, Gustav Heinze [ca. 1860]. Score and 2 parts. 34 cm., wove paper.
Alternate arrangement for viola included.   P.N.: G. 95 H.

2358. Sechs Sonaten (Suiten) für Violoncell allein. Genau bezeichnet für Unterricht und praktischen Gebrauch von Julius Klengel...Nr. 4 Es dur. ... Leipzig, Breitkopf & Härtel [1930?]. 1 l., 7 pp., 30 cm. (Edition Breitkopf, No. 3974.)   P.N.: E.B. 3974

SUITE NO. 5 IN C MINOR (S. 1011)

2359. Ioh. Seb. Bachs Compositionen für Violoncello solo. Mit Begleitung des Pianoforte herausgegeben von Dr. W. Stade...No. 6, Sonate No. V. ... Leipzig, Gustav Heinze [ca. 1860]. Score and 2 parts. 34 cm., wove paper.
Alternate arrangement for viola included.   P.N.: G. 96 H.

2360. Sechs Sonaten (Suiten) für Violoncell allein. Genau bezeichnet für Unterricht und praktischen Gebrauch von Julius Klengel...Nr. 5,

C moll. ... Leipzig, Breitkopf & Härtel [1928?]. 1 l., 13 pp., 30 cm.
(Edition Breitkopf, No. 3975.)   P.N.: E.B. 3975

SUITE NO. 6 IN D MAJOR (S. 1012)

2361. Ioh. Seb. Bachs Compositionen für Violoncello solo. Mit
Begleitung des Pianoforte herausgegeben von Dr. W. Stade...No. 7,
Sonata No. VI D dur. ... Leipzig, Gustav Heinze [ca. 1860]. Score
and 2 parts. 34 cm., wove paper.
Alternate arrangement for viola included.   P.N.: G. 97 H.
2362. Sechs Sonaten (Suiten) für Violoncell allein. Genau bezeichnet
für Unterricht und praktischen Gebrauch von Julius Klengel...Nr. 6
D dur. ... Leipzig, Breitkopf & Härtel [1913?]. 1 l., 9 pp., 30 cm.
(Edition Breitkopf, No. 3976.)   P.N.: J.S.B.Km. 27

TOCCATAS

Clavier, Collections (S. 910-916)

2363. Joh. Seb. Bach. Piano Works...Toccatas. ... London, Augener
[ca. 1910]. 1 l., 45 pp., 31 cm. (Augener's Edition, No. 7983.)
Contents: Toccatas in E Minor, F♯ Minor, C Minor & D Minor
                                                   P.N.: 16236
2364. Toccatas for Piano...Edited by Edwin Hughes. New York,
G. Schirmer, c 1930. viii, 3-85 pp.; 31 cm. (Schirmer's Library of
Musical Classics, No. 1538.)   P.N.: 34380
2365. Toccate e sonate per pianoforte. Rivedute, con note critiche, la
maniera di esecuzione di tutti gli abbellimenti e l'analisi della forma
da Bruno Mugellini. ... Milan, G. Ricordi [ca. 1900]. 5 ll., 97 pp.,
30 cm. (Edizioni Ricordi, No. 417.)
Preface by Gabriel Fauré.   P.N.: E.R. 417

Clavier, Single Works

TOCCATA IN F♯ MINOR (S. 910)

2366. Oeuvres originales J. S. Bach, Toccata et fugue en Fa♯. Paris,
M. Senart; B. Roudanez [ca. 1910]. 9 pp., 35 cm. (Nouvelle
Édition française de musique classique, Nos. 285-86.)
Published in two parts, without separate title for second part, and
with continuous pagination. General editor of series: Vincent
D'Indy. Revision by Blanche Selva.
                  P.N.'s: S.R. & Cie. 285; S.R. & Cie. 286.

TOCCATA IN C MINOR (S. 911)

2367. The Academic Edition of Works by Joh: Seb: Bach...263,
Toccata in C minor. ... London, A. Hammond [ca. 1895]. 1 l.;

2367. *(continued)*   15, [1] pp.; 30 cm. (Academic Edition, No. 263.)
Fingered and annotated by Gordon Saunders.
2368.   Oeuvres originales J. S. Bach, Toccata et fugue en Ut. Paris,
M. Senart; B. Roudanez [ca. 1910]. 9 pp., 35 cm. (Nouvelle
Édition française de musique classique, Nos. 287-88.)
Published in two parts, without separate title for second part, and
with continuous pagination. General editor of series: Vincent
D'Indy. Revision by Blanche Selva.
P.N.'s: S.R. & Cte. 287; S. R.& Cte. 288
2369.   Toccata C-moll, Ut-mineur. ... Berlin, Adolph Fürstner [ca.
1909]. 13 pp., 33 cm. (Bibliothek älterer und neuerer Klavier-Musik,
No. 14.)
Edited by Franz Kroll.   P.N.: 17
2370.   Toccata in do minore...[riveduti da] F. Kroll. ... Milan,
G. Ricordi [ca. 1875]. 1 l., 11 pp., 34 cm. (Scelta di pezzi classici,
No. 93594.)   P.N.: 93594

TOCCATA IN D MAJOR (S. 912)

2371.   Oeuvres originales J. S. Bach, Toccata et fugue en Ré. 1re partie
[and 2e partie]. Paris, Maurice Senart [ca. 1910]. 2 parts. 35 cm.
(Nouvelle Édition française de musique classique, Nos. 225-26.)
General editor of series: Vincent D'Indy. Revision by Blanche
Selva.   P.N.'s: S. 225; S.R. & Cte. 226.

TOCCATA IN D MINOR (S. 913)

2372.   Toccata per clavecembalo composta dal Signore Giov. Sebast.
Bach, No. 1. Vienna, Presso Hoffmeister & Comp.; Lipsia, nell
Bureau de Musique [1801?]. 11 pp., obl. fol., 24 × 34 cm., wove paper.
P.N.: 52
2373.   Toccata per clavecembalo composta dal Signore Giov. Sebast.
Bach, No. [1]. Leipzig, C. F. Peters [before 1834]. 11 pp., obl. fol.,
25 × 33 cm., wove paper
Formerly the property of Mme. Clara (Wieck) Schumann. P.N.: 52
2374.   Toccata und Fuga für die Orgel bearbeitet von Max Reger.
Munich, Jos. Aibl, c 1902. 11 pp., 32 cm.   P.N.: 3013

TOCCATA IN E MINOR (S. 914)

2375.   Joh. Seb. Bach, Toccaten für Klavier zu zwei Händen auf Grund
der Ausgabe von Hans Bischoff herausgegeben von Robert Teichmüller. Leipzig, C. F. Peters [ca. 1930]. 27 pp., 30 cm. (Edition
Peters, No. 4111.)
Contents: Toccatas in E Minor and D Minor.   P.N.: 10789
2376.   Toccata con fuga, E moll...Edition nouvelle, rédigée par
Fréd. Conr. Griepenkerl. ... Leipzig, au Bureau de Musique de
C. F. Peters [1851?]. 1 l., 23-29 pp., 33 cm., wove paper. (Pièces
détachées de la 4me livraison...(No. 3).)   P.N.: 2696

TOCCATA IN G MINOR (S. 915)

2377. Arrangements from the Scores of the Great Masters, for the Organ, by W. T. Best. London, Novello, Ewer [ca. 1890]. [1], 994-1006 pp.; 1 l.; obl. fol.; 26×35 cm. (No. 76 of this series.)
P.N.: 4285
2378. Oeuvres originales J. S. Bach, Toccata et fugue en Sol. Paris, M. Senart; B. Roudanez [ca. 1910]. 11 pp., 35 cm. (Nouvelle Édition française de musique classique, Nos. 349-50.)
Published in two parts, without separate title for the second part, and with continuous pagination. General editor of series: Vincent D'Indy. Revision by Blanche Selva.
P.N.'s: S.R. et Cie. 349; S.R. et Cie. 350

Organ, Single Works

TOCCATA IN D MINOR (S. 565)

2379. Johann Sebastian Bach Organ Works...Edited by Charles-Marie Widor and Albert Schweitzer...Toccata and Fugue in D minor. New York, G. Schirmer [c 1912]. 3 ll.; 13, [1] pp.; obl. fol.; 23×31 cm.
P.N.: 31144
2380. Moderne Hochschule des Klavierspiels...Berühmte Meister- und Konzertstücke in neuen Ausgaben ... Carl Tausig, bearbeitungen für den Konzertvortrag: Toccata und Fuge (D moll) für die Orgel. ... Berlin, Schlesinger'schen Buch- & Musikhandlung (Rob. Lienau) [1902]. 11 pp., 32 cm.
P.N.: S. 9204
2381. Toccata and Fugue, D minor, for Organ...Transcribed by Sidney Silber. New York, The University Society [c 1919]. 8 ll., 1 l., 29 cm. (University Course of Music Study, Grade 6, Chapter 9.)
P.N.: 894-14
2382. Toccata et Fuga. Erfurt, G. Wilh. Körner [1850?]. Pp. 141-52, obl. 4°, 24×28 cm., wove paper. (Sämmtliche Orgel-Compositionen, Heft 49.)
Joint editors: Gotthilf Wilhelm Körner and Friedrich Kühmstedt.
P.N.: 124

TRIOS

2383. J. S. Bach's Kunst des Trio-Spiels, Art of Part-Playing. (Hermann Keller – Stainton de B. Taylor.) London, Peters Edition & Hinrichsen Edition, 195? 16 pp., obl. 4°, 23×31 cm. (Edition Peters, No. 350k.)
P.N.: 6421
2384. Sechs dreistimmige Fugen von Johann Sebastian und Wilhelm Friedemann Bach, für Violine, Viola und Bass (Violoncell) eingerichtet und mit je einem einleitenden langsamen Satz versehen von

254 PUBLISHED MUSIC OF J. S. BACH

2384. *(continued)* W. A. Mozart...nach der Vorlage der Gesellschaft der Musikfreunde in Wien durchgesehen und bezeichnet von Joh. Nep. David. ... Leipzig, Breitkopf & Härtel [c 1938]. 3 parts (in 2 vols. each). 31 cm. (Edition Breitkopf, No. 5678.)
Imperfect: Vol. II wanting. P.N.: 30956
2385. Triostudien, 60 Klavier- und Kammermusikstücke von Johann Sebastian Bach als Orgeltrios eingerichtet und mit den zum Studium erforderlichen Bezeichnungen versehen von Franz Ewald Thiele. ... Leipzig, Steingräber, c 1911. 4 vols. in 1. Obl. fol., 26×34 cm. (Edition Steingräber, Nos. 1925-28.)
Imperfect: Vol. I wants all before the table of contents.
P.N.'s: 1790, 1791, 1812, 1813

DAS WOHLTEMPERIERTE KLAVIER
BOOKS I AND II (S. 846-893)

Listed Alphabetically by Editor

2386. Abert, Hermann. Das wohltemperirte Clavier oder Praeludia und Fugen durch alle Tone und Semitonia, so wohl tertiam majorem oder Ut Re Mi anlanged, als auch tertiam minorem oder Re Mi Fa betreffend. Zum Nutzen und Gebrauch der lehrbegierigen musicalischen Jugend, als auch derer in diesem Studio schon habil seyenden besondern Zeit vertreib auffgesetzet und verfertiget von Johann Sebastian Bach p.t. hochf. Anhalt-Cöthenischen Capell-Meistern und Directore derer Cammer Musiquen. Anno 1722. Leipzig, Breitkopf & Härtel, 1922. 3 ll., 202 pp., illus. (facs.), 36 cm.
P.N.: B.W.XIV.
2387. Albert, Eugène Francis Charles d'. Das wohltemperierte Klavier...herausgegeben von Eugen d'Albert. I Teil [and II Teil] mit Bachs Bildnis nach einem Gemälde von G. Haussmann. Dritte Auflage. Stuttgart, Berlin, J. G. Cotta, c 1906, c 1907. 2 vols. in 1. 33 cm. (Edition Cotta, Nos. 92, 93.) P.N.'s: 123, 124
2388. Bartók, Béla. "Wohltemperirtes Klavier" 48 preludium és fuga fokozatos összeállitásban, ujjrenddel, elöadási jelekkel és jegyzetekkel második átdolgozott kiadás ellátta Bartók Béla. ... Budapest, Rozsnyai Károly [ca. 1910]. 4 parts in 1. 33 cm. (Rozsnyai Károly Kiadása, Nos. 246-49.) P.N.'s: 246-249
2389. Bennett, William Sterndale. Das wohltemperirte Clavier, Forty-Eight Preludes and Fugues. ... Part I, in two parts. London, Leader & Cock [ca. 1860]. 2 vols. 36 cm. (The Students Edition.)
Imperfect: Book II wanting.
P.N.'s: L. & C. 1407 – L. & C. 1408; L. & C. 2278 – L. & C. 2280; L. & C. 3223 – L. & C. 3241

2390. Bertini, Henri Jérôme. Das wohltemperirte Clavier, 48 Fugen
und Präludien in allen Tonarten...eingerichtet für das Pianoforte zu
4 Händen von Henri Bertini. Mainz, Antwerp & Brussels, B. Schott
[1843?]. 2 vols. 33 cm., wove paper.
Second title: Ecole de la musique d'ensemble. Etude spéciale...
pour apprendre à éxécuter les ouvrages des grand maitres. Collection des préludes et fugues de Jean Sebastien Bach arrangés pour le
piano à quatre mains et dédiés à tous les écoles de musique d'Europe
par Henri Bertini.   P.N.: 6481
2391. ——— Another edition, with same title page and imprint, but
issued in 4 parts. Imperfect: parts 2 and 3 only (Nos. 15-38).
2392. Best, William Thomas. The Well Tempered Clavichord, Forty-
Eight Preludes & Fugues in all the major & minor keys...Edited and
collated with all former editions of the work, by W. T. Best, organist
of St. George's Hall, Liverpool. London, Novello [ca. 1900]. 1 l.;
197, [1] pp.; 35 cm.   P.N.: (2610)
2393. Bischoff, Hans. Le clavecin bien tempéré. Première partie
(1722); deuxième partie (1744). Edition critique révisée, doigtée et
commentée par Dr. Hans Bischoff. Leipzig, Steingräber [1883-84].
2 vols. in 1. 33 cm. (Edition Steingräber, Nos. 1638-39.)
                                                      P.N.'s: 153; 232

——— See also: Clavier Works, Collections. Joh. Seb. Bach's Klavier-
werke...Kritische Ausgabe... von Dr.Hans Bischoff (entry no. 1532.),
Vols. 5 and 6.
2394. Brooke, Harold. Forty-Eight Preludes and Fugues (The Well-
Tempered Clavier). Edited by Harold Brooke. Part 1 [and Part 2].
London, Novello [1928?]. 2 vols. in 1. 33 cm. (Novello Edition,
Nos. 1-2.)   P.N.'s: 14235; 14375
2395. Busoni, Ferruccio Benvenuto. The Well-Tempered Clavichord
...Revised, annotated and provided with parallel examples and
suggestions for the study of modern pianoforte-technique by Ferruccio
B. Busoni. New York, G. Schirmer; Leipzig, Fr. Hofmeister [c 1894-
99]. 3 vols. in 2. 33 cm.   P.N.'s: Vol. I, pt. 1: 11660;
                                          pt. 2: 11661; pt. 3: none
2396. ——— Das wohltemperierte Klavier bearbeitet, erläutert und mit
daran anknüpfenden Beispielen und Anweisungen für das Studium der
modernen Klavierspieltechnik herausgegeben von Ferruccio B. Busoni,
New York, G. Schirmer [c 1897]. 56 pp.; 34 cm. (Universal Edition)
No. 2023.)
Wrapper issued by Universal-Edition.
        P.N.'s: 11650 (p. 56 only); 11650a (Nachtrag p. only)

——— See also: Clavier Works, Collections. Bearbeitungen...für das
Pianoforte...von Ferruccio Busoni, Vols. 5 and 6 (entry no. 1526).

——— See also: Clavier Works, Collections. Joh. Seb. Bach Klavier-

2396. *(continued)* werke. Neue Ausgabe von Ferruccio Busoni, Egon Petri und Bruno Mugellini...Vols. 1 and 2 (entry no. 1527).

Another copy of Book II, but with statement at foot of imprint: In die Universal-Edition aufgenommen.

Cesi, Beniamino. *See*: Clavier Works, Collections. ... Metodo per lo studio del pianoforte...Composizioni di Gio. Seb. Bach...Vols. 7 and 8 (entry no. 1536).

Chrysander, Friedrich. *See*: Clavier Works, Collections. Sammlung der Clavier-Compositionen von...Bach. Herausgegeben von Friedrich Chrysander, Vol. 3 (entry no. 1537).

2397. Czerny, Carl. C. Czerny's New Edition of John Sebastian Bach's 48 Preludes and Fugues for the Piano Forte, or Organ, dedicated to his friend, I. Moscheles Esqr. London, printed and sold by R. Cocks & Co. [ca. 1845]. 3 ll.; [1], 2-91, 2-109 pp.; 36 cm.; wove paper. English translation of Griepenkerl's Preface for Vol. 2 of the complete organ works, dated 1844, is tipped between front pastedown and front flyleaf. Fingering indicated is so-called English fingering. Same plates as the Bishop revision of the Czerny edition. Signature on front flyleaf:L. Colborne. P.N.'s: 3233, 3234

2398. —— Le Clavecin bien tempéré ou préludes et fugues dans tous les tons et demi-tons sur les modes majeurs et mineurs par Jean Sebastien Bach. Edition nouvelle soigneusement revue, corrigée et doigtée ainsi que pourvue de notifications sur l'exécution et sur les mesures des temps (d'après le métronome de Maelzel) et accompagnée d'une préface par Charles Czerny. ... Milan, G. Ricordi [ca. 1925]. 2 vols in 1. 34 cm. (Biblioteca musicale didascalica, Nos. 105440, 105441.)   P.N.'s: 105440 (115896); 105441 (115897)

2399. —— Le Clavecin bien tempéré ou préludes et fugues dans tous les tons et demi-tons sur les modes majeurs et mineurs par Jean Sebastien Bach. Edition nouvelle, soigneusement revue, corrigée et doigtée, ainsi que pourvue de notifications sur l'exécution et sur les mesures des temps (d'après le métronome de Maelzel) et accompagnée d'une préface par Charles Czerny. Partie I [and II]. Leipzig, au Bureau de Musique de C. F. Peters [1837]. 2 vols. 33 cm., wove paper. (Oeuvres complets, Livres 1 & 2.)

Book I, front flyleaf, has signature: Walther Curtius; title page has signature: Friedrich Curtius.

Book II, front flyleaf, has signatures: Fritz Curtius; Walther Curtius. Another copy without signatures.   P.N.'s: 2635, 2636

2400. —— Le Clavecin bien tempéré ou préludes et fugues dans tous les tons et demi-tons sur les modes majeurs et mineurs par J. Seb. Bach. Edition nouvelle, revue et corrigée critiquement, doigtée, métronomisée et enrichie de notes sur l'exécution par Charles Czerny. Leipzig & Berlin, C. F. Peters [after 1837]. 2 vols. in 1. 30 cm. P.N.'s: 2635; 2636

2401. —— "Khorosho temperirovannyi klavesin" ("Das wohltem-perierte Klavier") 48 preludii & fug dlia fortepiano. Chast ' I [and II] (red. K. Cherni). Moscow, Gosudarstvennoe musykal'noe isdatel'stvo, 1933, [1931]. 2 vols. in 1. 30 cm.
Notes in Russian and French.   P.N.'s: 25522; 25523

2402. —— The Well-Tempered Clavichord, 48 Preludes and Fugues; Clavecin bien tempéré; Clavicordio bien templado...Revised and fingered by Carl Czerny. ... Boston, London, B. F. Wood [ca. 1930]. 2 vols. in 1. 31 cm. (Edition Wood, Nos. 657, 658.)
P.N.'s: B.F.W. 4034-118; B.F.W. 4035-131

2403. —— The Well Tempered Clavichord, 48 Preludes and Fugues. Edited and revised by Carl Czerny. London, Augener [ca. 1920]. 1 l., 249 pp., 1 l., 30 cm. (Augener's Edition, No. 8009a, 8009b.)
P.N.'s: 14850, 14865

2404. —— The Well-Tempered Clavichord, Forty-Eight Preludes and Fugues, in two volumes. Edited by Carl Czerny, with a bio-graphical sketch of the author by Philip Hale. New York, G. Schirmer; Boston, The Boston Music Co., c 1893. 2 vols. 30 cm. (Schirmer's Library of Musical Classics, Nos. 13-14.)   P.N.'s: 11015; 11016

2405. —— The Well-Tempered Clavichord, "Le clavecin bien tempéré," being the celebrated 48 preludes & fugues by J. Sebastian Bach...[listing of separate preludes and fugues, with their prices]. Boston, Oliver Ditson [1856]. 2 vols. 34 cm.
P.N.'s: Vol. I: none; Vol. II: 14010

2406. —— The Well-Tempered Clavichord, by Johann Sebastian Bach. Volume One: Twenty-four preludes and fugues in all keys edited by Carl Czerny with a biographical sketch of Johann Sebastian Bach. Philadelphia, Theodore Presser [ca. 1910]. 2 ll., 119 pp., illus. (frontis). (Presser collection, No. 259.)
Biographical sketch written by Theodore Presser.
P.N.: P.C. Vol. 259-117

2407. —— Das wohltemperierte Klavier, Clavecin bien tempéré, revidiert und mit Fingersatz versehen von Carl Czerny. Vienna, Leipzig, Universal-Edition Aktiengesellschaft [ca. 1905]. 2 vols. in 1. 30 cm. (Universal-Edition, Nos. 5-6.)
Front wrapper of each volume bears the signature: Ernst Krüger.
P.N.'s: U.E.5; U.E.6

2408. Czerny, Carl, and John Bishop. Book 1 of...J. S. Bach's Works for the Pianoforte, revised by John Bishop of Cheltenham. The Well-Tempered Clavichord; 48 Preludes and Fugues, in all the major & minor keys. Composed by John Sebastian Bach. This edition has been carefully fingered...by Charles Czerny by whom it is dedicated to his friend I. Moscheles, Esqr. London, Robert Cocks [1848-58]. 3 ll., 199 pp., 36 cm., wove paper.

2408. *(continued)*   Penciled inscription on front pastedown: Mi∫s
Lawes. | Dec. 4ᵗʰ. 1859.   P.N.'s: 3233; 3234

Czerny, Carl, Friedrich C. Griepenkerl, and F. August Roitzch.
See: Clavier Works, Collections. Klavierwerke von Joh. Seb. Bach
herausgegeben von Czerny, Griepenkerl und Roitzsch…Vol. 1
(entry no. 1535).

2409. Dallier, Henri. Le Clavecin bien tempéré, Préludes & fugues
pour piano. Edition revue et doigtée par H. Dallier…en deux
volumes. … Paris, Henry Lemoine, c 1917. 2 vols. in 1. 30 cm.
(Édition nationale française Panthéon des pianistes, Nos. 1071-72.)
                    P.N.'s: 21323P.1071. HL.; 21324.P.1072.HL.

2410. Dubois, Francis Clément Théodore. Le Clavecin bien tempéré,
48 préludes et fugues transcrits à 4 mains par Théodore Dubois. …
Paris, Maurice Senart, c 1914. 4 vols. in 1. 34 cm.
                    P.N.'s: M.S. & Cⁱᵉ. 3437 to M.S. & Cⁱᵉ. 3440

2411. Fauré, Gabriel Urbain. Clavecin bien tempéré. Volume I
[and Volume II]. Révision par Gabriel Fauré. Nouvelle édition
revue par Madame Marguerite Long. Paris, A. Durand, c 1915.
2 vols. in 1. 31 cm. (Édition classique A. Durand & fils, Nos. 9356-
57.)   P.N.'s: D. & F. 9356; D. & F. 9357

2412. Forkel, Johann Nicolaus. Le Clavecin bien tempéré ou preludes
et fugues dans tous les tons et demitons du mode majeur et mineur par
J. Seb. Bach. I Parthie. Vienna, chez Hoffmeister & comp.; Leipig,
au Bureau de Musique [1801-1802]. 2 vols. Obl. fol., 26 × 35 cm.,
23 × 33 cm., wove paper, faded red boards.
    Title page of Vol. II has signature: Po∫sⁱ. C F Rungenhagen.
Vol. II has inked stroke added to engraved Roman numeral I to
make II.   P.N.'s: 53, 91

2413. Franz, Robert, and Otto Dresel. Das wohltemperirte Klavier…
herausgegeben von Robert Franz und Otto Dresel. Leipzig &
Brussels, Breitkopf & Härtel, c 1890. 2 vols. in 1. 33 cm.
    Inscription on title page: Meinen lieben | Robi | zu Weihnachten |
1893. Inscription on front flyleaf: Bach wohltemperirtes Klavier. |
Robert Franz und | Otto Dresel. …   P.N.'s: 18471, 18472

2414. —— Another copy, variant, of Vol. II. Imprint in black letters
instead of Roman, and Preface reset.

2415. Germer, Heinrich. Das wohltemperirte Clavier (Le Clavecin
bien tempéré)…Akademische Neuausgabe. Kritisch revidiert…von
Heinrich Germer. Erster Teil [and Zweiter Teil]. Brunswick,
Henry Litolff [c 1895]. 2 vols. in 1. 31 cm. (Collection Litolff,
Nos. 2114a, 2114b.)   P.N.'s: COLLECTION LITOLFF NO. 2114A;
                              COLLECTION LITOLFF NO. 2114B

2416. Goetschius, Percy. The Well-Tempered Clavichord, 48 Preludes
and Fugues, in two volumes…Analytical edition by Percy Goetschius.

... Boston, Oliver Ditson, c 1922. 2 vols. in 1. 31 cm. (Ditson Edition, Nos. 352-53.) P.N.'s: 73980-117; 73981-131

2417. Hallé, Charles. No. 1 [and 2-48] of Charles Halle's edition of Das wohltemperirte Clavier. Forty-eight Preludes and Fugues, composed by John Sebastian Bach. London, Chappell [ca. 1850]. 48 parts in 2 vols. 35 cm.
Each part has separate title and pagination and plate number.
Watermark: Grosvenor Chater & Co.   P.N.'s: 13210 to 13257

2418. Harcourt, Eugène d'. Sébastien Bach, Le Clavecin bien tempéré (1re partie)...Musicalement révisé d'après les textes originaux de la Société de Bach par Eugène d'Harcourt, doigté par Czerny. [Paris, F. Durdilly, Ch. Hayet Succr., c 1915.] vii, 97 pp.; 32 cm. (Edition des Conservatoires, No. 2.)
Vol. II never published.   P.N.: C.6706.H.

2419. Haupt, Carl August. Le Clavecin bien tempéré ou 48 preludes et fuges [sic] dans tous les tons majeurs et mineurs pour le clavecin ou pianoforte composées par J. Seb. Bach. Berlin, chez J. J. Riefenstahl; Hambourg, chez Jean Aug. Böhme; Vienna, chez Anton Diabelli [1838?]. 2 vols. Obl. fol., 26 × 34 cm., wove paper.
Imperfect: Book I wanting.   P.N.: J.J.R.161.B.

2420. ———— Le Clavecin bien tempéré ou 48 préludes et fugues dans tous les tons majeurs et mineurs pour le clavecin ou pianoforte composées par Joh. Seb. Bach. Nouvelle édition. Leipzig, Breitkopf & Härtel [ca. 1850]. 2 vols. Obl. fol., 26 × 32 cm., wove paper.
Imperfect: Book II wanting. Preface, in two parts: the first stating that A. B. Marx was sponsoring the edition; the second, signed by Marx and dated 1838, recommending Haupt as an editor of Bach.
P.N.: J.J.R.161.A; J.J.R.161.B.

2421. Hughes, Edwin. The Well-Tempered Clavichord, in two books. Edited by Edwin Hughes. ... New York, G. Schirmer, c 1925. 2 vols. in 1. 30 cm. (Schirmer's Library of Musical Classics, Nos. 1483-84.)
Below main title is Spanish title: El clavicordio bien templade en dos libros. Editado por Edwin Hughes, traducido por Maria Paz Gainsborg.   P.N.'s: 31840, 31841

2422. Indy, Paul Marie Théodore Vincent d'. Le Clavecin bien tempéré. Edition nouvelle revue et corrigée sur le manuscrit original et corrigée par Blanche Selva et Vincent D'Indy. Paris, Heugel [c 1924]. 1 l., 125 pp., 31 cm. (Édition française de musique classique, No. 69.)
Book I only published.   P.N.: E.F.69.

2423. ———— Le Clavecin bien tempéré, Livre II. Révision et annotations par Vincent D'Indy. Paris, Maurice Senart, c 1920. 2 vols. 34 cm. (Édition nationale, No. 5132.)
Imperfect: Vol. I wanting.   P.N.: M.S. 5132

2424. Keller, Oswin. Le Clavecin bien tempéré...Revue et doigté par Oswin Keller. Vol. I [and Vol. II]. Brussels, A. Cranz [1920?]. 2 vols. in 1. 31 cm. (Edition Cranz, Nos. 515-16.)

P.N.'s: C.44457; C.44458

2425. Klindworth, Karl. Das wohltemperierte Klavier, 48 Präludien und Fugen durch Vortrags-Bezeichnungen erläutert und mit genauem Fingersatz versehen von Karl Klindworth. ... Mainz, Leipzig, B. Schott [c 1894]. 2 vols. in 1. 31 cm. (Edition Schott, Nos. 151-52.)

P.N.'s: 25694 (1) to 25694 (12)

2426. Köhler, Christian Louis Heinrich. Le Clavecin bien tempéré ou préludes & fugues dans tous les tons et demi-tons sur les modes majeurs et mineurs par J. Seb. Bach. Revu et doigté par Louis Köhler. Brunswick, Henry Litolff [ca. 1875]. 2 vols. in 1. 30 cm. (Collection Litolff, Nos. 339-40.) P.N.'s: COLLECTION LITOLFF NO. 339; COLLECTION LITOLFF NO. 340.

2427. Kroll, Franz. Das wohltemperirte Klavier...Kritische Ausgabe nach handschriftlichen Quellen bearbeitet und mit Fingersatz versehen von Franz Kroll. Band I [and Band II]. Leipzig, C. F. Peters [ca. 1905]. 2 vols. in 1. 31 cm. (Edition Peters, Nos. 1a, 1b.)

P.N.'s: 8400, 8401

2428. —— Das wohltemperierte Klavier...Kritische Ausgabe nach handschriftlichen Quellen bearbeitet und mit Fingersatz versehen von Franz Kroll. Band I [and Band II]. Leipzig, London, New York, C. F. Peters [1915?]. 2 vols. in 1. 31 cm. (Edition Peters, Nos. 1a, 1b.)

P.N.'s: 8400, 8401

2429. —— Das wohltemperirte Clavier oder Praeludien und Fugen in allen dur- und Molltonarten...Neue und kritische Ausgabe nach handschriftlichen Quellen bearbeitet und mit technischen Erläuterungen und Fingersatz versehen von Franz Kroll. Band I [and Band II]. Leipzig, Berlin, im Bureau de Musique von C. F. Peters [1862-63]. 2 vols. in 1. 33 cm., wove paper. P.N.'s: 4343, 4344

—— See also: Complete Works. Johann Sebastian Bach's Werke. Herausgegeben von der Bach-Gesellschaft...Vol. XIV (entry no. 544).

2430. Longo, Alessandro. Il clavicembalo ben temperato ossia preludii e fughe in tutti i toni e semitoni nei modi maggiori e minori. Edizione riveduta e diteggiata da Alessandro Longo ... Volume primo [and Volume secondo]. ... Milan, G. Ricordi [ca. 1920]. 2 vols. in 1. 31 cm. (Edizione Ricordi Nos. 190-91.)

P.N.'s: E.R.190; E.R.191

2431. Lott, Edwin Matthew. Forty-Eight Preludes & Fugues (Das wohltemperirte Klavier)...Analyzed, phrased, and fingered by Edwin M. Lott. ... London, Edwin Ashdown [ca. 1885]. 2 vols.

33 cm .(Ashdown Edition of Standard Pianoforte Music, Nos. 105-6.)
P.N.'s: Vol. I only:
E.A. N°. 24091 – E.A. N°. 24102;
E.A. N°. 24643 – E.A. N°. 24648;
E.A. N°. 25,219 – E.A. N°. 25,224
2432. Morgan, Robert Orlando. Wohltemperirtes Clavier, The Forty-Eight Preludes & Fugues. Phrased, fingered and annotated by Orlando Morgan. Book I [and Book II]. London, Edwin Ashdown [c 1923, c 1925]. 2 vols. 31 cm.   P.N.'s: E.A.34389; E.A.34390;
E.A.34404; E.A.34430; E.A.34433;
E.A.34434; E.A.34439; E.A.34524;
E.A.34560; E.A.35341; E.A.34606;
E.A.34616; E.A.35271 to E.A.
35282; E.A.35383 to E.A.35394;
E.A.35526 to E.A.35537
2433. Mugellini, Bruno. Das wohltemperierte Klavier. Erster [and Zweiter] Teil…Instruktive Ausgabe von Bruno Mugellini. Leipzig, Breitkopf & Härtel [c 1908, c 1909]. 2 vols. in 1. 30 cm. (Edition Breitkopf, Nos. 2374-2375.)
At head of title: Ad Arrigo Boito, il revisore.
P.N.'s: V.A. 2374; V.A. 2375
2434. Pauer, Ernst. Das wohltemperirte Klavier, 48 Preludes and Fugues by J. S. Bach, Edited by Ernst Pauer. London, Augener [ca. 1867]. ix, 2-230 pp.; frontis.; 27 cm.
Signature on verso of frontispiece: W. Howell Allchin | Oxford.
Signature on front flyleaf: W. Howell Allchin. Signature on front pastedown: W [?] T Taphouse | 6 Morton Road | Oxford | Jan. 20 1931.   P.N.: A. 17.
2435. —— Das wohltemperirte Klavier, 48 Preludes and Fugues, by J. S. Bach, Edited by Ernst Pauer. Complete, or in two books. London, Augener [after 1888]. 2 vols. 28 cm. (Augener's Edition, Nos. 8010ᵃ, 8010ᵇ.)   P.N.: 5768
2436. Potter, Philip Cipriani Hambly. Forty-Eight Preludes and Forty-Eight Fugues, comprised in two volumes in all the major & minor keys for the piano forte, composed by John Sebastian Bach. London, Addison & Hodges [1845?]. 2 vols. in 1. Obl. fol., 25 × 36 cm., wove paper.
At head of title: New edition, edited by Cipriani Potter. Based on Lavenu's old plates.   P.N.'s: I. S. Bachs Preludes & Fugues (Vol: I);
S. Bachs Preludes & Fugues (Vol: 2ᵈ.)

Reger, Max. *See:* Clavier Works, Collections. Joh. Seb. Bach Klavier-Werke vollständig neue … bezeichnete Bach-Ausgabe von Max Reger und Aug. Schmid-Lindner … Vols. I and II (entry no. 1531).

262 PUBLISHED MUSIC OF J. S. BACH

2437. Reinecke, Carl Heinrich Carsten. Das wohltemperirte Klavier
...Mit Fingersatz, Vortragszeichen und analytischen Erläuterungen
herausgegeben von Carl Reinecke. ... Leipzig, Breitkopf & Härtel,
c 1892. 2 vols. in 1. 32 cm. P.N.'s: J.S.B. Klav. 1; J.S.B. Klav. 2

———— See also: Clavier Works, Collections. Joh. Seb. Bach Klavierwerke mit Fingersatz und vortragszeichen...von Carl Reinecke...
Vols. 5-6 (entry no. 1534).

2438. Riemann, Hugo. Joh. Seb. Bach's wohltemperirtes Clavier mit
Phrasierungs und Fingersatzbezeichnung herausgegeben von Dr.
Hugo Riemann. Neue sorgfältig revidirte Ausgabe. Theil I, Heft 1
[and Heft 2, Heft 3, Heft 4; Theil II, Heft 5, Heft 6, Heft 7, Heft 8].
... London, Augener [ca. 1895]. 8 parts in 1 vol. 31 cm. (Augener's
Edition, Nos. 6011a – 6011d; 6012a – 6012d.)
  Heft 7 bears imprint of C. F. Kahnt Nachfolger, Leipzig, with
  P.N.: 3112 instead of Augener.   P.N.'s: 1004, 10295, 10254,
                                             10516, 10623, 10943

2439. Risler, Joseph Edouard. Le Clavecin bien tempéré, The Well-
Tempered Clavichord. Vol. I [and Vol. II]. Edition revue par...
Ed. Risler. Paris, Heugel [ca. 1928]. 2 vols. in 1. 31 cm. (Édition
française de musique classique, Nos. 196-97.) P.N.'s: E.F.196; C.O.209

Röntgen, Julius. See: Clavier Works, Collections. Joh. Seb. Bach
Klavierwerke...Nach den Urtexten revidiert von Julius Röntgen...
Vols. 1 and 2 (entry no. 1528).

2440. Ruthardt, Adolf. Das wohltemperierte Klavier...heraus-
gegeben von Adolf Ruthardt. Leipzig, C. F. Peters [ca. 1910].
2 vols. in 1. 30 cm. (Edition Peters, No. 2790a.)
  This is Bände 1 & 2 of Ruthardt's collected edition of 10 vols.
                                       P.N.'s: 7694, 7695

2441. Saunders, Gordon. The Academic Edition of Works by Joh:
Seb: Bach...328, Forty-Eight Preludes & Fugues. Book I, 1 to 12
[and 329-331; Book II, 13 to 24 to Book IV, 37 to 48]. London,
A. Hammond [ca. 1895]. 4 vols. 30 cm. (Academic Edition,
Nos. 328-31.)
  Imperfect: Books 1 and 2 wanting.

Schmid-Lindner, August. See: Clavier Works, Collections. Joh. Seb.
Bach Klavier-Werke vollständig neue...bezeichnete Bach-Ausgabe
von Max Reger und Aug. Schmid-Lindner... Vols. I and II (entry
no. 1531).

2442. Schüngeler, Heinz. Das wohltemperierte Klavier. Teil I,
Lieferung 1 [and Lieferung 2]. Urtext und Studienausgabe herausgegeben von Heinz Schlungeler, Herrn Otto Heinrich Nötzel gewidmet. Magdeburg, Heinrichshofen [c 1942, c 1943]. 2 vols. 31 cm.
(Urtext-Studien-Ausgabe.)

Imperfect: All wanting after Book I, No. 12. Signature on title page of Lieferung 1: Seiner sehr verehrten | Schulerin, Frau Else. Kevecordis | zur freundliche Erinnerung | H Schüngeler | Ostern 1943. Signature on title page of Lieferung 2: Else Kevecordis | Schmallenberg.   P.N.'s: H.V. 13498, H.V. 13499; H.V. 13531

2443.   Schwenke, Christian Friedrich Gottlieb. Préludes et fugues pour le forte-piano dans tous les tons, tant majeurs que mineurs par J. Seb. Bach. Dédiés au Conservatoire de musique par l'editeur. I Partie, Contenant 24 préludes et 24 fugues. Paris; Bonn, chez N. Simrock [1801?]. 2 vols. Obl. fol., 26 × 33 cm., laid paper.
Imperfect: Vol. II [i.e., Vol. I] wanting. Also, Vol. I [i.e., Vol. II] has title page which is not integral part of this edition. Also, leaves 43 and 44 (pp. 85-88) wanting.   P.N.: 138

2444.   —— 48 Préludes & fugues dans tous les tons tant majeurs, que mineurs pour le clavecin ou piano-forte composés par Jean Sebastien Bach. Bonn, chez N. Simrock [ca. 1825]. 2 vols. Obl. fol., 27 × 34 cm., wove paper.
Books I and II labeled II and I respectively.   P.N.'s: 138, 166

2445.   Sporck, Georges. [Le clavecin bien tempéré en quatre recueils de 12 préludes et fugues chacun. Paris, E. Ploix, c 1915, c 1925, c 1928, c 1929.] 4 parts in 2 vols. 31 cm. (Édition analytique des classiques.)
Biographical notes by Paul Landormy.
P.N.'s: M.447 S. – M.470 S.; M.471 S. – M.494 S.;
M.495 S. – M.518 S.; M.519 S. – M.542 S.

2446.   Stade, Friedrich Wilhelm. Die Fugen des wohltemperierten Klaviers partiturmässig dargestellt und nach ihrem Bau erläutert von Dr. F. Stade, 1. [and 2.] Teil. Neu durchgesehene Auflage. Leipzig, Steingräber [ca. 1900]. 2 vols. in 1. 33 cm. (Steingräber Edition, Nos. 605-6.)
Notice concerning ornaments signed by Dr. Hans Bischoff.
P.N.'s: 605, 606

2447.   Staub, Victor. Clavecin bien tempéré, 48 préludes et fugues. Edition revue et doigtée par Victor Staub. Paris, E. Gallet [ca. 1920]. 2 vols. in 1. 31 cm. (Édition française, Nos. 132A, 132B.)
P.N.'s: E.G.7690(1); E.G. 7690(2)

2448.   Tagliapietra, Gino. Il clavicembalo ben temperato edizione riveduta da Gino Tagliapietra. Parte prima [and seconda]. Milan, G. Ricordi, 1928, 1929. 2 vols. in 1. 31 cm. (Edizione Ricordi, Nos. 807-8.)   P.N.'s: E.R.807; E.R.808

2449.   Tovey, Donald Francis. Forty-Eight Preludes and Fugues by J. S. Bach, Pianoforte. Edited by Donald Francis Tovey, fingered by Harold Samuel. ... New York, Oxford University Press, 1924. 2 vols. 31 cm. (The Associated Board Edition.)
P.N.'s: A.B.99; A.B.100.

2450. Wesley, Samuel, and Carl Friedrich Horn. S. Wesley and
C. F. Horn's New and Correct Edition of the Preludes and Fugues of
John Sebastian Bach. ... London, Printed for the editors by Robert
Birchall [1810-13]. 4 vols. in 1. Obl. 4°; 24×34 cm.; laid, wove
paper.
  Books III and IV have as imprint: London, Printed for the Editors,
by R^t. Birchall, No. 133, & Chappell & Co. 124, New Bond Street.
Book IV, from p. 225, pagination corrected in ink. All four title
pages have signature: Wesley. Book I introduction has signatures:
S. Wesley [and] C. F. Horn. On inside front cover the following
notes: J. G. Emett | 1814 |; and, in another hand: Given by him
to his daughter | Sarah Harriet Emett | August 1st | 1837 |; Bk. I.
p. 28: | Oct^er 3rd 1837.   P.N.: Bk. IV: Bach's Fugues 4th Book.
2451. ——— S. Wesley and C. F. Horn's New and Correct Edition of
the Celebrated Forty-Eight Preludes and Fugues or "Le clavier bien-
tempéré" of John Sebastian Bach. In four books. London, Printed
and sold by C. Lonsdale (late Birchall and Co.) [ca. 1845]. 1 l.,
iii, [1]-239 pp.; obl. fol.; 26×35 cm.; wove paper.
  Original plates, with a very few supplementary directions added.
                      P.N.: Bach's Fugues 4th Book
2452. Wiehmayer, Johann Theodor. Das wohltemperierte Klavier...
Piano solo. ... Magdeburg, Heinrichshofen, c 1920, c 1914, c 1915.
4 parts in 1 vol. 30 cm. (Neu instruktive Ausgabe, Nos. 4a-4d.)
                      P.N.'s: H.V.9748; H.V.9843;
                              H.V.11360; H.V.11422
2453. Wiernsberger. Le clavecin bien tempéré. Édition nouvelle
revue d'après les manuscrits originaux. Paris, Heugel [c 1924]. 2 ll.,
120 pp., 31 cm. (Édition française de musique classique, No. 10.)
  Reviser of this edition was Wiernsberger, who died before complet-
ing the revision of the second volume.   P.N.: E.F.10
2454. Willborg, Wilhelm. Das wohltemperirte Clavier...I. Theil,
24 Präludien und Fugen. Nach zunehmender Schwierigkeit geordnet
und zu Studien und Unterrichts-Zwecken mit allem nöthigen Aus-
gestattet von W. Willborg. Heft I [and II-IV]. ... Moscow, P. Jurgenson [1900]. 4 parts in 1 vol.
  Imprint for parts 2-4 varies slightly from that of part 1.
                      P.N.: 25967-25970
2455. Wouters, François Adolphe. Nouvelles Éditions revues, doigtées
et annotées par Adolphe Wouters. Bach J. S....Le clavecin bien
tempéré. ... London, Boosey & Co. [ca. 1897]. 2 vols. in 1. 33 cm.
(Nouvelle Éditions par Adolphe Wouters.)
  Title for Vol. II has imprint for Schott Frères, Bruxelles. Wrappers
for both volumes give both Boosey and the Brussels branch of
Schott Frères in the imprint. Foreword signed by Gertrude Azulay.
                      P.N.'s: S.F.5861; S.F.5862

Listed Alphabetically by Publisher (no editor indicated)

2456. André, C. A.; Offenbach s/M.   Le clavecin bien tempéré ou
préludes et fugues dans tous les tons et demitons sur les modes majeurs
et mineurs composés par Jean Seb. Bach. Cah. 1, 2, 3, 4. Edition
nouvelle, soigneusement revue, corrigée et doigtée... Oeuvres complets
Liv. I. Offenbach s/M, C. A. André [1846?]. 4 parts. 31 cm.
    Signature on title page: Carl Baermann.   P.N.'s: 6601-6604
2457. Berra, Marco; Prague.   Das wohltemperirte Clavier 48 Praeludien und Fugen in allen dur und moll Tonarten von J. S. Bach.
Prague, Marco Berra [ca. 1840]. 4 parts. 34 cm., wove paper.
    Imperfect: Part 1 wanting.   P.N.'s: M:B:423; M:B:424; M:B:425
2458. Bote, Ed., & G. Bock; Berlin.   Le Clavecin bien tempéré ou
Préludes et fugues dans tous les tons et demi-tons sur les modes majeurs
et mineurs. Partie I [and II]. Berlin, chez Ed. Bote & G. Bock
[ca. 1850]. 2 vols. in 1. 33 cm., wove paper.
                          P.N.'s: B. & B. 2209; B. & B. 2210; B. & B. 2222
2459. —— Das wohltemperirte Klavier, Le Clavécin bien tempéré...
Band II. Berlin, Ed. Bote & G. Bock [ca. 1865]. 2 vols. 34 cm.,
wove paper.
    Imperfect: Book I wanting.   P.N.: B. & B. 2222
2460. Breitkopf & Härtel; Leipzig.   48 Préludes et fugues dans tous les
tons majeurs et mineurs pour clavecin ou pianoforte composées par
J. Seb. Bach. 1ère [and 2me] Partie. Leipzig, chez Breitkopf & Härtel
[1819]. 2 vols. in 1. Obl. fol., 25 × 33 cm., laid paper.
    Books I and II inverted in order.   P.N.'s: 2900, 2901
2461. —— Das wohltemperirte Klavier, 48 Präludien u. 48 Fugen
durch alle dur- u. molltonarten von Johann Sebastian Bach. IIr
Theil... Neue verbesserte Ausgabe. Leipzig, bei Breitkopf & Härtel
[1851?]. 2 vols. 33 cm., wove paper.
    Signature on front flyleaf: S. Franko. Imperfect: Book I wanting.
                                                    P.N.: 8226
2462. Broderip & Wilkinson; London.   Préludes et fugues pour le
forte-piano dans tous les tons, tant majeurs que mineurs par I. Seb.
Bach dédiés au Conservatoire de musique par l'Editeur, contenant
12 préludes et 12 fugues. London, par Broderip et Wilkinson [1802].
2 parts. Obl. 4°, 26 × 36 cm., laid paper.
    Imperfect: Part 1 only of the 24 preludes and fugues of Vol. II
originally published in 2 parts by Broderip & Wilkinson.
2463. Cotelle, A.; Paris.   Quarante-huit Fugues et préludes pour le
piano-forte, composé par le célèbre Jean Sebastien Bach... Nouvelle
édition revue avec soin. Paris, chez A. Cotelle [ca. 1850]. 2 vols. in 1.
34 cm., wove paper.
    Signature on first title page: C. Perugini. Reissue, from same plates,
of Janet et Cotelle's [1828?] edition.   P.N.: 732

2464.   Coventry & Hollier; London. Préludes et fugues pour le forte-piano dans tous les tons, tant majeurs que mineurs par I. Seb. Bach dediés au Conservatoire de musique par l'Editeur...Contenant 12 préludes et 12 fugues. London, Coventry & Hollier [1837?]. 2 vols. in 1. Obl. fol., 25 × 35 cm., wove paper.
     Plates are those used by Broderip & Wilkinson, based on Schwenke edition.

2465.   Janet & Cotelle; Paris. Quarante-huit Fugues et préludes pour le piano-forte composés par le célèbre Jean Sebastien Bach...Nouvelle édition revue avec soin. Paris, chez Janet et Cotelle [1820-24]. 2 vols. 33 cm., laid paper.
     Based on the Imbault publication of fugues only, with same P.N. [1809?].   P.N.: 732

2466.   Lavenu, E.; London. Forty-Eight Preludes and Forty-Eight Fugues, comprised in two volumes in all the major & minor keys for the piano forte, composed by John Sebastian Bach. London, Printed and sold by E. Lavenu [not before 1821]. 1 l., 109 pp., obl. fol., 25 × 34 cm., wove paper (watermarked: 1821).
     Book I only.   P.N.: I. S. Bachs Preludes & Fugues (Vol: 1)

2467.   —— Forty-Eight Preludes and Forty-Eight Fugues, comprised in two volumes in all the major & minor keys for the piano forte, composed by John Sebastian Bach. London, E. Lavenu [not before 1816]. 1 l., 123 pp., obl. fol., 23 × 31 cm., wove paper (watermarked: 1816).
     Book II only.   P.N.: S. Bach's Preludes & Fugues Vol: 2ᵈ

2468.   Lemoine, Henry; Paris. 48 Préludes et fugues dans tous les tons majeurs et mineurs pour le piano forte composés par Jean Sebastien Bach. Dédiés au Conservatoire de musique par l'editeur. ... Paris, Chez Henry Lemoine [ca. 1844-50]. 2 vols. in 1. 26 cm., wove paper.
     Books I and II interchanged in this edition. Imperfect: Book II, pp. 27-30 are wanting. Reprinting of plates originally printed by Omont [ca. 1813].   P.N.'s: O. 217; O. 218

2469.   Nägeli, Hans Georg; Zürich. Das wohltemperirte Clavier oder Präludien und Fugen durch alle Töne von Johann Sebastian Bach. 1er Theil [& 2er Theil]. Zürich, Hans Georg Nägeli [1801]. 2 vols. Obl. fol., 26 × 34 cm., laid paper.
     General title, bound before title in both vols.: Musikalische Kunstwerke im strengen Style von J. S. Bach u. andern Meistern. Zürich, bey Hans Georg Nägeli.

2470.   Omont; Paris. 48 Préludes et fugues dans tous les tons majeurs et mineurs pour le piano forte composés par Jean Sebastien Bach. Dédiés au Conservatoire de Musique par l'editeur. ... Paris, au trophée musical, chez Omont [ca. 1813]. 2 vols. in 1. Obl. fol., 25 × 34 cm., contemporary green marbled boards and calf back lettered in gilt.

Books I and II interchanged in this edition. Omont signature stamped on both title pages.   P.N.'s: O.217; O.218

2471. Peters, C. F.; Leipzig. Le Clavecin bien tempéré ou préludes et fugues dans tous les tons et demitons du mode majeur et mineur par Johann Sebast. Bach. Partie I [and II]. Leipzig, au Bureau de Musique de C. F. Peters [1815?]. 2 vols. Obl. fol., 25 × 33 cm., laid paper.

On front flyleaf of each vol. inscription reads: Beſitzer | Paul Schnöpf. New plates made by Peters, based on the Forkel edition published by Hoffmeister & Kühnel.   P.N.'s: 53, 91

2472. —— Le Clavecin bien tempéré ou Préludes et fugues dans tous les tons et demitons du mode majeur et mineur par Jean Sebast. Bach. Partie I [and II]. Édition nouvelle et corrigée. Leipzig, au Bureau de Musique de C. F. Peters [1825?]. 2 vols. in 1. Obl. fol., 24 × 32 cm., wove paper.

A later printing, made from new plates of Peters which were based on Forkel edition published by Hoffmeister & Kühnel.   P.N.'s: 53, 91

2473. —— Le Clavecin bien tempéré ou préludes et fugues dans tous les tons et demitons du mode majeur et mineur per Jean Sebast. Bach. Partie I, édition nouvelle et corrigée. London, chez Ths. Boosey & Comp.; Leipzig, au Bureau de Musique de C. F. Peters [1825?]. 2 vols. Obl. fol., 26 × 33 cm., wove paper, original boards.

Imperfect: Book II wanting. Signature on front flyleaf: Jacob Roſenhain. A later printing, made from new plates of Peters which were based on Forkel edition published by Hoffmeister & Kühnel.
P.N.: 53

2474. Preston; London. Préludes et fugues pour le forte-piano dans tous les tons, tant majeurs que mineurs par I. Seb. Bach. Dédiés au Conservatoire de musique par l'editeur...Contenant 12 préludes et 12 fugues. London, Preston [1811?]. 2 vols. in 1. Obl. 4°, 24 × 34 cm., laid paper (watermarked: 1811, 1809).

Based on Schwenke's edition published by Simrock and later by Coventry & Hollier. Inscription on front flyleaf: Thomas Close | Nottingham.

2475. Richault; Paris. Vingt-quatre Préludes et fugues dans tous les tons et demi-tons du mode majeur et mineur pour le clavecin ou piano-forte, composé par Jean Sebastien Bach. Paris, chez Richault [1828?]. 2 vols. in 1. Obl. fol., 27 × 34 cm., laid paper.
P.N.'s: 1169 R; 1168 R

2476. —— Vingt-quatre Préludes et fugues dans tous les tons et demi-tons du mode majeur et mineur pour le clavecin ou piano-forte, composés par Jean Sebastien Bach. Paris, chez Richault [ca. 1850]. 2 vols. in 1. Obl. fol., 26 × 34 cm., wove paper.

Signature on front flyleaf: E. G. Busby. Reissue, from same plates, of Richault edition of [1828?].   P.N.'s: 1169 R; 1168 R

2477. Schlesinger, Maurice; Paris. Préludes et fugues dans tous les tons & demi tons du mode majeur et mineur composés pour le piano forte par Jean Sébastien Bach. Paris, chez Maurice Schlesinger [ca. 1835]. 1 l., 217 pp., 34 cm., wove paper.
At head of title: Edition soigneusement doigtée. Signature on title page: Mary Stanford | Paris | Sep^t. 30^h. 1851 [?]. Based on the Schwenke edition. P.N.: M.S. 741

2478. Schott, B.; Mainz. Le Clavecin bien tempéré ou 48 préludes et fugues dans les tons majeurs et mineurs composées par J. Seb. Bach. En 2 livres. Mainz, chez les Fils de B. Schott [1838-40]. 2 vols. in 1. 33 cm., wove paper. P.N.'s: 15239.1; 15239.2.

2479. —— Le Clavecin bien tempéré, Das wohltemperirte Clavier, 48 Präludien und Fugen in allen dur & moll Tonarten von J. Seb. Bach. Ausgabe in sechs Heften. Mainz, B. Schott's Söhne [1838-40]. 2 vols. 35 cm., wove paper.
Imperfect: Vol. II wanting. P.N.: 15239.1

Selections, Arrangements

PRELUDES AND FUGUES

2480. Acht Fugen und vier Praeludien aus Joh. Seb. Bach's Wohltemperirtem Clavier als Trios für Violine, Viola und Violoncell arrangirt von Carl van Bruyck. Drei Hefte. Leipzig, Breitkopf & Härtel [1866?]. 3 parts. 34 cm., wove paper.
P.N.'s: 11029a, 11029b, 11029c

2481. Auslese aus Johann Sebastian Bach's instructiven Klavierwerken ...bearbeitet von Karl Eichler...Zweiter Band...Klavierpräludien... Dritter Band...Klavierfugen. ... Stuttgart, Deutsche Verlags-Anstalt [ca. 1910]. 2 vols. 34 cm.
This is Vols. 2 and 3 of Eichler's edition of selected keyboard works. Preludes and fugues arranged as duets. P.N.: II

2482. Eight Selected Preludes and Fugues from Well-Tempered Clavichord, edited by Carl Tausig. ... St. Louis, Kunkel [c 1893]. 34 pp., 33 cm. (Kunkel's Royal Edition.) P.N.: 1490-41

2483. Praeludium und Fugen im Quintenzirkel aus dem Wohltemperierten Klavier...Zur Erleichterung der Ausführung auf zwei Klaviere zu vier Händen übertragen von E. Humperdinck. Mainz & Leipzig, B. Schott [ca. 1920]. 73, [1] pp.; 31 cm. (Edition Schott, No. 548.) P.N.: 25001

2484. Das wohltemperirte Clavier ausgewählte Präludien und Fugen bearbeitet und herausgegeben von Carl Tausig mit einem Vorwort von Louis Ehlert. 18te Auflage. ... Berlin, M. Bahn (früher T. Trautwein) [1869?]. 86 pp., 34 cm. P.N.: 2500

2485. Das wohltemperierte Klavier...Ausgewählte Praeludien und Fugen herausgegeben von Carl Tausig revidiert von Adolf Ruthardt.

Leipzig, C. F. Peters [1929?]. 115 pp., 30 cm. (Edition Peters,
No. 3180.)   P.N.: 9046
2486.   Das wohltemperierte Klavier. Ausgewählte Präludien und Fugen
bearbeitet und herausgegeben von Karl Tausig. Neue korrekte Ausgabe unter Revision von Gustav Damm (Theodor Steingräber).
Leipzig, Steingräber [ca. 1900]. 87, [1] pp.; 34 cm.   P.N.: 1069

PRELUDES

2487.   J. S. Bach, Kompositionen herausgegeben von A. Siloti...
10 Präludien aus "Das wohltemperierte Klavier". ... Moscow, chez
A. Gutheil, fournisseur de la cour impériale et des théâtres impériaux
[not after 1917]. 26 pp., 34 cm.   P.N.: A. 9682 G.
2488.   J. S. Bach, Kompositionen herausgegeben von A. Siloti... 10
Präludien aus "Das wohltemperierte Klavier". ... Moscow, A. Gutheil
(S. et N. Koussewitsky) [not before 1919]. 26 pp., 33 cm.
                                                       P.N.: A. 9682 G.
2489.   Twelve Selected Preludes from Well-Tempered Clavichord,
edited by Carl Tausig. ... St. Louis, Kunkel [c 1893]. 13 ll., 36 cm.
(Kunkel's Royal Edition.)   P.N.: 1490-41

FUGUES

2490.   Classische Hochschule für Pianisten. Für den Unterricht mit
Fingersatz u. Vortragsbezeichnungen versehen [von] L. Köhler...
[Part] 8, 24 Fug. (Wohltemp. Kl.). ... Leipzig, J. Schuberth [1880].
3 ll., pp. 3 (221)-45(263).   P.N.: 4265
2491.   Eight Fugues from J. S. Bach's Well-Tempered Clavichord, with
analytical expositions in colors and appended harmonic schemes by
Bern. Boekelman. Designed for use in music schools, and for self-
instruction. Boston, Boston Music Co., c 1912. 1 l.; 1ª-16ª, [1] pp.;
1-16 pp.; 1 l.; 34 cm.
    Secondary title reads: Harmonic schemes as supplement to the
colored edition of the fugues from J. S. Bach by Bern. Boekelman.
Copyright 1895, 1912 by Bern. Boekelman. Double pagination;
black printing: [1], 1ª-16ª, [1] pp.; polychrome printing; 1 l.,
1-16 pp., 1 l. Text in five colors. At head of title: Serie I.
2492.   Eight Fugues from J. S. Bach's Well-Tempered Clavichord, with
analytical expositions in colors and appended harmonic schemes by
Bern. Boekelman. Designed for use in music schools, and for self-
instruction. Boston, Boston Music Co., c 1913. 1 l.; [1], 1ª-16ª,
[1] pp.; 1-16 pp.; 1 l.
    Secondary title reads: Harmonic schemes as supplement to the
colored edition of selected fugues from J. S. Bach's Well-tempered
clavichord by Bern. Boekelman. Copyright 1895, 1913 by Bern.
Boekelman. Double pagination; black printing: [1], 1ª-16ª, [1]

2492. *(continued)*   pp.; polychrome printing: 1 l., 1-16 pp., 1 l. Text in five colors. At head of title: Serie II.
2493. Ernst von Stockhausen, Die harmonische Grundlage von 12 Fugen aus Joh. Seb. Bachs wohltemperirtem Klavier sowie der As moll-Orgelfuge von J. Brahms nach den Grundsätzen von S. Sechter dargestellt und erläutert. Leipzig, Breitkopf & Härtel [ca. 1895]. 40 pp., 34 cm. (Breitkopf & Härtel's Klavier-Bibliothek.) Analyses printed in red and black.   P.N.: 23129
2494. The Forty-Eight fugues for the Wohltemperirte Klavier by J. S. Bach in score with proper clefs. Edited by Dr. Charles Vincent... Book I [and Book II]. ... London, E. Donajowski, 1891. 2 vols. 28 cm. (Students Edition.) Signature on front cover of Book II: A. Davidson Arndt.
2495. The Forty-Eight Fugues for the Wohltemperirte Klavier by J. S. Bach, in score with proper clefs. Edited by Dr. Charles Vincent ...Book II.... London, E. Donajowski, 1891. 75 pp., 28 cm. (Students Edition.)
2496. The Forty-Eight Fugues for the Wohltemperirte Klavier by J. S. Bach, in score with proper clefs. Edited by Dr. Charles Vincent ...Book II. ... London, Published by Charles Vincent [ca. 1910]. 75, [1] pp.; 28 cm. (Students Edition.)
2497. The Forty-Eight Fugues for the Wohltemperirte Klavier by J. S. Bach, in score with proper clefs. Edited by Dr. Charles Vincent, the fugue subjects set to words by Professor Ebenezer Prout...Preface to 1911 edition...Book I. ... London, The Vincent Music Co. [after 1911]. 2 vols. 28 cm. (Students Edition.) Imperfect: Vol. II wanting.
2498. 48 Fugues pour le piano composées par le célèbre Jean Sebastien Bach. ... Paris, chez Imbault [1809?]. 3 ll., 157 pp., 32 cm., laid paper.
    Issued in two books of two parts each, with half-titles for each part, but continuous pagination. Note on general title: N.B. Ces fugues sont ici rangées felon l'ordre des fuccessions harmoniques.
                                                            P.N.: 732
2499. Seb. Bach 6 fugues mises en partition analysées et doigtées par F. Le Couppey. ... Paris, Maison Maho, J. Hamelle, succr. [ca. 1884]. 1 l., 25 pp., 32 cm.   P.N.: J.3194H.
2500. Six Fugues du célèbre Jean Seb. Bach arrangées pour violon, viola et violoncelle par Guillaume Braun. (Deuxième Suite des fugues.) Berlin, T. Trautwein [1829?]. 3 parts. 34 cm., wove paper. Contents: Bk. I, Nos. 2, 21; Bk. II, Nos. 1, 6, 10, 21.   P.N.: 288
2501. Zwanzig ausgewählte Fugen aus Joh. Seb. Bach's Wohltemperirtem Clavier für die Orgel bearbeitet von J. G. Zahn mit Erläuterungen von S. Jadassohn. Leipzig, F. E. C. Leuckart [1887]. 2 ll.; 61, xxvii, [1] pp.; obl. 8°; 22 × 27 cm.   P.N.: F.E.C.L.3335.

DAS WOHLTEMPERIERTE KLAVIER, BOOK I

Selections, Arrangements

2502. Twelve Preludes from the Well-Tempered Clavichord (Vol. I) for piano by Johann Sebastian Bach. Compiled by Orville A. Lindquist. Philadelphia, Theodore Presser [ca. 1937]. 27 pp., 31 cm. (Presser Collection, No. 348.)

2503. Two Five-Voiced Fugues with Preludes, J. S. Bach. Arranged for strings by M. Wood-Hill. New York, H. P. Gray; London, Goodwin & Tabb [c 1923]. 2 ll., 17 pp., 26 cm.
Contents: Nos. 4 and 22.

Single Works

NO. I IN C MAJOR

2504. Méditation pour le piano avec un violon obligé et avec accompagnement d'un second violon, alto et violoncelle sur le premier prélude du clavecin bien tempéré de Jean Sebastien Bach. Leipzig, au Bureau de Musique de C. F. Peters [1853?]. 5 parts. 34 cm.
This is the Gounod arrangement, with the added melody later known as the Bach-Gounod *Ave Maria*.   P.N.: 3628

2505. Oeuvres originales J. S. Bach, Prélude et fugue en UT (Clavecin bien tempéré No. 1). Paris, Maurice Senart [ca. 1910]. 5 pp., 35 cm. (Nouvelle Édition française de musique classique, No. 25.) General editor of series: Vincent D'Indy. Revision by Blanche Selva.   P.N.: M.S. & Cie. 25

2506. Prelude in A Flat (Ave Maria). Based on the first prelude of the "Well Tempered Clavichord" of Johann Sebastian Bach [arranged by] Charles Gounod, transcribed for the organ by H. Clough-Leighter. Boston, Oliver Ditson [c 1908]. 5, [1] pp.; 34 cm. (Third Organ Series.)   P.N.: 5-39-66683-3

NO. 2 IN C MINOR

2507. 2 Méditations pour le piano avec accompagnement de 2 violons, viola et violoncelle sur les préludes No. 2 et No. 6 du Clavecin bien tempéré de Jean Sebastien Bach. Leipzig, au Bureau de Musique de C. F. Peters [1858?]. 5 parts. 34 cm., wove paper.   P.N.: 4152

2508. Oeuvres originales J. S. Bach, Prélude et fugue en *Ut* (Clavecin bien tempéré No. 2). Paris, Maurice Senart [ca. 1910]. 5 pp., 35 cm. (Nouvelle Édition française de musique classique, No. 26.) General editor of series: Vincent D'Indy. Revision by Blanche Selva.   P.N.: M.S. & Cie. 26

NO. 3 IN C SHARP MAJOR

2509. Oeuvres originales J. S. Bach, Prélude et fugue en UT #¦(Clavecin bien tempéré No. 3). Paris, M. Senart & B. Roudanez [ca. 1910]. 5 pp., 35 cm. (Nouvelle Édition française de musique classique, No. 217.)
General editor of series: Vincent D'Indy. Revision by Blanche Selva. P.N.: S.R. & Cie. 217

NO. 4 IN C SHARP MINOR

2510. Oeuvres originales J. S. Bach, Prélude et fugue en *Ut* # (Clavecin bien tempéré No. 4). Paris, M. Senart; B. Roudanez [ca. 1910]. 5 pp., 35 cm. (Nouvelle Édition française de musique classique, No. 124.)
General editor of series: Vincent D'Indy. Revision by Blanche Selva. P.N.: S.R. & Cie. 124

NO. 5 IN D MAJOR

2511. Oeuvres originales J. S. Bach. Prélude et fugue en RE (Clavecin bien tempéré No. 5). Paris, M. Senart; B. Roudanez [ca. 1910]. 5 pp., 35 cm. (Nouvelle Édition française de musique classique, No. 125.)
General editor of series: Vincent D'Indy. Revision by Blanche Selva. P.N.: S.R. & Cie. 125.

NO. 6 IN D MINOR

2512. 2 Méditations pour le piano avec accompagnement de 2 violons, viola et violoncelle sur les Préludes No. 2 et No. 6 du Clavecin bien tempéré de Jean Sebastien Bach. Leipzig, au Bureau de Musique de C. F. Peters [1858?]. 5 parts. 34 cm., wove paper. P.N.: 4153

2513. Oeuvres originales J. S. Bach. Prélude et fugue en *Re* (Clavecin bien tempéré No. 6). Paris, Maurice Senart [ca. 1910]. 5 pp., 35 cm. (Nouvelle Édition française de musique classique, No. 126.)
General editor of series: Vincent D'Indy. Revision by Blanche Selva. P.N.: M.S. & Cie. 126

NO. 7 IN E FLAT MAJOR

2514. Oeuvres originales J. S. Bach, Prélude et fugue en MI♭ (Clavecin bien tempéré No. 7). Paris, M. Senart; B. Roudanez [ca. 1910]. 5 pp., 35 cm. (Nouvelle Édition française de musique classique, No. 218.)
General editor of series: Vincent D'Indy. Revision by Blanche Selva. P.N.: SR. & Cie. 218.

NO. 8 IN E FLAT MINOR

2515. Oeuvres originales J. S. Bach, Prélude et fugue en *Mi*♭ (Clavecin

bien tempéré No. 8). Paris, M. Senart; B. Roudanez [ca. 1910].
6 pp., 1 l., 35 cm. (Nouvelle Édition française de musique classique,
No. 27.)
General editor of series: Vincent D'Indy. Revision by Blanche
Selva.   P.N.: S.R. & Cie. 27.

NO. 9 IN E MAJOR

2516.   Oeuvres originales J. S. Bach, Prélude et fugue en MI (Clavecin
bien tempéré No. 9). Paris, M. Senart; B. Roudanez [ca. 1910].
3 pp., 35 cm. (Nouvelle Édition française de musique classique,
No. 219.)
General editor of series: Vincent D'Indy. Revision by Blanche
Selva.   P.N.: S.R. & Cie. 219

NO. 10 IN E MINOR

2517.   Oeuvres originales J. S. Bach, Prélude et fugue en *Mi* (Clavecin
bien tempéré No. 10). Paris, M. Senart; B. Roudanez [ca. 1910].
1 l.; 3, [1] pp.; 35 cm. (Nouvelle Édition française de musique
classique, No. 220.)
General editor of series: Vincent D'Indy. Revision by Blanche
Selva.   P.N.: S.R. & Cie. 220

NO. 11 IN F MAJOR

2518.   Bach...Prelude and Fugue No. 11. ... New York, The American
Music Teachers Protective Association Publishing Co. [ca. 1908].
5 pp., 33 cm. (Teacher's Edition Royal.)
                          P.N.: The A.M.T.P.A. Publishing Co.;
                          Prelude and Fuge No. 11; Fuge No. 11.
2519.   Oeuvres originales J. S. Bach, Prélude et fugue en *FA* (Clavecin
bien tempéré No. 11). Paris, M. Senart; B. Roudanez [ca. 1910].
4 pp., 1 l., 35 cm. (Nouvelle Édition française de musique classique,
No. 127.)
General editor of series: Vincent D'Indy. Revision by Blanche
Selva.   P.N.: S.R. & Cie. 127

NO. 12 IN F MINOR

2520.   Oeuvres originales J. S. Bach, Prélude et fugue en *Fa* (Clavecin
bien tempéré No. 12). Paris, M. Senart; B. Roudanez [ca. 1910].
1 l., 3 pp., 35 cm. (Nouvelle Édition française de musique classique,
No. 221.)
General editor of series: Vincent D'Indy. Revision by Blanche
Selva.   P.N.: S.R. & Cie. 221

NO. 13 IN F SHARP MAJOR

2521.   Oeuvres originales J. S. Bach, Prélude et fugue en FA# (Clavecin

2521. *(continued)*   bien tempéré No. 13). Paris, M. Senart; B. Roudanez [ca. 1910]. 4 pp., 1 l., 35 cm. (Nouvelle Édition française demusique classique, No. 298.)
    General editor of series: Vincent D'Indy. Revision by Blanche Selva.   P.N.: S.R. & Cte. 298

NO. 14 IN F SHARP MINOR

2522.   Oeuvres originales J. S. Bach, Prélude et fugue en *Fa* [i.e., F ♯ minor] (Clavecin bien tempéré No. 14). Paris, M. Senart; B. Roudanez [ca. 1910]. 1 l.; 3, [1] pp.; 35 cm. (Nouvelle Édition française de musique classique, No. 299.)
    General editor of series: Vincent D'Indy. Revision by Blanche Selva.   P.N.: S.R. & Cte. 299

NO. 15 IN G MAJOR

2523.   Oeuvres originales J. S. Bach, Prélude et fugue en SOL (Clavecin bien tempéré, No. 15). Paris, M. Senart; B. Roudanez [ca. 1910]. 5 pp., 35 cm. (Nouvelle Édition française de musique classique, No. 300.)
    General editor of series: Vincent D'Indy. Revision by Blanche Selva.   P.N.: S.R. & Cte. 300

NO. 16 IN G MINOR

2524.   Oeuvres originales J. S. Bach, Prelude et fugue en *Sol* (Clavecin bien tempéré No. 16). Paris, M. Senart; B. Roudanez [ca. 1910]. 4 pp., 1 l., 35 cm. (Nouvelle Édition française de musique classique, No. 128.)
    General editor of series: Vincent D'Indy. Revision by Blanche Selva.   P.N.: S.R. & Cte. 128

NO. 17 IN A FLAT MAJOR

2525.   Oeuvres originales J. S. Bach, Prélude et fugue en LA♭ (Clavecin bien tempéré, No. 17). Paris, M. Senart; B. Roudanez [ca. 1910]. 1 l.; 3, [1] pp.; 35 cm. (Nouvelle Édition française de musique classique, No. 301.)
    General editor of series: Vincent D'Indy. Revision by Blanche Selva.   P.N.: S.R. & Cte. 301.

NO. 18 IN G SHARP MINOR

2526.   Oeuvres originales J. S. Bach, Prélude et fugue en LA♭ [i.e., G ♯ minor] (Clavecin bien tempéré No. 18). Paris, M. Senart; B. Roudanez [ca. 1910]. 1 l.; 3, [1] pp.; 35 cm. (Nouvelle Édition française de musique classique, No. 302.)
    General editor of series: Vincent D'Indy. Revision by Blanche Selva.   P.N.: S.R. & Cte. 302

NO. 19 IN A MAJOR

2527. Oeuvres originales J. S. Bach, Prélude et fugue en LA (Clavecin bien tempéré No. 19). Paris, Maurice Senart [ca. 1910]. 5 pp., 35 cm. (Nouvelle Édition française de musique classique, No. 340.) General editor of series: Vincent D'Indy. Revision by Blanche Selva. P.N.: S.R. & Cie. 340

NO. 20 IN A MINOR

2528. Oeuvres originales J. S. Bach, Prélude et fugue en *La* (Clavecin bien tempéré No. 20). Paris, Maurice Senart [ca. 1910]. 7 pp., 35 cm. (Nouvelle Édition française de musique classique, No. 341.) General editor of series: Vincent D'Indy. Revision by Blanche Selva. P.N.: M.S. & Cie. 341.

NO. 21 IN B FLAT MAJOR

2529. Bach... Prelude and Fugue No. 21. ... New York, The American Music Teachers Protective Association Publishing Co. [ca. 1908]. 5 pp., 33 cm. (Teacher's Edition Royal.)
P.N.: The A.M.T.P.A. Publishing Co.; Prelude and Fuge N°. 21.; Fuge N°. 21.

2530. Oeuvres originales J. S. Bach, Prélude et fugue en si♭ (Clavecin bien tempéré No. 21). Paris, Maurice Senart [ca. 1910]. 5 pp., 35 cm. (Nouvelle Édition française de musique classique, No. 342.) General editor of series: Vincent D'Indy. Revision by Blanche Selva. P.N.: M.S. & Cie. 342.

NO. 22 IN B FLAT MINOR

2531. Oeuvres originales J. S. Bach, Prélude et fugue en *Si*♭ (Clavecin bien tempéré No. 22). Paris, M. Senart; B. Roudanez [ca. 1910]. 4 pp., 1 l., 35 cm. (Nouvelle Édition française de musique classique, No. 343.)
General editor of series: Vincent D'Indy. Revision by Blanche Selva. P.N.: S.R. & Cie. 343.

NO. 23 IN B MAJOR

2532. Oeuvres originales J. S. Bach, Prélude et fugue en si (Clavecin bien tempéré No. 23). Paris, M. Senart; B. Roudanez [ca. 1910]. 1 l.; 3, [1] pp.; 35 cm. (Nouvelle Édition française de musique classique, No. 344.)
General editor of series: Vincent D'Indy. Revision by Blanche Selva. P.N.: S.R. & Cie. 344.

NO. 24 IN B MINOR

2533. Oeuvres originales J. S. Bach, Prélude et fugue en *Si* (Clavecin bien tempéré No. 24). Paris, M. Senart; B. Roudanez [ca. 1910].

2533. *(continued)*   7 pp., 35 cm.   (Nouvelle Édition française de musique classique, No. 345.)

    General editor of series: Vincent D'Indy.   Revision by Blanche Selva.   P.N.: S.R. & Cte. 345.

DAS WOHLTEMPERIERTE KLAVIER, BOOK II

Selections, Arrangements

2534.   Six Fugues du célèbre I. Seb. Bach, arrangées pour deux violons, viola et violoncelle par Guill. Braun...1re suite.   Leipzig, chez Fréderic Hofmeister [ca. 1825].   4 parts.   34 cm., laid paper.
    Contents: Book II, Fugues Nos. 2, 5, 7, 9, 22, and 23.   P.N.: 772

2535.   Das wohltemperirte Klavier...in progressiver Ordnung für die Orgel eingerichtet mit Angabe des Fingersatzes und der Pedal-Applicatur nebst Anweisung über den Gebrauch der Register versehen von J. A. Eijken.   The Hague, G. H. van Eck, n.d.   71 pp., obl. fol., 27×34 cm.   (Edition G. H. van Eck, No. 419.)
    Contents: Fugues from Book II only.   P.N.: G.H.v.E.419

Single Works

NO. 12 IN F MINOR

2536.   Präludium und Fuge F-moll aus dem Wohltemperierten Klavier Teil II bearbeitet von Armin Knab. [Berlin, Max Hesse, 1914.] 6 pp., 27 cm.
    This is the Notenbeilage for *Die Musik*, Vol. XIII, No. 7 (Jan., 1914).

NO. 16 IN G MINOR

2537.   Praeludium und Fuge in G-moll, Nr. 16 aus dem zweiten Teil des Wohltemperierten Klaviers. ... [Berlin, Max Hesse, 1905.]   6 pp., 27 cm.
    This is the Notenbeilage for *Die Musik*, Vol. V, No. 1 (Oct., 1905).

TITLES

INDEX TO CANTATAS:

Ach Gott, Vom Himmel sieh darein (No. 2), 581–85

Ach Gott, wie manches Herzeleid (No. 3), 586–91

Ach Gott, wie manches Herzeleid (No. 58), 532, 889

Ach Herr, mich armen Sünder (No. 135), 1200–1205

Ach, ich sehe, itzt, da ich zur Hochzeit gehe (No. 162), 1291

Ach, lieben Christen, seid getrost (No. 114), 959, 1128–30

Ach wie flüchtig, ach wie nichtig (No. 26), 725–31

Actus Tragicus (No. 106), 1090–1104: *see* Gottes Zeit ist die allerbeste Zeit

Allein zu dir, Herr Jesu Christ (No. 33), 765–67

Alles nur nach Gottes Willen (No. 72), 951–55

Alles, was von Gott geboren (No. 80a)

Also hat Gott die Welt geliebt (No. 68), 932–36

Am Abend aber desselbigen Sabbats (No. 42), 813–20

Amore traditore (No. 203), 1389

Angenehmes Wiederau (No. 30a)

Ärgre dich, o Seele, nicht (No. 186), 1344–45

Auf Christi Himmelfahrt allein (No. 128), 1180–82

Auf, mein Herz, des Herren Tag (No. 145), 1241–42

Auf, schmetternde Töne der muntern Trompeten (No. 207), 1395–99, 1413

Aus der Tiefe rufe ich, Herr, zu dir (No. 131), 1189–93

Aus tiefer Not schrei' ich zu dir (No. 38), 790–95

Barmherziges Herze der ewigen Liebe (No. 185), 1343

Bekennen will ich seinen Namen (No. 200)

Bereitet die Wege, bereitet die Bahn (No. 132), 1194

Bisher habt ihr nichts gebeten in meinem Namen (No. 87), 1015

Blast Lärmen, ihr Feinde (No. 205a)

Bleib' bei uns, denn es will Abend werden (No. 6), 604–12

Brich dem Hungrigen dein Brot (No. 39), 796–802

Bringt dem Herrn Ehre seines Namens (No. 148), 1259–60

Christen, ätzet diesen Tag (No. 63), 902–7

Christ lag in Todesbanden (No. 4), 592–600

Christ unser Herr zum Jordan kam (No. 7), 613–16

Christus, der ist mein Leben (No. 95), 1036–40
Christus wir sollen loben schon (No. 121), 1157–60

Das ist je gewisslich wahr (No. 141), 1229–30
Das neugebor'ne Kindelein (No. 122), 1161–65
Dazu ist erschienen der Sohn Gottes (No. 40), 534, 803–6, 812
Dem Gerechten muss das Licht (No. 195), 1364–67
Denn du wirst meine Seele nicht in der Hölle lassen (No. 15), 660–61
Der Friede sei mit dir (No. 158), 1279
Der Herr denket an uns (No. 196), 535, 1369–72
Der Herr ist mein getreuer Hirt (No. 112), 1120–25
Der Himmel lacht, die Erde jubilieret (No. 31), 756–761
Der Streit zwischen Phoebus und Pan (No. 201): see Geschwinde, geschwinde, ihr wirbelnde Winde
Der zufriedengestellte Aeolus (No. 205): see Zerreisset, zersprenget, zertrümmert die Gruft
Die Elenden sollen essen (No. 75), 962–66
Die Freude reget sich (No. 36b)
Die Himmel erzählen die Ehre Gottes (No. 76), 967–70
Die Zeit, die Tag und Jahr macht (No. 134a)
Du Friedefürst, Herr Jesu Christ (No. 116), 1137–39
Du Hirte Israel, höre (No. 104), 1071–79
Durchlaucht'ster Leopold (No. 173a)
Du sollst Gott, deinen Herren, lieben (No. 77), 971–73

Du wahrer Gott und Davids Sohn (No. 23), 707–14

Ehre sei Gott in der Höhe (No. 197a)
Ein' feste Burg ist unser Gott (No. 80), 988–1000
Ein Herz, das seinen Jesum lebend weiss (No. 134), 1198–99
Ein ungefärbt Gemüte (No. 24), 715–18
Erforsche mich, Gott, und erfahre mein Herz (No. 136), 1206–7
Erfreut euch, ihr Herzen (No. 66), 924–26
Erfreute Zeit im neuen Bunde (No. 83), 1009
Erhalt' uns, Herr, bei deinen Wort (No. 126), 1176–77
Erhöhtes Fleisch und Blut (No. 173), 1309–10
Er rufet seinen Schafen mit Namen (No. 175), 1312
Erschallet, ihr Lieder (No. 172), 1306–8
Erwählte Pleissenstadt (No. 216a)
Erwünschtes Freudenlicht (No. 184), 1341–42
Es erhub sich ein Streit (No. 19), 679–85
Es ist das Heil uns kommen her (No. 9), 625–28
Es ist dir gesagt, Mensch, was gut ist (No. 45), 826–32
Es ist ein trotzig und verzagt Ding (No. 176), 1313–15
Es ist euch gut, dass ich hingehe (No. 108), 1109–11
Es ist nichts Gesundes an meinem Leibe (No. 25), 719–24
Es reifet euch ein schrecklich Ende (No. 90), 1018
Es wartet alles auf dich (No. 187), 1346–48

Falsche Welt, dir trau' ich nicht (No. 52), 865

Freue dich, erlöste Schar (No. 30), 750-55

Gedenke, Herr, wie es uns gehet (No. 217)

Geist und Seele wird verwirret (No. 35), 778

Gelobet sei der Herr, mein Gott (No. 129), 1183-85

Gelobet seist du, Jesu Christ (No. 91), 1019-21

Geschwinde, geschwinde, ihr wirbelnde Winde (No. 201), 1382-86

Gleich wie der Regen und Schnee vom Himmel fällt (No. 18), 672-78

Gloria in excelsis Deo (No. 191), 1355

Gott, der Herr, ist Sonn' und Schild (No. 79), 981-87

Gott der Hoffnung erfülle euch (No. 218)

Gottes Zeit ist die allerbeste Zeit (No. 106), 1090-1104

Gott ist mein König (No. 71), 946-50

Gott ist unsre Zuversicht (No. 197), 1373-75

Gottlob, nun geht das Jahr zu Ende (No. 28), 739-45

Gott, man lobet dich in der Stille (No. 120), 1154-56

Gott, wie dein Name, so ist auch dein Ruhm (No. 171), 1303-5

Halt' im Gedächtnis Jesum Christ (No. 67), 927-31

Hercules auf dem Scheidewege (No. 213): see Lasst uns sorgen, lasst uns wachen

Herr Christ, der ein'ge Gottes-Sohn (No. 96), 1041-43

Herr, deine Augen sehen nach dem Glauben (No. 102), 1061-66

Herr, gehe nicht ins Gericht (No. 105), 1080-89

Herr Gott, Beherrscher aller Dinge (No. 120a)

Herr Gott, dich loben alle wir (No. 130), 1186-88

Herr Gott, dich loben wir (No. 16); 662-65

Herr Jesu Christ, du höchstes Gut (No. 113), 1126-27

Herr Jesu Christ, wahr'r Mensch und Gott (No. 127), 1178-79

Herr, wie du willt, so schick's mit mir (No. 73), 956-59

Herz und Mund und Tat und Leben (No. 147), 1246-58

Himmelskönig, sei willkommen (No. 182), 1332-39

Höchsterwünschtes Freudenfest (No. 194), 1362-63

Ich armer Mensch, ich Sündenknecht (No. 55), 875-77

Ich bin ein guter Hirt (No. 85), 1011-13

Ich bin in mir vergnugt (No. 204), 1390

Ich bin vergnügt mit meinem Glücke (No. 84), 1010

Ich elender Mensch, wer wird mich erlösen (No. 48), 843-46

Ich freue mich in dir (No. 133), 1195-97

Ich geh' und suche mit Verlangen (No. 49), 847

Ich glaube, lieber Herr, hilf meinem Unglauben (No. 109), 1112-14

Ich habe genug (No. 82), 1005-8

Ich habe meine Zuversicht (No. 188), 1349-50

Ich hab in Gottes Herz und Sinn (No. 92), 1022-24

Ich hatte viel Bekümmernis (No. 21), 689–701

Ich lasse dich nicht, du segnest mich denn (No. 157), 1278

Ich liebe den Höchsten von ganzem Gemüte (No. 174), 1311

Ich ruf' zu dir, Herr Jesu Christ (No. 177), 1316–17

Ich steh' mit einem Fuss im Grabe (No. 156), 1277

Ich weiss, dass mein Erlöser lebt (No. 160), 1283

Ich will den Kreuzstab gerne tragen (No. 56), 878–85

Ihr, die ihr euch von Christo nennet (No. 164), 1293

Ihr Menschen, rühmet Gottes Liebe (No. 167), 1298–99

Ihr Tore (Pforten) zu Zion (No. 193), 1360–61

Ihr werdet weinen und heulen (No. 103), 1067–70

In allen meinen Taten (No. 97), 1044–47

Jauchzet Gott in allen Landen (No. 51), 861–64

Jesu, der du meine Seele (No. 78), 974–80

Jesu, nun sei gepreiset (No. 41), 807–12

Jesus nahm zu sich die Zwölf (No. 22), 702–6

Jesus schläft, was soll ich hoffen (No. 81), 1001–4

Komm, du süsse Todesstunde (No. 161), 1284–90

Lass, Fürstin, lass noch einen Strahl (No. 198), 1376–81

Lasst uns sorgen, lasst uns wachen (No. 213), 1425

Leichtgesinnte Flattergeister (No. 181), 1330–31

Liebster Gott, wann werd' ich sterben (No. 8), 617–24

Liebster Immanuel, Herzog der Frommen (No. 123), 1166–69

Liebster Jesu, mein Verlangen (No. 32), 762–64

Lobe den Herren, den mächtigen König der Ehren (No. 137), 1208–12

Lobe den Herrn, meine Seele (No. 69), 937–40

Lobe den Herrn, meine Seele (No. 69a)

Lobe den Herrn, meine Seele (No. 143), 1235–37

Lobet Gott in seinen Reichen (No. 11), 636–46

Lobt ihn mit Herz und Munde (No. 220)

Manche dich, mein Geist, bereit (No. 115), 1131–36

Man singet mit Freuden vom Sieg (No. 149), 1261–63

Meinem Jesum lass' ich nicht (No. 124), 1170–71

Meine Seel' erhebt den Herren (No. 10), 629–35

Meine Seele rühmt und preist (No. 189), 1351

Meine Seele soll Gott loben (No. 223)

Meine Seufzer, meine Tränen (No. 13), 654

Mein Herze schwimmt in Blut (No. 199)

Mein Gott, wie lang', ach lange (No. 155), 1275–76

Mein Odem ist schwach (No. 222)

Mer hahn en neue Oberkeet (No. 212), 1416–22

Mit Fried' und Freud' ich fahr' dahin (No. 125), 1172–75

Nach dir, Herr, verlanget mich (No. 150), 1264–67

Nimm von uns, Herr, du treuer Gott (No. 101), 1056–60
Nimm, was dein ist, und gehe hin (No. 144), 1238–40
Non sa che sia dolore (No. 209), 1404
Nun danket alle Gott (No. 192), 1356–58
Nun ist das Heil und die Kraft (No. 50), 848–61
Nun komm, der Heiden Heiland (No. 61), 895–99
Nun komm, der Heiden Heiland (No. 62), 900–901
Nur jedem das Seine (No. 163), 1292

O angenehme Melodei (No. 210a)
O ewiges Feuer, O Ursprung der Liebe (No. 34), 768–77
O ewiges Feuer, o Ursprung der Liebe (No. 34a)
O Ewigkeit, du Donnerwort (No. 20), 686–88
O Ewigkeit, du Donnerwort (No. 60), 891–94
O heil'ges Geist- und Wasserbad (No. 165), 1294
O holder Tag, erwünschte Zeit (No. 210), 1405
O Jesu Christ, mein's Lebens Licht (No. 118), 1143–48

Preise dein Glücke, gesegnetes Sachsen (No. 215)
Preise, Jerusalem, den Herrn (No. 119), 1149–53

Schauet doch und sehet, ob irgend ein Schmerz sei (No. 46), 833–37
Schau, lieber Gott, wie meine Feind (No. 153), 1272–74
Schlage doch, gewünschte Stunde (No. 35), 866–71

Schleicht, spielende Wellen (No. 206), 1393
Schmücke dich, o liebe Seele (No. 180), 1322–29
Schweigt stille, plaudert nicht (No. 211), 1406–15
Schwingt freudig euch empor (No. 36), 779–783
Schwingt freudig euch empor (No. 36c)
Sehet, welch eine Liebe hat uns der Vater erzeiget (No. 64), 908–13
Sehet, wer geh'n hinauf gen Jerusalem (No. 159), 1280–82
Sei Lob und Ehr' dem höchsten Gut (No. 117), 1140–42
Selig ist der Mann (No. 57), 886–88
Siehe, es hat überwunden der Löwe (No. 219)
Siehe, ich will viel Fischer aussenden, spricht der Herr (No. 88), 1016
Siehe zu, dass deine Gottesfrucht nicht Heuchelei sei (No. 179), 1320–21
Sie werden aus Saba alle kommen (No. 65), 914–23
Sie werden euch in den Bann tun (No. 44), 821–25
Sie werden euch in den Bann tun (No. 183), 1340
Singet dem Herrn ein neues Lied (No. 190), 1352–54
Steigt freudig in die Luft (No. 36a)
Süsser Trost, mein Jesus kommt (No. 151), 1268
Tönet, ihr Pauken! Erschallet, Trompeten (No. 214)
Tritt auf die Glaubensbahn (No. 152), 1269–71
Tue Rechnung! Donnerwort (No. 168), 1300–1302

Unser Mund sei voll Lachens (No. 110), 115–17

Uns ist ein Kind geboren (No. 142), 1231–34

Vereinigte Zwietracht der wechselden Saiten (No. 207)

Vergnügte Pleissen-Stadt (No. 216), 1426

Wachet auf, ruft uns die Stimme (No. 140), 1218–28

Wachet, betet, seid bereit allezeit (No. 70), 941–45

Wahrlich, wahrlich, ich sage euch (No. 86), 1014

Wär Gott nicht mit uns diese Zeit (No. 14), 655–59

Warum betrübst du dich, mein Herz (No. 138), 1213–15

Was frag ich nach der Welt (No. 94), 1032–35

Was Gott tut, das ist wohlgetan (No. 98), 1048–50

Was Gott tut, das ist wohlgetan (No. 99), 1051–52

Was Gott tut, das ist wohlgetan (No. 100), 1053–55

Was mein Gott will, das g'scheh' allzeit (No. 111), 1118–19

Was mir behagt, ist nur die muntre Jagd (No. 208), 1400–1403

Was mir behagt, ist nur die muntre Jagd (No. 208a)

Was soll ich aus dir machen, Ephraim (No. 89), 1017

Was willst du dich betrüben (No. 107), 1105–8

Weichet nur, betrübte Schatten (No. 202), 1387–88

Weinen, Klagen, Sorgen, Zagen (No. 12), 647–53

Wer da glaubet und getauft wird (No. 37), 784–89

Wer Dank opfert, der preiset mich (No. 17), 666–671, 745

Wer mich liebet, der wird mein Wort halten (No. 59), 890

Wer mich liebet, der wird mein Wort halten (No. 74), 960–61

Wer nur den lieben Gott lässt walten (No. 93), 1025–31

Wer sich selbst erhöhet, er soll erniedriget werden (No. 47), 838–42

Wer sucht die Pracht, wer wünscht den Glanz (No. 221)

Wer weiss, wie nahe mir mein Ende (No. 27), 732–38

Widerstehe doch der Sünde (No. 54), 872–74

Wie schön leuchtet der Morgenstern (No. 1), 574–80

Wir danken dir Gott, wir danken dir (No. 29), 746–49

Wir müssen durch viel Trübsal in das Reich Gottes eingehen (No. 146), 1243–45

Wo gehest du hin (No. 166), 1295–96

Wo Gott, der Herr, nicht bei uns hält (No. 178), 959, 1318–19

Wohl dem, der sich auf seinen Gott (No. 139), 1216–17

Wo soll ich fliehen hin (No. 5), 601–3

Zerreisset, zersprenget, zertrümmert die Gruft (No. 205), 1391–92, 1413

GENERAL INDEX

Included in this index are editors, transcribers, and arrangers of music, composers, and common nicknames of larger works. Authors are included only if they have edited music in the catalog or if they do not receive separate listing in the section "Music Literature." Individual titles of chorales and songs, and most works listed in the Table of Contents have not been included. Also not included are translators of texts and of explanatory material, authors of texts, owners of music, and those merely responsible for fingering, bowing, and so forth. For cantata titles, see Index to Cantatas.

All references are to entry numbers in the catalog.

Aber, Adolf, as author, 489
Abert, Hermann, as editor, 2386
Achtzehn Choräle, 1498
Actus Tragicus (Cantata No. 106), 1090–1104
Albert, Eugène F. C. d', as editor, 1730, 2387
Alexanian, Diran, as editor, 2345
Alla Breve Fugue (Prelude and Fugue in D Major), 2097
Allen, Hugh P., as editor, 718, 1257, 1889
Altmann, Wilhelm, as author, 203; as editor, 2319, 2324, 2329, 2332
Angel, Clark B., as editor, 1506
Ansbacher, Luigi, as author, 402
Appel, Richard G., as editor, 1255, 1256
Archer, Frederic, as editor, 1692, 1695, 2088, 2094, 2099, 2100, 2102
Árpád, Szendy, as editor, 1760, 1791, 2055, 2070
Art of the Fugue, The (Die Kunst der Fuge), 1809–21
Ascension Oratorio (Cantata No. 11), 636–46
Atkins, Ivor A., editor of: cantatas, 789, 896, 986, 1003, 1135, 1368; chorale preludes, 1489; passions, 1981, 2010–11
Auer, Leopold, as editor, 2142

Bach, Anna Magdalena, Notebook for, No. 2 (1725), 1912–22, 2073, 2185, 2186, 2189, 2200, 2201
Bach, Carl Philipp Emanuel, as author, 9–11; biography of, by Carl Bitter, 33; as composer, 524–25; as editor, 1439, 1457
Bach, Johann Christian, biography of, by Carl Bitter, 33
Bach, Johann Christoph, as composer, 526–30

Bach, Johann Christoph Friedrich, biography of, by Carl Bitter, 33
Bach, Johann Jacob, 1427–31
Bach, Johann Ludwig, as composer, 531
Bach, Wilhelm Friedemann, biography of, by Carl Bitter, 33; in novel by A. E. Brachvogel, 45; Orgelbüchlein for, 1502–3; Klavierbüchlein for, 1793, 1808; fugues of, 2384
Bagge, Selmar, as editor, 1384, 2023
Baker, Harry E., as editor, 1412, 1419–20
Barge, J. H. Wilhelm, as editor, 2113
Bargiel, Woldemar, as editor, 1451–52
Barlow, J. Herbert, as editor, 1433
Barnes, Edward S., as editor, 1693, 2201
Bartók, Béla, as editor, 1913, 2388
Batka, Richard, as author, 26; as editor, 1912
Bauer, Harold, as editor, 1615, 1630, 2293
Becker, Albert, as editor, 990
Becker, C. F., as editor, 1439, 1440, 1450, 2190
Becker, Gustave L., as editor, 1748–50
Becker, Hugo, as editor, 2340
Beltz, Hans, as editor, 1598, 1602
Bennett, W. Sterndale, as editor, 1998, 2013, 2389
Berner, as editor, 1619
Bertini, Henri J., as editor, 2390–91
Besch, Hans, as author, 204
Best, William T., as editor, 2093, 2377, 2392
Beutter, A., as author, 63
Biehr, Oscar, as editor, 2132
Birthday Cantata (Cantata No. 208), 1400–1404

Bischoff, Hans, editor of: clavier works, 1532, 1681; clavier duets, 1669; inventions, 1704; Italian Concerto, 1803–4; preludes and fugues, 2062; suites, 2224, 2244, 2286; toccatas, 2375; Well-tempered Clavier, 2393
Bischoff, Heinz, as transcriber, 1797
Bishop, John, as editor, 2408
Bitter, Carl H., as author, 33–36, 189; as editor, 2200
Blankenburg, Walter, as author, 204
Boekelman, Bernardus, as editor, 1751–52, 1794–95, 2491–92
Bondeville, Emmanuel, as author, 65
Bonucci, Arturo, as editor, 1910
Boyd, Charles N., as editor, 1438
Brady, Edwin, as author, 192
Brahms, Johannes, 2493
Braun, Guillaume, as transcriber, 2500, 2534
Bret, Gustav, as author, 65
Bridge, John F., as editor, 1958
Brissler, Friedrich F., as editor, 1932, 1978
Brixel, Franz, as editor, 1766
Brooke, Harold, as editor, 2394
Bruyck, Carl D. van, as author, 49; as transcriber, 2480
Bülow, Hans G. von, as editor, 1552, 1774, 2233
Buonamici, Guiseppe, as editor, 1701, 1761
Burmeister, Richard, as editor, 1514
Busch, Adolf, as editor, 2147
Busoni, Ferruccio B., editor of: clavier works, 1526–27; concerto, 1592; inventions, 1740, 1743, 1762, 1771, 1767; Well-tempered Clavier, 2395–96
Buszin, Walter E., as author, 192; editor of: chorales, 1432, 1442, 1481; chorale preludes, 1492,

1509; organ works, 2033; songs, 2193

Button, H. Elliot, as editor, 1437

Canby, Edward T., as arranger, 2199

Canonische Veränderungen über "Vom Himmel hoch," 1512–13

Capriccio on the departure of his beloved brother (Capriccio sopra la lontananza del suo fratello dilettissimo), 1427–31

Cary, Tristram, as editor, 1911

Casadesus, Francis, as editor, 852

Casella, Alfredo, as editor, 1910

Catechism Chorales, Catechism Preludes, 1499–1501

Cathedral Fugue (Prelude and Fugue in E Minor), 2100–2001

Cellier, Allexandre, as author, 65

Cesi, Beniamino, as editor, 1536

Chapuis, Auguste, as editor, 1382

Chase, The (Cantata No. 208), 1400–1403

Christmas Oratorio (Weihnachts-Oratorium), 1925–46

Chromatic Fantasy and Fugue in D minor (Chromatische Fantasie und Fuge D-Moll), 1514–25, 1548, 1550–52

Chrysander, K. F. Friedrich, as editor, 1537

Clark, F. Scotson, as editor, 2082

Clavierbüchlein (Klavierbüchlein für Wilhelm Friedemann Bach), 1793, 1808

Clavier-Übung: Part I of (6 Partitas), 2274–2311; Part II of (French Overture and Italian Concerto), 1548, 1550–52, 1554, 1798–1807, 2312–13; Part III of (Catechism Chorales and 4 Duets), 1499–1501, 1669–73; Part IV of (Goldberg Variations), 547–54

Clough-Leighter, H., editor of: cantatas, 591, 624, 635, 713, 777, 1089, 1204, 1290, 1329, 1338; passion, 2031; Well-tempered Clavier, 2506

Coffee Cantata (Cantate No. 211), 1406–15

Concerto, Italian, 1548, 1550–52, 1554, 1798–1807

Corelli Fugue (Fugue in B Minor), 1688

Cramer, J. G., as composer, 522–23

Czerny, Carl, editor of: clavier works, 1535, 1540–43, 1685; inventions, 1719, 1722, 1724; Musical Offering, 1903; suites, 2205, 2245–46, 2275–76, 2281; Well-tempered Clavier, 2397–2408

Dallier, Henri, as editor, 1523, 1801, 2213, 2253, 2282, 2409

Damm, Gustav: see Steingräber, Theodor

Damrosch, Frank, editor of: cantatas, 1098, 1378; chorales, 1472; mass, 1858; motet, 1891

Darrah, Basil, as editor, 1772

David, Ferdinand, editor of: concerto, 1648; fugue, 1698; Musical Offering, 1908; sonatas, 2112, 2114, 2134–36, 2163, 2178, 2181, 2182; suites, 2328, 2330, 2333, 2356

David, Hans T., as editor, 73, 1815, 1904, 2312; as author, 74

David, Karl H., as editor, 1507

Davis, Katherine K., as editor, 1402

Dehn, Siegfried W., as author, 75; editor of: cantatas, 1408, 1416; Brandenburg Concerti, 1561, 1566, 1572, 1578, 1581, 1587; other concerti, 1588, 1595, 1599,

286   GENERAL INDEX

Dehn, Siegfried, W.,   *(Continued)*
    1600, 1603, 1609, 1611, 1633,
    1639, 1649, 1659; suites, 2317,
    2321, 2326
Deis, Carl, as editor, 1893
Diack, J. Michael, editor of: arias,
    570; cantatas, 789, 1368, 1412;
    chorales, 1471; passion, 1987
D'Indy, P. M. T.;Vincent: *see* Indy,
    P. M. T. Vincent d'
Dohnányi,Ernstvon,aseditor,2052
Dörffel, Alfred, as editor, 84, 1440
Dorian Fugue (Prelude and Fugue
    in D Minor), 2098
Dotzauer, Justus J. F., as editor,
    2335
Dragonetti, Domenico, as arranger,
    2077–78
Dresel, Otto, as editor, 2413–14
Drinker, Henry S., as author 85–
    87; editor of: choral works, 528;
    cantatas, 585, 599, 600, 612, 634,
    645, 646, 659, 661, 665, 684, 700,
    712, 724, 738, 767, 776, 783, 788,
    794, 801, 811, 832, 842, 846, 860,
    907, 913, 923, 935, 940, 945, 949,
    959, 980, 987, 998, 1031, 1047,
    1057, 1060, 1066, 1077, 1088,
    1102, 1124, 1125, 1136, 1148,
    1160, 1164, 1169, 1174, 1182,
    1188, 1193, 1205, 1211, 1215,
    1225, 1237, 1249, 1267, 1328,
    1336, 1348, 1359, 1397, 1423–24;
    chorales, 1444, 1468, 1477–78,
    1482, 1485; duets, 1676, 1677;
    mass, 1866; motets, 1885, 1890,
    1892, 1900; oratorio, 1939;
    passions, 1984, 2024
Dubois, François C. T., as author,
    88; as editor, 2410
Dunham, Henry M., as editor, 2087
Dupré, Marcel, as author, 91; as
    editor, 1954
Dürr, Alfred, as author, 92; as
    editor, 781

Easter Oratorio (Oster-Oratorium),
    560, 563, 1923–24
Ebner, Joseph, as author, 204; as
    transcriber, 2347
Eckhardt, William, as editor, 1963
Eichler, Karl, as arranger, 1557,
    2481
Eickemeyer, Willy, as editor, 1593
Eighteen Little Preludes for Clavier,
    2047–56
Eijken, J. A., as transcriber, 2535
Eldering, Bram, as editor, 2138
Elgar, Edward, as editor, 2011
Elsmith, Berta, as editor, 1469–70
Emmanuel, Maurice, as editor,
    1548, 2214, 2254, 2283
Engel, Carl, as author, 100; as
    arranger, 2201
English Suites, 536, 537, 539,
    2202–41
Erk, Ludwig, as editor, 1453–55
Espagne, Franz, as editor, 524–25
Ettler, Carl, as editor, 882
Evans, Frederic S., as editor, 1728

Faelten, Carl, as editor, 1734, 1735
Fantasia and Fugue in C Minor,
    1551
Fantasia in C minor, 1550, 1552,
    1679–81
Fantasies and Fugues (Preludes
    and Fugues), 2075–2109
Farlane, George, as editor, 1800
Farmer, Charles V., as author, 192
Farmer, John, as editor, 1538, 1784
Fauré, Gabriel U., as editor, 1956,
    2411
Ferchault, Guy, as author, 204
Fischer, Edwin, editor of: Chro-
    matic Fantasy and Fugue, 1517;
    concerto, 1605; fantasy, 1679;
    inventions, 1765, 1775; Italian
    Concerto, 1805; preludes, 2056;
    English Suites, 2219, 2221, 2225,
    2232, 2237, 2239; French Suites,

2258, 2260, 2262, 2264, 2266, 2271
Fischer, Kurt von, as author, 204
Fischer, Wilhelm, as editor, 848, 866, 881, 1091, 1406, 1517
Fleischer, Heinrich, as author, 192
Flesch, Karl, as editor, 2150
Foote, Arthur W., as editor, 1742
Forkel, Johann N., as author, 117–23, 368; as editor, 1516, 2412, 2471, 2472, 2473
Four Duets, 1669–73
Fox, Otto, as editor, 1727
Franz, Robert, as author 128–131; editor of: arias, 564 68; cantatas, 639, 689, 695, 699, 725, 730, 732, 752, 755, 768, 771, 775, 785, 818, 819, 826, 830, 839, 914, 921, 1090, 1101; Magnificat, 1824, 1830, 1831; oratorio, 1927; passions, 1989, 2016–18; songs, 2194–96; Well-tempered Clavier, 2413–14
French Overture, 1806, 2312–13
French Suites, 1538, 2242–73
Frey, Martin, as editor, 1732
Friedman, Ignaz, as editor, 1702
Fuga alla Giga (Prelude and Fugue in G Major), 2106
Fughetta in C Minor for Clavier, 1673

Gaillard, Frits, as editor, 2344
Gál, Hans, as editor, 1571
Gallon, Noël, as editor, 1710, 1917, 2065
Garban, L., as editor, 1920
Garcin, Jules A., as editor, 2144
Geehl, Henry E., as editor, 1764, 1792
Geer, E. Harold, as editor, 1079
Geiringer, Karl, as author, 137–38; as editor, 527, 530, 1577, 1582
Geistliche Lieder (Sacred Songs), 2183–99

Gerber, Heinrich N., 542
German Suites, 2274–2315
Germer, Heinrich, as editor, 555, 1429, 1774, 2035, 2043, 2047, 2415
Gevaert, François A., as editor, 2006
Giant Fugue, The (Fugue in D Minor), 1692–93
Glynn, Franklin, as editor, 1495
Goetschius, Percy, as editor, 1463, 2416
Goldberg Variations (Aria mit 30 Veränderungen), 547–54
Goldenweiser, Alexander B., as editor, 2287
Goldschmidt, Otto, as editor, 857
Goldsworthy, William A., as editor, 1246
Gounod, Charles F., as arranger, 2504, 2506
Grace, Harvey, as author, 146–47; as transcriber, 573, 653, 678, 701, 966, 1104, 1253, 1399, 1403
Graeser, Wolfgang, as editor, 1819
Great Fugue, The (Prelude and Fugue in G Minor), 2108
Griepenkerl, Friedrich K., editor of: chorale preludes, 1487–88; clavier works, 1535, 1541–43, 1544–45; concerti, 1612–13, 1617, 1621, 1624, 1626, 1628, 1637; clavier duets, 1671; inventions, 1724; Musical Offering, 1903; organ works, 1948–52; preludes, 2057; preludes and fugues, 2071; sonata, 2120; suites, 2204, 2281; toccatas, 2376
Grümmer, Paul, as editor, 2338
Grützmacher, Friedrich W. L., as editor, 2130, 2339, 2343
Guilmant, Félix A., editor of: cantatas, 597, 619, 638, 677, 694, 754, 774, 906, 955, 1083; oratorio, 1933; passion, 1982

288 GENERAL INDEX

Hallé, Charles, as editor, 2417
Hambourg, Jan H., as editor, 2146
Hänlein, A., as editor, 2079
Harcourt, Eugène d', as editor, 2418
Harris, Roy E., as transcriber, 1817
Hasler, Hans Leo, 1479
Haupt, Carl A., as editor, 2419–20
Heartz, H. L., as editor, 1723
Hellmesberger, Joseph, as editor, 1648, 1698, 1903, 2112, 2143, 2178, 2182, 2333
Hellwig, K. F. Ludwig, as editor, 1975, 2025, 2028
Henkel, Heinrich, as editor, 1755
Hermann, Friedrich, editor of: concerto, 1648; fugue, 1698; Musical Offering, 1908; sonatas, 2112, 2114, 2118, 2178, 2179, 2182, 2333
Herrmann, Eduard, as editor, 1640, 1651, 1662, 2141
Herzogenberg, Heinrich von, as editor, 669
Higgs, James, as editor, 1713, 1958, 2073
Hinkle, Norwood, as editor, 1226
Homeyer, Paul J. M., as editor, 1963
Honaas, Christopher O., as editor, 1274
Horn, August, as editor, 1978, 2021
Horn, Karl F., as editor, 2450–51
Hubay, Jenö, as editor, 2131
Hughes, Edwin, as editor, 1590, 2169–73, 2175, 2421
Hull, A. Eaglefield, as author, 198; as editor, 1957
Humiston, William H., as author, 199, 200; as editor, 1394
Humperdinck, Engelbert, as transcriber, 2483
Husmann, Heinrich, as author, 204

Indy, P. M. T. Vincent d', editor of: capriccio, 1431; Chromatic Fantasy and Fugue, 1525; clavier works, 1686; inventions, 1754, 1785; Italian Concerto, 1807; minuets, 1875; A. Bach's Notebook, 1921; suites, 2268, 2272, 2292, 2297, 2302, 2305, 2308, 2311, 2315, 2316; toccatas, 2360, 2368, 2371, 2378; Well-tempered Clavier, 2422–23, 2505, 2508, 2509, 2511, 2513–17, 1519–28, 2530–33
Inventions, 1538, 1539, 1699–1797, 2299
Irwin, Charles D., as editor, 1696
Italian Concerto, 1548, 1550–52, 1554, 1798–1807

Jackson, Bernard, as arranger, 2198
Jacob, Gordon, as editor, 1558, 1568, 1574
Jadassohn, Salomon, as author, 205–7; editor of: Magnificat, 1828; masses, 1846, 1865, 1869, 1871, 1874; oratorios, 1926, 1937–38; passions, 1983, 1991, 1995, 2005, 2019, 2022; Sanctus, 2109
Jeral, Wilhelm, as editor, 2337
Joachim, Joseph, as editor, 1643, 1666
Johnson, Thomas A., as editor, 1562, 1573
Jones, Ifor, editor of: cantatas, 642, 673, 683, 692, 710, 977, 1028, 1064, 1147, 1203, 1245, 1322, 1349, 1357; oratorio, 1940
Junk, Victor, 529

Katwijk, Paul van, as arranger, 2160
Keldorfer, Viktor, as editor, 1977
Kelk, A. Hastings, as editor, 1987

Keller, Hermann, as author, 215–17; as editor, 1502, 2383
Keller, Oswin, as editor, 1700, 2247, 2424
Kemp, Stephen, as editor, 858
Kinsky, Georg, as author, 219, 220; as editor, 2092
Kirkpatrick, Ralph, as editor, 551, 1515, 1706
Klengel, Julius, as editor, 2128, 2350, 2353, 2355, 2358, 2360, 2362
Klengel, Paul, as editor, 1645, 1656, 1658
Klindworth, Karl, as editor, 1712, 1802, 2050, 2203, 2425
Knab, Armin, as editor, 2536
Koch, Caspar P., as transcriber, 1736, 2085
Koemmenich, Louis, as editor, 2015
Köhler, C. Louis H., as editor, 1539, 1549, 2426, 2490
Körner, Gotthilf W., as editor, 1494, 2105, 2382
Kortschak, Hugo, as editor, 2169–73, 2175
Kretzmann, O. P., as author 192
Kretzschmar, A. F. Hermann, as editor, 78, 250, 306, 395–96, 1567, 1844, 1856–57, 1861; as author, 179, 211, 233–40, 491
Kroll, Franz, editor of: inventions, 1739, 1767; English Suites, 2223, 2229, 2235, 2236; partitas, 2294, 2295, 2298, 2299; toccata, 2369; Well-tempered Clavier, 2427–29
Krone, Max T., as editor, 1228, 1339, 1837, 1841–42
Kühmstedt, Friedrich, as editor, 2105, 2382
Kuhnau, Johann, 1430
Kurth, Ernst, as author, 242; as editor, 2139

Lachner, Vincenz, as arranger, 2200
Lack, Théodore, as editor, 1709, 1915, 2064
Landshoff, Ludwig, as author, 246, editor of: concerti, 1560, 1564, 1570, 1576, 1580, 1586; inventions, 1699, 1703; sonatas, 2177, 2180; songs, 2185
Lange, Samuel de, as editor, 1968
Langley, Alfred G., as editor, 775, 828
Le Couppey, Félix, as editor, 2499
Le Maître, Paul, as editor, 2151
Léonard, Hubert, as editor, 2145
Lessmann, Otto, as editor, 2045
Ley, Henry G., as transcriber, 1943
Leyden, Rolf van, as editor, 2129
Lillebridge, Frederic, as editor, 1720, 2230
Lindquist, Orville A., as editor, 2502
Liszt, Franz, as transcriber, 2083
Little Fugue in G Minor (Fugue in G Minor), 1694–98
Long, Marguerite, as editor, 2411
Longo, Alessandro, as editor, 1747, 1780, 2046, 2074, 2216–17, 2256, 2430
Lott, Edwin M., as editor, 2431
Lotti, Antonio, as composer, 531
Lubrich, Fritz, as editor, 370, 1434

MacPherson, Stewart, as author, 269–70; as editor, 1741, 1777, 2049
Mandyczewski, Eusebius, as editor, 1565, 1577, 1582
Marcello, Benedetto, as composer, 1529
Marpurg, Friedrich W., 1814
Marteau, Henri, as editor, 1642, 1653, 2149
Marx, Adolph B., as author, 272–73; editor of: cantatas, 572,

Marx, Adolph B., *(Continued)* 1056, 1061, 1067, 1071, 1078, 1080, 1094; mass, 1855; passions, 1998–99, 2008; Pastorale, 2034; preludes and fugues, 2076

Mason, William, as editor, 1726, 2072

Matthaei, Karl, as author, 204

Mendel, Arthur, as editor, 73

Mendelssohn-Bartholdy, J. L. Felix, as conductor, 110; as editor, 1490, 1491, 1493, 1511, 2328

Meyer, Joseph, as editor, 2207

Meyer, Waldemar, as editor, 1664

Mondesir, Elisabeth de, as author, 65

Moser, Andreas, as editor, 1646, 1657, 1667, 2115, 2148, 2164

Moreau, Raoul, as editor, 2007

Morgan, Robert O., as editor, 2432

Mottl, Felix, as arranger, 1385, 1417

Mozart, Wolfgang A., as arranger, 533, 538, 2384

Mugellini, Bruno, editor of: clavier works, 1527, 1547; inventions, 1716; suites, 2218, 2255, 2284–85; toccatas, 2365; Well-tempered Clavier, 2433

Müller, C. G., as editor, 1906

Müller, Fritz, as arranger, 554

Müller, Gottfried, as arranger, 781

Müller von Asow, E. H., as editor, 2338

Musical Offering, The (Musikalisches Opfer), 1903–11

Nachèz, Tivadar, as transcriber, 2348

Naumann, K. Ernst, editor of: cantatas, 641, 773, 831, 909, 916, 922, 1073; organ works, 1953; sonata, 2127; songs, 2186; suites, 2212, 2248

Naumann, Martin J., as author, 192

Nettl, Paul, as author, 192

Nevin, Gordon B., as editor, 1668

Nicholl, Horace W., as editor, 2012, 2032

Nies-Berger, Édouard, as editor, 1947

Noel-Gallon: *see* Gallon, Noel

Norton, M. D. Herter, as transcriber, 1817

Nowotny, Carl, as editor, 2165

Ochs, Siegfried, as editor, 1072, 1449, 1850, 1994

O'Meara, Eva J., as author, 512

Orem, Preston W., as editor, 1725, 2063

Orgelbüchlein für W. F. Bach, 1502–3

Overture, French, 1806, 2312–13

Overtures for orchestra, 2317–24

Pachulski, Henri, as editor, 2202, 2215

Parlow, Edmund, as editor, 1705

Partitas, 2274–2314

Passacaglia in C Minor (Fugue in C Minor), 1690–91

Pauer, Ernst, as editor, 2434–35

Peasant Cantata, 1416–24

Petri, Egon, as editor, 1527

Petri, Henri, as editor, 1647, 1655, 1663

Pfatteicher, Carl F., as author, 204

Philipp, Isidore, as editor, 1428

Phoebus und Pan (Cantata No. 201), 1382–86

Pittman, J., as editor, 2015

Pointer, John, editor of: cantatas, 741, 871, 920, 930, 1027, 1122, 1138, 1262; motet, 1902

Pölchau, Georg, as editor, 1512, 1822, 1867, 1872, 1905

Pollain, Fernand, as editor, 2346

Poltronieri, Alberto, as editor, 1910

Portnoff, Leo, as editor, 1641, 2166

Potter, P. Cipriani H., as editor, 2436

Preitz, Gerhard, as editor, 1733

Prelude and Fugue in A Minor, 1550, 1552

Preludes, Clavier, 1538, 1539, 1549, 2035–56

Prout, Ebenezer, as author, 346–49; editor of: arias, 556–59; cantata, 1223; clavier works, 1555; inventions, 1721

Ramin, Günther, as author, 204

Raphael, Günther, editor of cantatas, 579, 590, 608, 609, 614, 622, 693, 726, 760, 823, 859, 864, 869, 929, 952, 975, 984, 1037, 1085, 1146, 1189, 1209, 1266, 1268, 1282, 1289

Rauch, J. N., as editor, 2168

Raugel, Félix, as editor, 817

Reay, Samuel, as editor, 1410

Reger, Max, editor of: clavier works, 1531; concerti, 1583, 1618, 1625; inventions, 1737; suites, 2320, 2325; toccata and fugue; 2374

Rehberg, Willy, as editor, 1616, 1623, 1804

Reimann, Heinrich, as author, 357; as editor, 1971

Reinecke, Karl H. C., as editor, 1529, 1530, 1533–34, 1556, 2437

Reinhart, Walther, as author, 204

Richter, Bernhard F., as editor, 1458

Riemann, K. W. J. Hugo, as author, 362–65; editor of: concerti, 1584, 1597, 1606, 1610, 1636; inventions, 1753, 1781–83; Art of the Fugue, 1813; Well-tempered Clavier, 2438

Riemenschneider, Albert, 220, 499, 1228, 1515, 1835, 1952; as author, 366; as editor, 1438,

1467, 1498, 1503, 1505

Risler, Joseph E., as editor, 2439

Ritter, Max, as author, 370; as editor, 1811

Robert, Richard, as arranger, 547

Robinson, Raymond C., as editor, 1473

Roessel, Louis, as arranger, 2174

Rogers, James H., as editor, 2086, 2270

Roitzsch, F. August, editor of: chorale preludes, 1487–88; clavier works, 1535, 1541; concerti, 1588, 1595, 1599, 1600, 1603, 1609, 1611, 1631, 1633; inventions, 1724; Musical Offering, 1903; organ works, 1948–52; preludes, 2057; sonata, 2120; suites, 2281

Rolfe, Walter, as editor, 1770

Röntgen, Julius, as editor, 1528

Rosé, Arnold J., as editor, 2153

Rosenwald, Hans, as author, 192

Rösler, Gustav, editor of: cantatas, 575, 583, 589, 593, 601, 610, 613, 621, 626, 630, 637, 648, 656, 662, 667, 672, 680, 685, 686, 697, 705, 709, 715, 719, 731, 733, 739, 747, 751, 758, 763, 770, 779, 784, 790, 797, 804, 807, 814, 816, 822, 827, 834, 841, 843, 850, 862, 884, 887, 893, 895, 902, 908, 918, 924, 927, 932, 938, 941, 946, 953, 956, 962, 967, 971, 979, 982, 993, 1005, 1012, 1019, 1022, 1026, 1032, 1036, 1041, 1044, 1062, 1069, 1074, 1082, 1095, 1106, 1110, 1112, 1115, 1120, 1131, 1141, 1150, 1190, 1220, 1366, 1369, 1375, 1381; Magnificat, 1829; masses, 1853, 1864, 1868, 1870, 1873; oratorios, 1924, 1934–35; passion, 1976

Roth, Herman, editor of: cantatas, 868, 877, 1128, 1144, 1276, 1281,

Roth, Herman, *(Continued)* 1288, 1305, 1307, 1325; capriccio, 1430; Magnificat, 1826, 1833–35; passion, 1972; songs, 2184, 2189
Rust, Wilhelm, as editor, 616, 802, 1035, 1103, 1380, 1944–45
Ruthardt, Adolf, editor of: clavier works, 1553; concerto, 1591; inventions, 1718; preludes and fugues, 2060; suites, 2210–11, 2250, 2288–89; Well-tempered Clavier, 2440, 2485

Saar, Louis V., as arranger, 1768, 2197
St. Anne's Fugue (Prelude and Fugue in E flat Major), 2103
St. John Passion (Johannespassion), 570, 1969–87
St. Luke Passion (Lukaspassion), 1986–87
St. Matthew Passion (Matthäuspassion), 570, 1988–2032
Sanford, Charles V., as editor, 2004
Saran, August, as editor, 1658
Sauer, Emil von, as editor, 1519, 1922, 2267
Saunders, Gordon, as editor, 1738, 1773, 2257, 2290, 2367, 2441
Sauret, Emile, as editor, 1594, 1644, 1654
Schaab, Robert, as editor, 1840
Schäfer, Wilheim, as author, 143
Schemelli, Georg C., as editor of *Musikalisches Gesangbuch*, 2183, 2184, 2185, 2186, 2191, 2192, 2193, 2194, 2195, 2196
Schenker, Heinrich, as author, 393; as editor, 1518
Schering, Arnold, as author, 394–400; editor of: cantatas, 574, 592, 604, 617, 636, 647, 679, 690, 756, 769, 796, 833, 849,

861, 872, 875, 880, 892, 915, 947, 981, 989, 1001, 1011, 1081, 1092, 1149, 1166, 1219, 1284, 1313, 1332, 1391, 1409; Brandenburg Concerti, 1559, 1563, 1569, 1575, 1579, 1585; other concerti, 1589, 1604, 1614, 1622, 1627, 1629, 1632, 1635; Magnificat, 1825; oratorio, 1925; passion, 1973
Schicht, Johann G., as editor, 1486, 1876
Schmid-Lindner, August, as editor, 1531, 2288
Schmidt, Karl, as author, 63
Schmieder, Wolfgang, as author, 204
Schneider, Max, as editor, 308, 445, 560–63, 1990, 2000
Schnirlin, Ossip, as editor, 1666
Schop, Johann, 1484
Schrade, Leo, as author, 204
Schreck, Gustav, editor of: cantatas, 595, 598, 740, 742, 899, 925; concerti, 1608, 1646, 1657, 1667; sonatas, 2110–11, 2115, 2164
Schreyer, Johannes, as author, 411; as editor, 1964
Schröder, Otto, as editor, 674, 1100, 1232, 1283
Schübler Chorales, 541, 1504–5
Schultze-Biesantz, Clemens, as editor, 2002
Schulz, August, as editor, 2137
Schumann, Georg, as editor, 1426, 1993
Schumann, Robert A., as author, 414; as arranger, 2133, 2145, 2154–59
Schüngeler, Heinz, as editor, 1554, 2442
Schurich, Hans, as transcriber, 1820
Schütz, Johann Jacob, 1141

Schwalm, Robert, as editor, 1664
Schwebsch, Erich, as author, 415; as transcriber, 1819
Schwedler, Maximilian, as editor, 2110–11, 2115
Schweitzer, Albert, as author, 204, 416–22; editor of: fugues, 1693, 1697; organ works, 1947, 1955, 2090, 2097, 2101, 2103, 2108, 2379
Schwenke, Christian F. G., as editor, 2443–44, 2464, 2474, 2477
Scott, Charles K., as editor, 1270, 1286, 1883
Seiffert, Max, editor of: cantatas, 605, 882, 991, 1013, 1016, 1093, 1218; concerto, 1620; mass, 1860; organ works, 1951; passion, 1970; songs, 2192
Selva, Blanche, editor of: capriccio, 1431; chromatic fantasy and fugue, 1524; clavier works, 1686; inventions, 1711, 1754, 1785; Italian Concerto, 1798, 1807; minuets, 1875; A. Bach's Notebook, 1919, 1921; preludes, 2054; suites, 2289, 2292, 2297, 2302, 2305, 2308, 2311, 2315, 2316; toccatas, 2366, 2368, 2371, 2378; Well-tempered Clavier, 2505, 2508, 2509, 2511, 2513–17, 2519–28, 2530–33
Semper, Hans, as editor, 2206, 2245
Shepherd, Arthur, 541
Silber, Sidney, as transcriber, 2381
Siloti, Alexandre, as editor, 1524, 2487–88
Silver, Alfred J., as editor, 1965
Sinclair, G. R., as editor, 1894
Sinfonias (three-part invention), 1699–1737, 1773–97
Six Little Preludes for Clavier, 1538, 2035–40

Smend, Friedrich, as author, 204, 432, 433; as editor, 1453
Smend, Julius, as editor, 287
Söhle, Karl, as author, 143, 434–36
Soldan, Kurt, editor of: Goldberg Variations, 552; Brandenburg Concerti, 1560, 1564, 1570, 1576, 1580, 1586; other concerti, 1596, 1598, 1601, 1602; clavier duets, 1670; Italian Concerto, 1806; suites, 2277, 2313, 2318, 2322, 2327, 2331
Sonatas, Violoncello, 2334–62
Spengel, Julius H., as editor, 1856–57
Spicker, Max, as editor, 1929
Spiro, Friedrich, as editor, 1665
Spiro, Hermann, as editor, 2113
Spitta, Friedrich, as editor, 287; as author, 437
Sporck, Georges, as editor, 1746, 1779, 1916, 2048, 2058, 2445
Stade, F. Wilhelm, as editor, 2334, 2446; as arranger, 2349, 2351, 2354, 2357, 2359, 2361
Staub, Victor, as editor, 1707, 1918, 2447
Steiner, Hugo von, as editor, 1652
Steingräber, Theodor (Gustav Damm), as editor, 2486
Stern, Julius, as editor, 1851, 1978, 2003, 2004, 2009, 2016–18
Stockhausen, Ernst von, as editor, 2493
Stokowski, Leopold A. S., as author, 65
Straube, Karl, as author, 204, 467; editor of: cantata, 1200; inventions, 1737; Magnificat, 1823, 1833–35; organ works, 1962, 2084
Strieter, F. W., as editor, 685
Sturm, A., as editor, 1756, 1786, 2036, 2042, 2044, 2065, 2251

Such, Percy, as editor, 2341
Sundberg, John, as editor, 2188
Surette, Thomas W., as editor, 1462, 1469–70

Tagliapietra, Gino, as editor, 2448
Taubmann, Otto, as editor, 882, 1016, 1376, 1385
Tausig, Carl, as editor, 2380, 2482, 2484–86, 2489
Taylor, Franklin, as editor, 1717, 2051, 2059, 2209–10, 2249
Taylor, Stainton de B., as author, 457; as editor, 1427, 1497, 1510, 2383
Teichmüller, Robert, editor of: concerto, 1607; fantasies, 1681; inventions, 1704; Italian Concerto, 1803; prelude and fugue, 2062; suites, 2224, 2244, 2286; toccata, 2375
Telemann, Georg Philipp, 1529
Terry, Charles S., as editor, 117, 1411, 1447, 2187; as author, 458–69
Thiele, Franz E., as author, 471; as transcriber, 2385
Thomas, Gustav A., as transcriber, 1818
Thompson, John, as editor, 1763
Thorne, Edward H., as editor, 943, 1377, 1930
Three-Part Inventions, 1539, 1699–1737, 1773–97
Toccatas and Fugues (Preludes and Fugues), 2075–2109
Todt, Bernhard, as author, 474; editor of: cantatas, 582, 584, 611, 631, 633, 649, 652, 711, 720, 722, 737, 806, 825, 897, 963, 1002, 1007, 1025, 1084, 1271, 1298, 1327, 1354, 1365, 1422; oratorio, 1923; sonata, 2113
Tovey, Donald F., as author, 94, 495; as editor, 1812, 2449

Treharne, Bryceson, as editor, 1250, 1464, 1476
Twelve Little Preludes for Clavier, 2041–46
Two-Part Inventions, 1538, 1539, 1699–1772

Ulrich, Hugo, as editor, 1836, 1978

Valois, Jean de, as editor, 912
Vaughan Williams, Ralph, as editor, 706
Vené, Ruggero, as arranger, 1769
Vierne, Louis V. J., as editor, 2075
Vincent, Charles, as editor, 2494–97
Vivaldi, Antonio, 1529, 1631–32, 1637
Vockner, Josef, as editor, 1854, 1966, 2001
Vogler [Georg J.?], as editor, 1496
Vogrich, Max, as editor, 1552
Volbach, Fritz, as editor, 1845
Volckmar, Wilhelm V., as editor, 1967
Volkland, Alfred, as editor, 919
Vuataz, Roger, as editor, 1907

Wackernagel, Peter, as editor, 1508
Wagner, Richard, as author, 143
Weber, Carl M. von, 1496
Webster, Mary P., as editor, 1473
Wedding Cantata (Cantata No. 202), 1387–88
Wedge Fugue (Prelude and Fugue in E Minor), 2102
Well-tempered Clavier, The (Das wohltemperierte Klavier): Books 1 and 2, 540, 2386-2537; excerpts, 542, 543, 1526, 1527, 1528, 1531, 1534, 1536, 1537, 1539
Wesley, Samuel, as author, 494; as editor, 2450–51
West, John E., editor of: cantatas, 577, 596, 643, 650, 671, 723,

West, John E., *(Continued)* 734, 791, 799, 903, 1039, 1153, 1326, 1383; motets, 1882, 1887, 1897

Westrup, Jack A., as author, 204

Wetzler, Hermann H., as editor, 1893, 1895

Whittaker, W. Gillies, as author, 457, 497–98; editor of: arias, 569; cantatas, 670, 702, 729, 759, 856, 910, 936, 965, 970, 1050, 1086, 1108, 1159, 1162, 1165, 1195, 1212, 1240, 1252, 1254, 1258, 1296, 1334; chorales, 1435; Magnificat, 1838–39; motet, 1888, oratorio, 1942; passion, 2020; songs, 2183

Widor, Charles M., as author, 335–36, 382, 417, 419, 499; editor of: fugues, 1693, 1697; organ works, 1947, 1955, 2090, 2097, 2101, 2103, 2108, 2379

Wiehmayer, J. Theodor, as editor, 1551, 1731, 2061, 2243, 2452

Wiernsberger, as editor, 2453

Wilhelmj, August, as editor, 1661

Willborg, Wilhelm, as editor, 2454

Williams, Walter, as editor, 580, 795

Williamson, John F., as editor, 1884

Willner, Arthur, as editor, 891, 1091

Wilsing, Daniel F. E., as editor, 1936, 1997

Wolffheim, Werner J.: as editor, 445, 1426; as author, 505

Wolfram, Ernst H., as editor, 1960

Wolfrum, Philipp, as author, 506–8; as editor, 879, 1376

Wood, Henry J., as editor, 1881, 1896, 1898, 1901

Wood-Hill, M., as transcriber, 2503

Wouters, Adolphe F., editor of: Chromatic Fantasy and Fugue, 1521; fantasy, 1680; inventions, 1745, 1778; Italian Concerto, 1799; sonatas, 2220, 2222, 2228, 2234, 2238, 2241, 2314; Well-tempered Clavier, 2455

Zahn, Johannes G., as editor, 514; as transcriber, 2501

Zanzig, Augustus D., as editor; 1483

Zhiliaev, N., as editor, 1714–15, 2242

Zuschneid, Karl, as editor, 1729